WENNER-GREN CENTER
INTERNATIONAL SYMPOSIUM SERIES

VOLUME 24

BASIC MECHANISMS OF OCULAR MOTILITY AND THEIR CLINICAL IMPLICATIONS

Symposium on

BASIC MECHANISMS OF OCULAR MOTILITY AND THEIR CLINICAL IMPLICATIONS

PROCEEDINGS OF THE INTERNATIONAL SYMPOSIUM
HELD IN WENNER-GREN CENTER, STOCKHOLM,
JUNE 4–6, 1974

Edited by

Gunnar Lennerstrand

Department of Ophthalmology, Karolinska Hospital and Nobel Institute for Neurophysiology, Karolinska Institute, Stockholm, Sweden

Paul Bach-y-Rita

Smith-Kettlewell Institute and Department of Visual Sciences, Pacific Medical Center, San Francisco, California

Co-editors

Carter C. Collins   Arthur Jampolsky   Alan B. Scott

Smith-Kettlewell Institute and Department of Visual Sciences, Pacific Medical Center, San Francisco, California

PERGAMON PRESS

Oxford · New York · Toronto
Sidney · Paris · Braunschweig

U.K.	Pergamon Press Ltd., Headington Hill Hall, Oxford OX3 0BW England
U.S.A.	Pergamon Press Inc., Maxwell House, Fairview Park, Elmsford, New York 10523, U.S.A.
CANADA	Pergamon of Canada, Ltd., 207 Queen's Quay West, Toronto 1, Canada
AUSTRALIA	Pergamon Press (Aust.) Pty. Ltd., 19a Boundary Street, Rushcutters Bay, N.S.W. 2011, Australia
FRANCE	Pergamon Press SARL, 24 rue des Ecoles, 75240 Paris, Cedex 05, France
WEST GERMANY	Pergamon Press GMbH, 3300 Braunschweig, Postfach 2923, Burgplatz 1, West Germany

First edition 1975

Library of Congress Cataloging in Publication Data

Symposium on Basic Mechanisms of Ocular Motility and their Clinical Implications, Wenner-Gren Center, 1974.
Basic mechanisms of ocular motility and their clinical implications.
(Wenner-Gren Center international symposium series; v. 24.)
Includes index.
1. Eye—Movements—Congresses. 2. Eye—Muscles—Anomalies—Congresses. I. Lennerstrand, Gunnar. II. Bach-y-Rita, Paul, 1934–. III. Title. IV. Series. [DNLM: 1. Eye Movements—Congresses. 2. Eye Manifestations—Congresses. 3. Oculomotor Muscles—Physiology—Congresses. WS WE429 v. 24 1974/WW400 S9843b 1974.]
RE731.S93 1974   612'.846   75-9907
ISBN 0-08-018885-0

Printed in Great Britain by A. Wheaton & Co., Exeter

CONTENTS

FREE CONTRIBUTIONS

NEUROPHYSIOLOGY OF OCULOMOTOR SYSTEMS

SYSTEMS ANALYSIS OF OCULOMOTOR FUNCTIONS

CLINICAL ASPECTS OF OCULAR MOTILITY

CONTRIBUTORS AND INVITED PARTICIPANTS

Vivian C. Abrahams
Department of Physiology
Queen's University
Kingston
Ontario
Canada K7L 3N6

Jorge A. Alvarado
Department of Opthalmology
University of California
San Francisco
School of Medicine and the
Francis I. Proctor Foundation
   for Research in Ophthalmology
(Electron Microscopy Laboratory)
San Francisco
California 94143
USA

Rosa Alvarado-Mallart
Laboratoire Physiologie Générale
Université de Paris XI
91405 Orsay
France

Paul Bach-y-Rita
Smith-Kettlewell Institute and Department of Visual
   Sciences
Pacific Medical Center
2232 Webster Street
San Francisco
California 94115
USA

Neal H. Barmack
Laboratory of Neurophysiology
Good Samaritan Hospital
Portland
Oregon 97210
USA

Wolfgang Becker
Sektion Neurophysiologie
Universität Ulm
D-79 Ulm
West Germany

Emilio Bizzi
Department of Psychology
Massachusetts Institute of Technology
Cambridge
Massachusetts 02139
USA

C. Buisseret-Delmas
Laboratoire de Psycophysiologie
Université de Paris VI
75005 Paris
France

Ulrich Büttner
Psychiatrische Klinik
Universität Göttingen
D-3400 Göttingen
v.-Siebold-Strasse 5
West Germany

Jorge Alberto F. Caldeira
Rua Amália Noronha 289
05410 Sao Paulo S.P.
Brazil

Alberto O. Ciancia
Oro 2936
Buenos Aires
Argentina

David G. Cogan
Bldg. 10 Rm. 10 N 315
National Institute of Health
Bethesda
Maryland 20014
USA

Bernhard Cohen
Department of Neurology
Mount Sinai School of Medicine
New York
New York 10029
USA

Han Collewijn
Department of Physiology
Faculty of Medicine
Erasmus University
Postbus 1738
Rotterdam
The Netherlands

Carter C. Collins
Smith-Kettlewell Institute and Department of Visual
   Sciences
Pacific Medical Center
2232 Webster Street
San Francisco
94115 California
USA

Robert B. Daroff
Department of Neurology
University of Miami
School of Medicine
PO Box 875
Miami
Florida 33152
USA

Johannes Dichgans
Neurologische Universitätsklinik
D-78 Freiburg i.Br.
Hansastrasse 9
West Germany

Rolf Eckmiller
Physiologisches Institut
Freie Universität Berlin
D-1000 Berlin 33
Arnimallee 22
West Germany

Paul Enoksson
The Eye Clinic
Södersjukhuset
S-10064 Stockholm
Sweden

Curt von Euler
Nobelinstitute for Neurophysiology
Karolinska Institutet
S-104 01 Stockholm
Sweden

Peter Fells
Moorfields Eye Hospital
City Road
London EC1
England

Merton C. Flom
School of Optometry
University of California
Berkeley
California 94720
USA

Burkhart Fischer
Neurologische Universitätsklinik
D-78 Freiburg i. Br.
Hansastrasse 9
West Germany

Lars Frisén
The Eye Clinic
Sahlgrenska Sjukhuset
S-413 45 Göteborg
Sweden

Paul Gogan
Laboratoire de Physiologie
U.E.R. Saint Antoine
27 Rue de Chaligny
Paris 75012
France

A. Gonshor
Aviation Medical Research Unit
Department of Physiology
McGill University
Montreal PQ
Canada H3C 3G1

Ragnar Granit
Nobel Institute for Neurophysiology
Karolinska Institutet
S-104 01 Stockholm
Sweden

Jean Patrick Guéritaud
Laboratoire d'Antomie Comparée Université de Paris
   VII
75005 Paris
France

Genevieve M. Haddad
Department of Psychology
University of Maryland
College Park
Maryland 20742
USA

Volker Henn
Neurologische Klinik
Kantonsspital
CH-8006 Zurich
Rämistrasse 100
Switzerland

Nils Gunnar Henriksson
Department of Otolaryngology
Lasarettet
S-221 85 Lund
Sweden

Simon Heywood
Department of Psychology
University of Oxford
South Parks Road
Oxford OX1 3PS
England

Ginette Horcholle-Bossavit
Laboratoire de Physiologie
U.E.R. Saint Antoine
27 Rue de Chaligny
Paris 75012
France

Carol van Horn
Smith-Kettlewell Institute and Department of Visual
   Sciences
Pacific Medical Center
2232 Webster Street
San Francisco
California 94115
USA

William F. Hoyt
Neuro-Ophthalmology Unit
University of California
Medical Center
San Francisco
California 94122
USA

Tetsuo Ishii
Department of Otolaryngology
Teikyo University
School of Medicine
Kaga 2-11-1
Itabashi-ku
Tokyo
Japan

Robert S. Jampel
The Kresge Eye Institute
3994 John R. Street
Detroit
Michigan 48201
USA

Arthur Jampolsky
Smith-Kettlewell Institute and Department of Visual
　Sciences
Pacific Medical Center
2232 Webster Street
San Francisco
California 94115
USA

Geoffrey Melvill Jones
Aviation Medical Research Unit
Department of Physiology
McGill University
Montreal PQ
Canada H3C 3G1

Richard Jung
Neurologische Universitätsklinik
D-78 Freiburg iBr.
Hansastrasse 9
West Germany

Reinhart Jürgens
Sektion Neurophysiologie
Universität Ulm
D-79 Ulm
West Germany

H. J. Kleinschmidt
Department of Physiology
Faculty of Medicine
Erasmus University
Postbus 1738
Rotterdam
The Netherlands

Guntram Kommerell
Universitäts-Augenklinik
D-78 Freiburg i.Br.
West Germany

Fritz H. Körner
Universitäts-Augenklinik
D-74 Tübingen
West Germany

Jörgen Krüger
Neurologische Universitätsklinik
D-78 Freiburg i.Br.
Hansastrasse 9
West Germany

Eric Kugelberg
Department of Neurology
Karolinska Sjukhuset
S-104 01 Stockholm
Sweden

Phillip H. Landers
Royal Military College of Science
Shrivenham
Swindon
Wiltshire
England

Jan Lännergren
Nobel Institute for Neurophysiology
Karolinska Institutet
S-104 01 Stockholm
Sweden

Gunnar Lennerstrand
The Eye Clinic
Karolinska Sjukhuset
S-104 01 Stockholm
Sweden

Ermanno Manni
Istituto di Fisiologia Umana
Università Cattolica
S. Cuore
Via della Pineta Sacchetti 644
I-00166 Roma
Italy

Robert Mayr
A 1180 Wien
Geymüllergasse 4–6/4
Austria

Dietrich Lothar Meyer
Psychiatrische Klinik
Universität Göttingen
D-3400 Göttingen
V.-Siebold-Strasse 5
West Germany

David O'Meara
Smith-Kettlewell Institute and Department of Visual
　Sciences
Pacific Medical Center
2232 Webster Street
San Francisco
California 94115
USA

James E. Miller
St Louis Children's Hospital
500 S. Kingshighway
St Louis
Missouri 63110
USA

Eugenio Mira
Clinica Otorinolaringoiatrica
dell'Universita di Pavia
I-27100 Pavia
Italy

Ken Ñakayama
Smith-Kettlewell Institute and Department of Visual
  Sciences
Pacific Medical Center
2232 Webster Street
San Francisco
California 94115
USA

Ilse Nawratzki
Hadassah University
Department of Ophthalmology
Jerusalem
Israel

Alf Nilsson
Department of Psychology
University of Lund
Paradisgatan 5
S-223 50 Lund
Sweden

Gunter K. von Noorden
Texas Children's Hospital
Texas Medical Center
Houston
Texas 77025
USA

Karl-Gösta Nyman
The Eye Clinic
Sabbatsbergs Sjukhus
Box 6401
S-113 82 Stockholm
Sweden

John S. Outerbridge
OTL Research Laboratories
Royal Victoria Hospital
Montreal, PQ
Canada

Wolfgang Precht
Max-Planck-Institut
Neurobiologische Abteilung
D-6 Frankfurt/M-Niederrad
Deutschordenstrasse 46
West Germany

Robert D. Reinecke
The Albany Medical College of Union University
Department of Ophthalmology
Albany
New York 12208
USA

Graham Ratcliff
Department of Neurology
Churchill Hospital
Oxford
England

Stephan Réthy
Universitäts-Augenklinik
643 Bad Hersfeld
Gotzbertstrasse
West Germany

F. Richmond
Department of Physiology
Queen's University
Kingston
Ontario
Canada K7L 3N6

David A. Robinson
Department of Ophthalmology
The Johns Hopkins Hospital
Wilmer Institute
601 N. Broadway
Baltimore
Maryland 21205
USA

P. Kenneth Rose
Department of Physiology
Queen's University
Kingston
Ontario
Canada

Michael D. Sanders
National Hospital
Queen Square
London W1
England

Kurt-Peter Schaefer
Psychiatrische Klinik
Universität Göttingen
D-3400 Göttingen
v.-Siebold-Strasse 5
West Germany

Wolfgang Schlote
Pathologisches Institut
D-74 Tubingen
Liebermeister Strasse 8
West Germany

Ditmar Schott
Psychiatrische Klinik
Universität Göttingen
D-3400 Göttingen
v.-Siebold-Strasse 5
West Germany

Roberto Schmid
Institute of Electrical Engineering and Electronics
Polytechnic of Milan
Milan
Italy

Clifton Schor
College of Optometry
Pacific University
Forest Grove
Oregon
USA

Alan B. Scott
Smith-Kettlewell Institute and Department of Visual
    Sciences
Pacific Medical Center
2232 Webster Street
San Francisco
California 94115
USA

Kurt Simons
The Albany Medical College of Union University
Department of Ophthalmology
Albany
New York 12208
USA

Carlos Souza-Dias
Rua Cincinato Braga 59, conj. 5B2
01333 Sao Paulo S.P.
Brasil

Mario Stefanelli
Istituto di Elettronica
Universitá di Pavia
Via Strada Nuova 106/c
I-27100 Pavia
Italy

Robert M. Steinman
Department of Psychology
University of Maryland
College Park
Maryland 20742
USA

Jun-Ichi Suzuki
Department of Otolaryngology
Teikyo University
School of Medicine
Kaga 2-11-1
Itabashi-ku
Tokyo
Japan

Karl-Jens Süss
Psychiatrische Klinik
Universität Göttingen
D-3400 Göttingen
v.-Siebold-Strasse 5
West Germany

R. Täumer
Universitäts-Augenklinik
D-78 Freiburg i.Br.
Killianstrasse
West Germany

Anthony Taylor
Sherrington School of Physiology
St Thomas Hospital
London SE1 7EH
England

Björn Tengroth
The Eye Clinic
Karolinska Sjukhuset
S-104 01 Stockholm
Sweden

Hans Theopold
Universitäts-Augenklinik
D-78 Freiburg i.Br.
Killianstrasse
West Germany

Suzanne Tyc-Dumont
Laboratoire de Physiologie
U.E.R. St Antoine
27 Rue de Chaligny
75012 Paris
France

Gerald Westheimer
Department of Physiology-Anatomy
University of California
Berkeley
California 94720
USA

Barbara J. Winterson
Department of Psychology
University of Maryland
College Park
Maryland 20742
USA

Tutis Vilis
Department of Physiology
Medical Sciences Building
University of Western Ontario

Ontario
Canada

Gerhard Vossius
Institut für Biokybernetik und Biomedizinische Tech-
    nik der Universität Karlsruhe
D-75 Karlsruhe
Kaiserstrasse 12
West Germany

Syozo Yasui
Department of Applied Science and Biology
California Institute of Technology
Pasadena
California
USA

Laurence Young
Massachusetts Institute of Technology
Cambridge
Massachusetts 02139
USA

David Zee
Department of Ophthalmology
The Johns Hopkins Hospital
Wilmer Institute
601 N. Broadway
Baltimore
Maryland 21205
USA

Yngve Zotterman
Wenner-Gren Center
Sveavägen 166
S-113 46 Stockholm
Sweden

PREFACE

In 1969 the Smith-Kettlewell Eye Research Foundation sponsored a Symposium on the Control of Eye Movements. The primary emphasis was on finding common ground for physiologists and biophysicists working on basic aspects of eye movements. A number of the participants in that symposium agreed that the next one should emphasize involvement of clinical scientists as well, in order to reduce the time-lag between laboratory findings and clinical applications, and acquaint the laboratory scientists with clinical problems that required fundamental work. Thus, this Symposium on Basic Mechanisms of Ocular Motility and Their Clinical Implications was planned to meet this need to encourage interaction between laboratory and clinical scientists.

Each topic was first presented by a laboratory scientist and then discussed by a clinician. In some cases the individual speakers were equally competent in the laboratory and clinical aspects. After each session, a laboratory-clinical round table was held to further relate the two approaches to a common interest. The last day of the symposium was reserved for free communications by anatomists, physiologists, psychologists, engineers, and clinicians. These papers have been included in this volume.

The successful experience with this symposium has led us to suggest that the next symposium should be primarily planned from a clinical point of view, with laboratory scientists commenting on the clinical eye-movement problems and, hopefully, suggesting experiments to answer particular clinical questions.

This symposium would have remained as simply an idea, had it not been for the encouragement and support of individuals and institutions in Sweden and the United States. Dr. Ragner Granit and Dr. Curt von Euler, on hearing of our plans, generously offered to sponsor our application for financial support from the Swedish Medical Research Council and the Swedish Ministry of Education. Dr. Y. Zotterman offered the conference facilities of the Wenner-Gren Center in Stockholm. The Smith-Kettlewell Eye Research Foundation of San Francisco provided generous financial support. The participants are greatly indebted to this support for allowing this symposium to have become a successful reality.

GUNNAR LENNERSTRAND
PAUL BACH-Y-RITA

INTRODUCTION

EXPERIMENTAL AND CLINICAL RESEARCH ON EYE MOVEMENTS AND VISION

RICHARD JUNG

THIS symposium is distinguished from preceding conferences on eye movements (Bach-y-Rita *et al.*, 1971; Bender, 1964; Dichgans and Bizzi, 1972; Zikmund, 1973) by correlating basic and clinical research in parallel papers, aiming at a synthesis of fields which have often developed separately. This plan made by the organizers Lennerstrand and Bach-y-Rita has a special appeal to me, since I have myself tried to integrate experimental and clinical neurology for over three decades. It becomes increasingly difficult to combine both in a world of progressive specialization, but we are grateful for the opportunity to try it here. A discussion between neurophysiologists, engineers, ophthalmologists, otologists, neurologists and psychologists cannot fail to stimulate the field of oculomotor and visual research. I am convinced that this visuomotor area will be the main frontier of vision research over the next decade.

In 1938, when I began to record human eye movements after some preliminary experiments on the cat's brain stem, the experimental guides to oculomotor research and visuo-vestibular regulations were the classical publications of Magnus (1924), Lorente de Nó (1928, 1931, 1935, 1938), Spiegel (1929, 1933) and ter Braak (1936). The classic of eye movements and vision and their psychophysics was and still is Hering's handbook article of 1879. Dodge's fundamental paper (1903) and Ohm's lifework of nystagmography (1928) extending over more than two decades, albeit difficult to read, had described all forms of human eye movements, normal and abnormal nystagmus. Already Barany's early clinical work (1907) and Fischer's physiological vestibular studies in the 1920s (1928) had set a standard of vestibular testing on which objective studies, facilitated by the simple method of electronystagmography in man, could be built up (Jung, 1953). Ter Braak's discovery of visuomotor auto-regulation and negative feed-back in the visuomotor system (1936) was mainly based on the rabbit's optokinetic nystagmus but could soon be applied to man, although human optokinetic responses are more dependent on attention (Jung, 1953).

Looking over the rapidly increasing literature on eye movements and their visual and vestibular regulations I feel that these classical papers should be consulted more often to avoid repetition of findings already well described in the literature. These and the Scandinavian studies of Dohlman (1925), Nylén (1931) and their co-workers, and the German schools of Grahe (1926), Güttich (1934, 1944) and Frenzel (1955) which followed, are now quantitized by present-day neurophysiology. All these remain

1

the basis of modern research in our field. Recent work since 1960 is summarized in four symposia (Bach-y-Rita *et al.*, 1971; Bender, 1964; Dichgans and Bizzi, 1972; Zikmund, 1973).

Lorente de Nó's measurement of the synaptic delay of oculomotor neurons (1935) and his paper on the mechanisms of the reticular formation in the rabbit (1938) showed the way towards a neuronal physiology of vestibular and visuo-motor functions. Simple recording methods of the early years, which brought our first insights into visual-vestibular interaction and allowed classification of the various forms of nystagmus, have now given way to quantitative research and modelling. We are still far from a useful application of cybernetic models to clinical problems of nystagmus, but automatic analysis in nystagmography has begun to demonstrate how the computer can help the clinicians in their more practical problems of diagnosis.

I should like to show a rather old-fashioned example of recording and analysing eye movements without a computer. This may also demonstrate how a single case of pathological nystagmus can give us a better insight into physiological problems than vestibular stimulation in normals. In spite of the tremendous variety of nystagmic syndromes to which Henrikson and other clinicians will draw attention, a well-selected case may give us important clues to visual-vestibular interaction, as the following anecdote will show.

When Mittermaier and I investigated the interrelation of vestibular and optokinetic nystagmus by using various vestibular stimuli in normals, the short lasting effects of labyrinthine stimulation made this analysis difficult and we waited for clear cases of spontaneous vestibular nystagmus towards one side before compensation. In March 1939 a student walked into Mittermaier's room complaining of severe vertigo and showing a continuous regular nystagmus after an acute labyrinthine lesion. Mittermaier sent him over for optokinetic testing. We did, and within 1 hr we got all the information we wanted on visual-vestibular interaction and its phasic and tonic components (Jung and Mittermaier, 1939). This is shown in Fig. 1, which demonstrates that vestibular nystagmus to the left adds to the left optokinetic nystagmus when the eyes lag behind a high-velocity visual stimulus, and that it is subtracted from optokinetic nystagmus to the right. The record further shows clearly an opposite deviation of the nystagmic "Schlagfeld": to the side of the slow phase in vestibular, and to that of the quick phase in optokinetic nystagmus.

There are three reasons for this quick success. We had: (1) a good case, (2) a good DC-amplifier, (3) last not least a good question. This may demonstrate what I often tell my students who are somewhat spoiled by modern research facilities: a good idea is more important in research than a good on-line computer, although it may be nice to have both.

I may add that these plain results were not described so clearly in my first paper with Mittermaier (1939), which obnubilated the quantitative data in a rather lengthy casuistic description (Jung and Mittermaier, 1939). During the war I could not pursue this research but 8 years later I resumed the results more succinctly for the Physiological Society of Stockholm in 1947 (Jung, 1947). One may learn from this experience that investigations of general interest should not be hidden in clinical case descriptions.

In clinical neurophysiology one should avoid trifling analyses and casuistic curiosities, keeping an eye open for cases of general significance which may demonstrate physiological mechanisms through an experiment of nature.

Of course effective research in clinical neurophysiology needs some experience in the laboratory and a neurophysiological training. I had the luck to receive this training from two great neurophysiologists. The first was Paul Hoffmann in Freiburg, who—besides his basic work on monosynaptic reflexes in man—began to record eye muscle potentials during nystagmus in 1913 (Hoffmann, 1913). The second was W. R. Hess in Zürich, who had begun as an ophthalmologist and then became the leading neurophysiologist on the Continent, developing his brain stimulation method in the behaving cat.

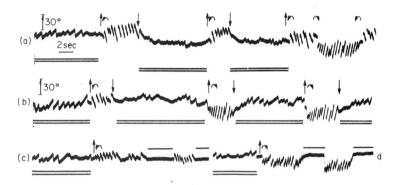

FIG. 1. Visuo-vestibular coordination in a case of spontaneous vestibular nystagmus influencing optokinetic nystagmus (OKN). D.C. recordings from Jung and Mittermaier (1939). Each record begins with spontaneous vestibular nystagmus beating to the left during closed eyes (marked by double lines ═). After eye opening (↑) a supra-maximal visual movement stimulus of a striped drum (rotating at >120/sec circular velocity) is applied. When the drum rotates to the left ∩) it elicits OKN to the right and vice versa (∩). OKN to the left shows much higher volocities of the slow phases when beating to the same left side as vestibular nystagmus. Right OKN causes after-inhibition of left vestibular nystagmus with eye closure (↓ in a and b); following left OKN vestibular nystagmus returns sooner in b. In c and d OKN is suppressed by steady fixation (marked ────). The *tonic deviation* is independent of slow phase facilitation or depression since left vestibular nystagmus diminishes OKN to the right in the same Schlagfeld (right) and facilitates left OKN which beats in the left opposite Schlagfeld. Algebraic summation is shown by *slow phase velocity maxima*: spontaneous vestibular nystagmus to the left had a slow phase velocity up to 24°/sec, the left optokinetic up to 115°/sec, the right optokinetic up to 65°/sec. This means that a *velocity at about 25°/sec of vestibular nystagmus is added to the OKN beating to the same side and subtracted from OKN to the opposite side* when both OKN would reach a maximal slow phase velocity of 90°/sec to either side in the normal state.

Following the suggestions of these teachers I have tried to coordinate animal experimentation with neurophysiological recording and psychophysical investigations in man for visual and oculomotor research. Both can, and should, be combined by using human visual perception as a guide for experiments.

Clearly, one must also have some luck in research and not least in selecting the right co-workers.

Looking over the program of this symposium I was gratified to see how many of my former co-workers have continued to contribute to the field of eye movements and vision, and indeed how their own pupils in turn are further developing the field. The appearance of one's "research grandsons" may be an appropriate sign that it is now time to retire from research and to give way to the younger generation.

I hope that the combined effort of clinical and non-clinical scientists at this symposium will provide new stimuli to oculomotor research by facilitating international contacts through our discussions, eliciting new ideas and preparing the way for new syntheses in the field of eye movements and vision.

REFERENCES

BACH-Y-RITA, P., COLLINS, C. A. and HYDE, E. (Eds.) (1971) *The Control of Eye Movements.* Academic Press, New York.

BARÁNY, R. (1907) *Physiologie und Pathologie (Funktions-prufung) des Bogengang-Apparates beim Menschen.* Klinische Studien. Deuticke; Leipzig. Wien.

BENDER, M. B. (Ed.) (1964) *The Oculomotor System.* Hoeber, New York.

BRAAK, J. W. G. TER (1936) Untersuchungen über optokinetischen Nystagmus. *Arch. néerl. Physiol.* **21**, 309–376.

DICHGANS, J. and BIZZI, E. (Eds.) (1972) Cerebral control of eye movements and motion perception. *Bibl. ophthal. (Basel)* **82**, 1–403.

DODGE, R. (1903) Five types of eye movement in the horizontal meridian plane of the field of regard. *Am. J. Physiol.* **8**, 307–329.

DOHLMAN, G. (1925) Physikalische und Physiologische Studien zur Theorie des Kalorischen Nystagmus. *Acta oto-laryng. (Stockh.)* Suppl. **5.**

FISCHER, M. H. (1928) Die Regulationsfunktion des menschlichen Labyrinthes und die Zusammenhänge mit verwandten Funktionen. *Ergebn. Physiol.* **27**, 209–379.

FRENZEL, H. (1955) *Spontan-u. Provokationsnystagmus als Krankheitssymptom.* Springer, Berlin.

GRAHE, K. (1926) Die Funktion des Bogengangsapparates und der Statolithen beim Menschen. BETHE, BERGMANN, EMBDEN, ELLINGER (Eds.), *Handbuch der normalen und pathologischen Physiologie*, Bd. **11**, pp. 909–984. Springer, Berlin.

GÜTTICH, A. (1934) Zur Physiologie der Augenbewegung bei der aktiven Kopf- und Körperdrehung. *Passow-Schaefers Beitr.* **31**, 109–113.

GÜTTICH, A. (1944) *Neurologie des Ohrlabyrinthes.* G. Thieme, Leipzig.

HERING, E. (1879) Der Raumsinn und die Bewegungen der Augen. HERMANN (Ed.), *Handbuch der Physiologie*, vol. **3**, pp. 343–601. Vogel, Leipzig.

HOFFMANN, P. (1913) Über die Aktionsströme der Augenmuskeln bei Ruhe des Tieres und beim Nystagmus. *Arch. Anat. Physiol. Physiol. Abt.* **1913**, 23–34.

JUNG, R. (1947) Die Registrierung des postrotatorischen und optokinetischen Nystagmus und die optisch-vestibuläre Integration beim Menschen. *Acta oto-laryng. (Stockh.)* **36**, 199–202.

JUNG, R. (1953) Nystagmographie. Zur Physiologie und Pathologie des optisch-vestibulären Systems beim Menschen. BERGMANN *et al.* (Eds.), *Handbuch der inneren Medizin*, 4. Aufl., vol. **5**, pp. 1325–1379. Springer, Berlin.

JUNG, R. and MITTERMAIER, R. (1939) Zur objektiven Registrierung und Analyse verschiedener Nystagmusformen: Vestibulärer, optokinetischer und spontaner Nystagmus in ihren Wechselbeziehungen. *Arch. Ohr.- Nas.- und Kehlkopf-Heilk.* **146**, 410–439.

LORENTE DE NÓ, R. (1928) *Die Labyrinthreflexe auf die Augenmuskeln nach einseitiger Labyrinthexstirpation nebst einer kurzen Angabe uber den Nervenmechanismus der vestibulären Augenbewegungen.* Urban und Schwarzenberg, Wien.

LORENTE DE NÓ, R. (1931) Ausgewählte Kapitel aus der vergleichenden Physiologie des Labyrinthes. Die Augenmuskelreflexe beim Kaninchen und ihre Grundlagen. *Ergebn. Physiol.* **32**, 73–242.

LORENTE DE NÓ, R. (1935) The synaptic delay of the motoneurones. *Am. J. Physiol.* **111**, 272–282.

LORENTE DE NÓ, R. (1938) Analysis of the activity of the chains of internuncial neurons. *J. Neurophysiol.* **1**, 207–244.

MAGNUS, R. (1924) *Körperstellung.* Berlin, Springer.

NYLÉN, C. O. (1931) A clinical study on positional nystagmus in brain-tumor. *Acta oto-laryng. (Stockh.)*, Suppl. 247, **15.**

OHM, J. (1928/29) *Zur Tätigkeit des Augenmuskelsenders.* 2 Bde. Selbstverlag, Bottrop.

SPIEGEL, E. A. (1929) Experimentalstudien am Nervensystem: Der Mechanismus des labyrinthären Nystagmus. *Z. Hals- Nasen-u. Ohrenheilk.* **25**, 200–217.

SPIEGEL, E. A. (1933) Role of vestibular nuclei in cortical innervation of the eye muscles. *Arch. of Neur. (Chicago)* **29**, 1084–1097.

ZIKMUND, V. (Ed.) (1973) *The Oculomotor System and Brain Functions.* Butterworth, London.

Symposium on

BASIC MECHANISMS OF OCULAR MOTILITY AND THEIR CLINICAL IMPLICATIONS

INTRODUCTORY REMARKS

ARTHUR JAMPOLSKY

THE Smith-Kettlewell Eye Research Foundation in San Francisco is happy to co-sponsor with the Wenner-Gren Center in Sweden this symposium on the "Basic Mechanisms of Ocular Motility and Their Clinical Implications".

The motivating goal is to bring together the laboratory investigators and clinical investigators interested in this area, to discuss their mutual problems, directions, and potentials.

We all owe a great deal of thanks to our Swedish hosts, for making available these marvelous symposium facilities, and for their gracious hospitality.

The motivating concept in the formation of the Smith-Kettlewell Institute of Visual Sciences in San Francisco was to provide an environment where laboratory investigators and clinical investigators could work together in a medical center environment, for their mutual benefit, and for the benefit of patients with strabismus and visual neurologic problems.

The San Francisco symposium 4 years ago, which marked the dedication of the Smith-Kettlewell Research Institute Building, provided the initial symposium environment where workers in these fields could come together and discuss their subjects. In this way the clinical scientists would become more aware of the laboratory tools and methods, and the laboratory scientists would become more aware of the related clinical problems. It was the hope and expectation that these mutual discussions would extend and augment the mutual working environments, to foster more and more such collaboration. Especially, it is their purpose to reduce the lag time between laboratory knowledge and practical clinical application. It is desirable to foster a mutual concern, even an obligation, for laboratory scientists to attempt to point out, even to speculate. as to the possible clinical usefulness of newly acquired knowledge; and it is a similar obligation of clinical scientists to attempt to formulate and state their problems in a communicable manner.

There are notable examples of real progress in the benefits to be derived from mutual exchanges between laboratory scientists and clinical scientists. For example, it was not too long ago that clinicians in this area restricted the examination to a single option of plotting eye *positions* in the different fields of *gaze* in order to analyze motility problems. Such devices as the Hess screen and Lancaster charts are such clinically useful methods.

Now however, thanks to engineers, neurophysiologists, and others, clinicians are asking, "How on earth the eyes got to these positions?" Clinicians now look for, and measure, eye movement velocities, accelerations, and other parameters easily adaptable for clinical observation and clinical measurement by available equipment.

There is a balanced appreciation of each other's methods and interpretations. Not all laboratory derived evidence constitutes pure valid science. Not all clinical insights constitute controlled observation.

Rather laboratory scientists appreciate that some clinicians are capable of some scientific methods, and some cogent clinical observations and measurements can be made by people with unpithed brains and untwitching legs. And, on the other hand, clinical scientists appreciate that laboratory scientists are willing and eager to apply their energies to clinical entities, if the problem is appropriately crystallized, formulated, and stated. And if there is mutual availability and interest to pursue the effort. Hence, the desirability of the physical environments in which to work together, and the symposia in which to discuss together.

Everyone at this symposium is probably aware of the conditions that exist when a laboratory scientist lectures, and presents data and conclusions to a clinical audience. The clinician believes the data, but secretly doubts the conclusions. The laboratory lecturer, on the other hand, is sure of his conclusions, but often secretly doubts his data.

Happily, these veils are being wiped away. There is the hope and expectation that these symposia will foster an ever closer collaboration of working together and discussing together.

We wish to thank our hosts and their co-workers for their many successful efforts for this symposium, and especially Paul Bach-y-Rita and Gunnar Lennerstrand for the organizational arrangements.

We all wish to extend our appreciation to the vision and benevolence of Mr. Wenner-Gren, to Mr. Jack Smith, and to Kitty and Bill Kettlewell, for helping make these environments possible.

Opening Address

COMPARING SOME CONTROL MECHANISMS IN SKELETAL AND EYE MUSCLES

RAGNAR GRANIT

FOR one who like myself has worked with the eye and with muscular afferents, but never with the two of them co-operating in extraocular muscles, it seems natural to discuss some points of contact between eye muscle and skeletal muscular control in the hope that this would be of some interest to an audience of specialists on eye movements.

There seems to prevail among many of those working on eye movements the misunderstanding that the stretch reflex is one only. Long ago I (1955) pointed out that there are three such reflexes or as many as there are types of stretch-sensitive endings. This has recently again been stressed by Matthews (1972). Of them the best known is the excitatory one of the primary spindle afferents which is both mono- and polysynaptic. This is the extensor stretch reflex of Liddell and Sherrington (1924). Another one from the muscle spindle's secondary endings is inhibitory on the leg extensors and thus opposes the former. It has excitatory effects in the flexors and in both places is wholly polysynaptic. The third stretch reflex derives from the Golgi tendon organs and so far, wherever seen, has been found to be inhibitory on its own muscle.

These statements refer to reflexes within the spinal cord but in addition all three sensory endings have cortical cerebral and cerebellar projections whose elaboration exceeds what one could anticipate a few years ago. It is not known what purposes they serve but, in view of the dominating alpha–gamma linkage in motor acts, it seems reasonable to expect the spindles to be coactivated in order to make possible feedback information about the resulting movement. My own favourite hypothesis is that their cerebral role is to check whether a demand has or has not been accomplished according to order. The recording of spindle activity in man, introduced by Hagbarth and Vallbo (1967) and perfected by Vallbo (1970, 1971) has shown voluntary movement to be carried out in alpha–gamma linkage and this, indeed, is a situation in which it is possible to vary demand and study accomplishment.

Considering that spindles mostly operate in alpha–gamma linkage, their role in eye muscles should be to accompany contraction. They would be feebly active in passive stretch as, for instance, in the particular motoneurons under reciprocal inhibition. If only the polysynaptic component were present in the extraocular muscular afferents—as we have reason to believe—the decisive factor would be the nature of the biasing activity. To pursue these problems the experimenter would need a preparation in which there is a large number of extraocular spindles. The monkey can hardly be called such a preparation. It has only about six spindles in each eye muscle (Greene and Jampel, 1966) whereas man has about fifty (Cooper and Daniel, 1949, 1963) and the goat a still greater number (Cooper *et al.*, 1951). We have no definite explanation of why this should be so, only the basic conviction that evolution does not support a meaningless increase of afference on such a scale.

To give my attitude to spindle physiology in a nutshell, the emphasis should be on the fact that these are organs under control of the gamma loop and that hence the chance of being able to elucidate their role in oculomotor mechanisms is tied to the chance of finding from where and under what circumstances the loop can be shown to become operative. This, in the first instance, means finding central stations which excite or inhibit the discharge of spindle afferents. It is impossible to advance such problems without putting next on the list the need for finding out to what an extent there is alpha–gamma linkage also in the oculomotor system and, again, this would begin with a search for places from which the ocular gamma system can be activated. Its existence has already been demonstrated by Whitteridge (1959).

I find it pointless to delay the proceedings of this conference by theorizing extensively about the possible role of extraocular muscular afferents in the various types of eye movements known. But it may be worth while to draw the attention of this gathering to the fact that a substantial body of evidence supports the general conclusion that the gamma efferents are activated also in general arousal which of course is highly pertinent to the experimental analysis of eye movements.

There is an amusing parallel between the two fields of skeletal and eye muscle control respectively. I mean the fact that the number of central sites from which activation somehow correlated with eye movements can be obtained, just as is the case in the field of skeletal muscle control, appears to increase virtually in proportion to the number of experimenters devoting themselves to central stimulation and recording. This actuates three general problems: (i) the definition of prime movers and the study of interactions and constraints in their operations; (ii) separation from prime movers of places merely in need of information to the effect that eye muscles are being or have been activated including the problem of why these places should require such knowledge; (iii) the question of whether there are sites which are activated merely for the sake of being prepared to play a role should need for this arise.

While the first two points are obvious enough and also recognized in the literature on eye movements, the third may seem obscure. However, I have in mind an analogy with skeletal muscle control which may be relevant also in the field of oculomotor physiology. This is the fact that commands to certain limb motor units to execute a definite, restricted movement can be shown to elicit changes of membrane potential in motoneurons which are not called upon to participate in the movement ordered from above. The evidence is derived by the technique of monosynaptic testing which is a way of measuring the number of excited or inhibited motoneurons raised above or suppressed below threshold within the pool of one specific muscle or synergic muscle group. For instance, when the right soleus alone was given the command to act in response to a warning signal, the Achilles tenden reflex was enhanced on both sides during the preparatory period (Requin, 1969). A number of experiments of this general type have been published recently and some were mentioned by Zalkind at the recent Conference on motor control in Varna. I was reminded of this kind of evidence for accompanying "ghost" motor activity not demanded for a specific act, when I found Westheimer and Blair (1972) stating, that "there is, physiologically speaking, no such thing as a single direction of pull of an extraocular muscle... In general, any saccadic movement involves all muscles". But in a wider context one might think of preparatory activity in, say, extraocular muscle nuclei, vestibular or mesencephalic reticular nuclei, neck muscle motoneurons and other sites when only one of them actually produces the given motor act.

Returning to the afferent side of control problems, it deserves to be emphasized that many inputs are relevant only in combination with others. There is, for instance, the recent experiment by Marsden et al. (1972) in which they studied the responses to loading and unloading of the flexor of the top joint of the thumb. When the hand was anaesthetized with the aid of a wrist cuff, the spindles and tendon organs in the muscle, whose tendon alone runs down to the top joint, could not by themselves produce the normal load compensation to a resistance. Seemingly redundant information proved to be non-redundant.

REFERENCES

COOPER, S. and DANIEL, P. M. (1949) Muscle spindles in human extrinsic eye muscles. *Brain,* **72,** 1–24.
COOPER, S. and DANIEL, P. M. (1963) Muscle spindles in man; their morphology in the lumbricals and the deep muscles of the neck. *Brain,* **86,** 563–586.
COOPER, S., DANIEL, P. M. and WHITTERIDGE, D. (1951) Afferent impulses in the oculomotor nerve, from the extrinsic eye muscles. *J. Physiol. (Lond.)* **113,** 463–474.
GRANIT, R. (1955) *Receptors and Sensory Perception.* Yale Univ. Press, New Haven.
GREENE, T. and JAMPEL, K. (1966) Muscle spindles in the extraocular muscles of the macaque. *J. Comp. Neurol.* **126,** 547–550.
HAGBARTH, K.-E. and VALLBO, Å. B. (1967) Mechanoreceptor activity recorded percutaneously with semi-microelectrodes in human peripheral nerves. *Acta physiol. scand.* **69,** 121–122.
LIDDELL, E. G. T. and SHERRINGTON, C. S. (1924) Reflexes in response to stretch (Myotatic reflexes). *Proc. Roy. Soc. B,* **96,** 212–242.
MARSDEN, C. D., MERTON, P. A. and MORTON, H. B. (1972) Servo action in human voluntary movement. *Nature (Lond.)* **238,** 140–143.
MATTHEWS, P. B. C. (1972) *Mammalian Muscle Receptors and Their Central Actions.* Arnold, London.
REQUIN, J. (1969) Some data on neurophysiological processes involved in the preparatory motor activity to reaction time performance. *Acta Psychol.* **30,** 358–367.
VALLBO, Å. B. (1970) Discharge patterns in human muscle spindle afferents during isometric voluntary contractions. *Acta physiol. scand.* **80,** 552–556.
VALLBO, Å. B. (1971) Muscle spindle response at the onset of isometric voluntary contractions in man. Time difference between fusimotor and skeletomotor effects. *J. Physiol. (Lond.)* **218,** 405–431.
WESTHEIMER, G. and BLAIR, S. M. (1972) Concerning the supranuclear organization of eye movements. In: *Cerebral Control of Eye Movements and Motion Perception,* DICHGANS, J. and BIZZI, E. (Eds.) pp. 28–35. Karger, Basel.
WHITTERIDGE, D. (1959) The effect of stimulation of intrafusal muscle fibres on sensitivity to stretch of extraocular muscle spindles. *Quart. J. Expl Physiol.* **44,** 385–393.

PERIPHERAL MECHANISMS

MUSCLE CELL TYPES OF THE CAT INFERIOR OBLIQUE†

Jorge A. Alvarado and Carol Van Horn

INTRODUCTION

Hess (1961) first demonstrated that mammalian extraocular muscle (EOM) has two major types of muscle fibers or cells: multi-innervated, non-twitch, and singly-innervated twitch fibers. Subsequent to this, electron microscopic and histochemical studies further subdivided EOM into a confusing number of cell types. This situation prompted Peachey (1971) to review the literature to reconcile discrepancies in the reported findings. He resolved the differences by following the classification of Mayr (1971) in the rat EOM. According to Peachey mammalian EOM cells probably can be subdivided into five cell types (Peachey, 1971).

Except for Harker (1972), subsequent papers have not conformed to the classification of Mayr and Peachey (1971). Harker (1972) studied sheep EOM and also found five cell types; there remained, however, substantial differences between the characteristics of the cells in the sheep and those described by Mayr. In a very recent paper by Durston (1974) only three cell types were found in the EOM of man and baboon.

It is clear that further study of EOM is needed. Since the physiologic, mechanical and motor unit properties of the inferior oblique muscle of the cat are best known (Bach-y-Rita, 1971, Lennerstrand, 1974), this muscle is ideal for morphologic-physiologic correlative studies, hindered only by the absence of a thorough morphologic description. Such a description is the object of this paper.

The findings best fit with those of Mayr. Additional and more readily identifiable characteristics of each cell type are reported. The organization of the EOM is related to that of other skeletal muscles. Compared to other mammalian skeletal muscles, EOM's are unusual in being among two or three muscles having multi-innervated cells, as shown by Hess. In comparison to all vertebrate skeletal muscles they are unusual in at least three respects: (1) the singly-innervated fiber system includes all the cell types found only in the most complex (varied) muscles; (2) the multi-innervated system is represented by every cell type so far described in such muscles; (3) EOM's are the only muscles, so far described, possessing within a single muscle every cell type present in vertebrate skeletal muscle.

METHODS

In cats anesthetized with diabutal, the inferior oblique muscle was isolated by removing the eye and surrounding soft tissues. The muscle was mounted on a plastic holder

†This work was supported in part by: USPHS EY-00799, Research to Prevent Blindness and NIH Grant No. EY 00299. Dr. Alvarado was the recipient of a Seeing Eye Fellowship during 1971–73.

15

under tension through sutures attached to the sclera, sufficient to approximate the resting length of the muscle. A solution of 2% paraformaldehyde and 3.5% glutaraldehyde in 0.15 M sodium cacodylate buffer at pH 7.4 at 37°C was dripped on the muscle for 30 min. Following this the muscle was carefully dissected from the orbit and further fixed by immersion for 2 to 4 hr in the same fixative.

For electron microscopy 2 × 4-mm pieces were cut from clearly identified areas of the whole muscle. These were post-fixed in 2% osmium tetroxide in veronal acetate buffer for 2 to 6 hr, stained *en bloc* in 2% uranyl acetate, dehydrated in cold acetone, embedded in araldite, allowed to stand at room temperature for 1 to 2 days, and slowly polymerized with heat. Thin sections were obtained using a Sorvall MT-2 microtome equipped with a diamond knife. The sections were stained with 2% aqueous uranyl acetate at 45°C for 30 min and lead citrate for 3 min. A Siemens Elmiskop I was used to examine and photograph the tissues. To correlate the appearance of muscle cells in longitudinal and cross-sections, some blocks were flat embedded to permit sectioning of tissues in two planes at 90° angles.

Three muscles were processed intact for fiber count studies by light microscopy; these tissues were post-fixed and embedded in the manner described for electron microscopy. Cross-sections (0·6 μm thick) were obtained at four equidistant points (4–6 mm apart) along the muscles' length. They were stained either with 1% Toluidine Blue or Methylene Blue, and photographed to make a montage having a final magnification of 600×. The cells were then counted by two observers. Numerous single cells were also dissected and their lengths were compared to the whole muscle.

RESULTS

The inferior oblique ranges in length between 15 and 20 mm; its width is from 4–6 mm. The muscle is flat and slightly oval in cross-section, and several zones or layers discerned are described as follows.

1. Orbital Layer

This is the most distinct layer and is situated along the muscle surface facing the orbital bone, partially separated from the rest of the muscle by a wide collagenous band (Fig. 1). This connective tissue band is not invariably present along the muscle length, but can be observed intermittently along 40–60% of the muscle belly, being absent near the insertion and origin of the muscle (Figs. 1A–B). It is still easily distinguished from the remaining muscle by its homogeneous population of small cells (Figs. 1 and 3). It occupies approximately 10–20% of the total area and contains 30–40% of the total number of cells. The cells are well separated from each other by an abundant connective tissue containing the richest capillary bed of the three zones of the muscle (Fig. 3B).

2. Global Layer and Central Zone

These two areas comprise the rest of the muscle. The two portions do not form distinct layers but are characterized by an outer zone of loosely arranged cells occupying

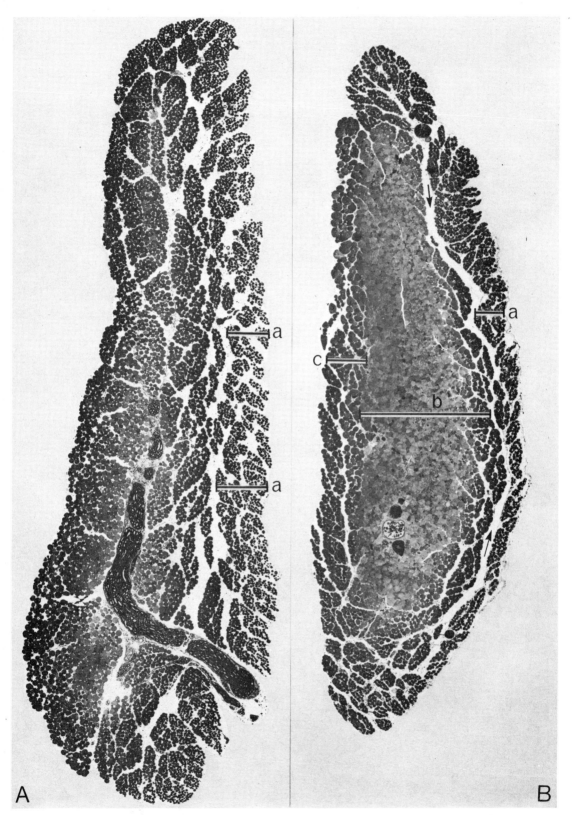

FIG. 1. Cross-sections of midportion of muscle, light micrographs. (A) Section at the level of nerve entry into the muscle. At this level, the orbital layer (a) is not well separated from the other zones. It can be differentiated, however, by its population of very small cells. × 50. (B) The orbital layer (a) is clearly separated by a band of collagenous tissue (arrows) from the dense, central zone (b) and the superficial global layer (c). × 50.

17

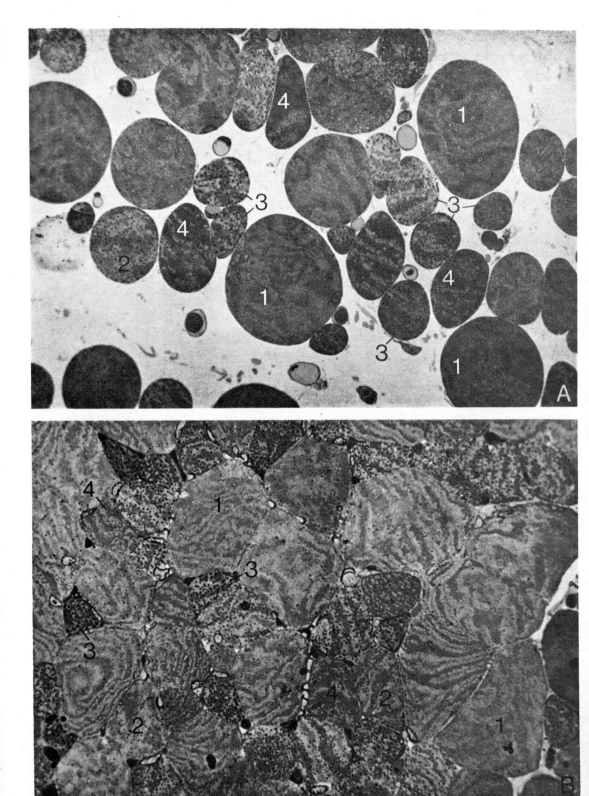

Fig. 2. Global and central zones, light micrographs. (A) Global cells are well separated from each other. Note large cells with scanty mitochondria (mito.) (2); smaller cells of moderate size and mitochondria content (2); very small cells, with large clearly seen mito. (3); distinct dark, dense cells with few mito. (4) are pointed out. ×830. (B) Note the close apposition of cells in the central zone; the same number of cell types may be noticed. ×830.

the surface facing towards the eye, called the *global layer*. The muscle core or *central zone* is surrounded by the orbital and global layers, and is composed of compactly arranged cells (Figs. 1, 2). The two zones contain a heterogenous population of cells varying widely in size and mitochondrial content (Fig. 2).

Fiber count and length

Figure 4 shows how cross-sections of the inferior oblique muscle were obtained at four different points along the muscles' length for fiber counts. The results of the counts are displayed in the bar graph. Sections from adjacent levels demonstrate different numbers of cells; an increasing number being found towards the belly portion of the muscle. The cells of the orbital layer terminate earlier than those in the other portions, so that 4–6 mm from the musculo-tendinous junction few or no cells are found (Fig. 4, Specimens I and II).

Dissection studies showed the largest cells in the central and global zones to be easiest to dissect intact; these cells most often extended the length of the muscle. Several cells in the orbital portion that were dissected intact also extended the length of the muscle.

Fiber types

Five distinct cell types can be distinguished on a morphologic basis; four occur in the global and central zone, and two in the orbital layer. One of the latter two is also found in the other layers. Major identifying characteristics of each type are summarized in Table 1.

Fibers of global and central zone

Type 1

Cells of type 1 are easily identified because of their very large size and paucity of mitochondria (Fig. 2). They constitute 38% of the cells of the global and central core, occupy 60% of this area and have an average diameter of 30.6 μm.

Electron microscopy reveals that the myofibrils are thin, uniform in width, and well separated from each other by an abundant sarcoplasmic reticulum (Figs. 5, 12, 13A). The transverse tubules are prominent and regularly disposed along the A/I band junction. The sarcomere is characterized by a prominent M-line 400 Å in average

TABLE 1. CHARACTERISTICS OF FIBER TYPES IN CAT INFERIOR OBLIQUE

Type	Layer	Average diameter μm	Mitochondria	Membranous: SR + TT	Sarcomere M-line Å	Z-line Å
1		30.6	Few/small	Much	400	480
2	Global	22.2	Moderate	Much	No	540
3		12.6	Many/large	Moderate	Thin/faint	760
4		23.2	Few	Poor	600	1000
3	Orbital	12.2	Many	Moderate	Thin/faint	730 Å
5		12.2	Many	Poor	600 Å	1180 Å

SR = sarcoplasmic reticulum; TT = transverse tubules.

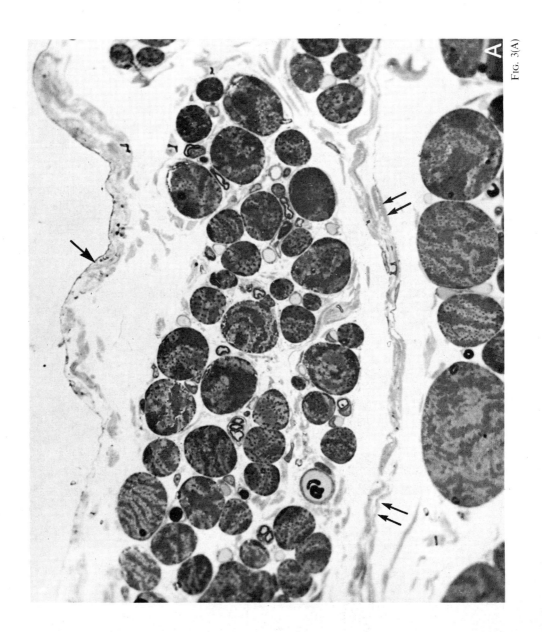

Fig. 3(A)

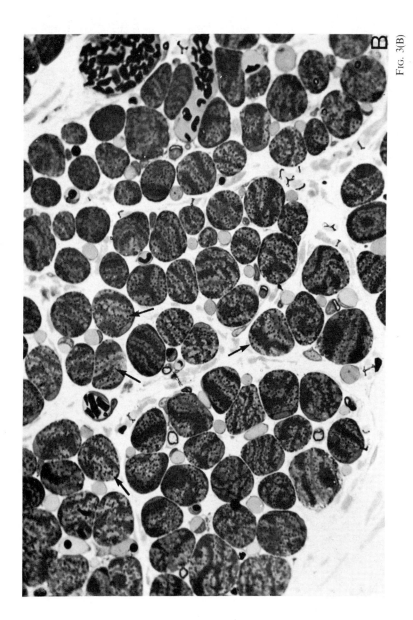

FIG. 3(B)

FIG. 3. Orbital layer. (A) Higher magnification of area seen in Fig. 1A. The surface of the muscle is covered by Tenon's capsule (single arrow); at the bottom of photograph are seen a few cells from the central zone, separated by a dense collagenous tissue (double arrow) from the smaller orbital cells. ×800. (B) Note the uniformity in size, the mito. content (dark dots shown by arrows) and the large number of capillaries found in this layer. ×800.

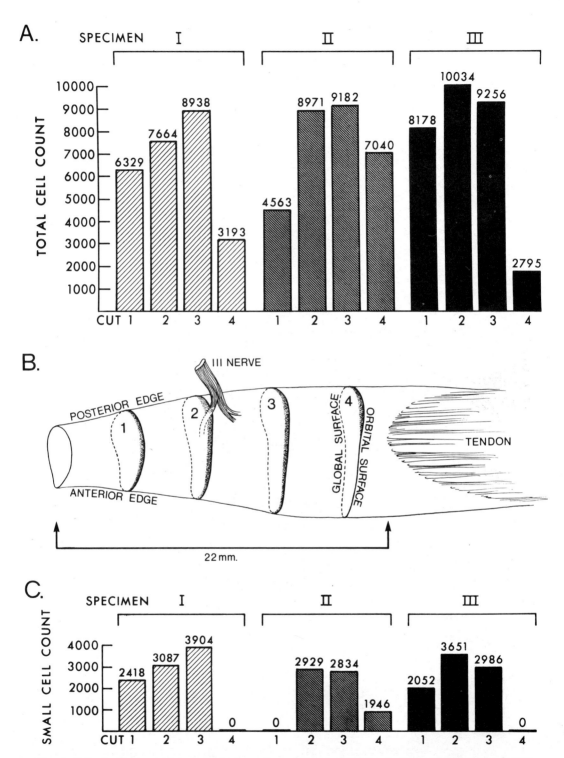

FIG. 4. Cell counts, at equidistant points, from three different specimens, I, II, III. (A) Note the largest number of cells are found in the midportion or belly of the muscle (cuts 2 and 3) and that the total number of cells declines toward the ends. (B) Schematic representation of the shape of the inferior oblique muscle, and the manner in which the cross-sections were taken. The stippled area represents the portion of the muscle cross-section occupied by the orbital layer. (C) This graph shows the proportion of orbital cells found at each level. Note the orbital cells represent a significant portion of the total number of cells, and that these cells terminate earlier than the cells from other zones.

22

Fig. 5. Type 1 muscle fiber. (A) The myofibrils are well aligned, clearly separated from each other by an extensive transverse tubular system (arrows) and sarcoplasmic reticulum; the sarcomere has thin Z-lines and a prominent M-line; the mitochondria (M) are few and very small. ×13,200. (B) Detail of the sarcomere showing the well-developed SR, especially along the I-band region. Note the complex interconnections among the SR tubules as well as the triads (arrow) formed with the transverse tubules. ×27,000.

FIG. 6. Type 2 muscle cell. The myofibrils are discrete, thin, and well separated from each other as in cell type 1; however, an M-line is not evident and the mito. are larger and more abundant. × 9600.

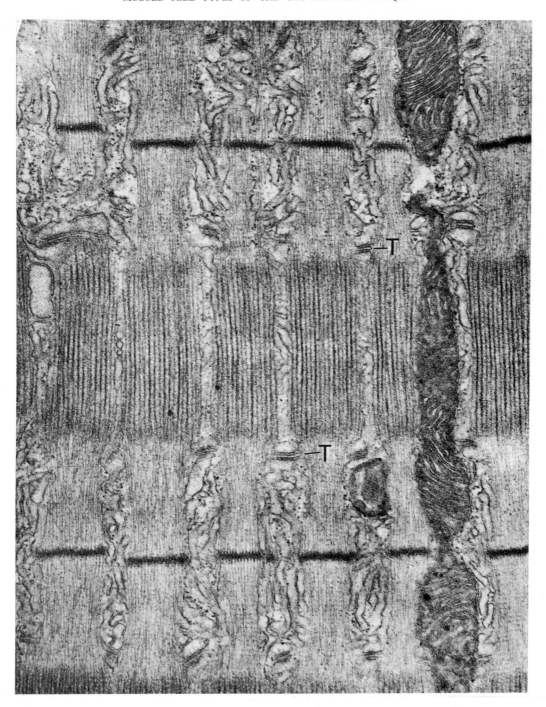

Fig. 7. Cell type 2. Note the tubular elements of the SR forming two and three layers along the I-band region, regularly interacting with the transverse (T) tubules. The SR extends through the A-band region. No M-line is discernible. × 30,000.

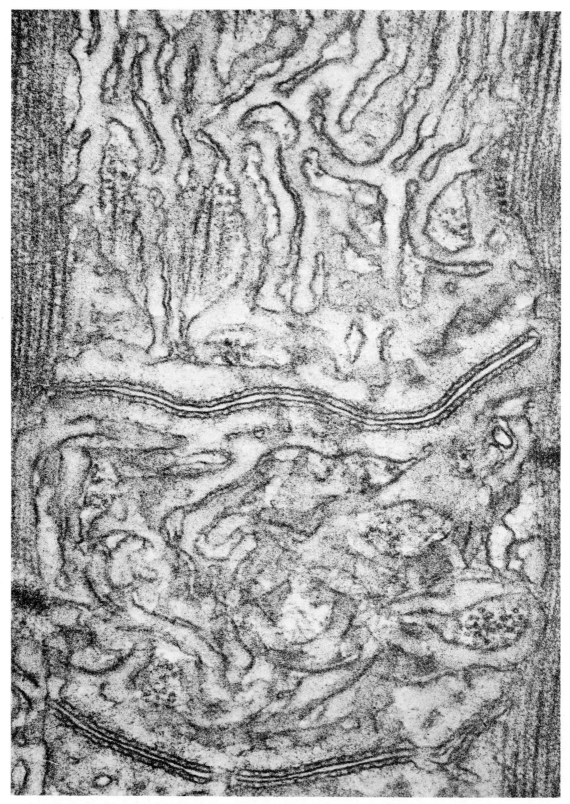

FIG. 8. Cell type 2. The interconnecting tubules of the SR are shown, being especially abundant in the I-band region, forming triads at the level of the A/I junction, extending into the A-band region, forming a single layer of interconnecting tubules. Note the absence of fenestrated cisternae of the SR present in other skeletal muscle. ×81,000.

width, as well as a straight, thin Z-band averaging 480 Å in width (SD 90 Å). The scarce very small mitochondria extend the length of the I-band, rarely measuring more than one micron in length (Fig. 5A).

Type 2

These are the most difficult to identify with certainty, especially by light microscopy, since they have many features in common with cell types 1 and 3. They are distinguished from cell type 1 with the light microscope by their smaller size and larger more numerous mitochondria (Fig. 2), and from type 3 by their larger size, smaller and less numerous mitochondria. Type 2 cells measure 22.2 μm in average diameter, constitute 20% of the cells from the global and central areas and occupy 16% of these areas.

By electron microscopy, type 2 cells can be identified best when sectioned in two planes at a right angle to each other. The same cell can be studied in cross-section for mitochondrial content and size, and in longitudinal section for the features of the sarcomere. The absence of an M-line differentiates these cells from type 1 and 3 cells (Figs. 6, 7). The myofibrils are thin, as in cell type 1, but the endoplasmic reticulum is more abundant, especially in the I-band region where the cisternae and tubes of the endoplasmic reticulum form double and triple layers (Figs. 7, 8, 12, 13B). The transverse tubular system is also prominent, forming triads which flank the myofibrils and course radially at the level of the A- and I-band junctions (Fig. 8). The Z-line measures 540 Å in average diameter (SD 95 Å). The mitochondria are more abundant and two or three times larger than those in type 1; usually they are equal in length to the sarcomere or about 2–3 μm (Fig. 6). They are not uniformly distributed throughout the cell, some areas containing large numbers of subsarcolemmal mitochondria and others in which they are scanty.

Type 3

These are the smallest cells found in the global and central zones, measuring 12.6 μm in diameter. They constitute 26% of the cells and occupy 8% of the global area.

Their mitochondria are largest of all cell types, being wider than the myofibrils, and frequently extend the length of two and occasionally four sarcomeres (3 to 8 μm). The mitochondrial cristae are unusually abundant and closely packed, giving the mitochondria a darker appearance than in other cell types. The mitochondria are arranged in long columns between the myofibrils or along the periphery of the fiber, and numerous lipid granules are closely associated with them (Fig. 9). The mitochondria may occupy as much as 30% of the cross-sectional area of the muscle fiber.

The sarcoplasmic reticulum (SR) is less developed than in cell types 1 and 2, and is especially apparent in cross-sections along the A-band, where a few profiles of SR separate the myofibrils (Figs. 12, 14). The transverse tubules are seen most often along the A- and I-band junctions, but they are not as abundant as in types 1 or 2. The most distinguishing feature of the sarcomere is its Z-line, measuring 760 Å (SD 92 Å), and thus is thicker than in fiber types 1 and 2. These cells appear to be susceptible to mechanical disruption during preparation, often resulting in irregular Z-lines and

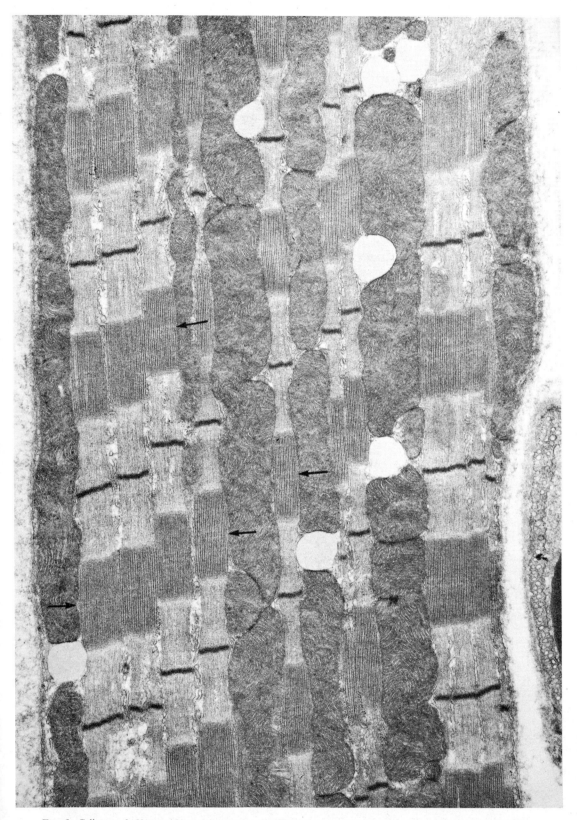

FIG. 9. Cell type 3. Very wide and long mitochondria, closely packed with cristae mitochondriales, form long columns. The mitochondria are closely associated with numerous lipid granules. The myofibrils are thin, separated by a relatively scanty SR. The Z-line is thicker than cell types 1 and 2. A faint M-line is recognized in some sarcomeres (arrows). × 16,750.

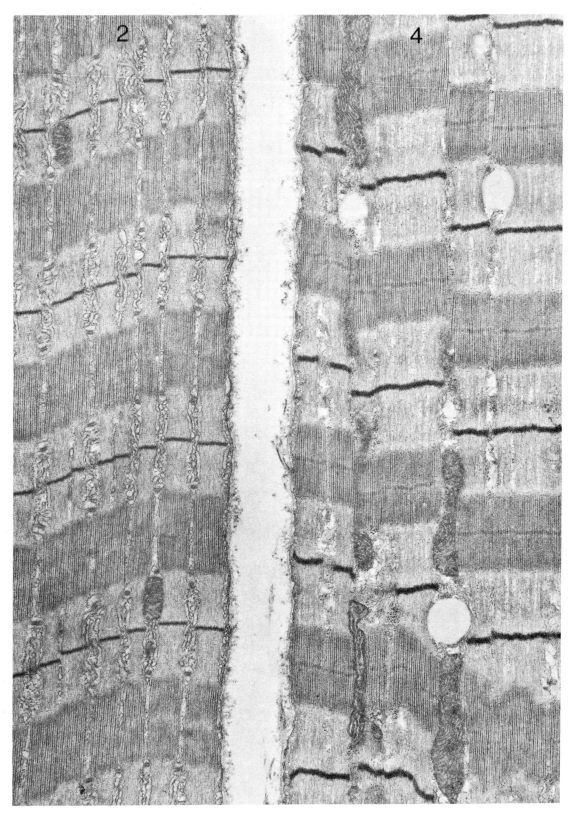

Fig. 10. Cell types 4 and 2. Contrast type 2, seen on the left side, with cell type 4, characterized by an extremely thick Z-line, a prominent M-line and by a scanty SR and transverse tubular system. × 18,000.

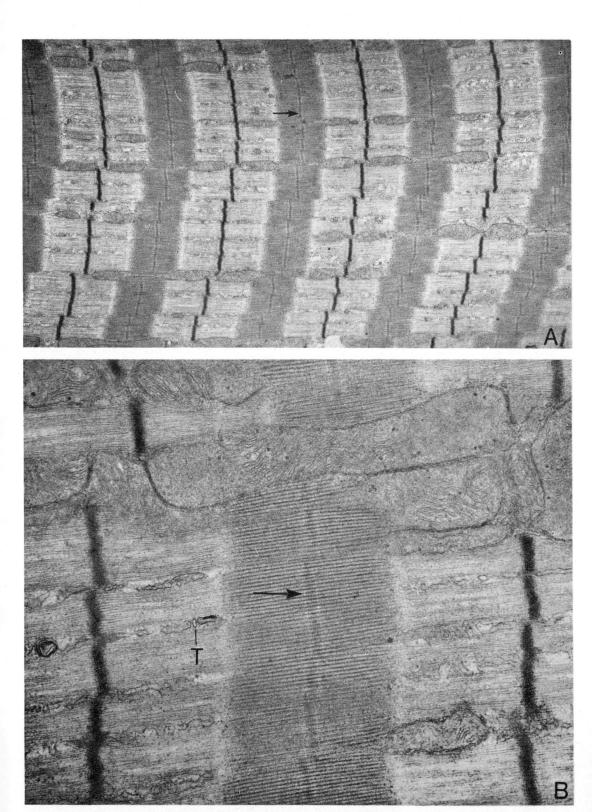

FIG. 11. (A) and (B). Further illustrations of type 4 cells. The mitochondria are generally small, disposed along the I-band on either side of the Z-line. The M-line is prominent (arrows). Figure (B) shows a few profiles of the seldom seen T-system (T). A, × 10,500; B, × 35,000.

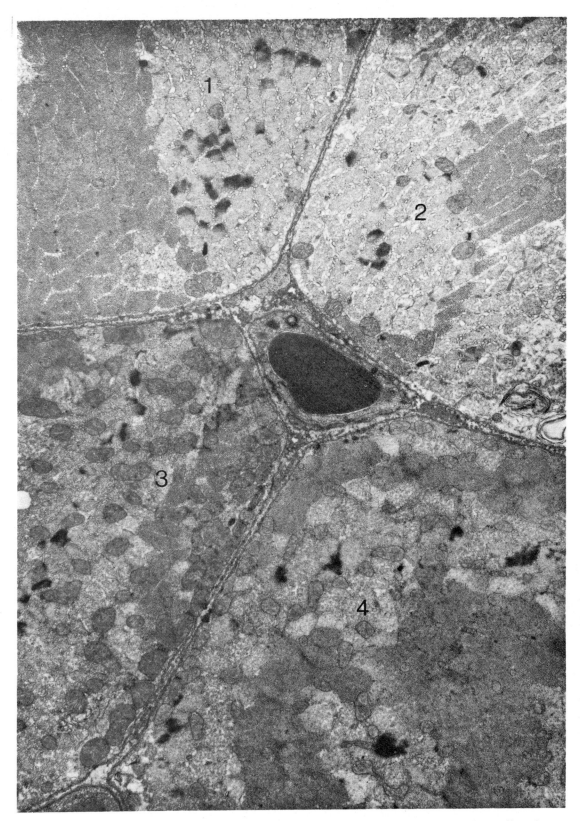

FIG. 12. Global fibers in cross-section. The myofibrils of cells type 1 and 2 are outlined by profiles of the SR; the mitochondria of cell type 2 are larger and more numerous than type 1. The SR of type 3 is seen mainly along the I-band region, the mito. are abundant. The myofibrils of type 4 appeared fused with each other, except in some areas sectioned across the I-band. × 14,200.

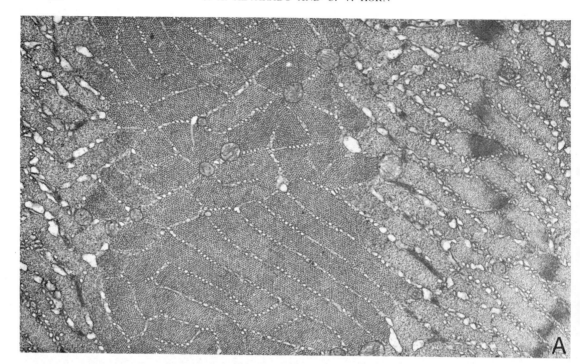

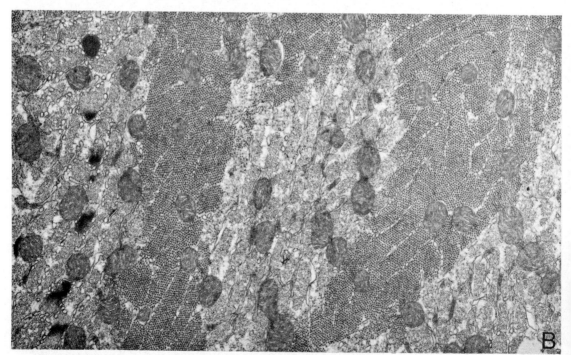

FIG. 13. (A) Cell type 1. Notice the regular separation of myofibrils by oval profiles of the SR; these form double-layer ribbons along the I-band region. × 19,200. (B) Cell type 2. The myofibrils are distinct; the mito. are observed in both the I- and A-band regions. × 15,000.

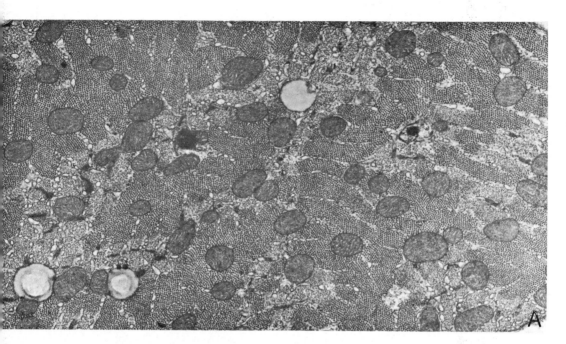

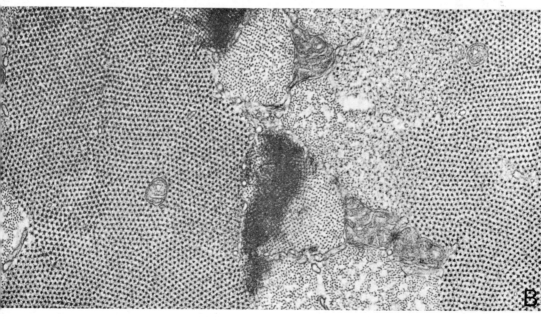

FIG. 14. (A) Cell type 3. Note the abundant mito., lipid granules and a moderate number of profiles of the SR. × 19,000. (B) Cell type 4. The paucity of SR elements and mitochondria makes it impossible to determine the boundaries of the myofibrils. The thick Z-line forms dark, wide patches in cross-section. × 45,000.

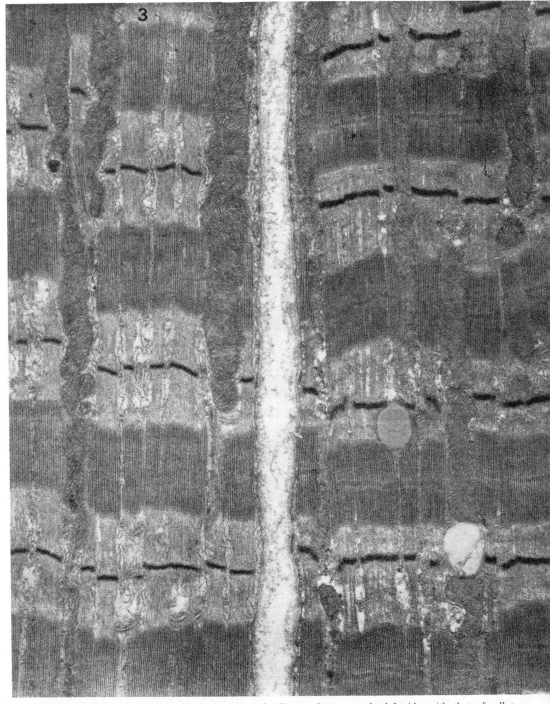

Fig. 15. Orbital cells. Contrast the appearance of cell type 5 seen on the left side, with that of cell type 3, present on the right side. Type 5 is distinguished by its thicker Z-line, prominent M-line but poorly developed SR. Both have numerous large mitochondria, but type 3 has a better developed SR and transverse tubules, especially along the I-band region. × 15,000.

poor demarcation of the A/I junction. There is an M-line, but it is often difficult to visualize, especially in cells showing misalignment of the myofilaments.

Type 4

These cells are easily identified by light and electron microscopy (Figs. 2, 10, 11, 12, 14B). Their average diameter is 23.2 μm, they comprise 15% of the cells in the global and central region and occupy 16% of this area. With the light microscope, they are the darkest and most compact cells and show few mitochondria. The electron microscope shows this compact appearance to be due to the close apposition of the myofibrils, barely separated from each other by a sparse SR. The reticulum is usually found in the I-band region, and rarely extends into the A-band. The transverse tubules are likewise the least developed of all the cell types, and are difficult to demonstrate (Fig. 11B). The sarcomere is characterized by a thick Z-band measuring 1000 Å (SD 127 Å) and a prominent M-line of 600 Å average width. The mitochondria are scanty, small, and usually disposed along the I-band (Fig. 11A).

Orbital layer

The cells of this layer appear homogeneous with the light microscope and were counted and measured as one cell type. They represent 30–40% of the total number of cells in the whole muscle. They measure 12.2 μm in average diameter. By electron microscopy they can be classified into two cell types.

Type 3

Previous authors (Mayr, 1973; Harker, 1972) have classified this cell as distinct from its counterpart in the global and central zones. The two cells are morphologically identical, and should be classified as type 3, until physiological or other studies indicate otherwise. This cell is best differentiated from its companion cell in the orbital layer (type 5) when observed in longitudinal section with the electron microscope (Fig. 15). Type 3 constitutes 60–70% of the cells from the orbital layer. Figures 15 and 16 show its morphology which is identical to its counterpart in the global and central zones.

Type 5

This cell type, while characteristic of the orbital layer, is occasionally found in the central zone, where it is easily confused with type 4. Type 5 cells are less common, it is estimated they represent 30–40% of the cells in the orbital portion. They are distinguished from cell type 3 by their thicker Z-line measuring 1180 Å (SD 110) and their prominent M-line, measuring 600 Å in average width. Type 5 cells resemble type 3 in having a large number of mitochondria and lipid granules. The myofibrils are closely apposed to each other, being separated from each other by a poorly developed sarcoplasmic reticulum.

Occasionally cells are seen in the orbital region which cannot be classified with certainty. They resemble type 5, except for the absence of an M-line, slightly fewer mitochondria, and a better developed sarcoplasmic reticulum.

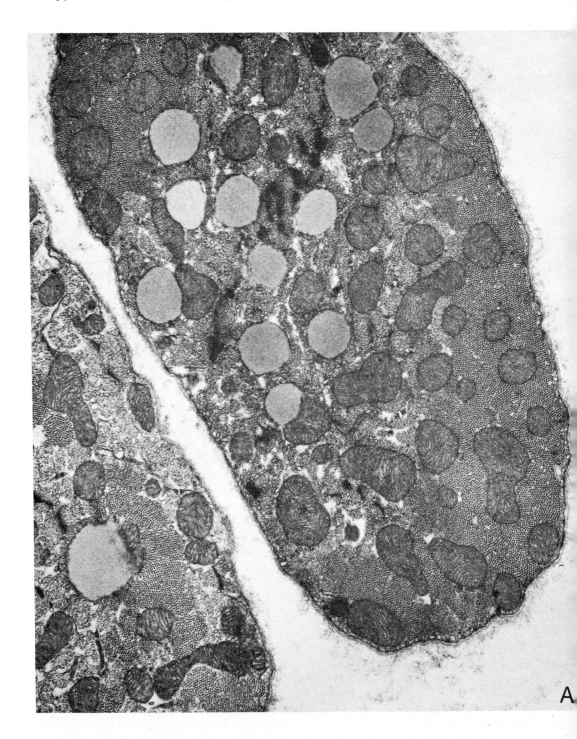

A

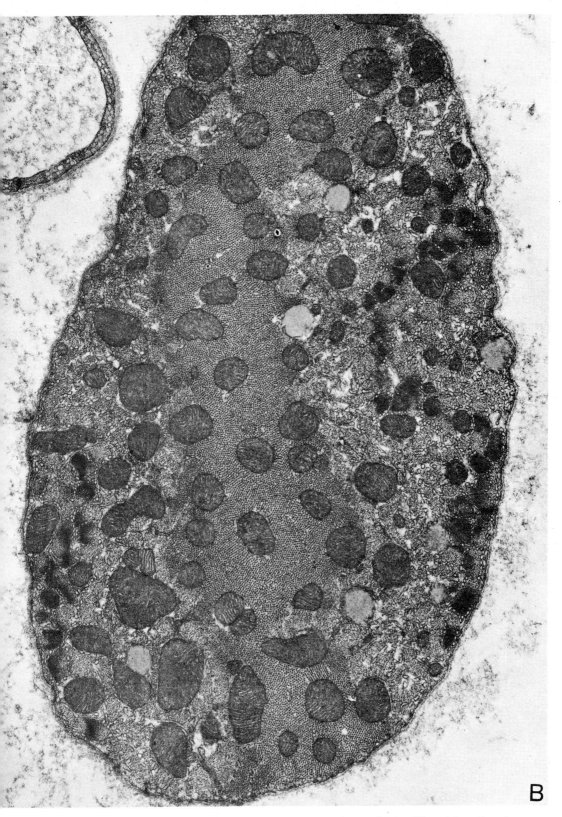

FIG. 16. (A and B) Cross-sectional views of the orbital cells are less useful in differentiating these two cell types. Both cells have numerous, large mitochondria and lipid vacuoles. The cell in Fig. B may be classified as type 3 because of its better developed SR, shown along the I-band region. A/B, ×18,000.

DISCUSSION

Fiber Length

The length of the EOM cells relative to the muscle's length has been a subject of controversy. Most textbooks (Cogan, 1970; Wolff, 1968) state the cells extend the length of the muscle. Hines (1931), however, described muscle fibers terminating in the middle third, as well as near the insertion in the rabbit EOM. Lockhart and Brandt (1938), without publishing supportive data, noted: "In the adult eye muscles the fibers run all the way."

In the past, accurate fiber counts could not be performed using traditional methods (e.g. paraffin embedding) because of the small size and close apposition of the muscle cells. Since the EOM are small, modern techniques using plastic resins for embedding can be employed. This permits the muscle to be sectioned thin enough to provide sufficient resolution for accurate fiber counts. Our data shows that the largest number of fibers occupy the middle third or belly of the cat inferior oblique muscle. The count drops rapidly within 4–6 mm from this point, then gradually decreases toward the origin and insertion of the muscle. Dissection studies showed some fibers to terminate several millimeters short of the tendon and others, especially the large ones, to extend the length of the muscle.

It is apparent from this study that a significant number of cells terminate within the muscle and that most of those that do are the small diameter fibers. The actual proportion of short fibers is unknown; such determinations might best be done by dissection studies which are tedious and difficult. Some short cells have been reported to form overlapping and end to end junctions (Floyd, 1970); these cells would extend the muscle's length when dissected out, while in reality they represent several cells joined together axially. The above data and observations may explain the wide range in size that has been observed in measurements of a given cell type; also very small fibers that have been described probably represent cells tapering down as they terminate within the muscle. This would be borne out by the fact that measurements of the fiber size in the middle third of the muscle show less variation than at the ends.

The findings regarding cell length in the cat inferior oblique are in agreement with those in other skeletal muscles. The latter were summarized by Gould (1973) in a recent review. He stated muscle fibers extend the muscle's length in short muscles such as the tensor tympani, and in long muscles whose fibers are arranged in parallel, such as the sartorius muscle. Most muscles are composed of fibers shorter than the muscle's length, the thicker fibers usually being the longest.

Muscle Cell Classification

Table 2 compares the number and terminology of muscle fiber types found in this study with those of other observers. The cells are designated by number until physiologic properties are demonstrated that may be used to designate the fiber types. Arabic numerals are used to avoid confusion with the classification employed in some histochemistry studies where roman numerals were employed to classify the muscle cell types (Brooke and Kaiser, 1970; Guth et al., 1969).

TABLE 2. COMPARISON OF SEVERAL RECENT STUDIES OF EOM

Author	Alvarado, 1974		Mayr, 1971 and 1973	Harker, 1973	Miller, 1971
Species	Cat		Rat	Sheep	Monkey
	Type				
Global		1	Large pale	1. Large "A"	White
	{	2	Intermediate	2. Intermediate "C"	Large red
	{	3	Small, dark	3. Small C	?
	{	4	Clear	4. Large "G"	Slow
Orbital	{	3	Dark	5. Small "C"	
	{	5	Clear	6. Small "G"	Small red
				7. Intermediate "C"	

The cells are listed in an order corresponding with those published by Mayr (1973). Two major aspects of the classification of EOM fibers are considered: (1) the arrangement of muscle cells into layers and (2) the separation of fibers into singly and multiply innervated cells. Studies of the properties of each layer have proved useful in clinical research, especially, those designed to interpret the findings of the electromyogram (EMG). For instance, the activity recorded with the EMG when the eyes are held "at rest" in the primary position was recently shown to stem largely from the orbital layer (Breinin, 1971; Scott and Collins, 1973).

We recently reported on the type of innervation of each cell by staining the motor endplates of fibers dissected to a single cell level (Alvarado, Nichols and Van Horn). The results showed cell types 1, 2, and 3 of the global region and three of the orbital layer are singly innervated, while types 4 and 5 are multi-innervated. As shown in Table 2, the fibers are separated according to innervation; singly innervated cells listed before multi-innervated ones. The cells are also listed in order of increasing mitochondrial content, decreasing size and sarcoplasmic reticulum content. Harker (1973) offered reasons to expect that cell types 1, 2, and 3 might correspond to the physiological types described by Burke (1973) in the cat gastrocnemius. These types are designated FF for fast, easily fatigued fibers, FR for fast, moderately fatigue resistant fibers, and S for slow, most fatigue resistant fibers. Again, the present classification suggests and anticipates such physiological relationships.

The thickness of the Z-line proved to be rather useful in differentiating cell types closely resembling each other, such as types 3 and 4 or types 4 and 5. These cells differ sharply in Z-line thickness (see Table 1).

There is close correspondence between the five fiber types of the cat and rat EOM with respect to size, sarcoplasmic (SR) and mitochondrial content. They differ most markedly in the presence or absence of an M-line. While only cell type 2 lacks an M-line in the cat EOM, only cell type 4 has an M-line in the rat. The M-line is easily disrupted by misalignment of the myofilaments, and it is best preserved in glutaraldehyde fixed tissues (Knappeis and Carlsen, 1968). Cheng-Minoda et al. (1968) examined type 4 muscle fibers from several species, variously fixed, and concluded that the presence or absence of an M-line was a species related property.

The sheep EOM and those of the cat and rat have fewer common properties. The sizes do not correspond, so that cell type 4 is the largest cell in the sheep instead of cell type 1. The orbital layer is described to contain a third cell type, instead of two. The muscle fibers are said to branch near their insertion, a phenomenon so far unreported on other EOM (Harker, 1972). The four fibers observed in the monkey EOM closely correspond to those in the cat and rat. Miller's classification (1967) is based largely on research performed before Peachey's review of the literature; more recent work is consistent with the presence of five cell types in the monkey (Miller).

Comparison of EOM and Other Skeletal Muscles

A. *Singly-innervated system*

Investigations to determine the fiber types of EOM and of other skeletal muscles (SM) in the past dozen years have led to parallel developments. In both fields observers were initially concerned with the ultrastructural characteristics of only two fiber types: red and white for SM's; "fast" and "slow" for EOM's. Subsequent studies involved the application of histochemical techniques and an ever-increasing number of cell types were reported, reaching as many as eight for SM and four for the EOM (Romanul, 1964; Miller, 1967). Recent physiologic and morphologic studies in singly-innervated skeletal muscles have resulted in the description of three muscle fiber types only. The muscles studied were selected because the properties of their motor units were well known or because strictly morphologic–physiologic correlative studies could be conducted on these muscles.

The motor unit properties of a fast muscle, the extensor digitorum longus (EDL), and a slow muscle, the soleus muscle, of the rat were studied by Close (1967). The EDL has fast motor units only composed of muscle fibers having an average twitch contraction time of 11 ms. The soleus is predominantly composed of slow motor units with contraction times averaging 38 ms. There exist, in addition, a few "intermediate" motor units with contraction times lasting 18 ms. Schiaffino *et al.* (1970) showed that the EDL is composed of a heterogenous fiber population, varying in size and mitochondria content; however, all these cells possess a well-developed sarcoplasmic reticulum (SR), which correlates well with the fast contraction time of the fibers. The slow soleus is predominantly composed of a homogeneous group of fibers characterized by a poorly developed SR and a moderate number of mitochondria. There is a small percentage of fibers with a better developed SR, presumably belonging to the motor units of "intermediate" speed of contraction mentioned above (Close, 1967).

Burke (1971, 1973) performed correlative morphologic–physiologic studies of the cat gastrocnemius. Three motor units were identified, each composed of a homogeneous fiber population. As mentioned, he proposed the terminology FF, FR, and S to designate the motor units. Each motor unit is composed of one of the three cell types found in the gastrocnemius. FF and FR fibers possess high levels of myofibrillar ATPase which accords with their faster contraction times; they also have high levels of non-oxidative glycolytic enzymes. The S fibers, on the other hand, have low levels of myofibrillar ATPase and high levels of oxidative glycolytic enzymes, in accordance with their low speed of contraction and high resistance to fatigue.

The singly-innervated fibers of extraocular muscles closely resemble those described in other mammalian skeletal muscles (see, for example, Schiaffino *et al.* 1970; Gauthier, 1969). The question is whether the EOM's are organized similarly to one of the three muscles previously described. That is, do the three singly-innervated fibers of the EOM belong to three distinct types of motor units, like the gastrocnemius muscle, or to one type of motor unit, like the EDL.

Table 3 is an analysis of the fiber composition of the inferior oblique. It shows the singly-innervated system accounts for a majority of the cells (70%); most of these cells are richly supplied with mitochondria and presumably fatigue resistant. At least half of the singly-innervated cells possess an extensive membranous system, implying the ability to contract rapidly (types 1 and 2). While type 3 has a modest membranous system, it might be adequate considering the unusually small size (diameter) of these cells. Indeed, morphometric analysis has shown that the sarcoplasmic reticulum to myofibril ratio of cell type 3 is nearly equal to that of cell types 1 and 2, which have a very well-developed SR (Mayr, 1973). It appears then, the twitch, singly-innervated system has the morphological attributes of a very fast, largely fatigue resistant system.

TABLE 3. ANALYSIS OF THE FIBER COMPOSITION OF THE CAT INFERIOR OBLIQUE MUSCLE

Type	Innervation	Percent of total number of cells	Mitochondria rich Type	Percent	S.R. + TT rich
1 2 3 3 orb.	Single	23% 12% 15% 20%	2 3 5 (3)	= 47%	} = 35%
		Subtotal 70%			
4 5	Multiple	15% 15% Total 100%	6 } 15%		Total 35%
			Total 62%		

Lennerstrand (1974) performed the first extensive study of extraocular muscle motor units using the cat inferior oblique muscle. He was able to identify one type of motor unit belonging to the singly innervated system and two types to the multi-innervated system. The recorded contraction times ranged from 3.5 ms to 18 ms. The motor units were remarkably fatigue resistant; those units that fatigued corresponded to the fibers with the fastest contraction times. These studies indicate that the singly-innervated fibers of the inferior oblique and presumably other EOM are organized in a similar manner to those of the EDL. That is, both muscles are composed of three muscle fiber types, but only one motor unit type, a fast, fatigue-resistant motor unit. The possibility still exists, however, that the duration of stimulation used by Lennerstrand to bring out differences in fatigue resistance was not sufficiently long. Burke (1973) has commented on the difficulty of determining the precise conditions that will bring out such differences; he found the use of subtetanic rates of stimulus quite useful. This manner of stimulation was not utilized by Lennerstand. The possibility still exists, then, that the different muscle fibers might belong to distinct motor units as found in the cat gastrocnemius.

B. *The multi-innervated system*

There are comparatively fewer studies of the multi-innervated skeletal muscle system than of the already discussed singly-innervated one. Two studies are particularly relevant to this paper and will be briefly described. Takeuchi (1958) recorded intracellular potential of red and white muscle fibers of the snake fish; he recorded overshoot action potentials from the white fibers and non-overshoot, MEPP-like, potentials from the red fibers. Nakajima (1969) later reported that both red and white fibers were multi-innervated, the red fibers containing numerous, small closely grouped end plates, while the white fibers have fewer, larger, evenly spaced motor end plates. The multi-innervated EOM system was first shown by Hess and Pilar to contain fibers producing non-conducted junctional potentials similar to those of the red fibers of the snake fish. A major point of contention has been whether multi-innervated fibers in EOM are also capable of producing conducted, over-shoot potentials as suggested by Bach-y-Rita (1971). The studies of Lennerstrand have shown that the inferior oblique muscle of the cat has two multi-innervated motor units; one capable of producing non-propagated junctional potentials and the other propagated overshoot spike potentials.

We have shown that the two multi-innervated fibers (types 4 and 5) correspond to a white, mitochondria-poor and a red mitochondria-rich fiber. Thus, it appears the multi-innervated system in the EOM closely resembles other multi-innervated skeletal muscles. Indeed, the multi- and singly-innervated muscle fibers of extraocular muscles have similar counterparts in other skeletal muscles, but EOM's are different in several regards. They, together with the tensor tympani and esophagus, are the only mammalian muscles having multi-innervated cells (Romanul, 1964). Furthermore, EOM's are unusual among all skeletal muscles in three other respects: (1) the singly innervated system is composed of the maximal number of cell types (three) described in these muscles; (2) the multi-innervated system has the two cell types so far described in such muscles; (3) EOM's are the only skeletal muscles, so far described, every type of vertebrate skeletal muscle fiber within a single muscle. This duality of functional systems, together with the great variety of cell types, is undoubtedly responsible for the unusual physiological properties of extraocular muscles. These muscles are capable of prolonged sustained contraction, of extremely fast saccadic movements, as well as very slow vergence movements, etc.

Future studies may now be carried out in the cat inferior oblique using intracellular microelectrodes to study the physiologic properties of single cells, which may then be labelled with a color dye for subsequent morphologic characterization. These studies will hopefully provide the information needed to relate structure to function, and a better classification of extraocular muscle fibers.

ACKNOWLEDGEMENTS

We wish to express our appreciation for the support given throughout this project by Dr. Paul Bach-y-Rita. Many thanks to Professor M. J. Hogan for reading the manuscript and offering many suggestions. Dr. Jane Hyde is also thanked for her editorial contributions.

REFERENCES

ALVARADO, J. A., NICHOLS, K. and VAN HORN, C. Innervation of the cat extraocular muscle fibers (in preparation).
BACH-Y-RITA, P. (1971) Neurophysiology of eye movements. In: *The Control of Eye Movements*, BACH-Y-RITA, P., COLLIN, C., and HYDE, J. (Eds.), pp. 7–45, Academic Press.

BREININ, G. M. (1971) The structure and function of extraocular muscle—an appraisal of the duality concept. *Am. J. Ophthal.* **72,** 1–9.

BROOKE, M. H. and KAISER, K. K. (1970) Muscle fiber types: how many and what kind? *Arch. Neurol.* **23,** 369–379.

BURKE, R. E., LEVINE, D. N., TSAIRIS, P. and ZAJAC, F. E. III (1973) Physiological types and histochemical profiles in motor units of the cat gastrocnemius. *J. Physiol.* **234,** 723–748.

BURKE, R. E., LEVINE, D. N., ZAJAC, F. E., TSAIRIS, P. and ENGEL, W. K. (1971) Mammalian motor units: physiological-histochemical correlations in three types in cat gastrocnemius. *Science, N.Y.* **174,** 709–712.

CHENG-MINODA, K., DAVIDOWITZ, J., LIEBOWITZ, A. and BREMIN, G. M. (1968) Fine structure of extraocular muscle in the rabbit. *J. Cell. Biol.* **39,** 193–197.

CLOSE, R. (1967) Properties of motor units in fast and slow skeletal muscles of the rat. *J. Physiol.* **193,** 45–55.

COGAN, D. G. (1970) *Neurology of the Ocular Muscles,* 2nd ed. Charles C. Thomas, publisher.

DURSTON, J. H. J. (1974) Histochemistry of primate extraocular muscles and the changes of denervation. *Brit. J. Ophthal.* **58,** 193–216.

FLOYD, K. (1970): Junctions between muscle fibers in cat extraocular muscles. *Nature,* **227,** 185.

GAUTHIER, G. F. (1969) On the relationship of ultrastructural and cytochemical features to color in mammalian skeletal muscle. *Z. Zellforsch. mikrosk. Anat.* **95,** 462–482.

GOULD, R. P. (1973) The microanatomy of muscle. In *The Structure and Function of Muscle,* BOURNE, G. H. (Ed.). Academic Press, Inc.

GUTH, LLOYD and SAMAKA, F. J. (1969) Qualitative differences between actomyosin ATPare of slow and fast mammalian muscle. *Exptl Neurol.* **25,** 138–152.

HARKER, D. W. (1972) The structure and innervation of sheep superior rectus and levator palpebra extraocular muscles. I. Extrafusal fibers. *Inv. Ophthal.* **11,** 956–969.

HESS, A. (1961) The structure of slow and fast extrafusal muscle fibers in the extraocular muscles and their nerve endings in guinea pigs. *J. Cell. Comp. Physiol.* **58,** 63–80.

HINES, M. (1931) Studies on the innervation of skeletal muscle. III. Innervation of the extrinsic eye muscles of the rabbit. *Am. J. Anat.* **47,** 1–53.

KNAPPEIS, G. G. and CARLSEN, F. (1968) The ultrastructure of the M-line in skeletal muscle. *J. Cell. Biol.* **38,** 202–211.

LENNERSTRAND, G. (1974) *Brit. J. Ophthal.* **58,** 193–216; Isometric tension and electrical activity in motor units of the cat's inferior oblique muscle. *Acta Physiol. Scand.* (in press).

LOCKHART, R. D. and BRANDT, W. (1938) Length of striated muscle fibers. *J. Anat.* **72,** 470.

MAY, R. (1971) Structure and distribution of fibre types in the external eye muscles of the rat. *Tissue and Cell.* **3,** 433–462.

MAYR, R. (1973) Morphometrie von Ratten–Augenmaskel fasern. *Vorh. Anat. G & S* **67,** 353–358.

MILLER, J. E. (1967) Cellular organization of rhesus extraocular muscle. *Invest. Ophthal.* **6,** 18–39.

MILLER, J. E. (Nov. 1971) Recent histologic and electron microscopic findings in extraocular muscles. *Trans. Am. Acad. Ophthal. Otolar.* **75,** 1175–85 (1973).

MILLER, J. E. Personal communication.

NAKAJIMA, YASUKA (1969) Fine structure of red and white muscle fibers and their neuromuscular junctions in the snake fish (*Ophiocephalus corgus*). *Tissue and Cell,* **1,** 229–246.

PACHTER, B. R. and BREININ, G. H. Fine structure and function of ocular tissues. Extraocular Muscle. *Int. Ophthal. Clin.* **13,** 263–271.

PEACHEY, L. (1971) The structure of the extraocular muscle fibers of mammals. In: *The Control of Eye Movement,* BACH-Y-RITA, P., COLLINS, C. and HYDE, J. (Eds.), pp. 45–67. Academic Press.

ROMANUL, F. C. A. (1964) Enzymes in muscle. I. Histochemical studies of enzymes in individual muscle fibers. *Arch. Neurol.* **11,** 355–368.

SCHIAFFINO, S., HANZLIKOVA, V. and PIEROBON, S. (1970) Relations between structure and function in rat skeletal muscle fibers. *J. Cell Biol.* **47,** 107–119.

SCOTT, A. B. and COLLINS, C. C. (1973) Division of labor in human extraocular muscle. *Arch. Ophthal.* **90,** 319–322.

TAKEGUCHI, A. (1958) Neuromuscular transmission fish skeletal muscles investigated with intracellular micro-electrodes. *J. Cell. Comp. Physiol.* **54,** 211–220.

WOLFF, E. (1968) *The Anatomy of the Eye and Orbit,* 6th ed. W. B. Saunders Co., Philadelphia.

Discussion Remarks of R. Mayr

I want to discuss two aspects of eye muscle morphology: (1) muscle fiber types, and (2) internal structure of extra-ocular muscles.

1. Dr. Alvarado's excellent presentation on the "Morphology of Eye Muscles" based on his detailed studies of cat extraocular muscle (EOM) and the recent literature has shown that, with respect to muscle fiber types, the situation has become much clearer since the last symposium in San Francisco (cf. Peachey, 1971). Irrespective of the absence (rat, cat) or presence (sheep) of muscle spindles, the oculorotatory EOM of mammals have essentially the same pattern of (extrafusal) muscle fiber composition. They are composed of two layers which may overlap to some extent. The global or central layer (GL) consists of four types of muscle fibers, one type of medium to large fibers with multiple motor innervation and a more or less continuous spectrum of large, intermediate and small fibers with focal innervation. The orbital or peripheral layer (OL) contains only two fiber types, both of small diameter, one with multiple and one with focal innervation. The multi-innervated types of the two layers are morphologically different and may conform with amphibian (GL) and avian (OL) type slow fibers, respectively. The focally innervated fibers of the OL are in many respects similar to the small focally innervated fibers of the GL, and the question arises whether their separate classification is justified. Morphometric studies in the rat (Mayr, 1973) show that on account of the amount of the sarcotubular system all three types of focally innervated fibers of the GL can be expected to be equally fast acting, whereas the focally innervated fibers of the OL contain less sarcoplasmic reticulum suggesting less rapid action. An additional fiber type seems to exist in the spindle containing periphery of sheep eye muscles (Harker, 1972).

Recent histochemical work in cat and rabbit (Asmussen *et al.*, 1972) supports the presence of six fiber types, four in the GL and two in the OL. In conclusion it can be stated that there is good agreement on number, distribution and many morphological features of fiber types in mammalian EOM now. However, several properties are subject to species-dependent variation, among them the behavior of the M-line, the diameter range of the different fiber types, the mitochondrial content especially of the multi-innervated fibers, etc. Because of these variations and the differences in terminology the literature is still confusing. Therefore a common terminology satisfying comparative demands should be proposed.

2. Concerning the internal structure of EOM, the old literature is even controversial on the question, whether the muscle fibers run the full length of the muscles or not (cf. Peachey, 1971). Alvarado's fiber counts at different levels of cross section give evidence that many muscle fibers of cat EOM must be shorter than the muscle itself. This is also true in the rat where fibers of the OL are generally shorter than those of the GL (Mayr, 1971). Correspondingly, a staggered arrangement of muscle fiber tendon junctions can be observed on the orbital surface. Beyond this, however, we know about the existence of myomyous junctions in EOM (Mayr *et al.*, 1967; Teräväinen, 1969; Floyd, 1970) indicating a more complex internal architecture. These junctions exhibit cholinesterase activity like many muscle fiber tendon junctions and are the sites of mechanical linkage of two different muscle fibers. Recent work from our laboratory in cat (Mayr, Gottschall, Gruber and Neuhuber, in preparation) revealed striking differences between the internal organization of cat and rat EOM. The investigations were performed in teasing preparations of fine muscle fiber bundles from both layers of cat EOM after cholinesterase staining. The main results can be briefly summarized as follows. In the OL large motor endplates are confined to a broad band in the middle third of the muscle. The occurrence of myomyous junctions is very rare in this layer and restricted to both ends of the layer. The muscle fibers run parallel to each other through the length of the layer which is considerably shorter than the GL. Thus the organization of the OL of cat EOM is similar to that of rat.

In the GL of cat EOM we found the large motor endplates distributed within five to eight more or less distinct bands, almost along the whole length of the muscle. This global pattern of endplate distribution is gradually changing to the orbital pattern in the interior of the muscle. The GL is further characterized by a high occurrence of myomyous junctions which are dispersed between both ends of the fiber bundles, especially between the different endplate zones. The multi-innervated muscle fibers of this layer generally run the whole muscle length and extend about 0.5 mm further into the distal tendon than any of the focally innervated ones. On the other hand, only few of the focally innervated fibers run from tendon to tendon without interruption; most of them are shorter, down to one-third of the length of the bundle, and are connected to other muscle fibers by means of myomyous junctions. These connections may be found in a one-to-one manner, but more often the muscle fibers are branched and connected to more than one other fiber. Often the junctions are organized in a step-like manner; one fiber is loosing diameter at each cholinesterase positive step, the other becomes gradually larger. Near the tendons in several instances focally innervated fibers were even found connected to multi-innervated ones in an end-to-side manner. The GL of rat EOM has a much simpler arrangement of muscle fibers: all muscle fibers run from end to end without interruption; as in the OL also in rat GL the large motor endplates are confined to a band in the middle third of the muscle.

Fiber branching, early reported in rabbit EOM by Hines (1931), and cholinesterase positive muscle fiber connections have also been found in sheep EOM (Harker, 1972).

44

The high occurrence of serially linked muscle fibers, as found in the GL of cat EOM, could be reflected in the mechanical properties of eye muscles. The question whether focally innervated muscle fibers connected to each other do belong to the same motor unit or not seems to be of functional importance. Large motor endplates of the same motor unit could be located far from each other and in several bands along the course of a muscle fiber bundle, especially on the global surface of cat EOM.

REFERENCES

ASMUSSEN, C., KIESSLING, A. and WOHLRAB, F. (1971) Histochemische Charakterisierung der verschiedenen Muskelfasertypen in den äußeren Augenmuskeln von Säugetieren. *Acta anat.* **79**, 526.

FLOYD, K. (1970) Junctions between muscle fibers in cat extraocular muscles. *Nature* **227**, 185.

HARKER, D. W. (1972) The structure and innervation of sheep superior rectus and levator palpebrae extraocular muscles. I. Extrafusal muscle fibers. *Invest. Ophthal.* **11**, 956.

HINES, M. (1931) Innervation of the extrinsic eye muscles of the rabbit. *Am. J. Anat.* **47**, 1.

MAYR, R. (1971) Structure and distribution of fiber types in the external eye muscles of the rat. *Tissue and Cell*, **3**, 433.

MAYR, R. (1973) Morphometrie von Ratten-Augenmuskelfasern. *Verh. Anat. Ges.* **67**, 353.

MAYR, R., ZENKER, W. and GRUBER, H. (1967) Zwischensehnenfreie Skeletmuskelfaser-Verbindungen. *Z. Zellforsch.* **79**, 319.

PEACHEY, L. (1972) The structure of the extraocular muscle fibers of mammals. In: *The Control of Eye Movements*, P. BACH-Y-RITA, C. C. COLLINS and J. H. HYDE (Eds.), p. 47. Academic Press, New York–London.

TERÄVÄINEN, H. (1969) Localization of acetylcholinesterase activity in myotendinous and myomyous junctions of the striated skeletal muscles of the rat. *Experientia (Basel)* **25**, 524.

AGING CHANGES IN EXTRAOCULAR MUSCLE†

JAMES E. MILLER

INTRODUCTION

The extraocular muscles are a diverse muscle mass that differ from skeletal muscle in numerous respects. Variations have been observed by morphology (Thulin, 1914; Garven, 1925; Wohlfart, 1938; Siebeck and Kruger, 1955), electrophysiology (Hess and Pilar, 1963; Bach-y-Rita and Ito, 1966), biochemistry (Smelser, 1944; Partsch et al., 1971), and kinesthesia (Breinin, 1962). Most recently there has been an emphasis on ultrastructure (Reger, 1961; Hess, 1961; Hess and Pilar, 1963; Dietert, 1965; Cheng and Breinin, 1965; Pilar and Hess, 1966; Peachey, 1966; Brandt and Leeson, 1966; Mayr et al., 1966; Cheng and Breinin, 1966; Miller, 1967; Mukuno, 1967; Sakimoto, 1968; Miller, 1971; Mayr, 1971; Harker, 1972), and histochemistry (Denny-Brown, 1929; Nachmias and Padykula, 1958; Cogan and Kuwabara, 1960; Cheng, 1964; Miller, 1967; Nemet and Miller, 1968; Yellin, 1969; Miller, 1971; Mayr, 1971; Aichmair, 1971; Harker, 1972; Minoda and Sato, 1973), where it was possible to subdivide eye cells and demonstrate alterations from skeletal muscle. Inherent in any discussion of this type is that of consistency; namely, the results from control and experimental or diseased tissue should always be reproducible. However, this assumption may not be valid for extraocular muscle from older animals since eye muscles undergo extensive degeneration with aging.

There are many previous observations relating to morphologic differences between young and older eye muscles from animals and humans. Adult eye muscles (age 30–40) had more sarcoplasm, fat droplets, pigment, and larger fibers when compared to children and infants (Attias, 1912). Ringbinden of fibers were observed in normal man and monkey to be more prevalent where the nerve penetrated the eye muscle, i.e. global surface of muscle (Thulin, 1914). Ringbinden have been found in specimens removed from adult dogs, rabbits, guinea pigs, and cats (Schwarz, 1925; Wohlfart, 1932), as well as monkey (Thulin, 1914) and man (Bucciante and Luria, 1934; Wohlfart, 1932).

A comparative study of eye muscles from humans of different ages (Bucciante and Luria, 1934) revealed the first change to be detectable around the age of 18 years with an increase in sarcoplasm and irregular myofibrils. During this interval it was also possible to find ringbinden or spiral annulets. Other changes concomitant with aging were an increase in fibrous and elastic tissue and progressive enlargement of fiber diameter. The increase in diameter was due to an accumulation of sarcoplasm accompanied by a loss of myofibrillar material until the fiber appeared as a pale sarcoplasmic mass or even a fibrous cord. The majority of these changes were further

†This investigation was supported in part by Public Health Service research grant EY 00519 from the National Institute of Neurological Diseases and Blindness.

documented in man, cow, guinea pig, dog, and cat (Wohlfart, 1938). The latter author was uncertain about the increase in fiber diameter with age, but recognized that the fibers undergoing change were those with fine myofibrils which he named A-fibers. He believed the major morphological alterations to be a marked increase in sarcoplasm and loss of myofibrils. Verification of these findings has continued to more recent time (Bergstrand, 1938; Cooper and Daniel, 1949; Mori, 1953; Voth and Rohen, 1962; Jonecko, 1963). The reports were consistent in indicating a histologic change in all extraocular muscles with advancing age.

We have also found alterations in eye muscles removed from man and monkey and have evaluated the tissue by electron microscopy. Our findings indicated that changes compatible with skeletal muscle disease occurred prior to middle age and with increasing frequency thereafter.

METHOD

Eye muscles were evaluated in thirty-seven monkeys and skeletal muscle was included in twelve of the group. Eight animals were born in captivity with verified ages of 2 months to 4 years. Other animals were estimated for age by bone and tooth structure. The two oldest animals were females obtained from primate colonies where they had been used for breeding purposes for 15 and 17 years. None of the animals were used in drug, nutritional, or deprivation experiments.

The human material for electron microscopy consisted of specimens from eight subjects age 5 months to 78 years and was obtained at the time of enucleation or orbital exenteration. The enucleations were usually performed for tumors or trauma and the eye muscles were not involved by the disease process. The origin of muscles that included a major band of motor end plates could only be evaluated in exenteration specimens. These were usually obtained from children with rhabdomyosarcomas and older adults with squamous cell carcinoma of the conjunctiva, melanomas of the choroid, or nasopharyngeal carcinoma.

Method of Preparation

The technique used for histochemistry, light microscopy, and electron microscopy has been previously described (Miller, 1967), but briefly consists of the following: monkeys were decapitated under barbiturate anesthesia, the brain and roof of the orbit removed, and entire muscles were dissected. For electron microscopy, the muscle was extended to its original length, clamped on a perforated support, incubated for 10 min in 1% buffered tetracaine solution at 0°C, then fixed in 4% or 6% glutaraldehyde and 2% acrolein for 1 hr, washed in 0.2 M Sorensen's phosphate buffer. Blocks of human muscles were pinned to supporting wax or wood at approximately resting length and prepared in a similar manner. Selected areas of the muscle were minced and post-fixed in Dalton's solution for 30 min, dehydrated in increasing strengths of ethyl alcohol, embedded and polymerized in araldite. Phase sections were stained with paraphenylenediamine and the blocks were reduced to selected areas for thin sectioning. Sections were picked up on uncoated copper grids and stained with 0.2% uranyl acetate for 15 min and Reynolds lead citrate for 5 min. Micrographs were obtained with a Siemens Elmiskop 1 and 1A electron microscope.

RESULTS

Rhesus eye muscles were similar to other skeletal muscles in the organization of the fibers. There was an orderly array of contractile elements, Z-bands, sarcoplasmic reticulum, and triads. However, the myofibrillar diameter was smaller and the sarcoplasm more abundant in all fibers evaluated except for a fiber of the Felderstruktur type (Miller, 1971). The fibers with the smallest cellular and myofibrillar diameter were concentrated about the periphery of an eye muscle, and larger fibers in the center of the muscle and adjacent to the globe. In contrast to skeletal muscle fibers of many other vertebrates where the sarcoplasmic reticulum is extensive in the A-band region, it was virtually absent in the small eye fibers. The two larger fibers located in the core and global surface of the muscle had a highly developed reticulum that subdivided the entire length of myofilaments into discrete myofibrils. In monkey these two may be distinguished by the presence of an M-line in one, and absence in the other. Eye muscle contained a fiber of intermediate or small diameter that had the morphology of "slow" cells. This fiber was deficient in sarcoplasmic reticulum and triads and poorly delineated into myofibrils. The latter is comparable with a Felderstruktur pattern of myofilaments.

The perinuclear area was the region of fibers with the greatest evidence of metabolic and myoneural activity. It usually contained mitochondria, Golgi apparatus, and myelin bodies, and was the only location where free ribosomes and rough surface endoplasmic reticulum were consistently located in young eye fibers.

The majority of eye cells contained large masses of mitochondria located adjacent to the sarcolemma. In the interior of fibers, mitochondria were interspersed between myofibrils and arranged in groups or as chains a single sarcomere wide. Mitochondria were generally ovoid in shape with tightly packed cristae, an electron dense matrix, and contained ribosome-like particles in young animals. Their dimensions varied between $\frac{1}{2}$ to 2 μ. In some small muscle cells from the periphery of an eye muscle they were fusiform, and in the slow fibers were often drumstick or dumb-bell in outline.

Thus, in monkey extraocular muscle, several cellular markers were available: the sarcoplasmic reticulum arrangement, mitochondrial morphology and distribution, and presence or absence of an M-line. Human fibers were less distinct since there was less variation of mitochondrial content and all fibers included M-lines. Sarcoplasmic reticulum arrangement, however, appeared similar to cat and monkey with small fibers having an I-band localization and "slow" fibers deficient in tubules.

In young animals, extraocular muscle fibers were characterized by sharpness of detail. In well-oriented, relaxed specimens, contractile elements were precisely aligned with excellent orientation of the sarcoplasmic reticulum network (Figs. 1 and 2). Sarcoplasmic spaces were filled with organelles and glycogen with a minimum of electron lucent spaces. Mitochondria and interspersed lipid droplets were relatively consistent in size, lying edge to edge with accurately repeating orientation. The mitochondria frequently showed small punctate densities equivalent to mitochondrial ribosomes (Fig. 1). However, all of the cell types contained structures which may be considered abnormal in other tissues. Myelin figures were frequently found adjacent to mitochondria (Fig. 1). Mitochondrial columns also contained ghost-like remnants of mitochondria that were bound by double membranes and included membranous whorls and networks which often incorporated glycogen particles (Fig. 2). These structures were interpreted as either the initial or terminal state in the development of mitochondria.

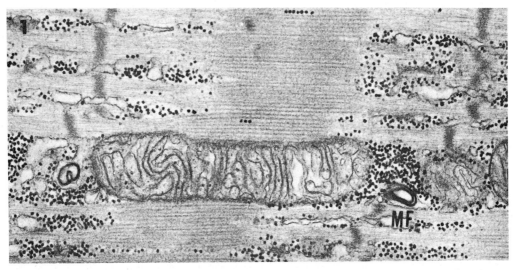

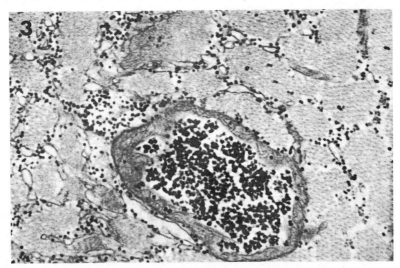

FIGS. 1–3. MF Myelin figure. MR Mitochondrial remnant.

FIG. 1. Six-week-old monkey, outer small fiber (30,000 ×). MF—myeline figure.

FIG. 2. Two-year-old monkey, global surface fiber (30,000 ×). MR—mitochondrial remnant.

FIG. 3. Three-year-old monkey, orbital surface. Glycogen surrounded by mitochondrial shell (30,000 ×).

Other unusual mitochondrial-like bodies were also found in fibers that contained a large number of ovoid mitochondria. These consisted of a mitochondrial shell with rudimentary cristae that encircled clumps of dark-staining particles interspersed on an electron lucent background (Fig. 3). The particles had the dimensions of glycogen but were unusual in their clumped arrangement. The entire body varied from the size of a single mitochondrion (0.75 μ^2) to those that had three to four times their cross-sectional area (Fig. 14). Another feature that seemed to predominate in prepubescent specimens were ovoid bodies approximately the same size and adjacent to peripheral nuclei (Fig. 4). These were not bound by a membrane and contained small particles measuring 10–15 mμ interspersed between microfilaments. Satellite cells were also more frequent in prepubertal animals (Fig. 5).

Fibrous tissue consisted of a few collagen and reticulin fibrils between muscle fibers that comprised a fascicle (Fig. 5). Fascicular boundaries were delineated by columns of collagen fibrils that were usually six to ten fibrils in depth. Young animals did not demonstrate pleomorphic or giant mitochondria or fragmentation and aimless orientation of myofilaments.

Beginning in early adulthood there was an increase in sarcoplasmic spaces with a dispersion of organelles and glycogen in the electron lucent matrix. This change was particularly evident in the en plaque motor end plate region where there was an increase in rough surface endoplasmic reticulum and polyribosomes (Fig. 6). The increase in sarcoplasm appeared to surround many nerve terminations to where they lay in a deep cleft. Occasional focal or cystic separation was found in the synaptic space with membrane whorls often occupying the dehiscent areas (Fig. 7). Vacuolation and disturbance of mitochondrial cristae, ghost mitochondria, membrane figures incorporating glycogen (Fig. 8), and dilatation of the sarcoplasmic reticulum was evident in a few cells. More varied myelin figures were also identified, occasionally one membrane enclosing a complex structure of tubules, glycogen, and other membranes (Fig. 9).

At approximately age 30 in humans and 5–6 years in monkeys, lipofuscin granules were located in many fibers beneath the cell membrane but were absent from the interior of the fibers (Fig. 10). Changes in orientation of myofilaments could also be recognized, but the fibers were infrequent and located predominantly in the small cell layer. The affected fibers often showed broadening and blurring of Z-lines similar to nemalin bodies (Shy et al., 1963) (Fig. 15). Sarcoplasmic spaces were slightly dilated in human fibers from the central core and monkey cells with M-lines. The same areas frequently contained polyribosomal particles in association with sarcoplasmic reticulum (Fig. 11).

Around age 40 in humans and 7–9 years in monkey, reduplication of Z-lines in peripheral fibers (Fig. 12) and fragmentation and loss of myofibrils in central cells were observed (Fig. 13). In monkey, myofibrillar changes were found in the larger cells with distinct M-lines. The loss of contractile substance was replaced by electron lucent material that contained lipofuscin pigment granules, polyribosomes, glycogen, pleomorphic mitochondria, and dilated portions of the sarcoplasmic reticulum (Fig. 14). Rough surface endoplasmic reticulum was frequently identified adjacent to the cell membrane in sections that did not contain nuclei which might represent T-tubular formation. An example that communicated with the cell surface and was oriented similar to transverse tubules is given in Fig. 6.

Ringbinden usually occurred abruptly within a normally organized fiber that often included other evidence of aging (Fig. 10). The region of circumferentially aligned

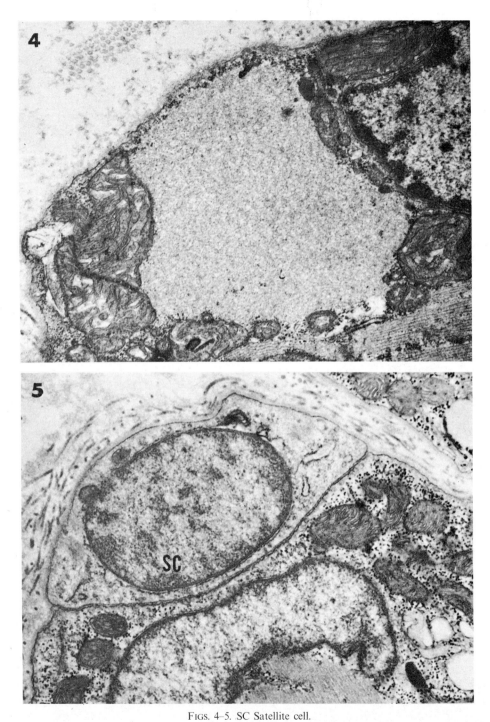

FIGS. 4–5. SC Satellite cell.

FIG. 4. Human, 2 years, peripheral fiber. Light body containing microfilaments (27,000 ×).

FIG. 5. Monkey, 3 years, satellite cell (SC), outer small cell (20,000 ×).

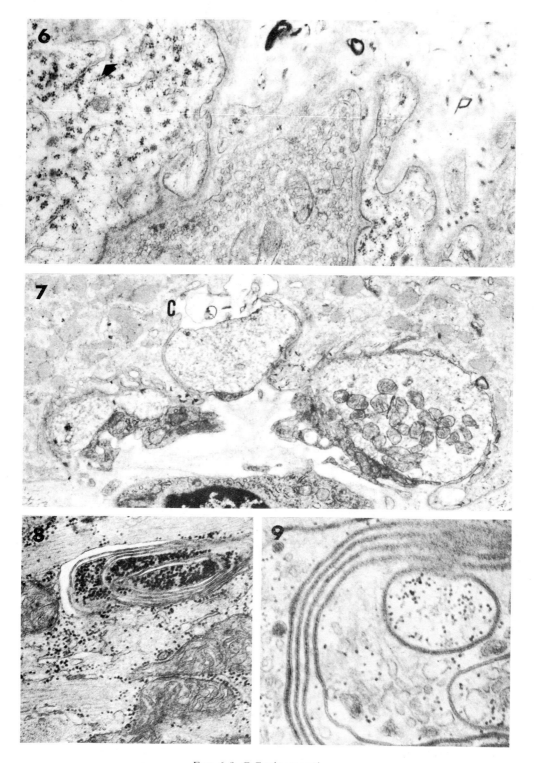

FIGS. 6–9. C Cystic separation.

FIG. 6. Monkey, age 6 years, center of muscle. Motor end plate region containing polyribosomes, tubules, and rough surface endoplasmic reticulum. Arrow = tubule communicating with fiber surface (46,000 ×).

FIG. 7. Human, age 36, fiber from global surface. Oval motor nerve terminals with cystic (C) separation of end plate (9600 ×).

FIG. 8. Monkey, 6 years. Membrane figure from outer fiber (30,000 ×).

FIG. 9. Monkey, age 6 years. Complex membrane figure containing glycogen, tubules and vesicles located in a large central cell without M-lines (55,000 ×).

53

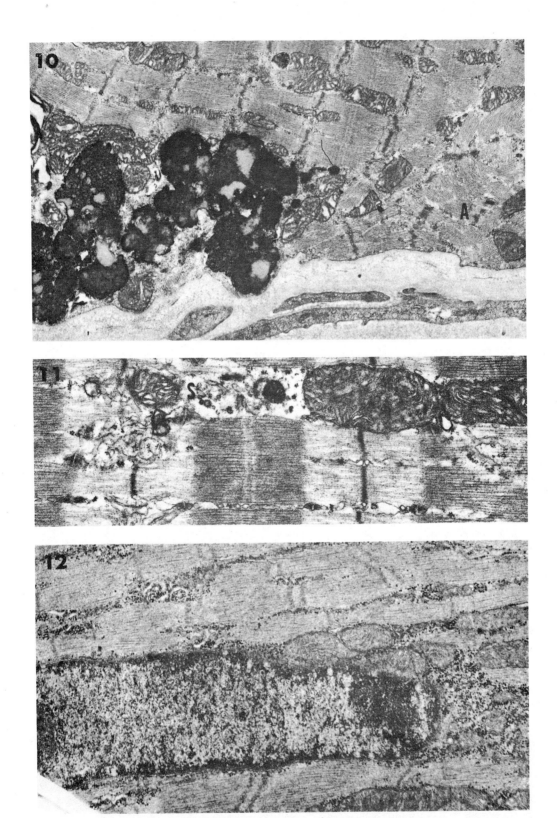

FIGS. 10–12. A Spiral annulet or Ringbinden.

FIG. 10. Human, age 36, small outer fiber including lipofuscin granules and spiral annulet (A) (10,000×).

FIG. 11. Monkey, age 6 years. Central fiber with M-lines, dilated sarcoplasmic reticulum spaces (S), and polyribosomes adjacent to sarcoplasmic reticulum (23,000×).

FIG. 12. Monkey, 9 years, double Z-lines and central nucleus in outer small cell (17,500×).

54

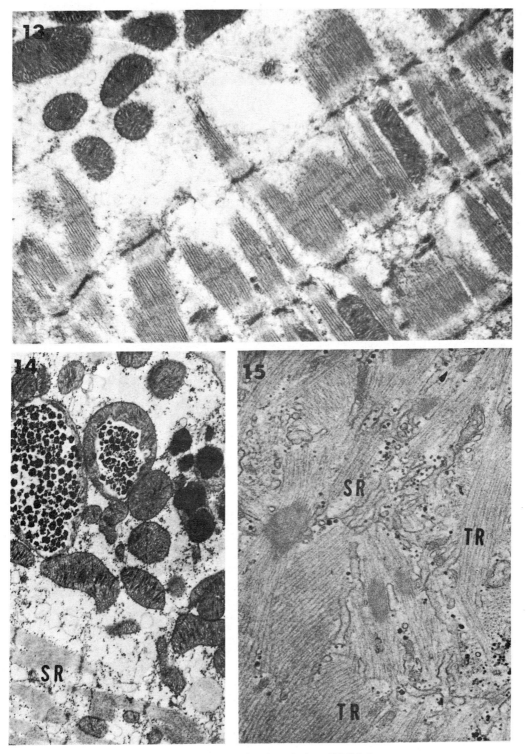

FIGS. 13–15. SR Sarcoplasmic reticulum. TR Triads.

FIG. 13. Human, 56 years. Global fiber with myofilament loss (16,000×).

FIG. 14. Monkey, age 9 years. Central fiber with dilated sarcoplasmic reticulum (SR), pleomorphic and large mitochondria incorporating glycogen (8500×).

FIG. 15. Monkey, age 8 years. Orbital cell including nemalin bodies and chaotic order of myofilaments. The sarcoplasmic reticulum (SR) appears intact. TR = triad (33,000×).

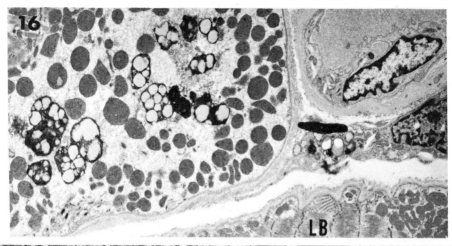

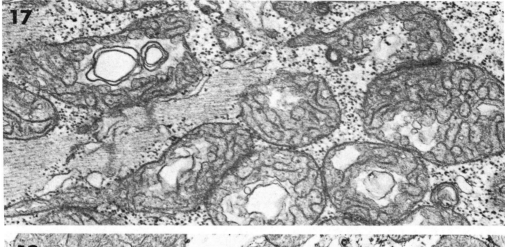

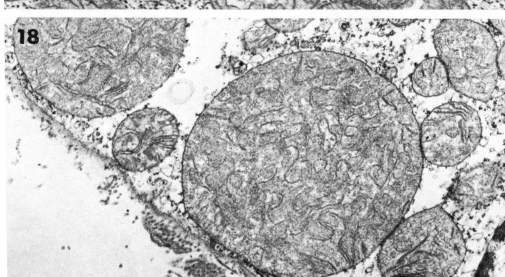

FIGS. 16–18. LB Leptomeric body.

FIG. 16. Human, age 66. Two fibers from global surface, one with extensive loss of myofibrils partially replaced by pleomorphic mitochondria, lysosomes, tubules, and amorphous sarcoplasm. The other fiber contains a leptomeric body (LB) (7500×).

FIG. 17. Monkey, 17 years. Pleomorphic mitochondria with membrane inclusions and loss of cristae and outer membrane (33,000×).

FIG. 18. Monkey, age 12 years. Giant mitochondrion in outer fiber (18,000×).

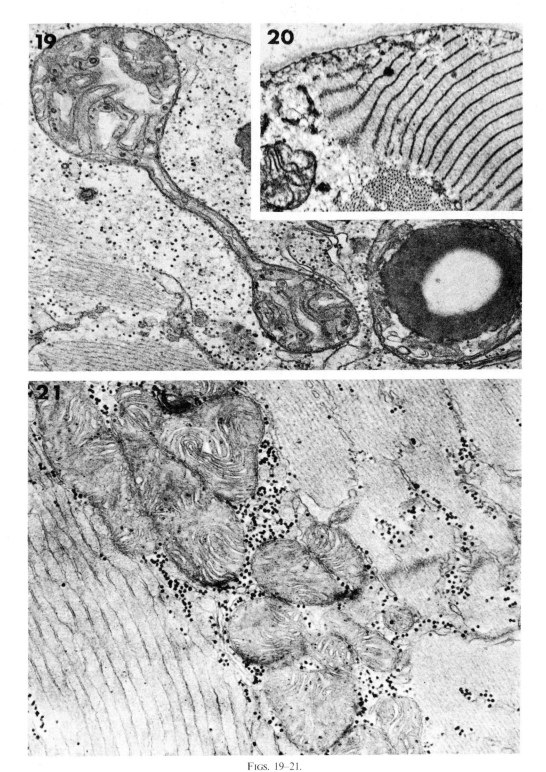

FIGS. 19–21.

FIG. 19. Monkey, 17 years, outer fiber. Bilobed mitochondrion and oval mitochondrion with lipid inclusion (33,000 ×).

FIG. 20. Leptomeric body in small peripheral fiber from human age 67 (21,000 ×).

FIG. 21. Monkey, age 17 years. Tubule formation in outer fiber (33,000 ×).

myofilaments was focal and extended a longitudinal distance of 20 to 50 μ. In addition, some areas demonstrated a total disarray with groups of filaments extending in any direction (Fig. 15). Both types of filamentous disorder included broad Z-lines similar to nemaline bodies. Although it was not possible to identify sarcoplasmic sleeves, the tubular apparatus appeared intact with elements of the carcoplasmic reticulum and triads readily evident.

In middle age there was an increase in collagen fibrils so that the interfiber space was equivalent to the fascicle septum in the young animal.

With advanced age there was accentuation of all of the previous findings (Fig. 16). Major alterations in mitochondria (Figs. 17, 18, 19) consisted of loss of orientation into columns, changes in shape, loss of membranes and cristae, and the formation of giant mitochondria. In addition, other unusual structures were found predominantly in older material. Leptomeric bodies (Figs. 16, 20) were identified in fibers that were moderately disturbed by aging. These were located in small "slow" cells in both the periphery and central regions. These fibers did not contain conglomerates of mitochondria, nuclear bags or chains, sensory nerve contacts, extracellular encapsulation, or other evidence indicating muscle spindle cells where leptomeric bodies are usually located (Karlsson and Andersson-Cedergren, 1968; Ovalle, 1972).

Another unique structure was a series of tubules with each unit incorporating a dense matrix (Fig. 21). The tubules measured 150 mμ in diameter and could be followed for distances of 8–10 μ in length. They were localized to one portion of an otherwise undisturbed fiber and occupied three-quarters of the cross-sectional area. A similar structure was recognized in a fiber from soleus muscle of a monkey 8 years of age, but it appeared to occupy only a small portion of the fiber and could be followed for a short distance in serial sections. Similar structures were also found in a survey of normal and slightly diseased human skeletal muscles (Engel *et al.*, 1970).

An occasional degenerating nerve was noted among eye fibers, but the vast majority of nerves and motor end plates were intact. This was true even of fibers showing extensive degeneration as well as nerves adjacent to separated end plates with myelin figures within the synaptic cleft. Synaptic vesicles of end plates were of normal configuration and were usually located in clusters adjacent to the presynaptic membrane.

DISCUSSION

The diffuse changes that occurs throughout eye muscles may account for alterations of eye movement observed in the aged. Ocular excursions (Holland, 1956; Chamberlain, 1971) gradually diminish throughout life. Ptosis, limitation of elevation of the lid, and convergence insufficiency are frequently observed in the elderly. All of these problems may be due to degeneration, loss of fibers within the muscle mass and increase of fibrous tissue.

The failure to select animals or subjects according to age may introduce variability into experiments. The gradual intracellular shift in cells with myofibrillar preponderance of childhood to sarcoplasmic excess of senescent and the addition of increased extracellular fibrosis is probably associated with changes in plasticity as well as contraction and relaxation phenomenon. Metabolism, energy transfer, and excitation–contraction coupling may be affected by sarcoplasmic reticulum dilatation, mitochondrial changes, tubular aggregates, and the increase in sarcoplasmic spaces. These factors may lead to alterations of intracellular potential, increased susceptibility to topically applied cholinergic drugs, and prolonged action potentials which are unique to eye fibers. All of the uncertainties may be reduced by using young animals for experiments.

As extraocular muscle and the tensor tympani muscle contained slow fibers (Erulkar et al., 1964) and both degenerated extensively with age (Malan, 1934), one assumption might be that the "slow" cells were atrophying. These, however, were the most resistant and only showed slight changes in the mitochondria and sarcoplasmic spaces, with occasional pigment and leptomeric bodies. The small fibers and the larger cells that contained the greatest mitochondrial mass were less immune and developed changes in mitochondrial configuration and inclusions, lipofuscin granules and ringbinden, but they did not include a marked loss of contractile elements. The fiber in eye muscle that most closely approximated a skeletal muscle fiber in the monkey, the cell containing M-lines, was extensively involved with progressive myofibrillar degeneration and changes within mitochondria.

Pleomorphism and enlargement of mitochondria is a phenomenon that has been noted in aging studies of insects. Evaluation of muscle from the house fly (Sohal et al., 1972) showed that with aging there was development and enlargement of irregular-shaped mitochondria, and it was indicated that this was from fusion of smaller units, occurring in all directions, longitudinal, vertical, or oblique. The pleomorphic changes in mitochondria in eye muscle were compatible with this interpretation since many of the sarcosomes contained indentations and irregular projections suggesting that fusion had occurred along many axes. Similar to eye muscle, aging in the blowfly was accompanied by glycogen inclusion into mitochondria and membrane whorls. Disturbed portions of mitochondria were also shown to be deficient in cytochrome oxidase (Sacktor and Shimada, 1972).

Muscle wasting is a normal occurrence with aging, and it has been suggested that this is due to a continuous loss of motor neurons (Jennekens et al., 1971). The remaining motor axons then sprout to reinnervate the denervated muscle fibers and confer upon the muscle cells the fast or slow histochemical properties of the nerve. Skeletal muscle from older humans was found to contain large conglomerates of cells with identical histochemical properties rather than the mosaic of younger individuals. There is very little to support this thesis in eye muscle. Only occasional motor terminals and nerves were abnormal. Changes within the muscle fibers were often focal rather than generalized. Furthermore, histochemical preparations of eye muscles obtained at the time of autopsy from the aged continue to show the normal pattern of smaller cells around the periphery surrounding a central mosaic of larger fibers.

In evaluating biopsies from patients suspected of having neuro-muscular disease, the age of the patient and the variations of eye muscle from "normal" must be considered. All surface biopsies will include the small cell layer covering the exterior of the muscle. Many of these fibers contain central nuclei and blend with larger, deeper cells. Consequently, there will be variation of cellular size and central nuclei in all tissue obtained from the surface. From early adulthood onward, there will be fibrosis, ringbinden, nemalin bodies, ribosomal accumulations, fragmentation, and dissolution of myofibrils, all suggesting disease of muscle. In older subjects, vacant sarcoplasm from loss of myofibrils, leptomeric bodies, and marked mitochondrial hypertrophy, pleomorphism and inclusions may be identified. Other findings that would be considered abnormal would be separation of nerve terminals, tubular formation, and splitting of Z-bands within muscle fibers.

In conclusion, eye muscle from humans and monkeys undergoes progressive degeneration throughout life. The muscle fiber that atrophied the greatest was the predominating cell within the central core of the muscle. In the monkey, this fiber had "whiter" histochemical characteristics (Miller, 1967) and an M-line in the center of the A-band. Although other cells did not have as great disturbances in their contractile proteins, they often included focal misalignment of myofibrils, lipofuscin granules, changes in mitochondrial shape and content, as well as foreign organelles.

It is recommended that in selecting animals or subjects for experiments that involve eye movements or measurements upon the muscles or muscle fibers that a limited age group be selected. Otherwise there may be discrepancies between younger and older animals. Young animals are necessary if muscle in its pristine state is desired.

REFERENCES

AICHMAIR, H. (1971) Stoffwechseluntersuchungen der äußeren augenmuskeln des menschen. *v. Graefes Arch. klin. exp. Ophthal.* **182,** 95.

ATTIAS, G. (1912) Über altersveränderungen des menschlichen auges. *v. Graefes Archiv fur Ophthal.* **81,** 405.

BACH-Y-RITA, P. and ITO, F. (1966) *In vivo* studies on fast and slow muscle fibers in cat extraocular muscles. *J. Gen. Physiol.* **49,** 1177.

BERGSTRAND, C. G. (1938) Zur morphologie der quergestreiften ringbinden. *Zschr. mikrostk.-anat. Forsch.* **44,** 45.

BRANDT, D. E. and LEESON, C. R. (1966) Structural differences of fast and slow fibers in human extraocular muscle. *Am. J. Ophthal.* **62,** 478.

BREININ, G. M. (1962) *The Electrophysiology of Extraocular Muscle.* University of Toronto Press.

BUCCIANTE, L. and LURIA, S. (1934) Trasformazioni nella struttura dei muscoli volontari dell'uomo nella senescenza. *Arch. Ital. Anat. Embriol.* **33,** 110.

CHAMBERLAIN, W. (1971) Restriction in upward gaze with advancing age. *Am. J. Ophthal.* **71,** 341.

CHENG, K. (1964) Distribution of succinic dehydrogenase in extraocular muscles. *Jap. J. Ophthal.* **8,** 116.

CHENG, K. and BREININ, G. M. (1965) Fine structure of nerve endings in extraocular muscle. *Arch. Ophthal.* **74,** 822.

CHENG, K. and BREININ, G. M. (1966) A comparison of the fine structure of extraocular and interosseus muscles in the monkey. *Inv. Ophthal.* **5,** 535.

COGAN, D. G. and KUWABARA, T. (1960) Tetrazolium studies on the retina: IV. Distribution of reductase in ocular tissue. *J. Histochem. Cytochem.* **8,** 380.

COOPER, S. and DANIEL, P. M. (1949) Muscle spindles in human extrinsic eye muscles. *Brain,* **72,** 1.

DENNY-BROWN, D. E. (1929) The histological features of striped muscle in relation to its functional activity. *Proc. Roy. Soc.* B, **104,** 371.

DIETERT, S. E. (1965) The demonstration of different types of muscle fibers in human extraocular muscle by electron microscopy and cholinesterase staining. *Inv. Ophthal.* **4,** 51.

ENGEL, W. K., BISHOP, D. W. and DUNNINGHAM, G. G. (1970) Tubular aggregates in Type II muscle fibers: Ultrastructural and histochemical correlation. *J. Ultrastruct. Res.* **31,** 507.

ERULKAR, S. D., SHELANSKI, M. L., WHITSEL, B. L. and OGLE, P. (1964) Studies of muscle fibers of the tensor tympani of the cat. *Anat. Rec.* **149,** 279.

GARVEN, H. S. D. (1925) The nerve-endings in the panniculus carnosus of the hedgehog, with special reference to the sympathetic innervation of striated muscle. *Brain,* **48,** 380.

HARKER, D. W. (1972) The structure and innervation of sheep superior rectus and levator palpebrae extraocular muscles: I. Extrafusal muscle fibers. *Inv. Ophthal.* **11,** 956.

HARKER, D. W. (1972) The structure and innervation of sheep superior rectus and levator palpebrae extraocular muscles: II. Muscle spindles. *Inv. Ophthal.* **11,** 970.

HESS, A. (1961) The structure of slow and fast extrafusal muscle fibers in the extraocular muscles and their nerve endings in guinea pigs. *J. Cell. & Comp. Physiol.* **58,** 63.

HESS, A. and PILAR, G. (1963) Slow fibres in the extraocular muscles of the cat. *J. Physiol.* **169,** 780.

HOLLAND, G. (1956) Untersuchungen über den einfluß des alters auf die physiologischen grenzen der augenbeweglichkeit. *Klin. Mbl. Augenh.* **129,** 655.

JENNEKENS, G. G. I., TOMLINSON, B. E. and WALTON, J. N. (1971) Histochemical aspects of five limb muscles in old age: an autopsy study. *J. Neurol. Sci.* **14**, 259.

JONECKO, A. (1963) Über die quergestreiften ringbinden der skeletmuskulatur bei wirbeltieren. *Anat. Anz.* **113**, 337.

KARLSSON, U. and ANDERSSON-CEDERGREN, E. (1968) Small leptomeric organelles in intrafusal muscle fibers of the frog as revealed by electron microscopy. *J. Ultrastruct. Res.* **23**, 417.

MAIER, A., ELDRED, E. and EDGERTON, V. R. (1972) Types of muscle fibers in the extraocular muscles of birds. *Expl Eye Res.* **13**, 255.

MALAN, E. (1934) Etude d'histologie comparée sur quelques modifications particulieres des fibres due tensor tympani dues à la sénescence. *Arch. de Biologie,* **45**, 356.

MAYR, R. (1971) Structure and distribution of fibre types in the external eye muscles of the rat. *Tissue & Cell,* **3**, 433.

MAYR, R., STOCKINGER, L. and ZENKER, W. (1966) Elektronenmikroskopische untersuchungen an unterschiedlich innervierten muskelfasern der äusseren augenmuskulatur des rhesusaffen. *Z. Zellforsch. mikrosk. Anat.* **75**, 434.

MILLER, J. E. (1967) Cellular organization of rhesus extraocular muscle. *Inv. Ophthal.* **6**, 18.

MILLER, J. E. (1971) Recent histologic and electron microscopic findings in extraocular muscle. *Trans. Am. Acad. Ophthal. Otolaryn.* **75**, 1175.

MINODA, K. C. and SATO, Y. (1973) Distribution of twitch and slow fibers in extraocular muscles. *Jap. J. Ophthal.* **17**, 2.

MORI, M. (1953) Striated annular fibers in ocular muscle. *Arch. Hist. Jap.* **5**, 485.

MUKUNO, K. (1967) Electron microscopic studies on the human extraocular muscles under pathologic conditions: Part 1. Pathologic findings, especially "rod formation", found occurring in normal extraocular muscles and those in the extraocular muscle of a patient with polymyositis. *Acta Soc. Ophthal. Jap.* **272**, 106 (1678).

NACHMIAS, V. T. and PADYKULA, H. A. (1958) A histochemical study of normal and denervated red and white muscles of the rat. *J. Biophysic. Biochem. Cytol.* **4**, 47.

NEMET, P. and MILLER, J. E. (1968) Evoked potentials in cat extraocular muscle. *Inv. Ophthal.* **7**, 592.

OVALLE, W. K. JR. (1972) Fine structure of rat intrafusal muscle fibers. *J. Cell Biol.* **52**, 382.

PARTSCH, G., AICHMAIR, H. and ALTMANN, H. (1971) Die bedeutung von α-glycerophosphat und 2,3-diphosphoglycerat im augenmuskelstoffwechsel des menschen. *Pflugers Arch.* **328**, 84.

PEACHEY, L. D. (1966) Fine structure of two fiber types in cat extraocular muscles. *J. Cell. Biol.* **31**, 84A.

PILAR, G. and HESS, A. (1966) Difference in internal structure and nerve terminals of the slow and twitch muscle fibers in the cat superior oblique. *Anat. Rec.* **154**, 243.

REGER, J. F. (1961) The fine structure of neuromuscular junctions and the sarcoplasmic reticulum of extrinsic eye muscles of *Fundulus heteroclitus. J. Biophysic. Biochem. Cytol.* **10**, 111.

SACKTOR, B. and SHIMADA, Y. (1972) Degenerative changes in the mitochondria of flight muscle from aging blowflies. *J. Cell Biol.* **52**, 465.

SAKIMOTO, T. (1968) Electron microscopic studies on human ocular muscles. (1) Filamentous and membranous structures in the extraocular muscle fibers. *Acta Soc. Ophthal. Jap.* **72**, 2325.

SCHWARZ, M. (1925) Uber das vorkommen quergestreifter ringbinden bei den augenmuskeln. *Zeitschr. f. d. ges. Anat. L. Abt.* **75**, 24.

SHY, G. M., ENGEL, W. K., SOMERS, J. E. and WANKO, T. (1963) Nemaline myopathy—A new congenital myopathy. *Brain,* **86**, 793.

SIEBECK, R. and KRÜGER, P. (1955) Die histologische struktur der äußeren augenmuskeln als ausdruck ihrer funktion. *v. Graefes Archiv für Ophthal.* **156**, 637.

SMELSER, G. K. (1944) The oxygen consumption of eye muscles of thyroidectomized and thyroxin-injected guinea pigs. *Am. J. Physiol.* **142**, 396.

SOHAL, R. S., MCCARTHY, J. L. and ALLISON, V. F. (1972) The formation of "giant" mitochondria in the fibrillar flight muscles of the house fly, *Musca domestica* L. *J. Ultrastruct. Res.* **39**, 484.

THULIN, I. (1914) Contribution a l'histologie des muscles oculaires chez l'hommes et chez les singes. *C.R. Soc. Biol., Paris,* **74**, 490.

VOTH, D. and ROHEN, J. W. (1962) Experimentelle und histochemische untersuchungen über die ringbinden der quergestreiften muskulatur. *Anat. Anz.* **111**, 165.

WOHLFART, G. (1932) Quergestreifte ringbinden in normalen augenmuskeln. *Zschr. mikr.-anat. Forsch.* **29**, 592.

WOHLFART, G. (1938) Zur kenntnis der altersveränderungen der augenmuskeln. *Zschr. mikr.-anat. Forsch.* **44**, 33.

YELLIN, H. (1969) Unique intrafusal and extraocular muscle fibers exhibiting dual actomyosin ATPase activity. *Exptl Neurol.* **25**, 153.

STRUCTURE AND FUNCTION OF TWITCH AND SLOW FIBRES IN AMPHIBIAN SKELETAL MUSCLE

Jan Lännergren

INTRODUCTION

The present account will deal almost exclusively with properties of amphibian skeletal muscle fibres, in particular with differences in structure, excitation-contraction coupling, and mechanical properties between fast, action potential propagating (*twitch*) fibres and more slowly contracting, non-propagating ("tonic" or *slow*) fibres. This may seem a bit out of place at a symposium where the topic is mammalian oculomotor physiology. However, the basic properties of muscle fibres from different animal species are very likely the same, and mechanical studies, in particular, can be performed under more rigorously controlled conditions on frog and toad muscles, from which single fibres can be isolated by fine dissection. Information about properties of amphibian slow fibres may also be of special interest in the present context since at least some mammalian extraocular muscles contain fibres which have many properties in common with those of amphibian slow fibres. Whereas a detailed study of mammalian slow fibres has just begun, the slow fibre system in Amphibia has been under investigation for several decades.

A number of workers in the twenties and thirties, especially in Germany, found that apart from giving the normal tetanic response to repetitive stimulation of their motor nerve fibres, many frog muscles would respond with "contractures", i.e. long-lasting, reversible contractions when substances such as potassium, choline or acetylcholine (ACh) were applied. (For a detailed review of the early literature as well as a discussion of excitation-contraction coupling in slow fibres, see Peachey, 1961).) Sommerkamp (1928) found that frog muscles could be divided into three categories on the basis of their response to ACh $(1:10^{-5})$; (a) muscles that give a series of twitches and/or a very short-lasting contraction (sartorius, semimembranosus, gracilis minor); (b) muscles that respond with a long-lasting shortening in which all fibres seem to participate (rectus abdominis, flexors and extensors of the shoulder); and (c) muscles in which only some of the fibres give a long-lasting response (gastrocnemius, iliofibularis, semitendinosus). Sommerkamp worked mainly with the iliofibularis muscle and named the region of the muscle surrounding the nerve entry point the tonus bundle (Tonusbündel) since this contains fibres which give a maintained response. Although "tonic" and "non-tonic" responses were found to be confined to different regions in some muscles it was not clear at Sommerkamp's time whether the different kinds of response were due to separate kinds of muscle fibres or if one individual fibre could give both types of response.

Tasaki and Mizutani (1944) demonstrated that there were two distinctly different types of mechanical response of toad motor units depending on the type of nerve fibre that was stimulated. Stimulation of large axons resulted in all-or-none twitches; stimulation of thin nerve fibres elicited no detectable response at frequencies below 7 Hz, above this a slow rise in tension was seen which was graded with stimulation frequency. No unit was found that gave both types of response. Their results were later confirmed and extended on frog and toad muscles by Kuffler and co-workers (Kuffler and Gerard 1947; Kuffler, *et al.*, 1947; Kuffler and Vaughan Williams, 1953 a,b).

INNERVATION OF TWITCH AND SLOW FIBRES

Twitch muscle fibres are innervated by large axons, 5-15 μm in diameter (e.g. Gray, 1957). The characteristic pattern of nerve endings on the surface of twitch fibres was described by nineteenth-century histologists as "boisson terminal" or "Endbüschel" (Ranvier, 1878; Bremer 1882) and consists of a number of long, thin, unmyelinated branches mainly oriented parallel with the long axis of the muscle fibre. The branches lie in synaptic gutters, or troughs, formed by invagination of the sarcolemma. Later investigations have shown that the longitudinal folds have secondary folds at right angles, which considerably increases the area of the subsynaptic membrane. The secondary folds show up particularly well with methods which are specific for cholinesterase activity (Couteaux, 1955, 1958) but are also seen in electron micrographs (Birks *et al.*, 1960). In mammalian muscle fibres there is a marked thickening of the subsynaptic sarcoplasm with a dense aggregation of mitochondria and nuclei which constitutes the end-plate proper. This thickening is much less conspicuous in frog fibres.

There is a considerable variation in the appearance of the nerve terminals on twitch fibres. The pattern described above with long, slender branches running mainly longitudinally is seen on fibres from sartorius and the non-tonic part of iliofibularis; there is usually only one "Endbüschel" per fibre. The terminals on twitch fibres in the tonus bundle are shorter, more branched and arranged in an irregular "bushy" pattern (Hess, 1960; Lännergren and Smith, 1966). Hess (1960) never found more than one ending of this type per muscle fibre in frogs; we observed the same type of ending in the iliofibularis muscles of *Xenopus* but often noted two, sometimes, three, synaptic regions on one and the same fibre.

Slow fibres are innervated by thin myelinated fibres 2-8 μm in diameter (e.g. Gray, 1957) which often run as bundles or "trusses" between the muscle fibres. The endings consist of fine varicosities, often arranged like a bunch of grapes—"terminaison en grappe". The subsynaptic arrangement is much simpler than in twitch fibres and junctional folds are almost completely absent (Page, 1965). The cholinesterase activity is much lower than in twitch fibres (Couteaux, 1952; Hess, 1960). There is a large number of synaptic regions on individual muscle fibres, figures between four (Gray, 1957) and thirteen (Hess, 1960) have been given.

STRUCTURE OF TWITCH AND SLOW FIBRES

Twitch and slow fibres have the same general structural features. The cell is invested by a multi-layered structure, the sarcolemma, consisting from inside to out of a plasma membrane, a basement membrane, a collagen layer, and a reticular layer. The contractile substance is arranged in myofibrils, consisting of actin filaments (I-filaments) and myosin filaments (A-filaments). The myofibrils are separated from each other by sarcoplasm containing various amounts of sarcoplasmic reticulum, mitochondria, lipid droplets, and glycogen. When viewed in the light microscope the fibre cross-section either has the appearance of "Fibrillenstruktur", i.e. a regular arrangement of discrete myofibrils or "Felderstruktur" with large, irregular myofibrils (Krüger, 1949, 1952). Krüger made a strong case for believing that fibres with Fibrillen structure are twitch fibres and those with Felder structure are slow fibres. This proposition was directly confirmed in experiments which combined electrical stimulation, light microscopy, and electron microscopy (Peachey and A. F. Huxley, 1962).

With the aid of electron microscopy further differences have been described. The sarcoplasmic reticulum in twitch fibres is arranged as double-walled, partially fenestrated sleeves surrounding each myofibril, usually extending over one sarcomere only. In slow fibres, the sarcoplasmic reticulum consists of a network of branching tubules, running freely from one sarcomere to the next (Page, 1965, 1968; see also Fig. 1). The other part of the sarcotubular system, the transverse tubules, forms an anastomosing network, which in twitch fibres is strictly arranged in the plane of the Z-line; a similar network exists in slow fibres but it is less orderly and extends longitudinally as well as transversely. The main difference is seen in the extent of contacts between transverse tubules and elements of the sarcoplasmic reticulum (triadic junctions) which are much fewer in slow fibres.

The length of A-filaments (1.5–1.6 μm) and I-filaments (1.95–2.05 μm) are the same in the two fibre types but a thickening at the middle of the A-filaments, giving rise to an M-line across the myofibrils, is absent in slow fibres. The Z-line is straight and thin in twitch fibres and displays a regular square lattice in fibre cross-sections; in slow fibres this lattice is missing and the Z-line appears in longitudinal sections as a broad, irregular "jagged" band (Page, 1965; Hess, 1967).

Histochemically, slow fibres are characterized by very low myofibrillar ATPase activity, low activity of oxidative and glycolytic enzymes and very sparse amounts of lipid droplets and glycogen grana (Lännergren and Smith, 1966; Engel and Irwin, 1967).

The characteristics of the innervation and structure of twitch and slow fibres, briefly summarized in the preceding sections, have been reviewed more fully by Hess (1970). The description above, and the review by Hess, imply that there are only two distinct fibre types in Amphibia. Recently, however, Smith and Ovalle (1973) have extended this classification and recognize on the basis of (1) mitochondrial distribution and staining intensity; (2) myofibril size and distribution; (3) relative fibre diameter, five fibre types in *Xenopus* limb muscles of which three are assumed to be twitch fibres and two held to be slow fibres. The possibility that three different types of twitch fibre may exist has been recognized by other investigators on histological and histochemical grounds (Engel and Irwin, 1967; Asmussen and Kiessling, 1970). The subdivision gains support from the results of a previous investigation (Lännergren and Smith, 1966) in which it was found that twitch fibres, classified on basis of their light-scattering properties (as observed in dark-field illumination in the dissecting microscope), differed in their pattern of nerve endings, enzyme activity, contraction and relaxation times, and susceptibility to fatigue. It is possible, but not yet proven, that the organization of twitch fibres in Amphibia is the same as that in mammals, i.e. that there are three types of motor units: (a) units composed of fast fibres susceptible to fatigue, (b) units containing fast fibres resistant to fatigue, and (c) units comprising slower fibres, very resistant to fatigue (cf., for example, Burke *et al.*, 1973).

The possibility that there are two types of slow fibres was discussed in relation to our findings (Smith and Länngergren, 1968) that in motor units, classified as slow on the basis of a lack of response to a single stimuli and graded rise in tension on repetitive stimulation, two classes of responses were seen at a stimulation frequency of 30/sec: (1) a very slow rise up to a maintained plateau and (2) a faster initial rise, later followed by a secondary increase in tension.

DISTRIBUTION OF SLOW FIBRES IN VARIOUS MUSCLES

The results of Sommerkamp, already referred to (p. 63), indicate that slow fibres occur to varying extents in different muscles. Wachholder and Ledebür (1930), also using ACh as a stimulating agent, performed a careful study of the distribution of "tonic" fibres in the upper limb of frogs and found them to be represented in all muscles which are active during amplexus (Umklammerung), but not in the antagonists; they also noted that the ACh response seemed to be more pronounced in males than in females. This suggested to them a specific role of tonic fibres in the mating behaviour. However, this cannot be the sole function of slow fibres since they also occur in various lower limb muscles such as the iliofibularis, semitendinosus, gastrocnemius, semimebranosus, tibialis med., ext. dig. long. IV (Kuffler and Vaughan Williams, 1953b; based on maintained response to ACh or KCl); pyriformis (Stefani and Steinbach, 1969; membrane characteristics); flexor tarsi (Smith and Ovalle, 1973; morphologic characteristics). Thus, it is more likely that they have a general postureal function. They are also found in extraocular muscles (Kuffler and Vaughan Williams, 1953b) and in rectus abdominis (Forrester and Schmidt, 1970; Uhrik and Schmidt, 1973). The exact proportion between twitch and slow fibres has only been determined in a few instances (Gray, 1957; Smith and Ovalle, 1973). The common pattern is that slow fibres are intermingled with twitch fibres and rarely grouped together; they are always by far outnumbered by twitch fibres in any muscle. This holds true also for rectus abdominis, sometimes taken to be a "pure" slow muscle.

MEMBRANE PROPERTIES AND SYNAPTIC TRANSMISSION

The electrical properties of twitch fibres have been much more thoroughly investigated and such fibres were in fact the first preparation used for potential measurements with glass microelectrodes. Measurements of this kind have shown that the resting membrane potential is 90–95 mV with the inside negative with respect to the outside (Adrian, 1956; Hodgkin and Horowicz, 1959). The steady membrane potential is determined by the concentration ratios of potassium and chloride ions, indicating a permeability both to K^+ and Cl^-. If $[K]_0$ is changed and the $[K]_0[Cl]_0$ product kept constant, the membrane behaves as a potassium electrode at $[K]_0$ above 10 mM; at lower concentrations the log $[K]_0$-membrane potential relation deviates from a straight line in a manner expected from a slight permeability to sodium ions. If changes in $[K]_0$ are made at constant $[Cl]_0$, or vice versa, more complicated changes in potential are observed, which can be explained on basis of the Donnan principle. The chloride permeability of fibres equilibrated in Ringer solution is about 4×10^{-6} cm/s, the potassium permeability is about half of this. The potassium permeability varies greatly with the direction of the driving force on the potassium ions and is higher for inward than for outward potassium current (anomalous rectification). The membrane resistance is of the order of 3–5.5 kΩ cm^2; the membrane capacitance is 4–7 μF/cm^2 (Adrian and Peachey, 1965; Stefani and Steinbach, 1969).

It has generally been held that the resting membrane potential of *slow* fibres is much lower than that of twitch fibres (-45 to -70 mV; Kuffler and Vaughan Williams, 1963a; Burke and Ginsborg, 1956; Kiessling, 1960). However, in a recent investigation Stefani and Steinbach (1969) found much higher values, about -80 mV. They also noted that the membrane resistance is about 20 times higher in slow than in twitch fibres. This means that measurements in slow fibres will be much more sensitive to a shunt produced around an impaling microelectrode, which may to a large extent explain the much lower values obtained by previous investigators. The membrane capacitance of slow fibres is 1.5–2.5 times lower than in twitch fibres (Adrian and Peachey, 1965; Stefani and Steinbach, 1969). This is to be expected if the wall of the transverse tubules is continuous with the surface membrane and if the relative amount of tubules is less than in twitch fibres which seems to be the case. The resting chloride permeability appears to be very low or absent, and the calculated potassium permeability is 10 times smaller than in twitch fibres; anomalous rectification is absent.

The arrival of a nerve impulse at the nerve terminals on a muscle fibre causes release of acetylcholine, which reaches the postsynaptic membrane by diffusion. ACh induces a permeability change in the end-plate membrane, which allows a depolarizing end-plate current to flow, usually recorded as an end-plate potential (EPP). When the end-plate region of a twitch fibre is depolarized to about -50 mV a propagated action potential is set up with an amplitude of 120–130 mV and a duration of about 2 ms at room temperature. The ionic mechanisms underlying the action potential in the twitch fibre membrane are essentially similar to those in the nerve membrane. The time course of the EPP is most easily studied when transmitter action is partially blocked so that the level for action potential initiation is not reached. Intracellular recording under these conditions shows the EPP as a brief depolarization followed by a slower repolarization with a half-time of 3–5 ms at room temperature.

When recordings are made from a *slow* fibre during stimulation of its thin motor nerve fibres, postsynaptic potentials are observed which differ from the twitch fibre EPP in amplitude, time course, and localization. The initial phase of these small-nerve junction potentials (s.j.p.; Kuffler and Vaughan Williams, 1953a) consists of a depolarization 5–10 mV in amplitude, followed by a slow repolarization phase (half-time 25–35 ms) which turns into a long-lasting hyperpolarization. In contrast to twitch fibre EPPs which usually can be recorded from one restricted region only, small-nerve junction potentials can be obtained along the entire length of slow fibres. This was taken to mean that individual slow fibres are densely innervated and have a large number of synaptic regions, an idea that is supported by histological findings (see above).

Repetitive stimulation of small nerve fibres causes summation of s.j.p.s and depolarization by about 25 mV. However, action potentials are not produced under normal circumstances. It is still not quite clear whether or not the slow fibre membrane entirely lacks regenerative properties. The reason for being cautious here is that Burke and Ginsborg (1956), using direct stimulation, on one occasion (out of 50 trials) found a slow fibre which after a hyperpolarizing step did give an action potential in response to depolarization. The claim by Shamarina (1963) that a large proportion of "tonic" fibres will respond with action potentials to repetitive stimulation, but not to single stimuli, has been refuted by several authors (Orkand, 1963; Forrester and Schmidt, 1970) who suggest that Shamarina was in fact recording from twitch fibres with a low safety factor of synaptic transmission. However, the possibility is still open that there are different types of slow fibres (cf. p. 66), one of which may conceivably possess the properties described by Shamarina.

EXCITATION–CONTRACTION COUPLING

This term comprises the chain of events which occur between membrane depolarization and tension production. A key role of calcium ions in the coupling process was suggested by the experiments of Heilbrunn and Wiercinsky (1947) in which they showed that of all normally occurring ions only calcium would produce a local contraction when injected into a frog muscle fibre. The tension of "skinned" frog fibres (sarcolemma removed) and of glycerol-extracted fibres (sarcolemma "dissolved") is related to the Ca^{++}-concentration of the surrounding medium by a steep S-shaped curve, starting at about 10^{-7} M and reaching a maximum at about 10^{-6} M (Hellam and Podolsky, 1969; Julian, 1971). Thus, the Ca^{++}-concentration in the sarcoplasm of intact, resting fibres is likely to be below 10^{-7} M. Since the total Ca^{++}-concentration of muscle is many times higher this implies that calcium is stored in some intracellular compartment which does not have free access to the sarcoplasm. The most likely candidate for such a compartment is the sarcoplasmic reticulum.

The first step in the coupling process is a depolarization of the surface membrane (Kuffler, 1946); passage of internal longitudinal current is ineffective in producing contraction (Sten-Kundsen, 1960). Changes in surface membrane potential are conveyed to the interior of the fibre via the walls of the transverse tubules. These make intimate contacts with the walls of the lateral cisternae of the sarcoplasmic reticulum in the form of triadic junctions (Fig. 1A). A potential change of the junctional membranes causes release of calcium from the lateral cisternae; the exact nature of this process is unknown. At low Ca^{++}-concentration ($<10^{-7}$ M) interaction between the actin and myosin filaments is prevented by a protein, tropomyosin, which is bound to the actin filaments. Tropomyosin is also closely associated with a second protein, troponin, with high Ca^{++} affinity. Released calcium ions bind to troponin, which induces a conformational change in the tropomyosin molecule such that actin–myosin interaction and force generation can occur. Relaxation is brought about by an (active) re-uptake of Ca^{++} into the sarcoplasmic reticulum. (For details of the role of Ca^{++} in E–C coupling see review by Ebashi and Endo, 1968.)

Depolarization of the surface membrane can be obtained either by electric stimulation or by an increase in external K^+-concentration. The latter method has the advantage that homogeneous depolarization of the entire surface membrane can be more easily obtained. When applied to single fibre preparations, mounted in a system specially designed for quick solution changes, very rapid steps in membrane potential can be

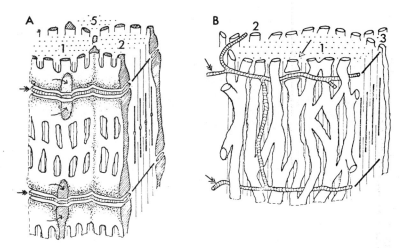

FIG. 1A. Schematic drawing to illustrate the organization of transverse tubules (double-headed arrows) and the sarcoplasmic reticulum in a frog twitch fibre. Single-headed arrows point at the terminal cisternae of the sarcoplasmic reticulum. B, Schematic drawing to represent the organization of transverse tubules (double-headed arrows) and the sarcoplasmic reticulum in frog slow fibres. One region of contact between a transverse tubule and the sarcoplasmic is shown (arrow), in which the small size of the terminal sacs may be noted. (Figures and caption from Page, 1969.)

achieved. Hodgkin and Horowicz (1960) used this method on isolated twitch fibres and studied the relation between tension development and membrane potential, recorded with an intracellular electrode. The mechanical response to a step change in potential consists of a relatively short-lasting, reversible increase of tension—a contracture, which starts at about $-50\,\mathrm{mV}$; above this threshold value tension rises rapidly and reaches a maximum at about $-30\,\mathrm{mV}$ (see also Fig. 2). The gradation of tension is probably

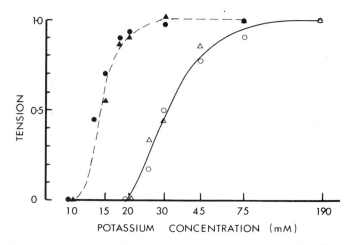

FIG. 2. Relation between contracture tension and external potassium concentration for two isolated twitch fibres (unfilled symbols) and two single slow fibres (filled symbols). Fibres dissected from the iliofibularis muscle of *Xenopus laevis*. Sarcomere length 2.2–2.3 μm. Depolarizing solutions had constant $[K]\cdot[Cl]$ product $= 300\ (mM)^2$.

due to a variation in the cross-sectional area of the fibre that is activated; sub-maximal depolarization results in activation of a peripheral ring of myofibrils, surrounding an inactive core (Gonzales-Serratos, 1965; Costantin and Taylor, 1973). Hodgkin and Horowicz also showed that twitch fibres maintain a steady tension for a few seconds only in high K^+-concentration solutions and then relax although the membrane remains depolarized (see also Fig. 6A). This has been explained by exhaustion of the calcium store (Hodgkin and Horowicz, 1960), or by inactivation of the release mechanism (Frankenhaeuser and Lännergren, 1967).

Excitation–contraction Coupling in Slow Fibres

Almost all of the information above has been derived from experiments performed on twitch fibres and relatively less is known about E–C coupling in slow fibres. Slow fibres respond with a long-lasting contracture to a number of agents, including KCl and ACh. The contracture response disappears after prolonged exposure to Ca^{++}-free solutions both in slow and in twitch fibres, but this does not prove that Ca^{++} constitutes the coupling agent since the permeability properties of the membrane are greatly affected by changes in $[Ca]_0$ (Frankenhaeuser and Hodgkin, 1957). Thus, the lack of response in Ca^{++}-free media might equally well be explained by a more pronounced inactivation of the release process when $[Ca]_0$ is lowered. However, it has been shown that application of Ca^{++} to fibres, which have had their sarcolemma removed, causes contraction in slow fibres as well as in twitch fibres and that the sensitivity of the two kinds of preparation is about the same (Costantin et al., 1967). Thus calcium ions very likely serve as the normal intracellular activating substance also in slow fibres.

The site of origin of activator-calcium in slow fibres is not clear. One possibility would be that Ca^{++} passes through, or is released from the surface membrane, rather than being released from the sarcoplasmic reticulum as in twitch fibres. This would explain the finding (Peachey and Huxley, 1960) that responses to local depolarization could be obtained from very many points on the surface of slow fibres in spite of the relatively small number of triads present. The idea that extracellular calcium ions play an important role in activation is further supported by findings that contracture tension in slow fibres is much more strongly dependent on $[Ca]_0$ than in twitch fibres (Lüttgau, 1963; Nasledov et al., 1966; Kirby, 1970). A difference in E–C coupling between twitch and slow fibres is further supported by the finding that the mechanical threshold is lower in slow fibres and the relation between tension and $[K]_0$ steeper (Lännergren, 1967; see also Fig. 2). Also, the mechanical threshold is markedly lowered by stretch in twitch fibres, but not in slow fibres (Lännergren, unpublished).

On the other hand, Nasledov, et al. (1972) have stressed the similarities in E–C coupling in the two fibre types. It has previously been shown (Eisenberg and Eisenberg, 1968; Howell, 1969) that exposing twitch fibres for 1 hr to Ringer solution made hypertonic by the addition of 400 mM glycerol and then transferring them to normal Ringer solution disrupts the transverse tubules and uncouples contraction from membrane depolarization. Although slow fibres seem to be more resistant to glycerol removal (Stefani and Steinbach, 1968) uncoupling can be achieved by this procedure if the experiment is performed on isolated slow fibres (as opposed to multi-fibre preparations as used by Stefani and Steinbach) as shown by Nasledov et al. (1972) which indicates that the tubules play an important role also in slow fibres.

A possibility, which has not been directly tested, would be that there is a dual source of activator-calcium in amphibian slow fibres, i.e. the external solution as well as the sarcoplasmic reticulum, as seems to be the case for chicken slow fibres (Page, 1969).

BASIC MECHANICAL PROPERTIES OF FROG MUSCLE FIBRES

Resting Muscle

An unstimulated muscle, for instance a frog's sartorius, is readily extensible and its tension does not rise significantly until it is stretched beyond 10–20% of its normal length in the body. At about 45% stretch the passive tension reaches the same value as that obtained at full activation at optimum length (A. V. Hill, 1953). Isolated fibres are even more extensible; the tension at twice the normal resting length being 10–50% of the maximum isometric tension. The difference between a whole muscle and an isolated fibre is mainly due to the presence of connective tissue between the fibres in the intact muscle. The resting tension of isolated fibres has been wholly (Ramsey and Street, 1940) or partly (Casella, 1951) attributed to stretch of the sarcolemma; recent investigations indicate that the sarcolemma does not contribute at sarcomere lengths below 3 μm (Podolsky, 1964; Rapoport, 1973). The origin of the very small resting tension which is observed in the range 2–3 μm sarcomere length is not clear. It has been suggested that it would be due to stretch of S-filaments, thought to connect the ends of the actin filaments across the H-zone (Huxley and Hanson, 1954), or reflect repulsive electrostatic forces between the filaments (Elliot et al., 1970). A third possibility suggested by D. K. Hill (1968) is that there is some active interaction between the actin and myosin filaments also in resting muscle, which would contribute to the resting tension.

The resting tension of isolated twitch and slow Xenopus fibres is about the same at 2.3 μm sarcomere length, but the length–tension curve is somewhat steeper for slow fibres in the range 2.3–2.8 μm sarcomere length (Lännergren, unpublished).

Active Tension Development Under Isometric Conditions

Isometric tension of fully activated muscle varies with muscle cross-sectional area and degree of extension. The reason behind the first statement is obvious: the larger the area the greater the number of contractile elements working in parallel. The maximum force per cm^2 seems to be very nearly the same for most vertebrate muscles; the most precise measurements have been performed on isolated frog fibres. The value for single twitch fibres is close to 300 mN/cm^2 (Hodgkin and Horowicz, 1960) and the figure for slow fibres is nearly the same (Nasledov et al., 1966; Lännergren, 1967).

The relation between muscle *length* and active tension was investigated by several workers in the early part of the century and it was usually found that maximum tension is produced at lengths corresponding to the greatest length the muscle can assume in the body. Complete length–tension curves for both active and passive tension of isolated frog twitch fibres were first published by Ramsey and Street (1940) who showed that maximum active tension was developed close to the resting length; from this maximum level there was an almost linear fall to zero tension at 100% extension.

The electron micrographs of Hanson and H. E. Huxley (1953) and H. E. Huxley (1953) clearly showed that the myofibrils are composed of two interdigitating sets of filaments: thick and thin. The thick filaments (about 11 nm in diameter) are confined to the A-band; the thin filaments (about 4 nm in diameter) are held together at their middle at the Z-line and extend through the I-band into the A-band on each side. It was also shown that the thick and thin filaments consist of myosin and actin, respectively (Hanson and H. E. Huxley, 1953). Observations with the light microscope of isolated myofibrils (H. E. Huxley and Hanson, 1954) and of isolated, living muscle fibres (A. F. Huxley and Niedergerke, 1954) showed that both during passive length changes and during active shortening the width of the I-band changed whereas the width of the A-band remained constant. These findings, together with the structural information obtained with the electron microscope, formed the basis for the sliding filament theory proposed almost simultaneously by H. E. Huxley and A. F. Huxley, in 1953–1954. According to this theory the two kinds of filaments are free to slide past each other in resting muscle. The force produced during active contraction is generated at a number of independent sites, identified with projections from the myosin filaments—crossbridges.

The theory gained strong support when A. F. Huxley and his colleagues (Gordon, Huxley and Julian, 1966) repeated the experiments of Ramsey and Street under very rigid conditions which enabled them to control precisely the length of a middle segment of an isolated fibre where intrinsic variations in sarcomere length are very small. The relation between active tension and sarcomere length obtained by Gordon et al. under this condition (Fig. 3) is easily interpreted in terms of the sliding filament theory: the plateau between 2.0 and 2.2 μm sarcomere length corresponds to a situation of

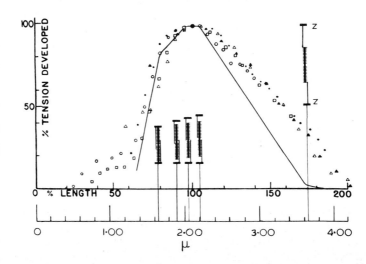

Fig. 3. Length–isometric tetanus tension relation for single twitch muscle fibres from the frog. Symbols refer to data from Ramsey and Street (1940; their fig. 5). Line in full summarizes results obtained with the improved length control system devised by A. F. Huxley and colleagues. The degree of overlap between thick filaments (length 1.6 μm) and thin filaments (length 2.05 μm including Z-line) for various critical sarcomere lengths (lower scale) is also indicated. (From Gordon et al., 1964.)

maximum overlap between the filaments and hence maximum number of crossbridges in position for force generation; the straight falling part between 2.2 and 3.6 μm corresponds to a linear decrease in overlap, and the zero point at 3.6 μm equals the point where overlap becomes zero and possibility for crossbridge action ceases. The basis for the steep fall in tension on the left-hand side of the plateau is less clear. It was originally interpreted as being due to structural interference with crossbridge action or filament movement but decreased efficiency of excitation-contraction coupling at short fibre lengths may also play a part (Taylor and Rüdel, 1970).

A corollary of the theory is that muscle fibres with long sarcomeres at resting length, i.e. fibres in which the filament lengths are greater, would produce more tension per cross-sectional area, since there would be a larger number of crossbridges acting in parallel on each thick filament. This has been shown to be true: maximum force per unit area of crayfish fibres (sarcomere length at rest about 10 μm) is 2 to 3 times higher than that of frog fibres (Zachar and Zacharová, 1966).

The isometric length–tension curve of slow fibres is very similar to that of twitch fibres (Nasledov and Lebedinskaya, 1971) as would be expected from the fact that A and I filament lengths are the same in the two fibre types.

Tension Time Course in Twitches and Tetani

So far, the steady tension level during a tetanus or a contracture has been discussed. The rise in tension following activation will now be considered. After the onset of stimulation—a single pulse to give a twitch, and a series of pulses to produce a tetanus— there is a short latent period followed by a minute drop in tension:latency relaxation. After this, tension rises along a steep S-shaped curve, passes through a maximum and falls again in a twitch, or approaches a steady level in a tetanus. The time course of these tension changes can be explained in terms of a simple analog model developed by A. V. Hill (1938). In its simplest form, applicable to muscle lengths where resting tension is negligible, the model consists of a contractile component (CC) which can produce force and/or shorten, connected with a series elastic component (SEC) with the properties of an undamped, non-linear spring (Fig. 4).

It must be emphasized here that the elements of the model were not identified with any specific structures in the muscle by Hill and the analog was developed long before the sliding filament theory was developed. The model has several shortcomings when it comes to explaining certain phenomena of muscle behaviour. (A number of these have been discussed in a recent article by Simmons and Jewell (1974) which also describes recent developments of the model for crossbridge force generation proposed in 1957 by A. F. Huxley.) However, in spite of its limitations, Hill's approach has been very useful for analysing the basic mechanical properties of muscle and is still widely used for studies of mechanical properties of mammalian muscle (see, for instance, the review by Close, 1972).

Part of the series elastic component is undoubtedly external to the muscle and corresponds to compliance of the connections between the muscle and the recording apparatus. With very rigid connections the length–tension curve of the SEC can be made so steep that full isometric tension is reached at an extension of 2% of L_o (L_o = optimum length for tension production; Jewell and Wilkie, 1958). About half

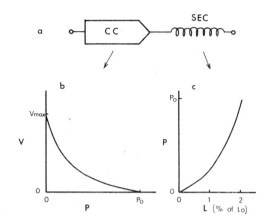

FIG. 4. (a) Analogue model of muscle (two-component model) consisting of a contractile component (CC) in series with a series elastic component (SEC). (b) Force-velocity curve, showing the relation between V (velocity of shortening of the CC) and P (force opposing shortening) when the CC is fully active. V_{max} denotes maximum shortening velocity (when external force opposing shortening is zero); P_0 denotes isometric tetanic tension. (c) Length–tension relation of the series elastic component as determined in isotonic release experiments. L_0 = muscle length for maximum isometric tension. The shape of the curves in (b) and (c) made to agree with the results of Jewell and Wilkie (1958).

of this compliance resides in the contractile material, possibly the crossbridges themselves.

The contractile component is characterized by its force–velocity relation, i.e. the speed at which the CC can shorten depends on the force acting against it (Fig. 4B). The curve in Fig. 4B represents a part of a rectangular hyperbola and can be adequately described by an equation of the form

$$(P + a)(V + b) = \text{constant},$$

where P is the force, V the shortening velocity, and a and b are constants, characteristic of a given muscle.

At the beginning of an isometric contraction (Fig. 5) the CC is supposed to change very quickly from a resting state to a fully active state. Since the force opposing shortening is zero at the beginning, the shortening speed of CC will be very high initially, but falls gradually as the SEC is extended and exerts an opposing force. If stimulation is continued, as in a tetanus, the tension will eventually reach a steady level = P_0. If only a single stimulus is given the activity of the CC will start to decline after some short time. At this instant the twitch tension curve separates from the tetanus curve, and its slope becomes zero at the instant when the CC no longer shortens = time of peak twitch tension. Beyond this point the SEC shortens at the expense of the CC, muscle tension falls and eventually becomes zero.

The way in which the activity of the CC changes with time cannot be directly assessed from the time course of the twitch. A. V. Hill (1949) introduced the concept of the "intensity of the active state" (AS in Fig. 5) defined as the tension the contractile component can just bear at a given instant without lengthening or shortening.

Various methods have been devised for determining the variation of active state intensity with time after a stimulus. These methods include: (a) a rapid stretch delivered soon after the stimulus by an amount just sufficient to extend the SEC to the length it acquires during the plateau of an isometric tetanus (Hill, 1949); this results in the full tetanus tension being developed, which has been taken to mean that the intensity of the active state rises very rapidly to its maximum value soon after the stimulus; (b) determination of the time at which the twitch tension curve starts to fall below the tetanus curve, which will mark the instant when the active state starts to decay during the twitch (MacPherson and Wilkie, 1954); (c) recording tension redevelopment when the tension in the SEC is discharged by a quick shortening step at various times after a single stimulus (Ritchie, 1954). This last method gives a family of twitch-like curves, the peaks of which, by definition, lie on the falling phase of the active state curve.

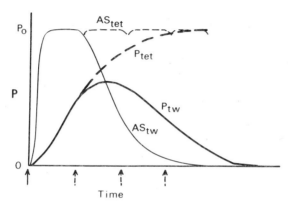

FIG. 5. Time course of tension during a twitch (P_{tw}, lines drawn in full) and during a tetanus (P_{tet} interrupted lines). Thin line, marked AS_{tw}, indicates time course of the active state in a twitch. During repetitive stimulation (arrows) the active state of the CC remains high and muscle tension (P_{tet}) rises gradually to reach P_0.

Active state determinations by methods which involve changes of the length or the tension of the muscle have been criticized since it has been shown that the duration of the active state is affected by such interventions (Jewell and Wilkie, 1960). It has furthermore been shown that the basic assumptions of the two-compartment analysis, i.e. that the SEC is a purely passive element, unaffected by the degree of activation, and that the shortening velocity of the CC changes instantaneously with changes in force (or vice versa) are not correct (see Simmons and Jewell, 1974 for a detailed discussion). However, determinations of the time course of the active state may still be useful since they provide at least some information about the time course of interaction of calcium with the contractile elements.

COMPARISON OF ISOMETRIC CONTRACTIONS OF TWITCH AND SLOW FIBRES

Twitch–tetanus Ratio and Rate of Tension Rise

The ratio of twitch amplitude to maximum tetanic tension for frog sartorius muscles or for single twitch fibres is 0.4–0.9, depending on temperature. Whereas the maximum tension per unit area is about the same in slow as in twitch fibres, the mechanical response of slow fibres to a single stimulus, as studied in nerve–muscle preparations with selective activation of thin nerve fibres, is extremely small and amounts to a few per cent of the maximum tension (Tasaki and Mizutani, 1944; Kuffler and Vaughan Williams, 1953b). Very likely this is due more to differences in membrane properties than in contractile properties. Because slow fibres are (normally) unable to generate action potentials, only local depolarization at the synaptic regions occurs, causing local contractions. These will produce very little overall tension if there are unactivated regions in between acting as series compliances. When repetitive stimulation is used a slow rise in tension is seen, which is graded with stimulus frequency. The greater efficacy of repeated stimulation is probably due to summation of synaptic potentials, causing a larger depolarization at each synaptic region and activation of larger portions of the fibre (Kuffler and Vaughan Williams, 1953a). Maximum tension is reached at about 50 Hz; stimulus rates greater than this merely increase the rate of tension rise. Even at very high stimulation frequencies tension development in slow fibres is many times slower than in tetanically stimulated twitch fibres. This might also be due to different properties of the membrane and/or the coupling system. However, recent experiments in which supramaximal amounts of calcium were directly applied to fibres from which the sarcolemma had been removed under oil, clearly demonstrated that the slow response is an inherent property of the contractile system of slow fibres (Costantin et al., 1967).

Maintenance of Tension

Slow fibres also differ from twitch fibres in their ability to maintain tension for long periods of time. This difference is seen both when repetitive, indirect stimulation is used and when membrane-depolarizing agents such as KCl and ACh are applied.

During repetitive stimulation, twitch fibre tension declines gradually, falling to zero in one to several minutes, depending on stimulation frequency and type of fibre. This fall in tension is usually attributed to fatigue, since essentially normal action potentials can still be generated.

When the membrane of a twitch fibre is continuously depolarized by the application of a K^+-rich solution a brief contracture is induced with a plateau of maximum tension lasting for a few seconds, followed by a quick relaxation (Fig. 6A). The fall in tension in this case is not due to fatigue but probably reflects inactivation of the calcium release mechanism (cf. p. 70).

Slow fibres maintain tension extremely well both during repetitive nerve stimulation (Kuffler and Vaughan Williams, 1953b; Smith and Lännergren, 1968) and during continuous, direct stimulation (Fig. 6B). Maximum tension can be maintained for several minutes at a potassium concentration of 20–40 mM (Nasledov et al., 1966; Lännergren, 1967); at very high $[K]_0$ some relaxation is seen, however, which seems to be more pronounced in Xenopus fibres than in frog fibres. Slow fibres are thus fatigue-resistant and show little inactivation.

In mammalian twitch fibres resistance to fatigue is closely related to the occurrence of a large number of mitochondria and lipid droplets and a high oxidative enzyme activity (for a review see Close, 1972). This is probably the case also for amphibian twitch fibres (Lännergren and Smith, 1966). Amphibian slow fibres, on the other hand,

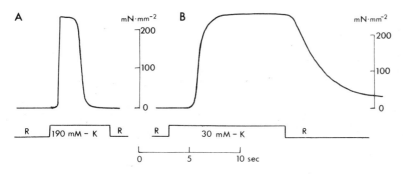

FIG. 6. Tension during a potassium contracture of a single twitch fibre (A) and of a single slow fibre (B). K-concentration chosen to give maximum tension. Note spontaneous relaxation of twitch fibre during depolarization and maintained tension of slow fibre. Relaxation of slow fibre after change back to Ringer solution (R) is slow. Fibres from the iliofibularis muscle of *Xenopus laevis*, held at 2.25 μm sarcomere length. Temperature 21–23°C.

have very few mitochondria and small energy stores (Lännergren and Smith, 1966; Engel and Irwin, 1967; Smith and Ovalle, 1973) which at first sight makes their high resistance to fatigue seem surprising. However, the anomalous situation may partly be explained by the very low shortening speed of slow fibres which implies a low turn-over rate of crossbridges (see below). Hence, maintenance of tension may be more "economic" in slow fibres.

Rate of Relaxation

After cessation of stimulation the intensity of the active state starts to decline when the calcium concentration at the contractile elements is reduced. The reduction is caused by lowering of the sarcoplasmic Ca^{++}-concentration, which in turn is the result of an active re-uptake of Ca^{++} by the sarcoplasmic reticulum. As discussed above, changes in muscle tension lag behind changes in active state intensity. Thus, relaxation is delayed relative to the fall in active state.

Relaxation is some 50 times slower in slow than in twitch fibres. At least two factors may contribute to this. First, the removal of Ca^{++} from the sarcoplasm is likely to be slow. The Ca^{++} uptake has not been directly measured but the finding by Costantin et al. (1967) that the spread of contraction was much wider in slow than in twitch fibres when calcium was directly applied suggests that Ca^{++} absorption is slow. The relative sparseness of the sarcoplasmic reticulum, as seen in electron micrographs is also consistent with the idea of less effective Ca^{++} pumping. Second, force-velocity measurements indicate that the breaking of attached crossbridges occurs at a much lower rate in slow fibres (see below). This will mean that tension falls more slowly when the Ca^{++}-concentration and the intensity of the active state has fallen to a low level.

ISOTONIC CONTRACTIONS

As explained above, the interpretation of results obtained under isometric conditions is complicated by the presence of a series compliance. For example, the contraction time of an isometric twitch, often used to classify a muscle or a motor unit as "fast" or "slow", does not only depend on the intrinsic shortening speed but will also be influenced by the stiffness of the SEC as well as the time course of calcium release and re-uptake. More reliable information about the intrinsic properties of a contracting muscle is obtained under isotonic conditions, in which case the speed at which the muscle shortens against a constant, opposing force (load) is recorded. During isotonic shortening of the fully active muscle, the tension in the CC is constant and equal to the external load; thus the shortening speed of the CC when producing a given force can be determined.

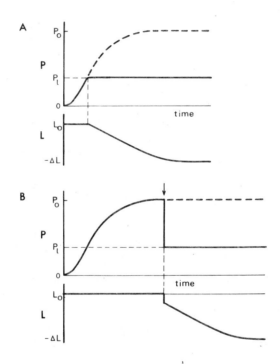

FIG. 7. Tension (P) and length (L) changes (shortening downwards) in a muscle during two types of isotonic experiment. A is an after-load contraction. Tension first rises isometrically to the value of the load (P_1), against which the muscle then shortens at constant velocity. Interrupted line indicates tension rise during an isometric tetanic contraction. B shows an isotonic release experiment. Tetanic tension is first developed at a fixed length. Arrow indicates when muscle is released and is exposed to the load. Note that shortening occurs with an initial, quick phase and a later, slow phase.

Isotonic experiments can be performed either as after-loaded contractions or as isotonic releases. In both cases, the experiments are usually done with the aid of a pivoted lever with small inertia. The muscle is connected to the lever on one side of the fulcrum and the load, in the form of a weight or a long stretched spring, is applied on the other side. In the after-loaded case a stop is used to prevent the load from stretching the unstimulated muscle, which is highly extensible. When the muscle is stimulated tetanically, tension starts to develop as in a normal isometric contraction but when the tension in the muscle matches the load, shortening begins at a constant velocity which depends on the load (Fig. 7A).

In isotonic release experiments (Fig. 7B) the muscle is first made to develop full isometric tension by stimulating it and checking the movement of the lever with another stop. When the stop is withdrawn, the tension falls abruptly to a level which corresponds to the load. The tension change is associated with a two-stage length change: a rapid initial shortening, attributable to recoil of the SEC, followed by a slower shortening at constant velocity, determined by the properties of the CC. In experiments performed on frog sartorius muscles the two methods were found to give almost identical force-velocity curves (Jewell and Wilkie, 1958). Measurements of the extent of quick shortening for releases to various loads can be used to determine the length–tension relation of the SEC.

The shape of the force–velocity curve of the CC (Fig. 4B) is adequately explained by the particular model for muscle contraction which was proposed by A. F. Huxley in 1957. In this model, force generation and shortening are assumed to depend on the cyclic action of crossbridges, each acting over a limited range (about ± 10 nm). The cycle involves attachment of a myosin bridge to an actin site in such a way that a shortening force is produced, splitting of ATP, and detachment of the bridge. The maximum force, P_0, is mainly determined by the number of possible contact points between the actin and myosin filaments in each half-sarcomere; it is thus linearly related to filament length and degree of overlap (cf. p. 72). During shortening, i.e. when the filaments slide past each other, less force is produced for two reasons. First, since the attachment rate is assumed to be finite, fewer bridges will attach during a given time; second, a large proportion of bridges will remain attached in a position which opposes shortening, since the detachment rate was also made to be finite.

The maximum shortening speed, V_{max}, obtained in the absence of an external load, is independent of the number of attached bridges, but will, according to the theory, depend on aspects of the cycling rate of the bridges, in particular the detachment rate. The cycling rate apparently varies greatly from one type of muscle to another, since very different values for V_{max} have been reported for different preparations. It has also been noted that there is a good correlation between V_{max} of a particular muscle and the ATPase activity of the actomyosin extracted from it (Bárány, 1967) which suggests that crossbridge turn-over rate is determined by the rate of ATP-splitting.

The total shortening speed of a muscle fibre is not only dependent on the rate of crossbridge turn-over, governing filament sliding rate, but it also depends on filament length and fibre length. If the filament lengths are the same, a long fibre will shorten more quickly than a short because there are more sarcomeres in series and their shortening speeds add up; if the fibre length is the same a fibre with shorter sarcomeres (and filaments) will shorten more quickly, again because there are more shortening elements in series.

Shortening Speed of Amphibian Twitch and Slow Fibres

The force-velocity relation of twitch fibres is well known from many studies of the frog's sartorius muscle, the favorite preparation of the A. V. Hill school. Most of those data pertain to 0°C, but values from experiments at room temperature are available (A. V. Hill, 1938). At 20–22°C the maximum shortening velocity is 6 muscle lengths/s, corresponding to about 12 μm/s per sarcomere. The value of a/P_0, which is a measure of the curvature of the force–velocity relation, is about 0.25.

Relatively few studies have been performed on slow fibres under isotonic conditions. Aidley (1965) studied the shortening properties of whole rectus abdominis muscles during the late, maintained phase of a potassium contracture, which probably represents slow fibre activity. Using an isotonic release technique, he found that the shortening speed at a given load was not constant as in twitch fibre preparations, but declined progressively during shortening. Thus, no simple force–velocity relation could be derived. Floyd and Smith (1971) encountered similar difficulties in their experiments with whole iliofibularis muscles, in which slow fibres were activated by selective stimulation of small-diameter nerve fibres: tension was not maintained during a constant-speed release, but fell progressively during the shortening. They furthermore found that isometric tension development at a given length was impaired if it was preceded by isotonic shortening from a greater length and ascribed the two effects to some form of "inactivation". Aidley's results, which were obtained at very short muscle lengths, may possibly be due to decreased efficiency of excitation–contraction coupling, which becomes evident at sarcomere lengths below 1.6–1.7 μm (Taylor and Rüdel, 1970). The "inactivation" observed by Floyd and Smith, however, cannot be explained in this way since it was observed at much longer sarcomere lengths, and its cause is unclear.

Isotonic experiments have recently been performed on isolated *Xenopus* slow fibres, activated by applying solutions with high K-concentration (Lännergren, unpublished). In most cases, after-loaded contractions were used, but a few isotonic release experiments were also performed. "Inactivation", evident as a progressive fall in shortening speed at constant load, was observed in the release experiments, both at low (30 mM) and at high (75 mM) K$^+$-concentration. In after-loaded contractions, however, a constant speed of shortening was obtained over more than 1 mm, provided a solution with

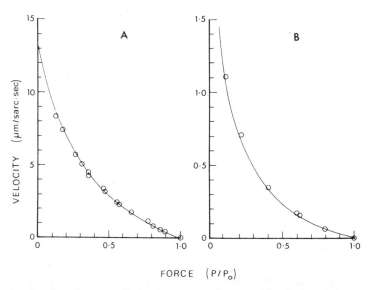

FIG. 8. Force–velocity data from after-load contractions of one twitch fibre (A) and one slow fibre (B) from *Xenopus laevis*. The twitch fibre was stimulated electrically at 100 Hz on a multi-electrode assembly; the slow fibre was activated by rapid application of 75 mM-K-solution. The curves fitted to the values obey Hill's equation (p. 74). For the curve in A, $a/P_0 = 0.40$, $b = 5$ μm/sarc.-sec; for the curve in B, $a/P_0 = 0.12$ and $b = 0.25$ μm/sarc.-sec. Temperature 21–24°C.

high K-concentration was used to activate the fibre. Data from after-loaded contractions were used to construct the force–velocity curve of Fig. 8B. It can be seen that it differs from a corresponding curve for an isolated twitch fibre (Fig. 8A) in two respects: V_{max} is about 6 times lower and the curvature is greater. The V_{max} value for the twitch fibre agrees well with that for sartorious fibres. A 10-fold difference in shortening velocity for twitch and slow fibres was observed in experiments on frog fibres, in which sarcomere shortening in response to local application of calcium was recorded (Costantin et al., 1967).

The fact that the force–velocity relation is more curved for slowly contracting fibres has been noted by other investigators (Woledge, 1968; Rall and Schottelius, 1973). It has been argued (Woledge, 1968) that a strongly curved force–velocity curve reflects a more efficient contractile process. If this is the case it would help to explain the puzzling situation that amphibian slow fibres are extremely resistant to fatigue although their metabolic capacity is very low.

ACKNOWLEDGEMENTS

The author is grateful to Dr. R. M. Simmons for reading the typescript and making helpful comments. This work was supported by grants from the Swedish Medical Research Council (Project No. 14X-3642) and Karolinska Institutets Fonder.

REFERENCES

ADRIAN, R. H. (1956) The effect of internal and external potassium concentration on the membrane potential of frog muscle. *J. Physiol. (Lond.)* **133**, 631–658.

ADRIAN, R. H. and PEACHEY, L. D. (1956) The membrane capacity of frog twitch and slow muscle fibres. *J. Physiol. (Lond.)* **181**, 324–336.

AIDLEY, D. J. (1965) Transient changes in isotonic shortening velocity of frog rectus abdominis muscles in potassium contracture. *Proc. Roy. Soc.,* B, **163**, 215–223.

ASMUSSEN, G. and KIESSLING, A. (1970) Die Muskelfasersorten des Frosches: Ihre Identifikation und die Gesetzmässigkeiten ihrer Anordnung in der Skeletmuskulatur. *Acta biol. med. germ.* **24**, 871–889.

BÁRÁNY, M. (1967) ATPase activity of myosin correlated with speed of muscle shortening. *J. Gen. Physiol.* **50**, 197–218.

BIRKS, R., HUXLEY, H. E. and KATZ, B. (1960) The fine structure of the neuromuscular junction of the frog. *J. Physiol. (Lond.)* **150**, 134–144.

BREMER, L. (1882) Über die Endigungen des markhaltigen und marklosen Nerven in quergestreiften Muskel. *Arch. mikroskop. Anat.* **21**, 165–201.

BURKE, R. E., LEVINE, P., TSAIRIS, P. and ZAJAC, F. E. (1973) Physiological types and histochemical profiles in motor units of the cat gastrocnemius. *J. Physiol. (Lond.)* **234**, 723–748.

BURKE, W. and GINSBORG, B. L. (1956) The electrical properties of the slow muscle fibre membrane. *J. Physiol. (Lond.)* **132**, 586–598.

CASELLA, C. (1951) Tensile force in total striated muscle, isolated fibre and sarcolemma. *Acta physiol. scand.* **21**, 380–401.

CLOSE, R. I. (1972) Dynamic properties of mammalian skeletal muscles. *Physiol. Rev.* **52**, 129–197.

COSTANTIN, L. L., PODOLSKY, R. J. and TICE, L. W. (1967) Calcium activation of frog slow muscle fibres. *J. Physiol. (Lond.)* **188**, 261–271.

COSTANTIN, L. L. and TAYLOR, S. R. (1973) Graded activation in frog muscle fibers. *J. Gen. Physiol.* **61**, 424–443.

COUTEAUX, R. (1952) Le système moteur a "petites" fibres nerveuses et a contraction "lente": contribution a son identification histologique sur les muscles de la grenouille. *C.R. Ass. Anat.* **39**, 264–269.

COUTEAUX, R. (1955) Localizations of cholinesterases at neuromuscular junctions. *Int. Rev. Cytol.* **4**, 335–375.

COUTEAUX, R. (1958) Morphological and cytochemical observations in the post-synaptic membrane at motor end-plates and ganglionic synapses. *Exptl Cell Res.,* Suppl. **5**, 294–322.

EBASHI, S. and ENDO, M. (1968) Calcium ion and muscle contraction. *Prog. Biophys.* **18**, 123–183.

EISENBERG, B. and EISENBERG, R. S. (1968) Selective disruptions of the sarcotubular system in frog sartorius muscle. *J. Cell Biol.* **39**, 451–467.

ELLIOTT, G. F., ROME, E. M. and SPENCER, M. (1970) A type of contraction hypothesis applicable to all muscles. *Nature (Lond.)* **226**, 417–420.

ENGEL, W. K. and IRWIN, R. I. (1967) A histochemical–physiological correlation of frog skeletal muscle fibers. *Am. J. Physiol.* **213**, 511–518.

FLOYD, K. and SMITH, I. C. H. (1971) The mechanical and thermal properties of frog slow muscle fibres. *J. Physiol. (Lond.)* **213**, 617–631.

FORRESTER, T. and SCHMIDT, H. (1970) An electrophysiological investigation of the slow muscle fibre system in the frog rectus abdominis muscle. *J. Physiol. (Lond.)* **207**, 477–491.

FRANKENHAEUSER, B. and HODGKIN, A. L. (1957) The action of calcium on the electrical properties of squid axons. *J. Physiol. (Lond.)* **137**, 218–244.

FRANKENHAEUSER, B. and LÄNNERGREN, J. (1967) The effect of calcium on the mechanical response of single twitch muscle fibres of *Xenopus laevis*. *Acta physiol. scand.* **69**, 242–254.

GONZALEZ-SERRATOS, H. (1965) Differential shortening of myofibrils during contractures of single muscle fibres. *J. Physiol. (Lond.)* **179**, 12–14P.

GORDON, A. M., HUXLEY, A. F. and JULIAN, F. J. (1964) The length-tension diagram of single vertebrate striated muscle fibres. *J. Physiol. (Lond.)* **171**, 28–30P.

GORDON, A. M., HUXLEY, A. F. and JULIAN, F. J. (1966) The variation in isometric tension with sarcomere length in vertebrate muscle fibres. *J. Physiol. (Lond.)* **184**, 170–192.

GRAY, E. G. (1957) The spindle and extrafusal innervation of a frog muscle. *Proc. Roy. Soc. B,* **146**, 416–430.

HANSON, J. and HUXLEY, H. E. (1953) The structural basis of cross-striations in muscle. *Nature (Lond.)* **172**, 530–532.

HEILBRUNN, L. V. and WIERCINSKY, F. J. (1947) The action of various cations on muscle protoplasm. *J. Cell. Comp. Physiol.* **29**, 15–32.

HELLAM, D. C. and PODOLSKY, R. J. (1969) Force measurements in skinned muscle fibres. *J. Physiol. (Lond.)* **200**, 807–819.

HESS, A. (1960) The structure of extrafusal fibers in the frog and their innervation studied by the cholinesterase technique. *Am. J. Anat.* **107**, 129–152.

HESS, A. (1967) The structure of vertebrate slow and twitch muscle fibers. *Invest. Ophthal.* **6**, 217–228.

HESS, A. (1970) Vertebrate slow muscle fibers. *Physiol. Rev.* **50**, 40–62.

HILL, A. V. (1938) The heat of shortening and the dynamic constants of muscle. *Proc. Roy. Soc. B,* **126**, 136–195.

HILL, A. V. (1949) The abrupt transition from rest to activity in muscle. *Proc. Roy. Soc. B,* **136**, 399–420.

HILL, A. V. (1953) The mechanics of active muscle. *Proc. Roy. Soc. B,* **141**, 104–117.

HILL, D. K. (1968) Tension due to interaction between the sliding filaments in resting striated muscle. The effect of stimulation. *J. Physiol. (Lond.)* **199**, 637–684.

HODGKIN, A. L. and HOROWICZ, P. (1959) The influence of potassium and chloride ions on the membrane potential of single muscle fibres. *J. Physiol. (Lond.)* **148**, 127–160.

HODGKIN, A. L. and HOROWICZ, P. (1960) Potassium contractures in single muscle fibres. *J. Physiol. (Lond.)* **153**, 386–403.

HOWELL, J. N. (1969) A lesion of the transverse tubules of skeletal muscle. *J. Physiol. (Lond.)* **201**, 515–533.

HUXLEY, A. F. (1957) Muscle structure and theories of contraction. *Prog. Biophys.* **7**, 255–318.

HUXLEY, A. F. and NIEDERGERKE, R. (1954) Structural changes in muscle during contraction. Interference microscopy of living muscle fibres. *Nature (Lond.)* **173**, 971–973.

HUXLEY, H. E. (1953) Electron microscope studies of the organisation of the filaments in striated muscle. *Biochim. biophys. Acta,* **12**, 387–394.

HUXLEY, H. E. and HANSON, J. (1954) Changes in the cross-striations of muscle during contraction and stretch and their structural interpretation. *Nature (Lond.)* **173**, 973–976.

JEWELL, B. R. and WILKIE, D. R. (1958) An analysis of the mechanical components in frog's striated muscle. *J. Physiol. (Lond.)* **143**, 515–540.

JEWELL, B. R. and WILKIE, D. R. (1960) The mechanical properties of relaxing muscle. *J. Physiol. (Lond.)* **152**, 30–47.

JULIAN, F. J. (1971) The effect of calcium on the force-velocity relation of briefly glycerinated frog muscle fibres. *J. Physiol. (Lond.)* **218**, 117–145.

KIESSLING, A. (1960) Das Ruhepotential der "tonischen" Skeletmuskelfasern des Frosches. *Pflüg. Arch. ges. Physiol.* **271**, 124–138.

KIRBY, A. C. (1970) Frog tonic muscle fibers: extracellular calcium and excitation-contraction coupling. *Am. J. Physiol.* **219**, 1446–1450.

KRÜGER, P. (1949) Die Innervation der tetanischen und tonischen Fasern der quergestreiften Skeletmuskulatur der Wirbeltiere. *Anat. Anz.* **97**, 169–175.

KRÜGER, P. (1952) *Tetanus und Tonus der quergestreiften Skeletmuskeln der Wirbeltiere und des Menschen.* Akademische Verlagsgesellschaft Geest u. Portig K.-G., Leipzig.

KUFFLER, S. W. (1946) The relation of electrical potential changes to contracture in skeletal muscle. *J. Neurophysiol.* **9**, 367–377.

KUFFLER, S. W. and GERARD, R. W. (1947) The small-nerve motor system to skeletal muscle. *J. Neurophysiol.* **10**, 383–394.

KUFFLER, S. W., LAPORTE, Y. and RANSMEIER, R. E. (1947) The function of the frog's small-nerve motor system. *J. Neurophysiol.* **10**, 395–408.

KUFFLER, S. W. and VAUGHAN WILLIAMS, E. M. (1953a) Small-nerve junctional potentials. The distribution of small motor nerves to frog skeletal muscle, and the membrane characteristics of the fibres they innervate. *J. Physiol. (Lond.)* **121**, 289–317.

KUFFLER, S. W. and VAUGHAN WILLIAMS, E. M. (1953b) Properties of the "slow" skeletal muscle fibres of the frog. *J. Physiol. (Lond.)* **121**, 318–340.

KÜHNE, W. (1887) Neue Untersuchungen über motorische Nervenendigungen. *Z. Biol.* **23**, 1–148.

LÄNNERGREN, J. (1967) Contractures of single slow muscle fibres of *Xenopus laevis* elicited by potassium, acetylcholine or choline. *Acta physiol. scand.* **69**, 362–372.

LÄNNERGREN, J. and SMITH, R. S. (1966) Types of muscle fibres in toad skeletal muscle. *Acta physiol. scand.* **68**, 263–274.

LÜTTGAU, H. C. (1963) The action of calcium ions on potassium contractures of single muscle fibres. *J. Physiol. (Lond.)* **168**, 679–697.

MACPHERSON, L. and WILKIE, D. R. (1954) The duration of the active state in a muscle twitch. *J. Physiol. (Lond.)* **124**, 292–299.

NASLEDOV, G. A. and LEBEDINSKAYA, I. I. (1971) Study of the contractile mechanism of frog tonic muscle fibres. *Sechenov Physiol. J. USSR*, **57**, 1307–1313.

NASLEDOV, G. A., MANDELSTAM, J. E. and RADZJUKEWICH, T. L. (1972) A study of excitation–contraction coupling in frog tonic muscle fibres of *Rana temporaria. Experientia*, **28**, 1305–1306.

NASLEDOV, G. A., ZACHAR, J. and ZACHAROVÁ, D. (1966) The ionic requirements for the development of contracture in isolated slow muscle fibres of the frog. *Physiol. Bohemoslovaca*, **15**, 293–306.

ORKAND, R. K. (1963) A further study of electrical responses in slow and twitch muscle fibres of the frog. *J. Physiol. (Lond.)* **167**, 181–191.

PAGE, S. G. (1965) A comparison of the fine structures of frog slow and twitch muscle fibres. *J. Cell Biol.* **26**, 477–497.

PAGE, S. G. (1968) Structure of the sarcoplasmic reticulum in vertebrate muscle. *Brit. Med. Bull.* **24**, 170–173.

PAGE, S. G. (1969) Structure and some contractile properties of fast and slow muscles of the chicken. *J. Physiol. (Lond.)* **205**, 131–145.

PEACHEY, L. D. (1961) Structure and function of slow striated muscle. In *Biophysics of Physiological and Pharmacological Actions*, SHANES, A. M. (Ed.), pp. 391–411. Am. Ass. Adv. Sci., Washington.

PEACHEY, L. D. and HUXLEY, A. F. (1960) Local activation and structure of slow striated muscle fibres of the frog. *Fed. Proc.* **19**, 257.

PEACHEY, L. D. and HUXLEY, A. F. (1962) Structural identification of twitch and slow striated muscle fibres of the frog. *J. Cell Biol.* **13**, 177–180.

PODOLSKY, R. J. (1964) The maximum sarcomere length for contraction of isolated myofibrils. *J. Physiol. (Lond.)* **170**, 110–123.

RALL, J. A. and SCHOTTELIUS, B. A. (1973) Energetics of contraction in phasic and tonic skeletal muscles of the chicken. *J. Gen. Physiol.* **62**, 303–323.

RAMSEY, R. W. and STREET, S. F. (1940) The isometric length-tension diagram of isolated skeletal muscle fibres of the frog. *J. Cell. Comp. Physiol.* **15**, 11–34.

RANVIER, L. (1878) *Leçons sur l'histologie du systeme nerveux.* Savy, Paris.

RAPOPORT, S. I. (1973) The anisotropic elastic properties of the sarcolemma of the frog semitendinosus muscle fiber. *Biophys. J.* **13**, 14–36.

RITCHIE, J. M. (1954) The effect of nitrate on the active state of muscle. *J. Physiol. (Lond.)* **126**, 155–168.

SHAMARINA, N. M. (1963) Electrical response of tonic skeletal muscle fibres to rhythmical stimulation. In: *The Effect of Use and Disuse on Neuromuscular Functions*, GUTMANN, E. and HNIK, P. (Eds.), pp. 499–514. Czech. Acad. Sci., Prague.

SIMMONS, R. M. and JEWELL, B. R. (1974) Mechanics and models of muscular contraction. In: *Recent Advances in Physiology*, LINDEN, R. J. (Ed.), pp. 87–147. J. and A. Churchill Ltd., London.

SMITH, R. S. and LÄNNERGREN, J. (1968) Types of motor units in the skeletal muscle of *Xenopus laevis. Nature (Lond.)* **217**, 281–283.

SMITH, R. S. and OVALLE, W. K. JR., (1973) Varieties of fast and slow extrafusal muscle fibres in amphibian hind limb muscles. *J. Anat.* **116**, 1–24.

SOMMERKAMP, H. (1928) Das Substrat der Dauerverkürzung am Froschmuskel. *Pflüg. Arch. ges. Physiol.* **128**, 99–115.

STEFANI, E. and STEINBACH, A. B. (1968) Persistence of excitation contraction coupling in "slow" muscle fibres after a treatment that destroys transverse tubules in "twitch" fibres. *Nature (Lond.)* **218**, 681–682.

STEFANI, E. and STEINBACH, A. B. (1969) Resting potential and electrical properties of frog slow muscle fibres. Effect of different external solutions. *J. Physiol. (Lond.)* **203**, 383–401.

STEN-KNUDSEN, O. (1960) Is muscle contraction initiated by internal current flow? *J. Physiol. (Lond.)* **151**, 363–384.

TASAKI, I. and MIZUTANI, K. (1944) Comparative studies on the activities of the muscle evoked by two kinds of motor nerve fibres. Part I, Myographic studies. *Jap. J. Med. Sci.*, Part III, Biophysics, **10**, 237–244.

TAYLOR, S. R. and RÜDEL, R. (1970) Striated muscle fibers: Inactivation of contraction induced by shortening. *Science*, **167**, 882–884.

UHRIK, B. and SCHMIDT, H. (1973) Distribution of slow muscle fibres in the frog rectus abdominis muscle. *Pflüg. Arch. ges. Physiol.* **340**, 361–366.

WACHHOLDER, K. and LEDEBÜR, J. VON (1930) Untersuchungen über "tonische" und "nichttonische" Wirbeltiermuskeln. I. Mitteilung. *Pflüg. Arch. ges. Physiol.* **225**, 627–642.

WOLEDGE, R. C. (1968) The energetics of tortoise muscle. *J. Physiol. (Lond.)* **197**, 685–707.

ZACHAR, J. and ZACHAROVÁ, D. (1966) Potassium contracture in single muscle fibres of the crayfish. *J. Physiol. (Lond.)* **186**, 596–618.

THE MOTOR UNIT: HISTOCHEMICAL AND FUNCTIONAL CORRELATIONS

ERIC KUGELBERG

SINCE Ranvier (1874), on the basis of extensive studies in the rabbit, associated the red and white colours of the muscle fibres with slow and fast contraction, it has been increasingly evident that morphological and histochemical properties of the muscle fibres are in some way correlated to function (e.g. Henneman and Olson, 1965; Olson and Swett, 1966). It has also been suggested that there is histochemical uniformity among muscle fibres innervated by a single motoneuron. Evidence in support of these hypotheses has until recently been indirect.

Two experimental approaches have been developed, which permit direct correlation between the histochemistry of individual muscle fibres and their contraction properties. Lännergren and Smith (1966) succeeded in comparing these in dissected single fibres of the toad muscle. For the mammalian muscle a relatively simple and effective method has been devised (Kugelberg and Edström, 1968; Edström and Kugelberg, 1968; Kugelberg, 1973). The muscle fibres making up a single motor unit can be demonstrated under the microscope by a combined physiological and histochemical technique. Repetitive stimulation of the motoneuron depletes the muscle fibres subserved by the neurone of glycogen, which permits mapping of the fibres in PAS-stained sections as unstained fibres, which can be further histochemically characterized in serial cross-sections (Fig. 1).

With this method it was proved that there is almost complete histochemical uniformity among the muscle fibres within the motor unit (Edström and Kugelberg, 1968; Doyle and Mayer, 1969; Burke *et al.*, 1971, 1973; Kugelberg, 1973). Thus the physiological properties of a motor unit at the same time reflect those of a given histochemical type of muscle fibre.

Homogeneity of the motor units is a prerequisite for the organization of the different types of muscle fibres in various types of movements according to their metabolic and functional capabilities. Homogeneity also indicates that the motoneuron determines the histochemical and physiological properties of its muscle fibres in keeping with the result of cross-union of the nerves to fast and slow muscles, initiated by Buller *et al.*, (1960) (cf. Romanul and Van Der Meulen, 1966, 1967; Dubowitz, 1967; Karpati and Engel, 1967).

The method of histochemical mapping reveals very clearly the distribution of muscle fibres in a single motor unit. The fibres are scattered, usually isolated and rarely more than two to four together, with extensive overlapping between different motor units (Fig. 1). In the rat soleus a single unit may be distributed almost over the

FIG. 1. Transverse section of rat soleus. PAS preparation showing the distribution of glycogen-depleted fibres of one type I motor unit. Note the wide scattering of fibres. × 21.

entire cross area of the muscle with an overlap of about thirty different motor units (Kugelberg, 1973). Similar but less extensive relative spread occurs in the cat gastrocnemius (Burke *et al.*, 1973b). It serves to spread contractile forces evenly in the muscle.

The enzymes most commonly used for histochemical fibre classification in clinical and experimental work are presented in Table 1.

The myofibrillar (actomyosin) ATPase reaction catalyses the hydrolysis of adenosine-triphosphate (ATP) to adenosine-diphosphate and inorganic phosphate and, as a result, provides the energy for the initiation of muscular contraction. The enzyme is part of the myofibril.

The routine histochemical ATPase method may be further modified by varying the condition of preincubation. For example, after preincubation at pH 4.3 the staining intensity is reversed, except in some type II fibres, which retain a moderate degree of reactivity at this pH (Brooke and Kaiser, 1970). The specificity of the reaction at pH 9.4 for actomyosin or fibrillar ATPase has recently come under attack. Guth

TABLE 1. ENZYMES FOR FIBRE TYPING

Myofibrils:	Myosin ATPase at pH 9.4
	Type I. Reaction light
	Type II. Reaction strong
Mitochondria:	Succinic dehydrogenase. SDH
	NADH diaphorase
Sarcoplasm:	Glucosan phosphorylase

(1973) admits that the procedure is truly an ATPase reaction, but considers it demon-strates total ATPase of the muscle fibre rather than permitting distinction between actomyosin ATPase and mitochondrial and sarcotubular ATPase activities. Biochemical studies indicate that the ATPase activity of myosin is the rate-limiting step in speed of shortening (Bárány, 1967, for further ref. see Close, 1972). Thus it is important to test empirically in different muscles the validity of the histochemical reaction for interpretation of contraction speed.

So far only single motor units of heterogeneous hindlimb muscles of rat and cat have been examined. However, the results were unequivocal. The type I fibre units are slow and type II fibre units fast (Burke *et al.*, 1971, 1973; Kugelberg, 1971, 1973).

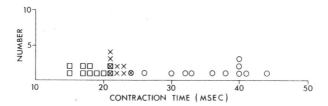

FIG. 2. Histochemical composition and isometric contraction times of rat soleus motor units. □ = units almost exclusively composed of fibres with ATPase intensity grade + + after formaldehyde fixation (type II); × = units with fibres of intermediate reactions, grade + (type II) and ○ = units with inhibited reaction, grade ○ (type I). ⊠ and ⊗ denote units of histochemically mixed composition. (From Kugelberg, 1973.)

Moreover, in the rat soleus, motor units were found with fibres of continuously variable intermediate intensities of various ATPase reactions associated with intermediate con-traction times (Kugelberg, 1973) (Fig. 2). I therefore think that in a given heterogeneous muscle the ATPase reactions give a good indication of the relative speed of the fibres.

Other factors, although likely correlated to myosin ATPase, may operate in determin-ing contraction time, such as the rate of release and uptake of Ca^{++}, morphological properties of the transverse tubular system and sarcoplasmic reticulum (Schiaffino *et al.*, 1970). For example, the type I fibre units of rat soleus are histochemically identical as regards intensity of ATPase, but their contraction time varies between 26 and 45 ms (Fig. 2). Differences between different species are still larger although the histochemical ARPase reactions appear to be identical. In the human eye muscles the majority of the fibres are type II and a minority type I. The latter are very probable slower than the type II fibres, but at present no exact figures as regards speed can be inferred from histochemical reactions alone.

SDH and NADH and other mitochondrial oxidative enzymes express the capacity of the muscle fibres for oxidative breakdown of lipids and other compounds, and phosphorylase capacity for anaerobic glycolysis (Dubowitz and Pearse, 1960; Romanul, 1964, and others). Since oxidation is a much more efficient source of energy than anaerobic glycolysis it is to be expected that the intensities of histochemical reactions of mitochondrial oxidative enzymes are correlated to resistance to fatigue. This has also been proved to be the case.

In the rat anterior tibial muscle there is a continuous spectrum of fibres from those with very low SDH and high phosphorylase activity to those with intense SDH and low phosphorylase activity organized into fast motor units. Among such fast units the content of mitochondrial oxidative enzymes seems to determine one physiological parameter, resistance to fatigue (Edström and Kugelberg, 1968). In the cat gastrocnemius (Burke *et al.*, 1971, 1973) essentially the same observations were made.

The intensities of mitochondrial oxidative enzymes may vary independently of myosin ATPase. For instance, in the skeletal muscles of man type I fibres have the most intense oxidative enzyme activity. In small animals with great rapidity of movements like the mouse or rat, some type II fibres have the most intense activity. An extreme example of the latter combination is found in the human extraocular muscles where many type II fibres are virtually packed with mitochondria with extremely high intensity of oxidative enzymes. The combination of high intensity of myosin ATPase and oxidative activity no doubt enables to combine speed and endurance.

The high mitochondrial enzyme activity in such fibres serves to compensate for the higher energy expenditure demanded by operation at high speed. The economy of tension maintenance in slow tonic fibres is greater than in fast phasic fibres, since to produce a given tension in a fused or partly fused tetanus the slow fibres require a much lower frequency of contraction than fast fibres and each contraction means consumption of ATP in making and breaking of cross-bridges and pumping of Ca^{++} back into sarcoplasmic reticulum.

Although in the rat soleus the type II fibres with a contraction time between 15 and 20 ms have a higher oxidative enzyme activity than the slower type I fibres with a mean contraction time of about 35 ms they are less efficient in maintaining tetanus. Some of this difference depends on a better matching between the capacity of neuromuscular transmission and tetanic fusion frequency in the slow fibres than in the fast fibres, and the safety factor for excitation-contraction coupling appears also greater in the slow fibres (Kugelberg, 1973). However, the high oxidative fast fibre units were very efficient in maintaining strong repetitive phasic contractions under long periods of time. Owing to the faster rate of rise and fall of tension such contractions can be repeated at a higher frequency than in slow motor units without interference between contractions. This is essential for rapid alternating movements.

In conclusion, the histochemical reactions for myosin ATPase is associated with contraction speed and mitochondrial oxidative enzymes activity with resistance to fatigue, but resistance to fatigue should be judged in relation to speed. The independent variability of both types of enzymes enables a wide range of specifications as regards speed and endurance required by muscles of different functions. Histochemical analysis makes it possible to "read" with some accuracy the functional competence of muscle fibres and motor units.

REFERENCES

BÁRÁNY, M. (1967) ATPase activity of myosin correlated with speed of muscle shortening. *J. Gen. Physiol.* **50**, 197.

BROOKE, M. H. and KAISER, K. K. (1970) Muscle fiber types: how many and what kind? *Arch. Neurol. (Chic.)* **23**, 369.

BULLER, A. J., ECCLES, J. C. and ECCLES, R. M. (1960) Interactions between motoneurones and muscles in respect of the characteristic speeds of their responses. *J. Physiol. (Lond.)* **150**, 417.

BURKE, R. E., LEVINE, D. N., ZAJAC, F. E., TSAIRIS, P. and ENGEL, W. K. (1971) Mammalian motor units: physiological-histochemical correlation in three types in cat gastrocnemius. *Science, N.Y.* **174**, 709.

BURKE, R. E., LEVINE, D. N., TSAIRIS, P. and ZAJAC, F. E. (1973a) Physiological types and histochemical profiles in motor units of the cat gastrocnemius. *J. Physiol.* **234**, 723.

BURKE, R. E. and TSAIRIS, P. (1973b) Anatomy and innervation ratios in motor units of cat gastrocnemius. *J. Physiol.* **234**, 749.

CLOSE, R. I. (1972) Dynamic properties of mammalian skeletal muscles. *Physiol. Rev.* **52**, 129.

DOYLE, A. M. and MAYER, R. F. (1969) Studies of the motor unit in the cat. *Bull. Sch. Med. Univ. Maryland.* **54**, 11.

DUBOWITZ, V. and PEARSE, A. G. E. (1960) A comparative histochemical study of oxidative enzyme and phosphorylase activity in skeletal muscle. *Histochemie*, **2**, 105.

DUBOWITZ, V. (1967) Cross-innervated mammalian skeletal muscle: histochemical, physiological and biochemical observations. *J. Physiol. (Lond.)* **193**, 481.

EDSTRÖM, L. and KUGELBERG, E. (1968) Histochemical composition, distribution of fibres and fatiguability of single motor units. *J. Neurol. Neurosurg. Psychiat.* **31**, 424.

GUTH, L. (1973) Fact and artifact in the histochemical procedure for myofibrillar ATPase. *Exptl Neurol.* **41**, 440.

HENNEMAN, E. and OLSON, C. B. (1965) Relations between structure and function in the design of skeletal muscles. *J. Neurophysiol.* **28**, 581.

KARPATI, G. and ENGEL, W. K. (1967) Transformation of the histochemical profile of skeletal muscle by "foreign" innervation. *Nature*, **215**, 1509.

KUGELBERG, E. and EDSTRÖM, L. (1968) Differential histochemical effects of muscle contractions of phosphorylase and glycogen in various types of fibres: relation to fatigue. *J. Neurol. Neurosurg. Psychiat.* **31**, 415.

KUGELBERG, E. (1971) Distribution, histochemical and physiological properties of normal and reinnervated rat motor units. In: *4th International Congress of Electromyography*, Brussels, 12–15 Sept., Symp. No. 1, pp. 85–86.

KUGELBERG, E. (1973) Histochemical composition, contraction speed and fatiguability of rat soleus motor units. *J. Neurol. Sci.* **20**, 177.

LÄNNERGREN, J. and SMITH, R. S. (1966) Types of muscle fibres in toad skeletal muscle. *Acta physiol. scand.* **68**, 263.

OLSON, C. B. and SWETT, C. P. (1966) A functional and histochemical characterization of motor units in a heterogeneous muscle (flexor digitorum longus) of the cat. *J. Comp. Neurol.* **128**, 475.

RANVIER, L. (1874) De quelques faits relatifs á l'histologie et á la physiologie des muscles striés. *Archs Physiol. norm. path.* **6**, 1.

ROMANUL, F. C. A. (1964) Enzymes in muscle. I. Histochemical studies of enzymes in individual muscle fibers. *Arch. Neurol. (Chic.)* **11**, 355.

ROMANUL, F. C. A. and VAN DER MEULEN, J. P. (1966) Reversal of the enzyme profiles of muscle fibres in fast and slow muscles by cross-innervation. *Nature (Lond.)* **212**, 1369.

ROMANUL, F. C. A. and VAN DER MEULEN, J. P. (1967) Slow and fast muscles after cross innervation. Enzymatic and physiological change. *Arch. Neurol. (Chic.)* **17**, 387.

SCHIAFFINO, S., HANZLIKOVÁ, V. and PIEROBON, S. (1970) Relations between structure and function in rat skeletal muscle fibers. *J. Cell. Biol.* **47**, 107.

STRUCTURAL–FUNCTIONAL CORRELATIONS IN EYE MUSCLE FIBERS. EYE MUSCLE PROPRIOCEPTION†

PAUL BACH-Y-RITA

INTRODUCTION

The present paper will be restricted to two aspects of oculomotor neurophysiology. First, I will discuss certain aspects of the structural–functional correlations of muscle fiber types in the peripheral oculomotor system. Secondly, I will present some physiological and anatomical studies related to the function of extraocular proprioception. This paper will primarily concern itself with research accomplished since 1969, when the symposium on the Control of Eye Movements (1971) was held.

I. STRUCTURAL–FUNCTIONAL CORRELATIONS

Alvarado (this Symposium) has described the morphological characteristics of eye muscles, including a description of clear morphological differences between outer (orbital) layer fibers and inner (core) fibers. In most biological systems, morphology reflects physiological properties, and both morphology and physiology reflect function. We have undertaken a series of studies on the properties of the fibers in eye muscles; our findings, combined with those of other investigators, indicate a close correlation between properties and functions.

A. Tonic and Phasic Fiber Types

The eye muscles perform several tasks, including those generally classified as fixation, slow movements and saccades.

1. Eye muscles hold the eye in one fixation position; due to head movement orientation, this fixation is usually in primary position. The muscle fibers that perform this function appear to be primarily the small outer layer muscle fibers (Collins and Scott, 1973; Collins, this Symposium) innervated by small nerve fibers (Yamanaka and Bach-y-Rita, 1968). In fact, only small motor nerve fibers were found to be active during tonic control of the eye in the absence of eye movements (Yamanaka and Bach-y-Rita, 1968). These muscle fibers maintain a constant tone measured to be approximately 7 g per eye muscle in the cat (Bach-y-Rita, 1971) and 12 g in the human

†This investigation was supported by NIH research grants No. PO1-EY-00299, No. PO1-EY-01176, Research Career Development Award No. EY-14,094, and the Smith-Kettlewell Eye Research Foundation.

(Collins, this Symposium). In humans, inhibition of the tonic contraction by neuro-muscular block results in up to 3 mm of exophthalmia (Tengroth, 1960).

The properties of the muscle fibers whose contraction maintains the tonic control of the eye reflect their function, since both the physiological properties (cf. Bach-y-Rita, 1971; 1973) and structural characteristics (Alvarado, this Symposium) are compatible with long-lasting activity. In fact, the physiological properties may be a product of this functional requirement: Buller *et al.* (1960) have demonstrated, by means of cross-innervation studies in cat limbs, that the physiological properties change to reflect the type of innervation; similarly Salmons and Vrbova (1969) and Barnard *et al.* (1970) have demonstrated morphological changes in response to functional demand.

2. The muscles move the eyes slowly, as in the slow phase of nystagmus and in the highly precise, slow following movements. The majority of these slow movements are generally not of large amplitude, usually being within a few degrees from the primary position (unless head movements are prevented). The slow movements are primarily mediated by the same slow small fibers which form the major contribution to maintaining fixation. These lower threshold slow ("tonic") fibers are active for a much greater percentage of the time than are the fast ("phasic") fibers during slow movements. This is reflected in the physiological and morphological properties of the muscle fibers.

3. The muscles move the eyes quickly, as in saccades or in the fast phase of nystagmus. Saccades are brief in time and the dominant activity, especially during large angle saccades, or saccades in eye positions far from primary position, is of the fast ("phasic") fibers (Collins and Scott, 1973), and fast nerve fibers have been demonstrated to be active during the fast phase of nystagmus (Yamanaka and Bach-y-Rita, 1968). The slower ("tonic") fibers are certainly contributing as much as they are capable of contri-buting to these saccades, but since their morphological and physiological characteristics reflect their principal role ("tonic") their contribution to the large angle saccades is overshadowed by that of the fast fibers (Collins and Scott, 1973).

While the tonic fibers contribute mainly to slow movements and fixation, and the phasic fibers mainly mediate fast movements, fibers of each type participate to some extent in each type of movement (cf. Bach-y-Rita, 1971; Collins, this Symposium). However, in view of the principal functional roles of the different eye muscle types, the terms "tonic" and "slow", as well as "phasic" or "fast", retain validity. Although not perfect, they do establish a functional framework.

B. Innervation of Tonic Fibers

There is considerable evidence that the extraocular muscles are subject to more than one type of innervational control. Thus the large fast ("phasic") muscle fibers, primarily located in the muscle core, are known to be singly innervated, while the small slow ("tonic") fibers, primarily found in the orbital layer, have multiple innervation (cf. Bach-y-Rita, 1971, 1973; Alvarado, this Symposium).

A muscle fiber with more than one end-plate region is multiple innervated. It may receive all its input from branches of the same nerve fiber; however, if more than one nerve fiber contributes input, the muscle fiber is polyneuronally innervated. Examples of polyneuronal innervation have been found in several types of vertebrate muscle (cf. P. Bach-y-Rita and G. Lennerstrand, 1975). The oculorotary muscles of the cat contain multiple innervated fibers (Hess and Pilar, 1963; Bach-y-Rita and Ito, 1966; Peachey, 1971; Lennerstrand, 1972; Alvarado, this Symposium). Earlier, on the basis of suggestive evidence, it was postulated that the multi-innervated eye muscle fibers might exhibit polyneuronal innervation (Bach-y-Rita, 1971). Therefore a study was designed (P. Bach-y-Rita and G. Lennerstrand, 1975) to obtain a definite answer to the question of the existence of polyneuronal innervation in extraocular muscles of the cat. Techniques for eliciting "tension excess" and post-tetanic potentiation, described by Brown and Matthews (1960) and by Bagust et al. (1973), were employed since these had proven of value in demonstrating polyneuronal innervation in other muscle systems. In addition we developed a new technique, referred to as cross-fatigue, to provide one more conclusive demonstration of the presence or absence of polyneuronal innervation.

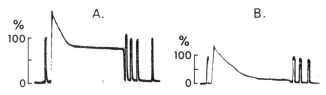

FIG. 1. Cross-fatigue test for polyneuronally innervated cat extraocular muscle fibers. A (lateral rectus) and B (retractor bulbus) tetanic responses to stimulation of one division of the abducens nerve before (first response to left) and after (responses to the right) the long-lasting tetanic stimulation of the other division of the nerve (broad trace second from the left). Stimulation was 1.5 V, 0.1 ms, at 300/sec for the first nerve branch, and 400/sec for the second. No cross fatigue was noted, thus confirming the absence of polyneuronally innervated muscle fibers in the cat lateral rectus and retractor bulbi muscles. [Reprinted with permission from J. Physiol. (1975)].

These three techniques were applied to the two muscles innervated by the abducens nerve; the lateral rectus, which contains multiple innervated fibers, and the retractor bulbus, a phasic muscle (Bach-y-Rita and Ito, 1965; Steinacker and Bach-y-Rita, 1967) which does not (Alvarado et al., 1967).

The excess of the sum of twitch tensions elicited from separate stimulation of two branches of the abducens nerve over tension from the whole nerve was 6.5% (S.D. ± 5.3%) for the lateral rectus and 1.2% (S.D. ± 8.6%) for the retractor bulbus; tetanic (300 stimuli/sec) tension excesses were −0.03% (S.D. ± 7.6%) for the lateral rectus and −0.9% (S.D. ± 3.4%) for the retractor bulbus. The small tension excesses could be attributed to mechanical properties. Twitches elicited by stimulation of one branch of the abducens nerve showed slight potentiation when preceded by a tetanic stimulation to the other nerve branch. This effect, which was probably due to mechanical properties of the muscle, could be readily differentiated from true post-tetanic potentiation, greater and longer lasting, elicited by applying both twitch and tetanic stimuli to the whole nerve. Muscle fatigue produced by intensive stimulation of one nerve branch did not decrease the amplitude of the tetanic contraction elicited by stimulation of the other branch. In fact, instead of crossed fatigue, a small potentiation (lateral rectus, 2.5%, S.D. ± 3.6%; retractor bulbus 3.8%, S.D. ± 4.1%) was observed, which appears to be due to mechanical factors.

Analysis of the results of the three tests led to the conclusion that polyneuronal innervation of the propagated impulse fibers in cat extraocular muscles could not be demonstrated. The small population of slow, non-propagated impulse fibers (Alvarado, this Symposium) could not be evaluated by these methods since, in such fibers, contraction does not spread beyond the immediate area of innervation.

Multiple innervation of twitch fibers can be expected to increase the rate at which a muscle fiber develops tension (Hunt and Kuffler, 1954). On the other hand, polyneuronal innervation would appear to afford little or no advantage for fast or fine muscle action. Indeed Bagust et al. (1973) point out that the neuronal control of muscle contraction must necessarily be less precise in polyneuronally innervated muscles; these authors suggest that polyneuronal innervation is primarily a condition of immature muscle.

The absence of evidence for polyneuronal innervation of propagated impulse fibers suggests that the end-to-end junctions revealed by histochemical techniques (Floyd, 1970; Mayr, 1970) do not transmit impulses electrotonically. If they did, a fiber connected by the end-to-end junctions to fibers distal and proximal to it would contract either when its own nerve supply delivered impulses to its own neuromuscular junction(s), or when a connecting fiber was innervated, producing an impulse that crossed the end-to-end junction. This would produce tension excess, post-tetanic potentiation and crossed-fatigue, all of which were minimal or absent in our studies (Bach-y-Rita and Lennerstrand, 1975).

C. Studies With Succinylcholine

Bach-y-Rita and Ito (1966) concluded that the orbital layer multi-innervated "twitch" and "slow" fibers of cat extraocular muscles were responsible for the contracture produced by the intravenous administration of Sch, a depolarizing neuro-muscular blocking drug. Kern (1965) had previously noted that the orbital layers of rabbit eye muscles contracted selectively on administration of Sch. Muscles which do not have multi-innervated fibers do not contract to Sch. Thus, the retractor bulbi, which is composed of singly innervated fibers (Bach-y-Rita and Ito, 1965; Alvarado et al., 1967), does not contract to succinylcholine (Bach-y-Rita, Levy and Steinacker, 1967).

We have recently completed a morphological study of muscle fibers depolarized by succinylcholine. Cat superior rectus muscle fibers were penetrated with glass micropipettes filled with a dye solution. Cells that responded to intravenous succinylcholine

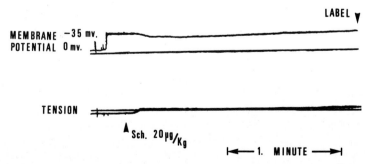

FIG. 2. Succinylcholine-induced depolarization of an eye muscle fiber. A fiber with a recorded membrane potential of 35 mv revealed a depolarization and repolarization following an intravenous injection of 20 μg/kg of succinylcholine, with a time course similar to that of the total muscle contraction and repolarization (lower line).

injection by membrane depolarization and repolarization in phase with the muscle tension changes were labeled (Fig. 2).

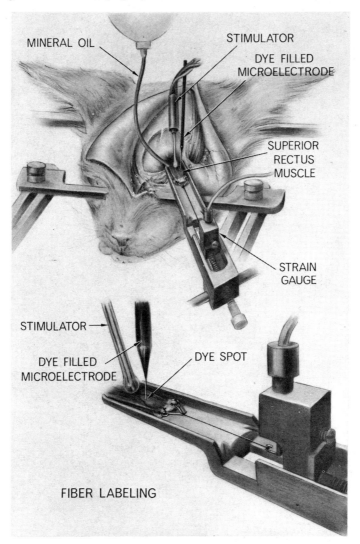

FIG. 3. Technique for intracellular labeling of extraocular muscle fibers. The anesthetized cat is shown mounted in a head holder. The globe has been removed and the superior rectus muscle, with a portion of sclera, has been mounted on a muscle holder. The spread-out insertion of the muscle has been maintained, and the muscle attached to a strain gauge. A dye-filled microelectrode is lowered into individual muscle fibers. Physiological recordings, including the response to local muscle stimulation, can be obtained, while the temperature of the muscle is maintained with a drip of warm mineral oil following the physiological recording. A current is passed through the microelectrode, thus iontophoretically labeling the fiber.

Figures 3 and 4 demonstrate our intracellular labeling techniques (preliminary description in Peachey *et al.*, 1971) for physiological–morphological–functional correlations. Extraocular muscle fibers are penetrated with glass microelectrodes filled with a saturated solution of procion Rubine. The physiological properties (e.g. membrane potential,

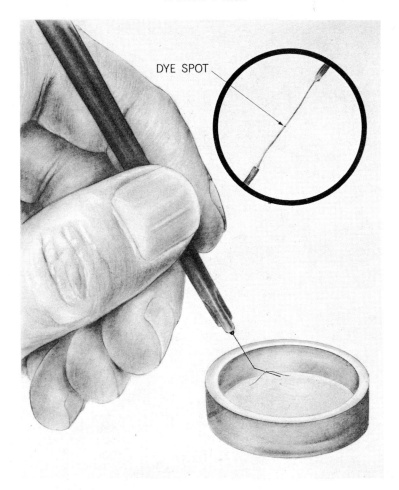

DYE SPOT

FIG. 4. Dissection of labeled extraocular muscle fiber for histochemical and morphological preparations. A fiber bundle containing the dye-labeled muscle fiber has been dissected from the fixed eye muscle. The fiber bundle is shown being moved carefully following the dissection. Further dissection has reduced the preparation to one, or a few fibers, including the labeled fiber (insert, upper right).

presence or absence of propagated impulse) and muscle fiber layer are determined, and with techniques such as those of the succinylcholine contracture studies described here, the function of the fiber can be determined. The fiber can then be labeled ionto-phoretically (by electrically driving dye from the microelectrode into the fiber). The labeled fiber can then be teased out of the fixed muscle and prepared for electron microscopic identification. In some cases, histochemical studies can also be undertaken, in order to identify the motor end-plate structure and organization of the fiber.

In the studies described above, only multi-innervated muscle fibers, in the orbital layer as well as in other layers, demonstrated the depolarization–repolarization response. They correspond to types 4 and 5, described by Alvarado (this Symposium). Studies are continuing to determine the precise physiological properties and functional role of these tonic-type fibers.

II. PROPRIOCEPTION

Afferent signalling of EOM stretch, or proprioceptive input, continues to be a subject of debate to this date. As summarized in 1971 (Bach-y-Rita), and previously indicated by other authors, the confusion in regard to the presence or absence of eye muscle proprioception has a number of origins: the definition of "proprioception" in terms of conscious position sense or subconscious nervous control of muscle contraction; extensive species variation in regard to the presence and distribution of organized stretch receptors (e.g. muscle spindles); afferent pathways into, and connections within, the central nervous system; and postulated functional roles for oculomotor proprioception. In the present section I will first summarize our recent experiments on one type of stretch receptor, the muscle spindle of the pig EOM; this will be followed by a compilation of varied data on CNS pathways for proprioception, and finally by a summary of some of the current hypotheses regarding the possible functional roles for afferent input from the EOMs.

A. Muscle Spindle Responses from Pig Eye Muscles

Muscle spindles have been demonstrated in the eye muscles of different species including pig, sheep, goat and man, but not in those of the common laboratory animals such as cat, dog, rat or rabbit although the eye muscles of all animals studied have some types of stretch receptors (cf. Bach-y-Rita, 1971 for summary). We (Lennerstrand and Bach-y-Rita, 1974) have utilized mini-pigs (14–25 kg), whose eye muscles contain well-defined muscle spindles, in an attempt to gain further insight into the types of afferent responses obtainable by EOM stretch. Microelectrode recordings were made

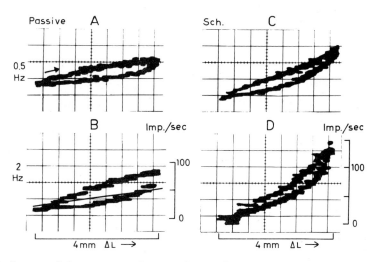

FIG. 5. f–ΔL diagram of the responses of a secondary ending subjected to triangular length changes of 4 mm/s (A and C) and 16 mm/s (B and D). Afferent instantaneous impulse frequency on the ordinate and muscle length change on the abscissa. Solid line in B is steady-state curve. Arrow indicates phase lead in spindle response over muscle length change. A and B before, C and D 2 min after the i.v. injection of 250 g/kg b.w.Sch. Note reduction in dynamic response, i.e. decrease in f–ΔL loop width, and increase in slope of the loops as an effect of the drug. (Reprinted by permission of *Acta physiol. scand.*)

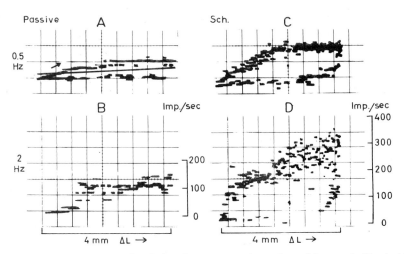

FIG. 6. f–ΔL diagrams of a primary ending during the same experimental conditions as in Fig. 1. At 16 mm/s before injection of Sch (B) the ending fired very few impulses during release of stretch, which is typical of primary endings. The effect of Sch was in this case to increase the dynamic response (C and D). Figures retouched. (Reprinted by permission of *Acta physiol. scand.*)

from single cells of the Gasserian ganglion, the structure implicated by Manni *et al.* (1968) as containing the cell bodies of EOM stretch receptors in pigs and goats. Spindle endings were identified by a reduction in firing during muscle twitch. The individual oculorotary muscles were connected to a muscle puller. In order to differentiate between primary and secondary endings, sinusoidal vibrations of high frequencies were applied; primary endings can follow higher frequencies of vibration than secondary endings (Brown *et al.*, 1967). The muscles were also stretched and released along a triangular curve, the frequency of which varied between zero and 16 Hz. The peak-to-peak amplitude was 4 mm.

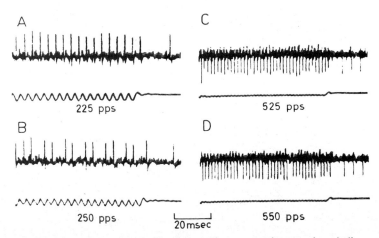

FIG. 7. Frequency-following of secondary and primary pig extra-ocular muscle spindle receptors A and B reveal the muscle vibration frequency following capability of a secondary ending (the response of the receptor is illustrated in Fig. 5), A and B, of a primary ending (shown in Fig. 6). The primary ending is capable of following higher frequencies of muscle vibration.

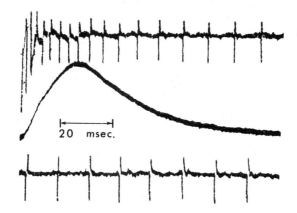

FIG. 8. In-series response of a pig extraocular muscle Golgi tendon organ. The lower trace was recorded in the absence of stimulation and thus reveals a spontaneous discharge. The middle trace shows the muscle tension produced by two pulses of stimulation to the motor nerve. The upper trace shows the afferent discharge recorded with a tungsten microelectrode from the semilunar ganglion. The increase in discharge frequency during muscle contraction indicates that the receptor is in series with the contractile elements of the muscle.

Static and dynamic responses were determined from spindle afferent impulse frequency–muscle length diagrams [(f–ΔL diagrams), Lennerstrand, 1968a]. Responses from both primary and secondary endings were identified. We have recorded responses similar to those of limb secondary endings (Fig. 5) and primary endings (Fig. 6). Figure 7 reveals the frequency following capabilities of each of the two types of endings.

In limb muscles, succinylcholine-induced intrafusal muscle fiber contraction has been used as a tool to differentiate between primary and secondary responses (Smith, 1966; Lennerstrand, 1968b; Lennerstrand and Thoden, 1968). We found similar succinylcholine effects on responses from pig eye muscle spindles (Figs. 5 and 6).

These functional studies have demonstrated primary and secondary afferent responses and dynamic and static fusimotor innervation in the eye muscle spindles of the pig. We have also demonstrated Golgi tendon organ responses. These increased in frequency during twitches (Fig. 8) and followed less than 300 pps (Fig. 9). Whether the Golgi

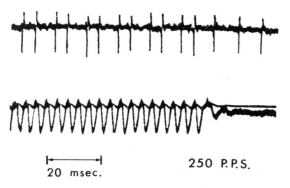

FIG. 9. Frequency-following capabilities of a pig extraocular muscle Golgi tendon organ. With 10 g of pre-tension, the Goldi tendon organ (the same as illustrated in Fig. 8) was unable to follow a muscle vibration of 250/sec.

and spindle machinery is used in the same way in the oculomotor control as in the spinal motor control (Matthews, 1972) has yet to be determined.

B. Central Nervous System Pathways for Proprioception

A number of studies have implicated the trigeminal complex as the location of the cell bodies of eye muscle stretch receptors. Some of these will be reviewed briefly in view of the discrepancy among authors as to the role of the different components of this complex. Further there is new evidence regarding second- (and higher) order projections of afferent information to other CNS structures.

With respect to the location of the cell bodies for muscle afferents, there is evidence in favor of both the mesencephalic nucleus of the trigeminal and the Gasserian ganglion. The studies of Cooper *et al.* (1955) revealed that responses to eye muscle stretch could be recorded in the mesencephalic nucleus in goats. Further, Fillenz (1955) had suggested that the mesencephalic nucleus contains the primary afferent cell bodies of the eye muscle proprioceptors in cats. However, the latencies she recorded ranged from 11–40 ms, which suggests second or higher order responses. Manni *et al.* (1966) demonstrated that the cell bodies of the stretch receptors in goats were located in the Gasserian ganglion of the trigeminal nerve; they showed that most of the responses described by Cooper *et al.* (1955) were second- (or later) order responses. At the present symposium Alvarado–Mallart, *et al.*, have reported primary afferent responses in the mesencephalic nucleus in the cat; they have also demonstrated the presence of afferent cell bodies in this structure anatomically, by horseradish peroxide studies. Thus the cell bodies of EOM afferents appear to occupy different parts of the trigeminal complex in different species.

The afferent input in the goat has been shown to be via the ophthalmic branch of the trigeminal nerve and via the "motor" nerves (Cooper *et al.*, 1953, 1955). In the cat, an animal with no demonstrable muscle spindles in eye muscles, the situation is less clear. The Gasserian ganglion does not contain the cell bodies of the extraocular stretch receptors (Manni *et al.*, 1968). At least some of the stretch receptor afferent fibers enter the brain stem via the motor nerves (Bach-y-Rita and Murata, 1964; Batini and Buisseret, 1974). However, Baker and Precht (1972) have recently demonstrated an afferent nerve from cat superior oblique muscle that enters the ophthalmic branch of the V nerve, and Batini and Buisseret (1974) have demonstrated that the ophthalmic branch of the trigeminal nerve of the cat contains a large per cent of those afferent fibers from stretch receptors which project to the cerebellum.

Manni *et al.* (1974) have extended their studies to demonstrate the central pathways of extraocular proprioception in lambs, utilizing both evoked potential and degeneration techniques. The cellular pool of the trigeminal ganglion which innervates the eye muscle spindles was stimulated with single shocks. Evoked potentials could be recorded from some ipsilateral mesodiencephalic sites (tectum, tegmentum, medial lemniscus, postero-ventromedial nuclei) which also responded to the manual stretch of the ipsilateral extraocular muscles. The latencies of the onset of the responses ranged from 1 to 5 ms. In chronic experiments in lambs, the pontine representation of the eye muscle proprioception was electrophysiologically identified in the oral part of the ipsilateral descending trigeminal nucleus; the identification area was then lesioned by means of a discrete electrolysis. The animals were sacrificed after 8–13 days. Histological examination showed degenerated nerve fibers along the medial lemniscus and the dorsal trigemino-thalamic tract. All degeneration was ipsilateral and terminated in the posteroven-trolateral and posteroventromedial nuclei of the thalamus. The results confirmed that the oral part of the descending trigeminal nucleus contains the perikarya of the second-order neurons of the eye muscle proprioceptors whose axons reach the mesodiencephalic regions through the medial lemniscus and the dorsal trigeminothalamic tract.

There is considerable evidence relating to the direct and indirect projections of the EOM afferents to other parts of the CNS. These include the superior colliculus, the cerebellum, and the oculomotor nuclei themselves.

Abrahams *et al.* (1974) have found that afferents from extraocular and neck muscles constitute the richest projection to the superior colliculus; 60% of the cells of origin of the tectospinal tract within the superior colliculus are excited by this muscle afferent input. Their discussion of the functional role of this representation will be found in the next section.

The cerebellum receives an input from extraocular muscles. Cooper *et al.* (1953) described responses to stretch of goat extraocular muscles in the superior cerebellar peduncle, and responses in the vermal cortex of the cat cerebellum to eye muscle stretch. Baker *et al.* (1972) confirmed the latter report and noted that single-shock stimulation of the superior oblique afferents in cats generated clear potentials in climbing fibers and typical Purkinje cell spike bursts in the molecular layer of the cerebellar cortex of lobule VI near the junction between this lobule and the paravermal zone. The latencies of the climbing fiber potentials ranged from 18 to 22 ms. However, the microelectrode recordings revealed Purkinje cell activation, via mossy fiber granule cell pathways, at 5–6 ms, followed by a burst of climbing fiber response with a latency of 18 ms.

Although it is now firmly established that the superior colliculus and the cerebellum receive an input from extraocular muscle afferents, it is still not clear to what extent these muscle afferents project more directly to motoneurons. Baker and Precht (1972) were unable to demonstrate a direct effect of muscle afferents on motoneurons of the trochlear nucleus in anesthetized preparations (see Section C-7). This would appear to provide evidence against a direct projection, at least in regard to the larger motoneurons (which would be most likely to permit stable intracellular recording).

An indirect pathway to the motoneurons, via the premotor pool, must also be consi-dered; other inputs also arrive at the motor neurons indirectly. Descending pathways from the cortex arrive in the premotor (or internuncial) pool (cf. Bach-y-Rita, 1956); further, Bertholz *et al.* (1974) have demonstrated that vestibular nystagmus is organized at a premotor level; these authors suggest that convergence with other influences modify-ing vestibular nystagmus will occur at this premotor (reticular and vestibular) level.

Following an extensive series of studies on goat extraocular stretch responses, Cooper *et al.* (1953) stated that the discharges from eye muscles probably have fairly direct pathways to the vestibular nuclei, the superior colliculus, the center for neck muscles and other regions of the central nervous system, and that via these structures the afferent discharges eventually reach the final motoneuron, or more probably, the premo-tor neuronal pool. These authors had demonstrated both excitatory and inhibitory responses. They noted single unit, and/or multi-unit long latency (20–200 ms) responses to muscle stretch in various central structures, including the motor nuclei, the central tegumental tract, the medial longitudinal fasciculus, the superior cerebellar peduncle, the colliculo-tegumental fibers, and the fiber bundles emerging from the motor nuclei.

C. Postulated Functional Roles of Extraocular Proprioception

In humans the eye muscles have one of the greatest concentrations of muscle spindles of all of the muscles of the body in addition to containing numerous other stretch receptors (Cooper and Daniel, 1949). Until recently, functional roles for these receptors were virtually unknown. However, in the last few years numerous functions of stretch receptors in EOMs have been demonstrated or proposed. The first three of these relate eye muscles to vestibular and postural mechanisms.

1. EOM-vestibular Interaction

Gernandt (1968) has described the interaction of EOM afferent activity with vestibular stimulation, and noted that EOM muscle stretch inhibited the vestibular activity, travelling over the slower reticular formation route to the EOM motor nuclei. Similarly, Ito *et al.* (1969) noted that the latency of motor fiber activity (recorded intracellularly in cat lateral rectus muscle fibers) to vestibular stimulation decreased with increasing stretch. This might be due to a stretch receptor inhibition of the slower vestibular activity.

The functional role of this interaction between EOMs and the vestibular system is not clear. It would be tempting to postulate a mechanism whereby increasing tension development toward the end of the slow phase of nystagmus would inhibit the slow vestibular activity, thus presenting a decreased viscous resistance to the opposite fast phase, or that inhibition of the slow vestibular pathways might prevent impulses initiating in the vestibular system from arriving at the motoneurons after the end of the slow phase of the nystagmus. If impulses were to arrive at this stage over the slow pathways, they would presumably oppose the movement to the opposite direction, thus adding a considerable force requirement to the agonist.

2. Facilitation of Labyrinthine Reflexes

Easton (1971, 1972) has provided evidence that eye muscle stretch (especially of the medial rectus) inhibited neck and limb muscles (Fig. 10) in the cat. He noted that "...horizontal rotation of the eye, stretching the horizontal recti, evokes inhibition of the EMG of the neck, biceps, and triceps muscles of both sides. By tallying the number of trials on which inhibition was observable, frequencies of inhibitions were obtained for each muscle under both directions of rotation for each eye. These frequencies differed systematically, suggesting a reflex from eye muscle stretch that could serve to facilitate the labyrinthine reflexes and, perhaps, to time their oscillations." Manni (discussion, this paper) has confirmed some of Easton's findings.

Easton suggested that this has an obvious significance if one pictures a cat on a turntable. The turning of the table evokes the labyrinthine reflexes, a bracing of the limbs against the turn together with movement of the head and eyes (labyrinthine nystagmus) in the direction opposite to the turn in order to stabilize the background. Both of these latter movements are periodically interrupted by nystagmic jerks recentering the neck and eyes. He suggests a plausible interaction would be that as the eyes approach the limit of their excursion the inhibition reaches a maximum, facilitating the reverse movement of the neck and at the same time facilitating the bracing effect of the limbs by emphasizing the difference in tone between the limbs of the two sides of the body. Similarly, the reflex pattern he described might tend to facilitate

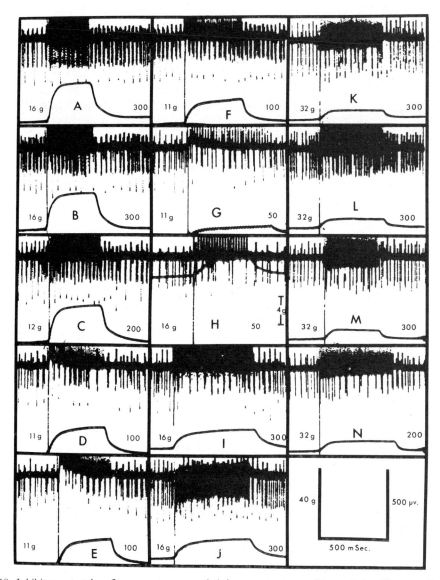

FIG. 10. Inhibitory stretch reflex responses recorded from motor nerve fibers of the VI nerve. Fourteen consecutive photographs of responses to stimulation of a portion of the VI nerve, while recording from another portion of the nerve, are illustrated (not all responses were photographed, so these records do not represent the responses to fourteen consecutive stimulus bursts). The number to the right represents the stimulus frequency. The calibrations in the lower right apply to all except for the strain gauge calibration in H, for which a separate calibration is illustrated. Inhibition is apparent in A, B, D, E, G, and I. It may be present in F, J, and N. In C, H, K, L, and M, inhibition cannot be identified (the spikes of the largest motor fiber have been retouched). [Reprinted by permission from *Arch. ital. Biol.* **11**, 1–15 (1972).]

a turn of the whole animal during locomotion. Thus the start of the turn might induce labyrinthine ocular nystagmus which would facilitate the neck movement and decrease the tonic activity in the limbs, thereby allowing the neck reflexes and volitional effort to work without hinderance.

3. *Control of Head Movement*

The regulation of head movement constitutes a special case of postural control, for head movement must be integrated with eye movement. Evidence has been obtained by Bizzi *et al.* (1971) that some combined head and eye movements are integrated in such a way as to suggest that a central mechanism develops patterned motor output simultaneously to neck muscles and extraocular muscles. This output might be controlled and corrected during the execution of the movement by peripheral input.

Abrahams *et al.* (1974) suggest the existence of a central organization which could suspend the dominant control of head position by labyrinthine structures, and would thus allow the systems originating in extraocular and neck muscle afferents to exert an extensive role in the control of head movement.

The next three hypotheses relate EOM afferents to eye motor control.

4. *Cerebellar Feedback Mechanisms*

Fuchs and Kornhuber (1969) demonstrated cerebellar responses to eye muscle stretch in cats and suggested that these receptors are part of a cerebellum mediated proprioceptive feedback loop for the control of eye movements, providing information to the cerebellum as to the magnitude of the end point of saccades. Baker *et al.* (1972), who confirmed and extended Fuchs and Kornhuber's results, suggest that the finding that the same region of the cerebellum generates field potentials which clearly precede saccadic eye movements may be of considerable functional interest. The cerebellar cortex may, therefore, be involved in the "correction" of movement prior to its execution, and this predictive ballistic type of correction may be continuously updated by the presence of a feedback from the extraocular muscle receptors.

5. *Eye Position Signal*

Recent studies by Rose and Abrahams (personal communication) have shown that the EOM receptors serve to indicate that the eye has arrived at a given position. While not wholly independent of velocity, the receptors fire when the eye reaches a given position. Depending on the initial position, the eye will have to move a greater or lesser distance to fire the receptors. Thus the receptors signal arrival at the new position.

6. *Comparison of Speed of Input from Retina and Eye Muscles*

Cooper *et al.* (1953) suggested one possible functional role of extraocular proprioception may be related to the relative speeds at which impulses from the muscles and those from the retina reach the brain; 1 or 2 ms compared to 25–80 ms. Thus, they note, by the time the retinal discharges reach the brain, messages from the eye muscles may have reached all the centers that may be concerned with eye movement.

The two remaining subsections deal with the demonstration of stretch reflexes and with the question of conscious eye position sense.

7. *Stretch Reflexes in EOMs*

Excitatory and inhibitory responses to stretch of EOMs were reported by Cooper *et al.* (1953). However, although they interpreted their results as demonstrating reflex activity, most authors deny the existence of EOM stretch reflexes.

Recently a stretch reflex in eye muscles has been uncovered, utilizing motor nerve stimulation techniques. In limbs, electrical stimulation of the motor fibers to a muscle had previously been employed by Granit (1950) to uncover an inhibitory stretch reflex in the gastrocnemius muscle. Bach-y-Rita (1972) has demonstrated an active inhibitory stretch reflex in cat extraocular muscles. The VI nerve was exposed intracranially at the emergence from the pons, through a ventral approach. A small branch was cut 1 cm from the emergence, and placed over recording electrodes to monitor the motor fiber activity. A larger bundle was cut as close as possible to the emergence from the pons, and placed over stimulating electrodes in order to produce contraction of the muscle. The major portion of the VI nerve remained intact, since afferent impulses are known to travel in this nerve from the lateral rectus (L.R.) to the brain. The L.R. was freed from the globe (which was then removed) and attached to a strain gauge. In encéphale isolé preparations a decrease in the motor nerve discharges could be noted during contraction, thus demonstrating inhibition.

Granit (1950) had found in gastrocnemius preparations that, in general, the greater the initial tension, the more pronounced the autogenic inhibition. He noted that greater inhibition could be obtained by combining stretch with contraction than by either alone. The extraocular muscles differ from the gastrocnemius in that initial tension or applied passive strength alone was ineffective; inhibitory responses of EOM stretch receptors were found only when the muscle contracted actively. This may be an indication that the reflex is not monosynaptic (Section B).

Bach-y-Rita's (1972) findings show that an extraocular stretch reflex can be demonstrated under certain conditions. It is not reasonable to expect a typical extensor muscle response comparable to a knee-jerk; the eye muscles are not extensors. Further, as Granit (1971) pointed out, stretch reflexes are also absent in skeletal musculature unless the fusimotor neurons are specifically activated and the alpha motoneurons are sufficiently depolarized.

The inhibitory reflex was not always present in the lateral rectus, even on the same motor unit discharge (Fig. 10). The presence or absence of the reflex may have depended on the state of activity of the motoneuron, and its role in any given organized movement (Granit, 1971).

Occasionally, an excitatory reflex was noted (Bach-y-Rita, 1972). Previously, Cooper et al. (1953) had shown excitatory reflex activity recorded from the intracerebral portion of EOM motor nerve fibers, and Baichenko et al. (1967) had recorded excitatory stretch reflexes during EMG studies of rabbit eye muscles. Baichenko et al. (1967) concluded that a tonic stretch reflex exists in rabbit eye muscles. Similarly, in Bach-y-Rita's (1972) studies, the effects of stretch were only observed on the tonic system, since only alterations of resting motor discharges could be evaluated.

At the level of the oculomotor nuclei, Sasaki (1963) demonstrated hyperpolarization of III nerve motoneurons by extraocular muscle stretch. However, the extensive studies of Baker and Precht (1972) have not confirmed this finding; in anesthetized cats, they were unable to demonstrate a direct effect of stimulation of the eye muscle afferent branch from the superior oblique muscle on intracellular or extracellularly recorded potentials of trochlear motoneurons.

The functional role of the stretch reflexes described by Cooper et al. (1953), Baichenko et al. (1967), and Bach-y-Rita (1972) is still not clear. Granit (1971) has pointed out that the stretch reflex in other muscles is an adjunct to contraction, with alpha and gamma motoneurons activated together in working muscles. A comparable functional role has yet to be demonstrated in eye muscles.

8. *Eye Position Sense*

Sherrington (1918) supported the concept of a perceptual role for EOM proprioception, a concept which was debatable in his time and which has not yet been clearly substantiated. Indeed Bringley and Merton (1960) provided evidence against conscious perception of eye position. Recently Skavenski (1972) has re-evaluated the literature demonstrating the absence of a conscious or unconscious eye position sense. He feels that previous experiments do not conclusively demonstrate that the eye is without a conscious position sense, because the psychophysical method of subjective reports used in the previous studies can be considered to be insensitive, or to have distracted the subjects due to discomfort and thus masked subtle eye position sensation. Skavenski developed a stress-free method by which he determined that subjects could detect the presence of a load and could report the direction of pull on their eyes. However, the studies of Skavenski *et al.* (1972) demonstrated that perception of direction depends primarily on commands sent to the eye muscles (outflow), and that the proprioceptive signal (inflow) has little or no influence when the inflow message from one eye is in conflict with the outflow sent to both eyes.

Skavenski (1972) showed that subjects were able to maintain eye position in the dark, correcting for passively applied loads. The subjects did not allow large errors to build up before they began corrective action. They compensated appropriately for small changes in the applied force or orientation of their eyes. The errors that occurred when the subjects corrected for loads are of about the same magnitude as the errors they made when they used extraretinal signals to control eye position in the dark with no external forces applied to their eyes.

Further, Skavenski (1972) noted that the loads required for detection in the psychophysical procedure were larger than the loads applied when the subjects corrected eye-position deviations. He suggested that, since the subjects could correct eye position for smaller loads than they required for the psychophysical report, the oculomotor response is more sensitive and perhaps unconscious.

D. Summary

The last several years have seen considerable progress in clarifying the properties of stretch receptors, in defining the muscle afferent pathways to the brain, and in suggesting of the functional roles of extraocular proprioception.

The studies reported by Lennerstrand and Bach-y-Rita (1974, and in preparation) have revealed that the eye muscles of pigs contain all of the types of stretch receptors that are found in limb muscles. The studies of Manni and his co-workers have clarified the central pathways of the eye muscle afferents in lambs, and data is accumulating in other animals. Baker *et al.* (1972) have demonstrated the mossy and climbing fiber projections of extraocular muscle afferents to the cat cerebellum, and Abrahams and collaborators have demonstrated the projection to the superior colliculus.

Several important studies relating to the functional role of extraocular proprioception have been published since the last review was prepared (Bach-y-Rita, 1971). Skavenski's studies demonstrated the existence of an extraretinal inflow signal that does not arise from the conjunctiva of eye lids. On the other hand, Skavenski *et al.*, have shown that when the inflow and outflow signals conflict, the outflow signal dominates.

The studies of Baker *et al.* (1972) confirmed and extended the findings of Fuchs and Kornhuber (1969) regarding the importance of extraocular proprioceptive input to the cerebellum in the control of eye movements. The studies of Abrahams and of Bizzi and their co-workers have documented the interaction between head- and neck-movement control systems, while Easton has demonstrated a role for extraocular proprioception in the control of the tone of body musculature.

Suggestive evidence exists for a functional role of extraocular proprioception in eye muscle stretch reflexes, and in vestibulocular reflexes. Further studies are needed to confirm or disprove these possible functional roles.

REFERENCES

ABRAHAMS, V. C., RANCIER, F. and ROSE, P. K. (1973) Neck muscle and extraocular receptors and their relationship to the tectospinal tract. In: *Control of Posture and Locomotion*, STEIN, R. B. PEARSON, K. G., SMITH R. S. and REDFORD, J. B. (Eds.). Plenum Press, New York.

ALVARADO, J. This symposium.

ALVARADO, J., STEINACKER, A. and BACH-Y-RITA, P. (1967) The ultrastructure of the retractor bulbi muscle of the cat (abstract). *Invest. Ophthal.* **6**, 548.

ALVARADO-MALLART *et al.* This symposium.

BACH-Y-RITA, P. (1956) El sistema internuncial oculomotor. *Acta neurol. latinoamer.* **2**, 65–71.

BACH-Y-RITA, P. (1971) Neurophysiology of eye movements. In: *The Control of Eye Movements*, BACH-Y-RITA, P. and COLLINS, C. C. (Eds.), pp. 7–45. New York, Academic Press.

BACH-Y-RITA, P. (1972) Extraocular muscle inhibitory stretch reflex during active contraction. *Arch. ital. Biol.* **110**, 1–15.

BACH-Y-RITA, P. (1973) Separate central and peripheral mechanisms controlling slow and fast eye movements. In: *The Oculomotor System and Brain Functions*, ZIKMUND, V. (Ed.), pp. 88–100. London, Butterworths.

BACH-Y-RITA, P. and ITO, F. (1966) *In vivo* studies on fast and slow muscle fibers in cat extraocular muscles. *J. Gen. Physiol.* **49**, 1177–1198.

BACH-Y-RITA, P. and LENNERSTRAND, G. (1975) Absence of polyneuronal innervation in cat extraocular muscles. *J. Physiol.* **244**, 613–624.

BACH-Y-RITA, P., LEVY, J. V. and STEINACKER, A. (1967) The effect of succinylcholine on the isolated retractor bulbi muscle of the cat. *J. Pharm. Pharmacol.* **19**, 180–181.

BACH-Y-RITA, P. and MURATA, K. (1964) Extraocular proprioceptive responses in the VI nerve of the cat. *Quart. J. Expl. Physiol.* **49**, 407–416.

BAGUST, J., LEWIS, D. M. and WESTERMAN, R. A. (1973) Polyneuronal innervation of kitten skeletal muscle. *J. Physiol.* **229**, 221–255.

BAICHENKO, P. I., MATYUSHKIN, D. P. and SUVOROV, V. V. (1967) Participation of fast and tonic oculomotor systems in stretch reflexes and labyrinthine reflexes of extraocular muscles. *Fiziol. Zh. SSSR*, **53**, 82–90.

BAKER, R. and PRECHT, W. (1972) Electrophysiological properties of trochlear motoneurons as revealed by IV nerve stimulation. *Expl. Brain Res.* **14**, 124–157.

BAKER, R., PRECHT, W. and LLINAS, R. (1972) Mossy and climbing fiber projections of extraocular muscle afferents to the cerebellum. *Brain Res.* **38**, 440–445.

BARNARD, R. J., EDGERTON, V. R. and PETER, R. B. (1970) Effect of exercise on skeletal muscle, I. Biochemical and histochemical properties. *J. Appl. Physiol.* **28**, No. 762–770.

BATINI, D. and BUISSERET, P. (1974) Sensory peripheral pathway from extraocular muscles. *Arch. Ital. Biol.* **112**, 18–32.

BERTHOLZ, A., BAKER, R. and GOLDBERG, A. (1974) Neuronal activity underlying vestibular nystagmus in the oblique oculomotor system of the cat. *Brain Res.* **71**, 233–238.

BIZZI, E., KALIL, R. E. and TAGLIASCO, V. (1971) Eye–head coordination in monkeys: evidence for centrally patterned organization. *Science*, **173**, 452–454.

BRINDLEY, G. and MERTON, P. (1960) The absence of position sense in the human eye. *J. Physiol.* **153**, 127–130.

BROWN, M. C., ENGBERG, I. and MATTHEWS, P. B. (1967) Fusimotor stimulation and the dynamic sensitivity of the secondary ending of the muscle spindle. *J. Physiol. (Lond.)* **189**, 545–550.

BROWN, M. C. and MATTHEWS, P. B. C. (1960) An investigation into the possible existence of polyneuronal innervation of individual skeletal muscle fibres in certain hind-limb muscles of the cat. *J. Physiol.* **151**, 436–457.

BULLER, A., ECCLES, J. C. and ECCLES, R. (1960) Interactions between motoneurons and muscles in respect of the characteristic speed of their responses. *J. Physiol.* **150**, 417–439.

COOPER, S. and DANIEL, P. M. (1949) Muscle spindles in human extrinsic muscles. *Brain,* **72**, 1–24.

COOPER, S., DANIEL, P. M. and WHITTERIDGE, D. (1953) Nerve impulses in the brainstem of the goat. Responses with long latencies obtained by stretching the extrinsic eye muscles. *J. Physiol.* **120**, 491–513.

COOPER, S., DANIEL, P. M. and WHITTERIDGE, D. (1955) Muscle spindles and other sensory endings in the extrinsic eye muscles; the physiology and anatomy of these receptors and of their connections with the brain stem. *Brain,* **78**, 564–583.

COLLINS, C. C. This Symposium.

COLLINS, C. C. and SCOTT, A. B. (1973) The eye movement control signal. *Proc. Second Bioengineering Conf. Ophthal. Section, Milan, Italy.*

EASTON, T. A. (1971) Inhibition from cat eye muscle stretch. *Brain Res.* **25**, 633–637.

EASTON, T. A. (1971) Patterned inhibition from horizontal eye movement in the cat. *Exptl Neurol.* **31**, 419–426.

FILLENZ, M. (1955) Responses in the brainstem of the cat to stretch of extrinsic ocular muscles. *J. Physiol.* **128**, 182–199.

FLOYD, K. (1970) Junctions between muscle fibres in cat extraocular muscles. *Nature (Lond.)* **227**, 185–186.

FUCHS, A. F. and KORNHUBER, H. H. (1969) Extraocular muscle afferents to the cerebellum of the cat. *J. Phys.* **200**, 713–722.

GERNANDT, B. E. (1968) Interactions between extraocular myotatic and ascending vestibular activities. *Exptl Neurol.* **20**, 120–134.

GRANIT, R. (1950) Reflex self-regulation of muscle contraction and autogenic inhibition. *J. Neurophysiol.* **13**, 351–372.

GRANIT, R. (1971) The probable role of muscle spindles and tendon organs in eye movement control. In: *The Control of Eye Movements,* BACH-Y-RITA, P. COLLINS, C. C. and HYDE, J. (Eds.), pp. 3–5. Academic Press, New York.

HESS, A. and PILAR, G. (1963) Slow fibres in the extraocular muscles of the cat. *J. Physiol. (Lond.)* **169**, 780–798.

HUNT, C. C. and KUFFLER, S. W. (1954) Motor innervation of skeletal muscle: multiple innervation of individual muscle fibres and motor unit function. *J. Physiol.* **126**, 203–303.

ITO, F., BACH-Y-RITA, P. and YAMANAKA, Y. (1969) Extraocular muscle intracellular and motor nerve responses to semi-circular canal stimulation.

KERN, R. (1965) A comparative pharmacologic–histologic study of slow and twitch fibers in the superior rectus muscle of the rabbit. *Invest. Ophthal.* **4**, 901–910.

LENNERSTRAND, G. (1968a) Position and velocity sensitivity of muscle spindles in the cat. I. Primary and secondary endings deprived of fusimotor activation. *Acta physiol. scand.* **73**, 281–299.

LENNERSTRAND, G. (1968b) Position and velocity sensitivity of muscle spindles in the cat. IV. Interaction between two fusimotor fibres converging on the same spindle ending. *Acta physiol. scand.* **74**, 257–273.

LENNERSTRAND, G. and BACH-Y-RITA, P. (1974) Spindle responses in pig eye muscles. *Acta physiol. scand.* **90**, 795–797.

LENNERSTRAND, G. and THODEN, U. (1968) Position and velocity sensitivity of muscle spindles in the cat. III. Static fusimotor single-fibre activation of primary and secondary endings. *Acta physiol. scand.* **74**, 30–49.

MANNI, E., BORTOLAMI, R. and DESOLE, C. (1966) Eye muscle proprioception and the semilunar ganglion. *Exptl Neurol.* **16**, 226–236.

MANNI, E., BORTOLAMI, R. and DESOLE, C. (1968) Peripheral pathway of eye muscle proprioception. *Exptl Neurol.* **22**, I, 1–12.

MANNI, E., PALMIERI, G. and MARINI, R. (1974) Central pathway of the extraocular muscle proprioception. *Exptl Neurol.* **42**, 181–190.

MATTHEWS, P. B. C. (1972) Mammalian muscle receptors and their central actions. Physiological Society No. 23, London, Edward Arnold.

MAYR, R. (1971) Structure and distribution of fibre types in the external eyemuscles of the rat. *Tissue and Cell* **3** (3), 433–462.

PEACHEY, L. (1971) The structure of the extraocular muscle fibers of mammals. In: *The Control of Eye Movements,* BACH-Y-RITA, P. COLLINS, C. C. and HYDE, J. (Eds.), pp. 47–66. New York, Academic Press.

PEACHEY, L. D., HUDSON, C. and BACH-Y-RITA, P. (1971) Marking extraocular muscle fibers for physiological–morphological correlation. *Proc. XXV International Congress of Physiological Sciences, Munich,* p. 443.

SALMONS, S. and VRBOVA, G. (1969) The influence of activity on some contractile characteristics of mamalian fast and slow muscles. *J. Physiol.* **201**, 535–549.

SASAKI, K. (1963) Electrophysiological studies on oculomotor neurons of the cat. *Jap. J. Physiol.* **13**, 287–302.

SHERRINGTON, C. (1918) Observations on the sensual role of the proprioceptive nerve supply of the extrinsic eye muscles. *Brain*, **41**, 332–343.

SKAVENSKI, A. A. (1972) Inflow as source of extraretinal eye position information. *Vision Res.* **12**, 221–229.

SKAVENSKI, A., HADDAD, G. and STEINMAN, R. (1972) The extra-retinal signal for the visual perception of direction. *Perception and Psychophysics*, **II**, 287–290.

SMITH, R. S. (1966) Properties of intrafusal muscle fibers. In: *Nobel Symposium I. Muscular Afferents and Motor Control*, GRANIT, R. (Ed.), pp. 69–80. Almqvist and Wiksell.

STEINACKER, A. and BACH-Y-RITA, P. (1968) The fiber spectrum of the cat VI nerve to the lateral rectus and retractor bulbi muscles. *Experientia (Basel)* **24**, 1254–1255.

TENGROTH, B. (1960) The influence of the extraocular muscles on the position of the eye. *Acta Ophthal. (Copenhagen)* **38**, 698–700.

YAMANAKA, Y. and BACH-Y-RITA, P. (1968) Conduction velocities in the abducens nerve correlated with vestibular nystagmus in cats. *Exptl Neurol.* **20**, 143–155.

Discussion Remarks of Ermanno Manni

The lecture of Doctor Bach-y-Rita has been so clear and extensive that it requires only a short comment. I have to point out mainly two aspects of the problem: the former is concerned with our investigations on the arrangement of the peripheral and central pathways of the eye muscle proprioception in the Ungulata, the latter is concerned with influence of eye muscle stretch on the electrical activity of the neck muscles.

In the lamb, pig, and calf unitary responses to stretching single extraocular muscles were recorded from the medial dorsolateral region of the semilunar ganglion. The firing of the units during stretching was inhibited by contraction of the muscle, a fact which shows that activity from eye muscle spindles was recorded. The units responding to stretch of extraocular muscles were unaffected by stimulation of other trigeminal fields or by jaw movements. The responses were not abolished by acute or chronic section of ipsilateral third nerve, while they were suppressed by acute or chronic section of the trigeminal ophthalmic branch, which provoked also degeneration of the sensory innervation of the eye muscle spindles.

On the other hand, cutting the trigeminal root did not abolish the semilunar responses to stretch of eye muscles and did not provoke degeneration of the ophthalmic branch and of the eye muscle spindles. Simultaneous chronic section either of the trigeminal root and the throclear nerve or of the trigeminal root and the abducent nerve did not suppress the Gasserian responses to the stretch of the superior oblique or of the lateral rectus muscles, respectively. In another group of experiments the cellular pool of the semilunar ganglion which innervates the eye muscle spindles was chronically destroyed by means of a discrete electrolysis. Degenerations occurred not only in the ipsilateral ophthalmic branch and in the eye muscle spindles, but also in the medial portion of the trigeminal root and in the ipsilateral descending trigeminal tract and nucleus. Unitary responses to stretch of single eye muscle could be recorded also from the ipsilateral trigeminal root, rostral part of descending trigeminal tract and trigeminal nucleus. Single-shock stimulation of the eye muscle representation in the semilunar ganglion elicited evoked potentials in the ipsilateral oral part of descending trigeminal tract and nucleus: the responses exhibited a very short latency (0.31–0.42 ms) when the records were taken from the tract, but they were longer when the responses were recorded from the nucleus (0.90–0.92 ms); one can suppose that in this case a synapse was intercalated. All such findings support the view that the semilunar ganglion contains the first-order neurons of the eye muscle proprioception; the peripheral process attains the eye muscle spindles through the ophthalmic branch and probably through the branches described by Winckler, while the central process enters the brainstem through the trigeminal root and the descending trigeminal tract and ends in the oral pole of the homonymous nucleus.

The descending trigeminal nucleus contains the second-order neurons of the eye proprioception, which send axons into the mesencephalon and which terminate in the ventrobasal nuclear complex of the ipsilateral thalamus. This statement is supported by the following data:

1. Responses to stretch of single eye muscles were recorded from the mesencephalic tectum and tegmentum, along the medial lemniscus and from the posteroventromedial and posteroventrolateral nuclei of the ipsilateral thalamus.

2. Single-shock electrical stimulation of the eye muscle representation in the semilunar ganglion and in the rostral pole of the descending trigeminal nucleus elicited evoked potentials in the same ipsilateral mesodiencephalic areas from which responses to stretching single extraocular muscles were recorded.

The latencies were shorter when the pons was stimulated (0.33 ms), showing that no synapse was intercalated, and longer when the stimulating electrode tip was in the semilunar ganglion (1–5 s); in this case at least a synapse was intercalated along the neural pathway.

3. Chronic destruction of the projection of the eye muscle proprioception in the rostral pole of the descending trigeminal nucleus provoked degenerations of nervous fibers which could be followed along the ipsilateral medial lemniscus and the dorsal trigemino-thalamic tract; the degenerations terminated in the posteroventromedial and posteroventrolateral nuclei of the ipsilateral thalamus.

In other experiments we have controlled the hypothesis according to which the first-order neurons of the eye proprioception could be represented by the ganglion cells scattered along the oculogyric nerves. In order to check this possibility we have carried out experiments on the calf since numerous ganglion cells may be found in the intracranial portion of the oculomotor nerve. Thus we have chronically cut the left third nerve in nine calves just where it enters the cavernous sinus. Responses to stretching individual eye muscles either of the left or of the right side were recorded from the ipsilateral trigeminal ganglion. They were of the type induced by muscle spindle excitation. However, no responses to stretching eye muscles were obtained from the intracranial course of the right oculomotor nerve. The spindles of the muscles innervated by the left oculomotor nerve were normal in several calves in which the central oculomotor stump contained only a few ganglion cells; however, very few degenerated spindles were found in the extraocular muscles of two calves in which the intracranial stump of the nerve exhibited more than 100 ganglian cells. Thus we conclude that the trigeminal ganglion of the calf contains some of the afferents from the eye muscle spindles as is the case for the lamb and the pig and the ganglion cells along the oculomotor nerve can play only an accessory and negligible role in innervating the eye muscle spindles.

Our results are not in agreement with those of other investigators as far as the peripheral arrangement of eye muscle proprioception is concerned in other animals. For example, Dr. Bach-y-Rita has recorded responses to stretch of the lateral rectus muscle from the trunk of the abducent nerve in the cat. We have not been able up to now to record responses to stretch of single eye muscles from the semilunar ganglion in the cat and in the dog. This fact supports the view that in such animals the peripheral arrangement of the eye muscle proprioception is quite different from that found in the lamb, pig, and calf.

Dr. Bach-y-Rita has reported the interesting results of the investigations carried out by Easton who discovered that stretch of single eye muscles can inhibit the electrical activity of the dorsal neck and forelimb muscles. The results by Easton have been confirmed in our laboratory. However, we have seen that stretch of eye muscles may not only inhibit but also activate the unitary discharge of the dorsal neck and forelimb muscles. Frequently we have seen, for example, ipsilateral activation and contralateral inhibition of neck muscles. I make only two remarks: the former is that the threshold is rather high (20–30 g); the latter that often pinching the skin of the eyelids could provoke the same effect.

REFERENCES

MANNI, E., BORTOLAMI, R. and DERIU, P. L. (1970) Presence of cell bodies of the afferents from the eye muscles in the semilunar ganglion. *Archs ital. Biol.* **108**, 106–120.

MANNI, E., BORTOLAMI, R. and DERIU, P. L. (1970) Superior oblique muscle proprioception and the throclear nerve. *Exptl Neurol.* **26**, 543–550.

MANNI, E., BORTOLAMI, R. and DESOLE, C. (1966) Eye muscle proprioception and the semilunar ganglion. *Exptl Neurol.* **18**, 226–236.

MANNI, E., BORTOLAMI, R. and DESOLE, C. (1968) Peripheral pathway of eye muscle proprioception. *Exptl Neurol.* **22**, 1–12.

MANNI, E., DESOLE, C. and PALMIERI, G. (1970) On whether eye muscle spindles are innervated by ganglion cells located along the oculomotor nerves. *Exptl Neurol.* **28**, 333–343.

MANNI, E. PALMIERI, G. and MARINI, R. (1971) Peripheral pathway of the proprioceptive afferents from the lateral rectus muscle of the eye. *Exptl Neurol.* **30**, 46–53.

MANNI, E., PALMIERI, G. and MARINI, R. (1971) Extraocular muscle proprioception and the descending trigeminal nucleus. *Exptl Neurol.* **33**, 195–204.

MANNI, E., PALMIERI, G. and MARINI, R. (1972) Pontine trigeminal termination of proprioceptive afferents from the eye muscles. *Exptl Neurol.* **36**, 310–318.

MANNI, E., PALMIERI, G. and MARINI, R. (1972) Mesodiencephalic representation of the eye muscle proprioception. *Exptl Neurol.* **37**, 412–421.

MANNI, E., PALMIERI, G. and MARINI, R. (1974) Central pathway of the extraocular muscle proprioception. *Exptl Neurol.* **42**, 181–190.

Discussion remarks of Robert S. Jampel

Five morphologically and histochemically different types of muscle fibers have been described in the extraocular muscles of primates. Also, three physiologically different types of muscle fibers have been identified:

fast-twitch fibers, singly innervated slow fibers and multi-innervated slow fibers. It is reasonable to assume that the fast-twitch fibers are associated with saccadic movements and the slow fibers with tonic movements. Also, the extraocular muscles contain a relatively large muscle mass when compared to other muscles and are capable of exerting many times more contractile power than is required to move the eye between two fixation points. These facts suggest that the various motor units that comprise the extraocular muscles subserve different functions rather than simply adding to the contractile power of the muscle.

In the ontogeny of eye movements in man more complex oculomotor functions are superimposed on more primitive functions in a definite order: the earliest eye movements (actually ocular stabilization when the head or body moves) are tonic and initiated by vestibular stimulation. Grafted onto these primitive stabilization movements are involuntary saccadic movements, tonic following or pursuit movements, voluntary or exploratory saccadic movements, and tonic vergence movements in that sequence. It is interesting to note that slow and fast movements are alternately added—*slow* vestibular, *fast* involuntary, *slow* pursuit, *fast* exploratory, and *slow* vergence—and that there are *five* types of movement.

In diseases of the central nervous system normally integrated, smooth-functioning eye movements may be broken down into their component parts, the so-called oculomotor dissociations. In these dissociations slow eye movements are frequently isolated from fast eye movements and conversely.

The following clinical situations have been observed as the result of central nervous system lesions: (1) a loss of convergence with the preservation of voluntary, pursuit, and vestibular movements; (2) the preservation of convergence with the loss of voluntary, pursuit, and vestibular movements to one side (in internuclear ophthalmoplegia); (3) the loss of convergence and voluntary movements with the preservation of pursuit and vestibular movements; (4) the loss of convergence, voluntary, and pursuit movements with the preservation of vestibular movements (in congenital and acquired ocular motor "apraxia"); (5) the loss of convergence, voluntary, and pursuit movements with the preservation of involuntary saccades directed towards moving objects and vestibular movements (in patients in semicoma). Thus clinically as well as ontogenetically *five* component parts of the integrated oculomotor function may be identified.

From the above information an important question arises: Are the *five* morphologically and histochemically different types of extraocular muscle fibers somehow related to the *five* functional components that appear integrated in normal oculomotor function?

PHORIA AND EOM AFFERENCE: PRELIMINARY SUPPORT FOR A NEW THEORY†

ROBERT D. REINECKE and KURT SIMONS

PHORIA is typically viewed as a form of latent squint, different in degree but not kind from tropia (e.g. Duke-Elder and Wybar, 1973, pp. 516 ff.). Yet this seems a less than satisfying classification since in its two key diagnostic respects phoria acts precisely opposite to tropia.

(1) In hetertropia fusion is poor, if present at all, and stereopsis virtually never seen (Reinecke and Simons, in press). The phoria patient, on the other hand, has by definition good fusion (and usually normal stereopsis) for his condition to exist.

(2) The response to the cover test by the phoria patient differs not in degree from that of the tropia patient, but in kind. The tropia response is fully conjugate, in the sense that the non-occluded eye is always involved in the response to the cover. The phoria response, however, is always assymetric.

The theory of phoria function that we are investigating derives from these two distinctions. In keeping with (1) and (2), respectively, we hypothesized:

(a) The phoria mechanism does not involve any fusional mechanism (since, again, fusion is normal), and

(b) rather than being "forced" into its occluded position by contralateral influence, as appears to be the case in tropia, the monocular phoria response to cover appears to behave as if its vergence position control were dropping down a step in a hierarchy, with some other control "taking over" when the visual feedback control signal is interrupted by occlusion.

The resulting overall hypothesis of phoria etiology that arises from these assumptions is a simple one. Phoria is the result of a discrepancy at the vergence control center between the interocular alignment signal arising from visual-retinal input and the alignment signal arising from extraocular muscle (EOM) stretch receptor afferent inputs. In other words, our hypothesis proposes that phoria is the difference between what the binocular visual input specifies as normal alignment and what the EOM afferents indicate is a condition of balanced tonus in the lateral muscle forces on the eyes. Thus, according to this hypothesis, when the visual stimulus—normally the dominant alignment cue—is removed through occlusion, EOM afference-based alignment cues "take over". If there is a difference between the visual and EOM signals, phoria movement occurs.

†Supported by grants EY-00752 and EY-00044 from the National Eye Institute, USPHS and a research grant from Research to Prevent Blindness, Inc.

While afference signals are known to be sent by the extrinsic EOMs in man, little is known about these signals (Bach-y-Rita and Collins, 1971; Duke-Elder and Wybar, op. cit.). Demonstration of their possible role in phoria thus only seems at present possible by indirect means. Our initial approach to this had been to observe latencies of eye-movement response to the cover–uncover test, and pilot runs prior to the conference appeared to support this as a valid measure. Further testing has failed to support this parameter as consistently related to the phoria, however.

The means we are at present using is examination of vergence velocities, using a variant of the "velocity matrix" technique introduced by Fricker (1971). Since (a) the weight of evidence available (cf. Toates, 1974) suggests that vergence control system is proportional rather than integral, i.e. that vergence velocity is positively correlated with the size of vergence movement required by the stimulus, and (b) it seems reasonable to assume that the visual and EOM afferent signals are algebraically summed in the vergence control center, our hypothesis can be extrapolated into the following testable form: If phoria is a result of conflict of visual and EOM afferent input, insertion of a prism so oriented as to increase the size of this discrepancy will give rise to a lower vergence velocity (EOM afference in opposition to visual input) than insertion of a prism of opposite polarity (EOM afference and visual input add).

Two corollary hypotheses can be added to this main one:

1. If a prism is inserted in front of the eye of an orthophoric patient, in effect producing a pseudo-phoria, the associated latency should be greater than that associated with removal of the prism and, in effect, relief of the phoria.

2. A further hypothesis, following from the assumption that the visual cue is a more powerful cue than the EOM afference cue, is that vergence velocity in response to occlusion (i.e. visual cue "turned off") will be lower than velocity in response to removal of occlusion (visual cue "turned on"), regardless of the direction of phoria.

METHOD

A computer-based system is used both to administer cover and prism tests to the subjects and to analyze the results. The subject views a fixation target with his head held in a headmount. Attached to the headmount are occluders and prism insertion devices operated by servomechanisms under computer control. Eye movements are detected by a DC-coupled infrared scleral reflectance-type photosensor (Biometrics model SG-200 Eye Movement Monitor). The output of the eye movement monitor undergoes analog-to-digital conversion at a 100-Hz sample rate and is stored digitally on the computer's mass storage device (a disc).

Calibration is achieved independently for each eye by occluding the contralateral eye and inserting a four-diopter prism in front of the eye to be calibrated. The resulting saccadic movement (or movements) is taken by the computer program as the definition for four diopters worth of excursion (i.e. approximately 2 degrees) and other movements are scaled to this standard. In addition to the calibration frame, the computer administers cover–uncover tests and insertion and removal of prism (base-out or base-in, as desired) OS and OD.

For analysis, the computer records of eye movement are plotted on a cathode-ray tube (CRT) display (Tektronix 4002) in segments 1.2 sec in duration, with time zero

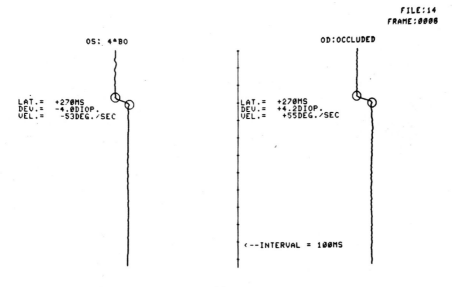

FIG. 1.

set immediately following completion of the particular occlusion, prism insertion, etc., being recorded. A sample record or "frame" is illustrated in Fig. 1. The time axis is top-to-bottom, OS and OD located left and right, respectively, and time markers indicated every 100 ms. As the column headings note, a four-diopter base-out prism has just been introduced OS prior to time zero while OD is "open" (i.e. not occluded) on fixation. The two circles on each eye movement trace are positioned by the operator to demarcate the beginning and end of any segment of interest. On command the computer calculates and prints out the size of excursion and velocity of the demarcated segment and latency of its beginning measured from time zero.

RESULTS

The vergence velocity data collected thus far, while indicating some trends in the direction predicted, does not yet provide any definitive support (or rejection) of our hypothesis. Data collection is continuing. One complicating factor has resulted from the strong support found in the data for our second corollary hypothesis. Virtually without exception, and regardless of the direction of phoria, the vergence velocity in response to removal of occlusion is greater—sometimes by a margin of 3 or 4:1—than the response to occlusion.

Support was also obtained for the first corollary hypothesis. In ten runs on five orthoptic patients, the latency of saccadic response to prism introduction was significantly ($P < 0.018$, t-test) longer than response to removal of the prism (and relief of the induced phoria).

A further, unexpected, piece of evidence apparently supporting our hypothesis was found in the occurrence of sudden, rapid eye movements of very short latency in

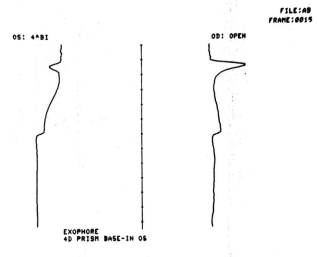

FIG. 2.

many of our phoria patient records. These movements, an example of which is illustrated in Fig. 2 (an exophore), were initially assumed to be blink artifacts. They occurred following change of visual stimulus of any kind (e.g. insertion or removal of prism, etc.).

Closer re-examination of the records, however, following a remark by Dr. Cogan that he had observed movements of this kind in some patients, indicated that they were a reliable phenomenon associated with the direction of phoria. Their fast response time suggests that they result from an afferent input available prior to the "new" visual input. In effect, a continuously available EOM afferent impulse associated with phoria would seem a logical origin of such a signal.

DISCUSSION

It must be emphasized that the above-reported results are preliminary. Some patients tested have provided more equivocal data (and sometimes data contradictory within the same patient on different test runs). Attention factors seem to strongly affect the results, fixation distance appears to affect the results in some patients but not in others, and shortcomings of the prototype servo-operated occlusion/prism insertion device used in these runs add further uncontrolled variables. Studies are continuing with a new version of this device and a larger group of patients.

Further data supporting the hypothesis can be found in the clinical realm:

When a muscle is *recessed*, as for an exotropic patient, the input to the vergence control center indicating the ortho position as too far eso is removed. Following surgery, the EOM afferent from the lateral rectus indicates the eye has already corrected the relative eso position. As time goes by, the normal tension of the muscle returns and the clinical condition may return as well.

When a muscle is *resected* (a notoriously ineffective operation unless combined with a recession), such as a medial rectus resection for an exophoria, the lateral rectus afferent impulses are now increased, due to an increase in the stretch, and the signals from that muscle would indicate the eye is now even more eso, with the result that the eye is moved into the exo position again. (The ineffectiveness of the resection is usually explained on the basis of the stretchtension relationship, but that relationship has never been overly convincing as an explanation.)

Explaining divergence paralysis as a partial paralysis of the lateral recti is another idea that is not very convincing to me. This doubt has been strengthened through observation of a patient with this condition by our automated tests. No weakness could be demonstrated in the form of reduced velocity laterally as opposed to medially in this patient. Consider what the case would be if the efferent impulses from the lateral rectus were partially or completely abolished. If we regard the stretch afferent impulses from the lateral and medial rectus muscles as usually canceling each other as they are processed when the phoria position is reached, and increasing appropriately when stretched as the eye moves past that point of phoria position, then when the patient has his eye moved medially in respect to the other eye—either actively or passively, the stretch receptor output of the lateral rectus would be increased and that of the medial rectus would be decreased. If a lesion caused the receptors of the lateral recti to be less effective than the signals from the medial recti, then the phoria position would be that of an esophore, where the two signals would be balanced, i.e. the low signals from the lateral recti and the decreased signals from the medial recti when the eye is in the eso position. Thus the eyes would be relatively ortho for near fixation since the convergence needed would satisfy the near fixation requirement, although the patient would be eso for distance. Here the ideal condition for a pure resection of the lateral recti to selectively increase the deficient afferent impulses from the lateral recti should be present. Clinically this is indeed the case, and is in fact one of the few conditions where resections work well by themselves.

If we can obtain a patient who is to have an ablative procedure of the Gasserian ganglion we should be able to make a clear test of our hypothesis through testing the patient before and after the surgical procedure.

Finally, it should perhaps be noted that the accommodative-convergence response required for any given fixation distance would not influence the phoria mechanism postulated here, since the eye's position can usually be explained by the distance phoria position plus the effect of accommodative convergence to describe the near phoria position.

REFERENCES

BACH-Y-RITA, P. and COLLINS, C. C. (Eds.) (1971) *The Control of Eye Movements*. New York, Academic Press.

DUKE-ELDER, S. and WYBAR, K. (1973) *Ocular Motility and Strabismus*, vol. VI. DUKE-ELDER, S. (Ed.) *System of Ophthalmology*. St. Louis, Mosby.

FRICKER, S. (1971) Dynamic measurements of horizontal eye motion. F. acceleration and velocity matrices. *Invest. Ophthal.* **10,** 724.

REINECKE, R. D. and SIMONS, K. A new stereoscopic test for amblyopia. *Am. J. Ophthal.* (in press).

TOATES, F. M. (1974) Vergence eye movements. *Documenta Ophthal.* **37,** 153.

MOTOR UNITS IN EYE MUSCLES

GUNNAR LENNERSTRAND

THE eye-movement apparatus is unique among mammalian motor systems in that it combines extremely swift and precise movement with a high capability to sustain a position. This wide range of action requires a rather complicated muscle machinery as is evident from the description of eye muscle morphology and physiology made by the previous speakers (Alvarado; Bach-y-Rita, this Symposium). How it is reflected in the organization of the eye muscles on the motor unit level is the topic of the present paper.

The motor unit in the eye muscles, defined in the usual manner (Sherrington, 1925) as the motoneuron, its axon and the muscle fibres it innervates, is "the final common path" for all eye-movement control. The variety of acts in which the eye motor units function has been reviewed by Robinson (1968) and by several contributors in a previous symposium on eye-movement control (see Bach-y-Rita and Collins, 1971). There are several fundamental types of eye movements. Conjugate eye movements are the rapid saccades, which can be of small amplitude and high frequency during fixation (so called microsaccades) or of large amplitude for refixation; the slower smooth pursuit movements; the stabilizing vestibular and optokinetic reflex movements with fast phases in the saccadic velocity range and slow phases in the speed range of smooth pursuit movements. Among normal disjunctive movements are the sluggish vergence movements, so important for fusion and binocular vision in man and other primates (Walls, 1962). Further, the eye muscles show an appreciable degree of activity at resting length, i.e. with the globe in the so-called primary position. In man the resting tension is 10–20 gs, which is relatively large, if one considers that the maximal eye-muscle tension developed during saccatic movements amounts to about 100 g (Collins, 1971). More detailed descriptions of the neurological control systems for eye movements will be given during this conference.

In this paper recent work on single motor units in cat extraocular muscle (in this case the inferior oblique, the lateral rectus and the retractor bulbi muscles) will be described, after a brief introductory review of motor unit studies in other muscles and of previous work on eye muscle physiology. Three types of motor units have been distinguished in the inferior oblique muscle. In the retractor bulbi muscle all units are of the same type. On the basis of the electrical and mechanical data some suggestions can be made with regard to the type of muscle fibres in each kind of unit. Further, the results will serve as a basis for a discussion on the motor unit organization of eye movements. More comprehensive reports on the material presented here have been given by Lennerstrand (1972, 1974 a, b) and Goldberg and Lennerstrand (1974).

119

SINGLE MOTOR UNITS IN OTHER MAMMALIAN
MUSCLE

In recent years several studies have been published on mechanical properties of single motor units in various muscles: in cat triceps surae and other hind-leg muscles (Devanandan et al., 1965; Henneman and Olson, 1965; McPhedran et al., 1965; Wuerker et al., 1965; Appelberg and Emonet-Dénand, 1967; Burke, 1967; Burke et al., 1973; see also Burke, 1973; Granit and Burke, 1973), in rat hind-leg muscles (Edström and Kugelberg, 1968; Kugelberg, 1973) and tail muscles (Steg, 1964; Andrew and Part, 1972), cat middle ear muscles (Teig, 1972) and in hand muscles of the monkey (Eccles et al., 1968) and man (Milner-Brown et al., 1973). Almost all of the muscles investigated have singly innervated muscle fibres, generating action potentials. Multiple innervated fibres have been described only in eye muscles (Alvarado, Bach-y-Rita; this Symposium) and in the tensor tympani and stapedius muscles (Erulkar et al., 1964; Fernand and Hess, 1969). It is important to keep in mind this variation in muscle-fibre innervation between eye muscles and other muscles when contractile properties of the motor units are compared.

The most extensive motor-unit studies have been made on the cat triceps surae muscles where intrinsic properties of the motoneurons have been correlated with the mechanical properties of the muscular part of the same motor unit. Important information has also been acquired concerning the motor-unit organization of different motor acts. Reviews of this work have been given in reports by Burke (1973) and Granit and Burke (1973). Variations in the rise time (contraction time) and the decay time of the twitch contraction in response to motoneuron or single axon stimulation were used to separate rapidly (fast) and slowly contracting (slow) units. The histochemical characteristics of the fibres in the single units were determined with the techniques described by Edström and Kugelberg (1968) and Kugelberg (this Symposium). The oxidative enzyme systems are better developed in slow units, which renders them less susceptible to fatigue (Burke et al., 1973). Many of the fast units are dependent for their energy mainly on anaerobic glycolysis but the energy supply within each fibre is limited and these fibres fatigue quickly after prolonged stimulation (the FF units of Burke et al., 1973). Other fast units have an enzyme machinery more similar to that of the slow units and they are more resistant to fatigue (the FR units of Burke et al., 1973). All three types of units are represented in the gastrocnemius muscle. In this muscle there also seems to exist a fairly strict correlation between the force produced in the motor unit and the size of the innervating motoneuron. Slow units, which give rather low tensions to tetanic stimulation, are mostly innervated by small motoneurons (Burke, 1967) and axons with low condition velocity (McPhedran et al., 1965; Wuerker et al., 1965). Fast units, producing higher tetanic tensions, are innervated by large motoneurons with thicker axons of high conduction velocity. The small motoneurons of the slow units have a higher membrane resistance and probably also a denser synaptic impingement than the motoneurons of fast units (Burke, 1968a; Mendell and Henneman, 1971). They would therefore be excited before the fast units by synaptic inflow from proprioceptive and supraspinal sources. A recruitment order of slow before fast units has also been shown in the anaesthetized or decerebrate animal (Henneman et al., 1965; Olsson et al., 1968; Burke, 1968a, 1973; Granit and Burke, 1973). Most of the FR units and all the slow units are innervated by motoneurons that respond tonically (with sustained firing) to excitatory synaptic activation (Burke, 1968b). The FF units are innervated by motoneurons that show phasic (rapidly decaying) responses to steady excitatory inputs.

From a functional point of view it has been suggested that these observations might be comprised in the so-called "size principle" of motoneuron recruitment (Henneman et al., 1965). According to this principle small motoneurons innervating slow motor units are always recruited before the fast units, irrespective of the type of motor act. The slow units would mainly regulate the tonic muscle activity needed, for example, in postural control, upon which stronger, quicker and usually short-lasting muscle contractions would be superimposed by recruitment of phasic motoneurons and fast motor units.

However, some recent findings indicate that motor unit recruitment according to the "size principle" is in many cases an oversimplification. Burke (1973) has pointed out that the motoneurons of fast and slow hind-limb units can be activated differently from the same supraspinal regions; in some instances excitation was seen in one kind of motoneuron, while the other was inhibited by the same input. It is also known that areas in the mesencephalon can influence the small gamma motoneurons leading to the intrafusal muscle fibres of the muscle spindles differently; by the stimulation of some areas the so-called dynamic gamma motor system is activated but not the so-called static gamma system (Appelberg and Jeneskog, 1972). This selective activation of one gamma system alone cannot be explained by the "size principle" since the sizes of dynamic and static gamma motoneurons seem to fall within the same range (Adal and Barker, 1965). Further variations in the recruitment pattern of motor units have been observed in man. The voluntary rapid limb movements have been shown predominantly to involve units with phasic firing patterns (Grimby and Hannerz, 1973; Hannerz, 1974). A recruitment order of tonic before phasic units could be obtained in the same movements if some pre-excitation (supraspinal or over muscle afferents) was induced. The implications for the efferent eye movement control of the "size principle" and its modification will be discussed later.

THE EYE MUSCLES

The extrinsic muscles of the eye include the four recti and the two oblique muscles (here called the oculorotatory muscles), the levator palpebrae and, in some species, the retractor bulbi muscle. First studies on motor units of the retractor muscle will be described. The levator palpebrae has not been investigated.

The Retractor Bulbi Muscle

1. *Previous studies*

The retractor bulbi muscle (RB) exists in several species among them the cat, but is lacking in man. In the cat it consists of four muscle slips originating at the apex of the orbit from the tendinous ring common also to the four rectus muscles and the superior oblique muscle. The slips run inside the recti in the muscle cone. They insert in each of the four quadrants of the globe approximately at the level of the equator (Motais, 1885; Key-Åberg, 1934). The RB has protective function of retracting the globe and raising the nictitating membrane (Bach-y-Rita, 1971). It is innervated together with the lateral rectus by the abducens nerve (Motais, 1885; Bach-y-Rita and Ito, 1965). Morphologically the muscle is composed of large, singly innervated fibres (Alvarado *et al.*, 1967; Asmussen *et al.*, 1971). Electrophysiological studies have shown them to be twitch fibres, generating action potentials, with an average resting potential of 71 mV. No evidence for multiple innervation could be obtained. It has also been shown that the RB motor nerve lacks the small diameter fibres found in other eye muscle nerves (Steinacker and Bach-y-Rita, 1968a), to some extent responsible for the multiple innervation (see below). Further, administration of succinylcholine intravenously caused long-lasting contraction of the oculorotatory muscles but not in the RB (Bach-y-Rita *et al.*, 1967). As mentioned below the muscle fibres responsible for the contraction of oculorotatory muscles are supposed to be multiply innervated slow contracting ones (Bach-y-Rita, 1971), and the RB like most skeletal muscles evidently lacks such fibres. A mechanical study of RB bulbi slips was performed by Steinacker and Bach-y-Rita (1968b), but no single motor unit studies existed.

2. *Motor units*

Stimulation of single motoneurons to the RB was done by means of a tungsten microelectrode placed in the abducens nucleus (Lennerstrand, 1974a). The motor units were all found to be of the same, fast type. The contractile properties fell within a rather narrow range as shown for values of twitch contraction time and half-decay time in Fig. 1. It was also demonstrated that dynamic mechanical parameters such as twitch contraction time and half-decay time, fusion frequency and fatiguability corresponded very closely in individual single units and the RB slips (Lennerstrand, 1974a), strongly indicating that the RB is composed of a mechanically homogeneous group of fast units. These units are much more susceptible to fatigue than most fast units in oculorotatory muscles (Fig. 11B), and the whole muscle fatigues at the same rate as its units (Fig. 2). These fast units could correspond to the FF motor units identified in the cat gastrocnemius muscle by Burke *et al.* (1973). From the standpoint of function, it is clear from the fatigue studies that the retractor muscle plays no part in the tonic control of eye movements. Between short periods of activity in protective reflexes it is probably at total rest. It has been suggested that the RB might also rotate the eye globe, but it has not been conclusively demonstrated that the slips can be activated one at a time from a supranuclear source.

The RB can be used as a convenient control in experiments on extrinsic eye muscles. In mechanical studies it can serve as an example of a pure fast unit muscle, and its properties can be compared with the oculorotatory muscles of mixed (fast and slow unit) type. In studies on polyneuronal innervation (see Bach-y-Rita, this Symposium) the RB was used as the singly innervated fibre control, against which all tests aimed at revealing multiple innervation of oculorotatory muscles had to be related. Since the RB shares motor nerves with the lateral rectus muscle, muscle responses could be compared under exactly the same experimental conditions.

Oculorotatory Muscles

These muscles will in the following often be referred to simply as eye muscles or extraocular muscles.

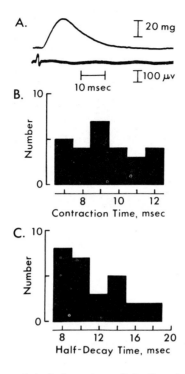

FIG. 1. (A) Twitch response of a typical single motor unit in the retractor bulbi muscle. Histograms of twitch contraction times (B) and half-day times (C) of a sample of retractor units. The rather narrow range of values and the absence of multiple peaks suggest that all units are of the same, fast type. [Reprinted by permission of *J. Physiol.* (*Lond.*) **236**, 43–55 (1974).]

1. *Previous studies*

The early discoveries of a variety of muscle fibre types and nerve endings in extraocular muscles suggested to some workers that motor systems with quite different properties might exist together in these muscles (see Siebeck and Krüger, 1955, also for references). The results of the physiological studies by Cooper and Eccles (1930) and Duke-Elder and Duke-Elder (1930) support these ideas. Cooper and Eccles showed that eye muscles are the most rapidly contracting of all mammalian muscles with a contraction time of 7.5–10 msec, compared with values of around 25 msec for the fastest hind-limb muscles. The stimulus frequency to reach a fused tetanus, the so-called fusion frequency, was much higher for the eye muscles than for fast hind-limb muscles, the values being 300 and 100 pulses per sec (pps) respectively. Duke-Elder and Duke-Elder (1930) demonstrated that the eye muscles are exceptionally sensitive to agents acting on the neuromuscular junction. When exposed to acetylcholine the eye muscles developed a long-lasting contraction, a property they share with tonic (or slow) muscle fibres in amphibian and avian muscle (Brown and Harvey, 1941; Kuffler and Vaughan Williams, 1953b; Ginsborg, 1960b). It does not seem possible that these properties, i.e. very rapid contractions and tonic contracture would combine within the same muscle fibre system. Rather, they indicate that eye muscles have at least one fast and one slow motor component. Further work has clarified much of the mechanical and electrical properties of these

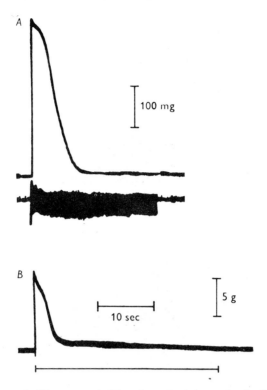

FIG. 2. Fatigue in a retractor bulbi motor unit (A) and a retractor muscle slip (B) at 200 pps stimulation for approximately 30 sec. EMG in A recorded simultaneously with tension to eliminate possibility of breakdown of neuro-muscular transmission as a cause of the tension decline. The similarity in time course of the two curves strongly indicates that the retractor muscle is composed of only one type of motor unit. [Reprinted by permission of *J. Physiol. (Lond.)* **236,** 43–55 (1974).]

motor systems. This research has been reviewed recently by Bach-y-Rita (1971), Breinin (1971) and Matyushkin (1972) and it will therefore be presented rather briefly here. Particular emphasis will be put on some controversial points where single unit studies might prove revealing.

In the absence of extensive single unit studies of eye muscles, information on contractile properties have been obtained in experiments using selective activation of different muscle fibre populations. Although morphologists have differentiated five or even more muscle fibre types (Peachey, 1971; Alvarado, Mayr, this Symposium) physiologists have been able to demonstrate only two (or three) motor systems, one fast and one (or two) slowly contracting (Matyushkin, 1961, 1964a, b; Hess and Pilar, 1963; Bach-y-Rita and Ito, 1966; Pilar, 1967; Ozawa *et al.*, 1969; Matyushkin and Drabkina, 1970; Bach-y-Rita, 1971; Breinin, 1971; Matyushkin, 1972). Most of the physiological studies have been made on cat and rabbit eye muscles. Although all six oculorotatory muscles of each species show morphological evidence of slow and fast components, the proportions differ as suggested by Peachey (1968) and showed more conclusively by Alvarado (this Symposium). Species differences as well as variations between individual oculomotory muscles might account for part of the contradictory results to be presented below.

The *fast motor component*, also called the phasic system (Matyushkin, 1961), is inner-vated by large nerve fibres. It can be rather selectively activated by low-threshold, cathodal stimulation of the motor nerve, although recently part of the slow component has been shown to have low stimulus threshold (see below). The fast component is composed of twitch fibres, i.e. muscle fibres capable of impulse conduction, both in the cat (Hess and Pilar, 1963; Matyushkin, 1964b; Bach-y-Rita and Ito, 1966) and in the rabbit (Matyushkin, 1961, 1964b; Ozawa, 1964; Ozawa *et al.*, 1969). These fibres, which from all available electrophysiological evidence are single innervated, i.e. with one end-plate region on each cell, are the largest of eye muscle fibres and have a conduction velocity of 3.0 m/sec (Bach-y-Rita and Ito, 1966). Their membrane poten-tials range between 60 and 100 mV and they produce over-shoot action potentials in response to direct and indirect stimulation (Matyushkin, 1961; Hess and Pilar, 1963; Bach-y-Rita and Ito, 1966; Pilar, 1967). This motor system has a contraction time of 5–8 msec and a half-decay time of about 7 msec (Matyushkin, 1964b; Bach-y-Rita and Ito, 1966). Somewhat slower contractions are obtained at supramaximal motor nerve stimulation (Cooper and Eccles, 1930; Brown and Harvey, 1941; Barmack *et al.*, 1971) indicating that both fast and slow systems are activated. The fusion frequency of the fast motor component is 350–450 pps depending on the recording system and the muscle preparation (Hess and Pilar, 1963; Matyushkin, 1964b; Bach-y-Rita and Ito, 1966). At this frequency of stimulation the tension output of the whole muscle had reached its maximum (Cooper and Eccles, 1930; Matyushkin, 1964b; Barmack *et al.*, 1971; Fuchs and Luschei, 1971b) and a further increase in stimulus frequency has only the effect of augmenting the rate of tetanic tension rise (Barmack *et al.*, 1971; Fuchs and Luschei, 1971b) in the same manner as in other skeletal muscle (Buller and Lewis, 1965).

As for the *slow motor component* or the tonic system (Matyushkin, 1960) all workers agree that its fibres are multiply innervated, i.e. each muscle fibre has several end plates (Matyushkin, 1961, 1964a; Hess and Pilar, 1963; Bach-y-Rita and Ito, 1966; Ozawa *et al.*, 1969; Matyushkin and Drabkina, 1970). It is innervated predominantly by small nerve fibres. These can be selectively activated by so-called anodal block stimulations of the motor nerve (Matyushkin, 1964b; Bach-y-Rita and Ito, 1966), a technique also used by Kuffler and Vaughan Williams (1953a), Ginsborg (1960a, b) and Floyd and Smith (1971) to activate slow muscle fibres with multiple innervation in amphibian and avian muscle. Another method of slow component activation is the selective curarization blocking all twitch fibres, employed by Hess and Pilar (1963).

According to Matyushkin (1961, 1964a, b), Hess and Pilar (1963), Ozawa (1964), Ozawa *et al.* (1969) and Matyushkin and Drabkina (1970), the slow system fibres are incapable of impulse conduction and respond only with local depolarizations to nerve stimulation, in the same manner as amphibian (Kuffler and Vaughan Williams, 1953a, b; Orkand, 1963) and some of the avian slow fibres (Burke and Ginsborg, 1956; Ginsborg, 1960a, b). Bach-y-Rita and Ito (1966), on the other hand, claimed that the fibres in the slow system were able to generate action potentials, and that only damaged fibres were non-conducting. They suggested the fibres in the slow system to be similar to the multiply innervated, impulse-conducting muscle fibres in muscle spindles of amphibia (Koketsu and Nishi, 1957a, b; Smith, 1964) and cat (Eyzaguirre, 1960; Bessou and Laporte, 1965) and the slow muscle fibres in birds (Ginsborg, 1960b).

The slow system fibres in eye muscles are smaller than those in the fast system, as indicated by measurements of membrane potentials (ranging between 30 and 60 mV) (Hess and Pilar, 1963; Bach-y-Rita and Ito, 1966; Matyushkin and Drabkina, 1970), and conduction velocity (2.16 m/sec) (Bach-y-Rita and Ito, 1966). According to Matyushkin (1964a) and Matyushkin and Drabkina (1970) two varieties of slow (or tonic) fibres can be separated in the rabbit, both of them with non-conducted membrane activity. Hess (1961, 1970), Peachey (1968), Harker (1973), and Alvarado (this Symposium) have observed two types of multiple innervated fibres with different density of end plates in eye muscles, an addition to the singly innervated (see also below). As Peachey (1968) pointed out, the conflicting findings on electrical properties of the slow component could be explained, if one assumes that these two types of multiple innervated fibres represent subdivisions of the slow component. Experimental evidence in favour of a separation of the slow component into two types of motor units will be presented below.

In rabbit and cat eye muscles, Matyushkin (1964b) was unable to obtain twitch responses from the slow (tonic) component, although tetanic stimulation gave rise to an appreciable tension output. Other studies on cat eye muscles have showed that the twitch contraction time of the slow component was about 25 msec (Bach-y-Rita and Ito, 1966). Fusion frequency for tetanus was as low as 25–30 pps (Hess and Pilar, 1963; Bach-y-Rita and Ito, 1966). However, this finding has been challenged by Barmack et al. (1971), who found that they had to stimulate cat eye muscles at rates above 40 pps to produce a steady tension increase. Similar results were obtained by Fuchs and Luschei (1971b) in eye muscles of monkeys.

2. Motor units

Recently, Close and Luff (1974) have recorded twitch responses to threshold and suprathreshold stimulation of the muscle nerve in rat eye motor units. They found evidence only for fast, twitch units with contraction times of about 5 msec and half-relaxation times of about 6 msec in this species, but the material was rather limited. From these findings and from mechanical studies of the whole muscle they concluded that the slow component must be much smaller in rat than in cat eye muscles. It is peculiar, though, that these differences are not reflected in the eye muscle morphology. Rat and cat eye muscles are quite similar with respect to fibre types (Mayr, 1971; Alvarado, this Symposium).

All the following data have been obtained from cat eye muscle. The safest way to ensure activation of single motor units is by intracellular stimulation of motoneurons with glass micropipettes (Burke et al., 1973). This technique has been used for a small number (20–30) units in the lateral rectus muscle (Goldberg and Lennerstrand, 1974). However, the instability of cells that had been penetrated made the interpretation of tests performed on these units rather restricted. Extracellular stimulation of single units in the inferior oblique muscle was therefore used in order to obtain more extensive data. The results obtained with both methods of motor unit activation were in very good agreement. This strongly supports the notion that single and not multiple units were studied with the extracellular technique as well. Both methods favour the activation of units innervated by large motoneurons with large axons, since these are most easily

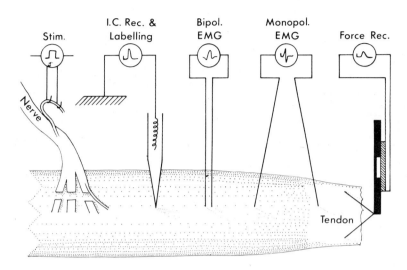

FIG. 3. Schematic presentation of single unit isolation and recording in the inferior oblique preparation. Extensive denervation of the muscle and stimulation of split neurofilaments made the activation of single units possible. In the units tension, monopolar and bipolar EMG and intracellular responses were recorded.

impaled in intracellular work and are the first to be activated by low intensity stimulation in extracellular approaches. The sample of motor units to be presented is therefore not representative as far as the proportions of the various types of units are concerned.

In order to stimulate single motor units extracellularly the inferior oblique muscle was extensively denervated until only a thin nerve filament remained. The muscle nerve was sectioned as far back in the orbit as possible and split into filaments positioned over platinum electrodes for cathodal stimulation. Functional isolation of single motor units was considered at hand when all or nothing responses to single and tetanic stimulation were obtained. The experimental methods are described in detail elsewhere (Lennerstrand, 1974b). From the units mechanical and electrical responses were recorded as shown schematically in Fig. 3. The glass microelectrodes for intracellular recordings were filled with a dye solution, permitting labelling of impaled muscle fibres for later morphological identification.

(a) Electrical properties

Non-conducting units. A small number of the motor units fired no action potentials but showed local responses that summated as the rate of tetanic stimulation exceeded 50 pulses per sec (pps). It was possible to record these responses extracellularly either with Ag–AgCl electrodes from the muscle surface (Fig. 4A) or with low resistance glass pipettes inserted in the muscle close to the unit (Fig. 4C). In the intracellular recordings from these units no impulse activity was demonstrated even during repetitive stimulation (Fig. 6D). The fibres of these units are probably of the slow type described in cat eye muscle by Hess and Pilar (1963). These authors pointed out the strong morphological and functional resemblance of the non-conducting eye muscle fibres to the slow multiply innervated muscle fibres of amphibian and avian muscle. A detailed

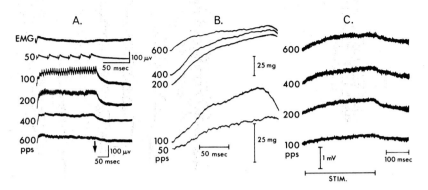

FIG. 4. Electrical (A and C) and mechanical (B) responses of MINC units to stimulation at the rates marked. In A monopolar, dc-EMG is recorded from one unit. Local responses to single stimulus (top trace) summate at repetitive stimulation of 60 pps and above. Arrow in lowest trace signifies stimulus removal. B and C, from another unit. The tetanus fuses at approximately 60 pps (B). The electrical activity presented in C is recorded with a micropipette close to the unit. Because of the high noise level of this dc-recording, individual local responses cannot be separated. [Reprinted by permission of *Acta physiol. scand.* (1974).]

physiological description of the amphibian slow fibre has been given by Lännergren (this Symposium). It should only be pointed out here that the slow fibres are well suited for the prolonged tonic activity known to occur in eye muscles. They are innervated by small-diameter nerve fibres in other species and it is likely that in eye muscles, too, they are supplied by fibres in the lower range of the nerve fibre diameter spectrum. In order to distinguish these units from other multiply innervated eye muscle units with conducted activity (Bach-y-Rita and Ito, 1966; see below), they will, in the following, be denoted multiply innervated, non-conducting units or MINC units for short. They would probably correspond to the type 5 fibre of Alvarado (this Symposium and personal communication).

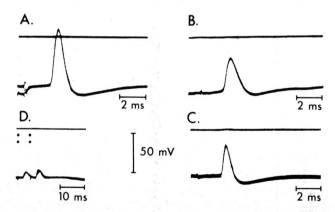

FIG. 5. Intracellular responses to single shocks in a SI unit (A) and in two different MIC units (B and C), and to double shocks in a MINC unit (D). Top line is reference (zero) potential. Unit in A is the same as in Fig. 7A, and unit in D same as in Fig. 4B and C. Action potentials are seen in A, B and C. In the MINC unit (D) no action potentials were fired even at increased stimulus strength (marked by stimulus dots); two superimposed traces coincide. [Reprinted by permission of *Acta physiol. scand.* (1974).]

Conducting units. The majority of motor units studied consisted of fibres capable of producing action potentials (Fig. 5 A, B, and C; Fig. 6 A and B).

Bach-y-Rita and Ito (1966) suggested that part of this fibre population is multiply innervated in cat eye muscles. Multiple innervation implies that end-plate regions are widely distributed over the fibres. If two or more end plate regions can be localized with physiological techniques within a single motor unit this would strongly indicate multiple innervation of that unit. The units were explored with bipolar electrodes moving along the muscle, parallel to the fibre direction. In passing over an end-plate region a reversal of the polarity of the bipolar EMG will occur (Jarcho *et al.*, 1952).

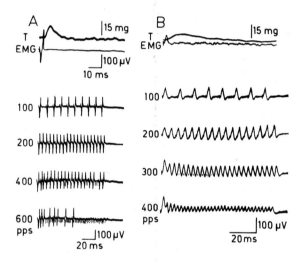

Fig. 6. Two top traces show mechanical twitch response (T) and monopolar dc-EMG to single pulse stimulation of a SI unit (A) and a MIC unit (B). Lower panels show EMG to repetitive stimulation at rates marked. The twitch contraction time is typically shorter in the SI-unit (4 ms) than in the MIC unit (13 ms). As seen from the EMG recordings to tetanic stimulation the MIC unit can follow higher stimulus rates (over 400 pps) than the SI unit (below 400 pps) before blocking of electrical transmission occurs.

With this method a large part of the impulse conducting extraocular units was shown to have multiple end-plate regions (Fig. 7B). These regions were distributed over a much larger distance (5–8 mm) than the narrow band of 1–2 mm usually thought to be occupied in the muscle by end plates of single innervated fibres (Hess and Pilar, 1963; Zenker and Anzenbacher, 1964; Dietert, 1965). Recently Mayr (this Symposium) has found several bands of single end plates in cat eye muscle. However, before it has been conclusively shown that the end plates of one single innervated unit can occupy positions in several of these bands, the conclusion of the EMG study with a bipolar electrode must be that the dispersed end plates are located on the same fibre and would not represent single end plates on different fibres within the same unit. The units would thus show true multiple innervation. [Another possibility for an explanation derives from the finding of a high occurrence of myomyous junctions between singly innervated eye muscle fibres (Mayr, this Symposium). Electrical activity may be transmitted between fibres, in which case a bipolar recording pattern resembling that of multiple innervation would be obtained. However, indirect evidence presented

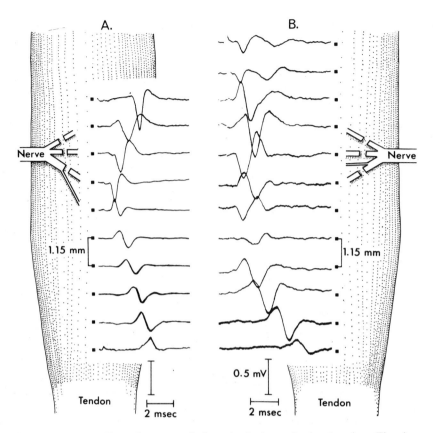

FIG. 7. Bipolar EMG recordings along two single units both conducting impulses. The denervation to isolate the units and the recording points are shown in the schematic drawing of the inferior oblique muscle and its motor nerve. A, The EMG sequence has one location of polarity reversal indicating a single end plate region. This is a SI unit. B, Several locations (4 or 5) of polarity reversals, indicating multiple innervation. The activity is clearly conducted, and the latency of response increases in the recordings beyond the innervation band (4 lowest traces). This is a MIC unit. [Reprinted by permission of *Acta physiol. scand.* (1974).]

by Bach-y-Rita (this Symposium) suggests that the myomyous junctions are non-conducting.]

The rest of the conducting units had only one end plate region (Fig. 7A), and they were regarded as singly innervated. These two types of conducting units will be denoted as singly innervated (SI) units and multiply innervated, conducting (MIC) units in the following.

Multiply innervated fibres, with end-plate regions 0.5–1.0 mm apart, have been described in the extraocular muscles of guinea-pig (Hess, 1961), rat (Mayr, 1971), sheep (Harker, 1972), and cat (Alvarado, personal communication). In all species except the sheep, these fibres are of small diameter and situated in the outer (orbital) layer of the muscle. In sheep they are generally found in the core of the muscle. The same authors also found some fibres with much denser multiple innervation in the orbital as well as in the central layers. The slow fibres of Hess and Pilar (1963) were located centrally in the muscle. In this context it is interesting to note that the fibres of

MIC units conduct action potentials at a significantly lower average velocity (1.72 m/sec) than the fibres in SI units (2.93 m/sec), and that the membrane potential generally is lower in MIC units than SI units (Fig. 5 A, B, and C). These observations would indicate that fibres in MIC units are thinner than those in SI units, and support the morphological findings.

With regard to electrical characteristics and innervation, the fibres of MIC units seem to be very similar to the fibres of the slow muscle component described by Bach-y-Rita and Ito (1966). It has been suggested that these slow fibres are responsible for the contracture in cat eye muscle induced by depolarizing neuromuscular agents like succinylcholine (Bach-y-Rita, 1971, this Symposium). Bach-y-Rita, Lennerstrand, Nichols and Alvarado (unpublished observation) found succinylcholine responding fibres to be located in the orbital layer. All this makes it very tempting to propose that the MIC units are formed by orbital, thin fibres with distributed multiple innervation, corresponding to muscle fibre type 4 in the classification of Alvarado (personal communication). The SI units would be composed of the singly innervated types 1, 2, and 3 of Alvarado (this Symposium).

(b) Isometric contractions

Speed of contraction as reflected in twitch responses and in fusion frequency was highest in the SI units. Their twitch contraction time ranged between 3.5 and 9 ms (Fig. 8A) and their fusion frequencies between 175 and 350 pps (Fig. 8B). MIC units had slower contraction times (5–18 ms) and lower fusion frequencies (120–225 pps). In the MINC units studied no response to single stimulus could be recorded with the present recording system. Fusion frequencies of MINC units were between 50 and 100 pps (Fig. 8B). Thus, it was found that SI units were the fastest and MINC

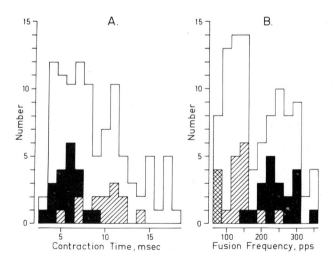

FIG. 8. Histogram to show distribution of twitch contraction time (A) and fusion frequency (B) for all units mechanically tested in the inferior oblique. The units that were identified from their electrical responses are marked separately: SI units with filled bars, MIC with striped bars, and MINC units with cross-hatched bars. Note that in MINC units no twitch response could be recorded. [Reprinted by permission of *Acta physiol. scand.* (1974).]

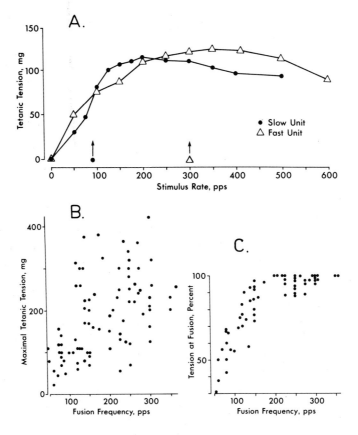

FIG. 9. (A) Tetanic tension at different rates of stimulation of a slow unit (MINC) and a fast unit (SI). Fusion frequency of each unit marked by arrow. Note the large discrepancy for the slow unit between fusion frequency (90 pps) and stimulus rate for maximal tetanic response (200 pps). (B) Maximal tetanic tension in a sample of inferior oblique units plotted against their fusion frequencies. (C) Tetanic tension at fusion in per cent of maximal tetanic tension, plotted against fusion frequency. The units with fusion frequencies below some 150 pps, which is within the range of MIC and MINC units, had to be stimulated at rates above fusion to reach maximal tension. [Reprinted by permission of Acta physiol. scand. (1974).]

units the slowest. MIC units were grouped in between. Discrepancies in fusion frequency values between the slowest (MINC) units in the present study and the previously studied slow component (Hess and Pilar, 1963; Bach-y-Rita and Ito, 1966) can be explained on mechanical grounds. When the whole slow component was activated, temporal and spatial variation in the contraction of a large group of multiply innervated fibres might very well reduce the fusion frequency to the low values (30 pps) reported earlier.

Tetanic tension. Speed of isometric contraction in a unit was more accurately determined from fusion frequency than from twitch characteristics in the present preparation (Lennerstrand, 1974b). Parameters of tetanic contractions in the units were correlated to fusion frequency. The maximal tetanic tension of the units increased with rising fusion frequency (Fig. 9B). However, in the units with fusion frequencies below 200 pps, maximal tension was obtained not at fusion of tetanus but at higher rates of stimulation (Fig. 9 A and C), which is out of the ordinary for muscles with singly innervated units (Cooper and Eccles, 1930; Lennerstrand, 1974a). On the other hand, it has been shown to occur for multiply innervated, slow amphibian fibres (Floyd and Smith, 1971) and also for the tonic component of cat and rabbit eye muscles (Matyushkin, 1964b). It may therefore be a property of multiply innervated units. It is also interesting to note that the maximal rate of steady-state firing of motoneurons in alert monkeys seldom is below 200 pps and often reaches values of 300–400 pps (Fuchs and Luschei, 1970, 1971a; Robinson, 1970; Schiller, 1970). Such firing rates would be needed in order to extract maximal tension from eye muscle units, both singly and multiply innervated.

The tetanic tension (25–425 mg) elicited from eye muscle units is low compared to that of other motor units. Only units in middle ear muscles have values in the same range (Teig, 1972). The retractor bubli showed average unit tensions of 400 mg. In the small superficial lumbrical muscle of the cat's foot, unit tetanic tensions between about 0.5–30 g were recorded (Appelberg and Emonet-Dénand, 1967). These variations between muscles must reflect to the greatest part differences in innervation ratio, i.e. the number of muscle fibres innervated by one nerve fibre. The innervation ratio of oculorotatory muscles of the cat was estimated by Torre (1953) to be approximately 1:10, as compared to 1:300–600 in cat hind-limb muscles (McPhedran et al., 1965; Burke and Tsairis, 1973). Corrections for the small number of afferent fibres in the eye muscle nerves (Bach-y-Rita and Murata, 1964) was not made. No correction is needed for intrafusal innervation since muscle spindles are missing in cat eye muscles (Cooper et al., 1955).

The *rate of tension rise* to tetanic stimulation was higher in fast units with high fusion frequencies than in slower units (Fig. 10). It was also found that the range of stimulus frequencies over which the rate of rise would increase, extended in most of the faster units up to 600–800 pps but only to about 400 pps in the slower units (those with fusion frequencies below 175 pps in Fig. 10). Stimulation at still higher frequencies would not yield any stronger output, even in the form of rate of tension rise. These values probably represent the maximal frequency at which the units are fired under natural conditions. In recording from alert animals characteristical differences have been observed between individual eye muscle motoneurons in the maximal firing rates during saccadic movements (Fuchs and Luschei, 1970; Robinson, 1970; Schiller, 1970). These variations may very well correspond to those just described for fast and slow eye motor units. This may offer a means of separating different types of units in alert animals, when no information can be achieved on unit mechanical properties.

Fatiguability of single units. Most eye muscle motoneurons in the monkey discharge at a steady rate during fixation (Fuchs and Luschei, 1970, 1971a; Robinson, 1970; Schiller, 1970; Henn and Cohen, 1972, 1973). Electrical activity in human eye muscle is known to continue at a high steady level during fixation (Björk and Kugelberg, 1953). Selective recordings in humans from different eye-muscle layers believed to contain different types of units (see below) (Collins and Scott, 1973) indicate that steady contraction during fixation is generated in both fast and slow units. In view of these observations it may not be surprising to find that most units are capable of long lasting contraction to continuous nerve stimulation (Fig. 11 A and B), in turn suggesting that tonic force production in eye muscles is shared between fast, singly and slow, multiply innervated units although the slow units may contribute the most. The tension after 30 sec of

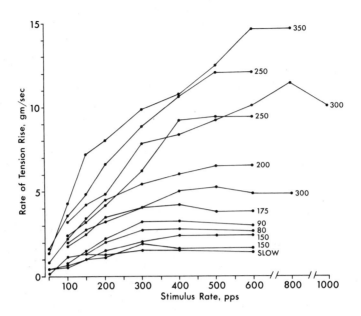

FIG. 10. Rate of tension rise in tetanic contraction plotted against stimulus rate, in a representative sample of inferior oblique units, identified by their fusion frequencies (marked at the end of each curve; the unit marked "Slow" was a MINC unit in which no fusion frequency could be determined). The fastest units show the highest rates of tension rise and their responses also increase over a wider range of stimulus rates (up to 800 pps) than those of the slower units (up to 400 pps). [Reprinted by permission of *Acta physiol. scand.* (1974).]

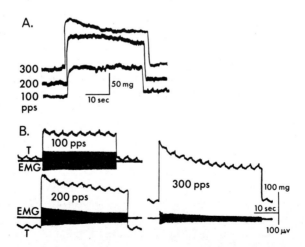

FIG. 11. (A and B) Fatigue in a MINC unit (fusion frequency 90 pps, A) and in SI unit (fusion frequency 250 pps, B). About 30 sec continuous stimulation was applied at the rates marked. In B EMG as well as tension (T) has been recorded. The endurance is high also in fast units, particularly in comparison with the rapid fatigue in retractor bulbi units (see Fig. 2A). [Reprinted by permission of *Acta physiol. scand.* (1974).]

high rate stimulation (200–300 pps) remained at 30% or more of the initial value. A few of the fast units fatigued completely. They behaved like fast units in other skeletal muscle (Steg, 1964; Burke *et al.*, 1973) including the retractor bulbi (see Fig. 2).

In the outer, orbital layers of the muscle, containing small fibers which we have reason to believe form part of the slow units (see above), the density of capillaries is high and the fibres are rich in mitochondria and oxidative enzymes (Mayr, 1971; Peachey, 1971). These are requirements needed for muscle fibers to be able to maintain contraction for long periods. Many of the fibres in the central part of the muscle have similar characteristics and would also seem suited for tonic activity. It is known that the relative blood flow is proportionally much higher in eye muscles than in any other muscles (Wooten and Reis, 1972). It is also known that prolonged exercise of adult muscle can convert fast but rapidly fatiguing units into more fatigue resistant ones (Barnard *et al.*, 1970; Burke *et al.*, 1973) by increasing the number of mitochondria and the oxidative capacity of the fibres. Eye-muscle fibres become adapted to long periods of tonic activity early in ontogeny and this may induce a permanent increase in the fatigue resistance of fast contracting units. All these factors would make the proportion of slow-fatiguing units larger in eye muscles than in other muscles. However, some of the core fibres have morphological and histochemical characteristics of twitch fibres in white hindlimb muscles (Mayr, 1971; Alvarado, this Symposium) shown to fatigue rapidly (see Granit and Burke, 1973). They may represent the small number of fast units with low endurance, which with respect to other mechanical properties were indistinguishable from the fatigue resistant fast units.

(c) *Functional implications*

Motor units in the fast and slow components. It is seen from the description of unit electrical and mechanical properties that the motor unit types can be tied to the previous subdivision of eye muscle function into a fast and a slow component. With regard to electrical properties the resemblance is most obvious. The fast component comprises the singly innervated (SI) units and the slow component the multiply innervated (MIC and MINC) units. It has also been shown that mechanical properties of the three types of units are compatible with such a separation in that SI units contract faster than the MIC and MINC units. It is likely, though, that MIC units, which have mechanical properties overlapping those of SI units, have to some extent remained unactivated by the selective stimulation used in earlier studies. This could explain why such a distinct separation with respect to mechanical properties into a fast and a slow component was obtained in these studies but not in the single unit work.

Speculations on the functional significance of multiple innervation. A large proportion of the muscle fibres in oculorotatory muscles has been found to be multiply innervated. The functional reason for this can only be speculated. The fibres with no conducted activity (the MINC units) have their counterpart in amphibian muscle, where they are supposed to produce the slow and exceedingly long-lasting contraction that are used in some of these animals' motor acts (Kuffler and Vaughan Williams, 1953b). The function of MINC units in the eye muscles could be similar, i.e. to supply at least partly the strong tonic activity in eye fixation (Scott, 1971).

More puzzling is the existence in eye muscles of multiple innervation of twitch fibres, i.e. fibres with impulse activity. These fibres form the MIC units which combine fairly fast and strong contractions with a remarkable resistance to fatigue. The fibres are rather thin and the impulse propagation is slower than in fast twitch fibres and they would perhaps contract much slower, were they not multiply innervated. The excitation wave travels faster in the nerve branches to the different end plates on the same muscle fibre than in the muscle fibre itself (Katz and Miledi, 1965) and by means of multiple innervation the fibres become activated within a shorter time span than single innervated fibres of the same size. Fibres with the same electrical characteristics have been observed in some avian muscle (Ginsborg, 1960 a,b). Also the intrafusal muscle fibres are multiply innervated and fire action potentials both in amphibians and mammals (Koketsu and Nishi, 1957 a, b; Smith, 1964; Bessou and Laporte, 1965). These may all be examples of motor systems where demands on speed and endurance have been met in a similar manner.

A possible advantage of multiple over single innervation can be extracted from Fig. 6, showing the EMG of a SI unit (Fig. 6A) and a MIC unit (Fig. 6B) during repetitive stimulation at different rates. In the SI unit the synaptic mechanisms could follow repetitive stimulation of 300 pps for several seconds but at 400 pps the one-to-one relation between stimulus and fibre response broke down quickly. The MIC unit could follow at least 400 pps for much longer periods. Similar differences has previously been observed in eye muscle EMG by Pilar (1967). Most likely the multiple innervation has been a very important factor in determining the high following frequency of the MIC unit. In the fibres of SI units transitory blocks in the neuromuscular transmission seem to occur at high rates of stimulation. The chances that all end-plate regions should be blocked at the same time are, of course, much smaller in multiply innervated fibres. Eye muscle units in alert monkeys are known to discharge for long periods at rates that approach and even exceed 300 pps (Robinson, 1970) so arrangements to avoid transmission block must be of great importance at least for the tonic eye-movement control.

Possible utilization of the motor units in different eye movements. Concerning the functional organization of eye movements it has been suggested that the slow motor component is used mainly in tonic, fixational activity and in slow vergence movements and that the fast component is put into operation in phasic activity (faster pursuit and saccadic movements) (Alpern and Wolter, 1956; Jampel, 1967; Robinson, 1968; Bach-y-Rita, 1971). This scheme would correspond to the operation of tonic and phasic motor unit activity observed in limb movments of animals (Burke, 1968b; Granit, 1970) and man (Grimby and Hannerz, 1973), implying that tonic motoneurons, innervating slow motor units would be used for postural control and phasic motoneurons, innervating fast motor units, in fast and strong but relatively short-lasting activity. Extraocular EMG responses in cat and rabbit to vestibular stimulation have suggested involvement of fast (phasic) fibres in rapid eye movements and of slow (tonic) fibres in slow movements (Nemet and Miller, 1965; Baichenko et al., 1967). The latter authors also showed that stretch reflexes, claimed to be nonexistent in eye muscles of cat (McCoach and Adler, 1932; McIntyre, 1939) and monkey (Keller and Robinson, 1971), excited the slow (tonic) system alone in the rabbit. This should be compared with the conditions in the spinal cord, where slow motor units controlled by tonically firing motoneurons are the ones most easily affected by proprioceptive inputs (Henneman et al., 1965; Burke, 1973; Granit and Burke, 1973).

However, recent experimentation on the eye motor units in the intact animal indicate that the organization of eye movements is different from that of limb movements.

Very few purely phasic motoneurons have been found in the eye motor nuclei of alert monkeys (Henn and Cohen, 1973). Instead most workers claim that the majority of the motoneurons show steady tonic discharge at constant eye position (Fuchs and Luschei. 1970, 1971a; Robinson, 1970; Schiller, 1970).

Further, while variations in the order of motor unit recruitment can occur in the spinal region depending both on the type of movement and the level of pre-excitation (Grimby and Hannerz, 1973; Hannerz, 1973), the recruitment pattern seems very fixed in the eye muscles. Irrespective of the type of movement, whether a fast saccadic or a slow vergence movement, each motor unit is brought into action at a moment that is strictly determined by the eye position and movement velocity (Robinson, 1970; Keller and Robinson, 1972; Skavenski and Robinson, 1972). This can be taken as an expression of the strictly preprogrammed control of eye movements (Robinson, 1968). It also implies that all eye motor units take part in all types of eye movement irrespective of whether they are predominantly phasic or tonic. EMG recordings in man support the findings in monkeys. By means of an electrode with multiple recording sites, Scott and Collins (1973; this Symposium) have been able to record simultaneously from fibres in the different layers of human eye muscles. They have demonstrated that while the fibres in the outer layers are the ones predominantly responsible for tonic activity in the primary position, the inner layer fibres take part in the fixational activity when the eye is deviated. Further, fibres from all layers are active in the phasic motor activity during movements, although inner layer fibres seem to contribute most of the force. If, as seems to be the case, the anatomical arrangements are similar in animals and man (Kato, 1938; Dietert, 1965) this would imply that both motor components are active in both phasic and tonic eye-muscle contractions of man.

With regard to the motor-unit recruitment pattern, experiments on nystagmus movements in the cat have shown that the small eye motoneurons with low conduction velocity of their axons have a lower threshold of activation than larger motoneurons with high conduction velocities (Yamanaka and Bach-y-Rita, 1968). Thus, the "size principle" of motoneuron recruitment would seem to hold for eye muscle. However, this cannot be taken to indicate that slow motor units always become activated before fast units. Motoneuron size, determined from the conduction velocity of its axon, is not as well correlated to the contractile properties of the motor unit in eye muscles as it is in hind-limb muscle. Slow conducting, i.e. small motoneurons, as well as rapidly conducting, i.e. large motoneurons, are connected to slow motor units (Fig. 12 A and B). Fast motor units, however, were mostly innervated by large motoneurons (Fig. 12A).

It is thus suggested that the motor unit recruitment in eye muscles is less orderly with respect to fast and slow types than in other muscle. Other evidence for this idea comes from threshold experiments on nerve stimulation. The first units to be activated in stimulation of the muscle indirectly over its nerve are the ones innervated by large axons. Increasing stimulus intensity activates a larger and larger portion of thinner axons. In most skeletal muscle this procedure evokes mechanical responses getting slower as the intensity of stimulation is increased, since nerve fibres to fast units usually have the lowest threshold and an increasing number of slow units become activated as the stimulus intensity increases. In the retractor bulbi the time course of a twitch contraction remains unchanged with intensity of stimulation since all units are of the same (fast) type. In the oculorotatory muscles, on the other hand, there

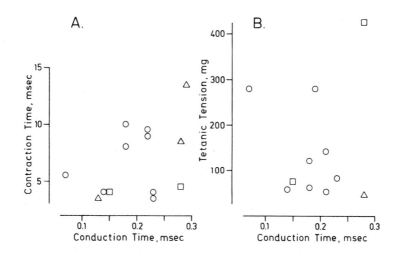

FIG. 12. Activation of single motor units in the lateral rectus muscle by means of intracellular stimulation of abducens motoneurons. Twitch contraction time (A) and maximal tetanic tension (B) of the units plotted against conduction time for antidromic impulse recorded in the motoneuron. The point of stimulation, at the entry of the abducens nerve in the brainstem, was stereotactically determined. This location and subsequently the conduction distance was kept constant in each experiment but the conduction distances probably varied between individual experiments. Units from three experiments have been marked with different symbols. Low conduction time would indicate high conduction velocity and large size of the axon and the motoneuron and vice versa. There is no clear correlation between speed or force of contraction in the units on the one hand and the size of the motoneuron on the other, although the tendency is for the fast conducting motoneurons to innervate the most rapidly contracting motor units (see A).

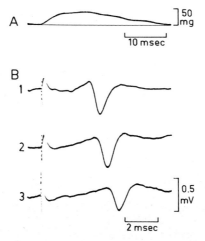

FIG. 13. Twitch response (A) and bipolar EMG at three positions 1.15 mm apart (B 1, 2, 3) in a partially denervated inferior oblique muscle. The contraction time (13 ms) of the twitch (A) indicates activation of predominantly slow units. The low conduction velocity of the activated muscle fibres (1.98 m/s) supports this idea.

is an initial decrease in both twitch contraction time and half-decay time followed by the expected slowing of the twitch, as also noted by Barmack *et al.* (1971) and Vilis (1973). Evidently some of the units with the low threshold to nerve stimulation belong to the slow group. This has been verified with mechanical and electrical recordings from threshold activation of eye muscles as seen in Fig. 13. The muscle fibres activated by barely threshold nerve stimulation had contraction times and conduction velocities in the range of fibres in MIC units. In the movement control the order of recruitment is reversed and this group of MIC units is the last one to be engaged. Thus large amplitude eye movements also involve a slow unit component, probably to give tonic support when the faster units tire and fail to supply the force needed for extended binocular fixation in large angle eye deviations.

In conclusion it seems reasonable, in spite of the uncertainty on the exact recruitment order, to assume that the multiply innervated mechanically slow units are responsible for most of the tonic activity both in the primary position and when the eyes are deviated. Singly innervated, fast units would seem most important to generate the larger forces needed for rapid eye movements, but can also deliver tonic support. It is clear, however, that we are still quite far from a complete understanding of how the supranuclear commands for a given movement are distributed to eye motor units of the different types.

ACKNOWLEDGEMENTS

These studies were performed while the author was a Visiting Scientist to the OTL Research Labs at Royal Victoria Hospital and the BioMedical Engineering Unit at McGill University, Montreal, Canada, and a Visiting Scientist to the Smith-Kettlewell Institute of Visual Sciences, San Francisco, U.S.A. The work was supported by the Canadian Medical Research Council (Visiting Scientist Award, Grant No. MRC-MA-4483), the United States Public Health Service Program (Project Research, Grant No. P01-EY00299), the Swedish Medical Research Council (Grant No. B74-14R-4123), P.E. Lindahl stipendiefond, Stiftelsen Vera och Carl J. Michaelssons donationsfond and Erik och Edith Fernströms fond för medicinsk forskning.

REFERENCES

ADAL, M. N. and BARKER, D. (1965) Intramuscular branching of fusimotor fibres. *J. Physiol. (Lond.)* **177,** 288–299.

ALPERN, M. and WOLTER, J. R. (1956) The relation of horizontal saccadic and vergence movements. *Arch. Ophthal., N.Y.* **56,** 685–690.

ALVARADO, J. and VAN HORN, C. (1975) This volume, pp. 15–43.

ALVARADO, J., STEINACKER, A. and BACH-Y-RITA, P. (1967) The ultrastructure of the retractor bulbi muscle of the cat. *Invest. Ophthal.* **6,** 548.

ANDREW, B. L. and PART, N. J. (1972) Properties of fast and slow motor units in hind limb and tail muscles of the rat. *Quart. J. Exp. Physiol.* **57,** 213–225.

APPELBERG, B. and EMONET-DENAND, F. (1967) Motor units of the first superficial lumbrical muscle of the cat. *J. Neurophysiol.* **30,** 154–160.

APPELBERG, B. and JENESKOG, T. (1972) Mesencephalic fusimotor control. *Exptl Brain Res.* **15,** 97–112.

ASMUSSEN, G., KIESSLING, A. and WOHLRAB, F. (1971) Histochemische Charakterisierung der verschiedenen Muskelfasertypen in den äusseren Augenmuskeln von Säugetieren. *Acta anat.* **79,** 526–545.

BACH-Y-RITA, P. (1971) Neurophysiology of eye movements. In *The Control of Eye Movements*, BACH-Y-RITA, P. and COLLINS, C. C. (Eds.), pp. 7–45. Academic Press, New York and London.

BACH-Y-RITA, P. (1975) This volume, pp. 91–108.

BACH-Y-RITA, P. and COLLINS, C. C. (Eds.) (1971) *The Control of Eye Movements*. Academic Press, New York and London.

BACH-Y-RITA P. and ITO, F. (1965) *In vivo* microelectrode studies of the cat retractor bulbi fibers. *Invest. Ophthal.* **4**, 338–342.

BACH-Y-RITA, P. and ITO, F. (1966) *In vivo* studies on fast and slow muscle fibers in cat extraocular muscles. *J. Gen. Physiol.* **49**, 1177–1198.

BACH-Y-RITA, P., LEVY, J. V. and STEINACKER, A. (1967) The effect of succinylcholine on the isolated retractor bulbi muscle of the cat. *J. Pharm. Pharmac.* **19**, 180–181.

BACH-Y-RITA, P. and MURATA, K. (1964) Extraocular proprioceptive responses in the VI nerve of the cat. *Quart. J. Exptl Physiol.* **49**, 408–416.

BAICHENKO, P. I., MATYUSHKIN, D. P. and SUVOROV, V. V. (1967) Participation of fast and tonic oculomotor systems in stretch reflexes and labyrinthine reflexes of extraocular muscles. *Fiziol. Zh. SSSR*, **53**, 82–90.

BARMACK, N. H., BELL, C. C. and RENCE, B. G. (1971) Tension and rate of tension development during isometric responses of extraocular muscle. *J. Neurophysiol.* **34**, 1072–1079.

BARNARD, R. J., EDGERTON, V. R. and PETER, J. B. (1970) Effect of exercise on skeletal muscle. II. Contractile properties. *J. Appl. Physiol.* **28**, 767–770.

BESSOU, P. and LAPORTE, Y. (1965) Potential fusoriaux provoqués par la stimulation de fibres fusimotrices chez le Chat. *C. R. Acad. Sci., Paris*, **260**, 4827–4830.

BJÖRK, A. and KUGELBERG, E. (1953) The electrical activity of the muscles of the eye and eyelids in various positions and during movement. *Electroen. Clin. Neurophysiol.* **5**, 595–602.

BREININ, G. M. (1971) The structure and function of extraocular muscle—An appraisal of the duality concept. *Am. J. Ophthal.* **72**, 1–9.

BROWN, G. L. and HARVEY, A. M. (1941) Neuro-muscular transmission in the extrinsic muscles of the eye. *J. Physiol. (Lond.)* **99**, 379–399.

BULLER, A. J. and LEWIS, D. M. (1965) The rate of tension development in isometric tetanic contractions of mammalian fast and slow skeletal muscle. *J. Physiol. (Lond.)* **176**, 337–354.

BURKE, R. E. (1967) Motor unit types of cat triceps surae muscle. *J. Physiol. (Lond.)* **193**, 141–160.

BURKE, R. E. (1968a) Group Ia synaptic input to fast and slow twitch motor units of cat triceps surae. *J. Physiol. (Lond.)* **196**, 605–630.

BURKE, R. E. (1968b) Firing patterns of gastrocnemius motor units in the decerebrate cat. *J. Physiol. (Lond.)* **196**, 631–654.

BURKE, R. E. (1973) On the central nervous system control of fast and slow twitch motor units. In: *New Developments in EMG and Clinical Neurophysiology*, vol. 3, DESMEDT, J. E. (Ed.), pp. 69–94. Karger, Basel.

BURKE, R. E., LEVINE, D. N., TSAIRIS, P. and ZAJAC III, F. E. (1973) Physiological types and histochemical profiles in motor units of the cat gastrocnemius. *J. Physiol. (Lond.)* **234**, 723–748.

BURKE, R. E. and TSAIRIS, P. (1973) Anatomy and innervation ratios in motor units of cat gastrocnemius. *J. Physiol. (Lond.)* **234**, 749–765.

BURKE, W. and GINSBORG, B. L. (1956) The electrical properties of the slow muscle fibre membrane. *J. Physiol. (Lond.)* **132**, 586–598.

CLOSE, R. I. and LUFF, A. R. (1974) Dynamic properties of inferior rectus muscle of the rat. *J. Physiol. (Lond.)* **236**, 259–270.

COLLINS, C. C. (1971) Orbital mechanics. In: *The Control of Eye Movements*, BACH-Y-RITA, P. and COLLINS, C. C. (Eds.), pp. 283–325. Academic Press, New York and London.

COLLINS, C. C. (1975) This volume, pp. 145–180.

COLLINS, C. C. and SCOTT, A. B. (1973) The eye movement control signal. *Proc. 2nd Bioengineering Conf., Ophthalmology Sect.*, Milan.

COOPER, S., DANIEL, P. M. and WHITTERIDGE, D. (1955) Muscle spindles and other sensory endings in the extrinsic eye muscles; the physiology and anatomy of these receptors and of their connexions with the brain-stem. *Brain*, **78**, 564–583.

COOPER, S. and ECCLES, J. C. (1930) The isometric responses of mammalian muscles. *J. Physiol. (Lond.)* **69**, 377–385.

DEVANANDAN, M. S., ECCLES, R. M. and WESTERMAN, R. A. (1965) Single motor units of mammalian muscle. *J. Physiol. (Lond.)* **178**, 359–367.

DIETERT, S. C. (1965) The demonstration of different types of muscle fibers in human extraocular muscle by electron microscopy and cholinesterase staining. *Invest. Ophthal.* **4**, 53–63.

DUKE-ELDER, W. S. and DUKE-ELDER, P. M. (1930) The contraction of the extrinsic muscles of the eye by choline and nicotine. *Proc. Roy. Soc. B.* **107**, 332–343.

ECCLES, R. M., PHILLIPS, C. G. and WU, C-P. (1968) Motor innervation, motor unit organization and afferent innervation of m. extensor digitorum communis of the baboon's forearm. *J. Physiol. (Lond.)* **198**, 179–192.

EDSTRÖM, L. and KUGELBERG, E. (1968) Histochemical composition, distribution of fibres and fatiguability of single motor units. *J. Neurol. Neurosurg. Psychiat.* **31**, 424–433.

ERULKAR, S. D., SHELANSKI, M. L., WHITSEL, B. L. and OGLE, P. (1964) Studies of muscle fibers of the tensor tympani of the cat. *Anat. Rec.* **149**, 279–298.

EYZAGUIRRE, C. (1960) The electrical activity of mammalian intrafusal fibers. *J. Physiol. (Lond.)* **150**, 169–185.

FERDINAND, V. S. V. and HESS, A. (1969) The occurrence, structure and innervation of slow and twitch muscle fibres in the tensor tympani and stapedius of the cat. *J. Physiol. (Lond.)* **200**, 547–554.

FLOYD, K. and SMITH, I. C. H. (1971) The mechanical and thermal properties of frog slow muscle fibres. *J. Physiol. (Lond.)* **213**, 617–631.

FUCHS, A. F. and LUSCHEI, E. S. (1970) Firing patterns of abducens neurons of alert monkeys on relationship to horizontal eye movement. *J. Neurophysiol.* **33**, 382–392.

FUCHS, A. F. and LUSCHEI, E. S. (1971a) The activity of single trochlear nerve fibers during eye movements in the alert monkey. *Exptl Brain Res.* **13**, 78–89.

FUCHS, A. F. and LUSCHEI, E. S. (1971b) Development of isometric tension in simian extraocular muscle. *J. Physiol. (Lond.)* **219**, 155–166.

GINSBORG, B. L. (1960a) Spontaneous activity in muscle fibres of the chick. *J. Physiol. (Lond.)* **150**, 707–717.

GINSBORG, B. L. (1960b) Some properties of avian skeletal muscle fibres with multiple neuromuscular junctions. *J. Physiol. (Lond.)* **154**, 582–598.

GOLDBERG, S. and LENNERSTRAND, G. (1974) Motor effects of intracellular stimulation of abducens neurons. To be published.

GRANIT, R. (1970) *The Basis of Motor Control*, Academic Press, New York and London.

GRANIT, R. and BURKE, R. E. (1973) The control of movement and posture. *Brain Res.* **53**, 1–28.

GRIMBY, L. and HANNERZ, J. (1973) Tonic and phasic recruitment order of motor units in man under normal and pathological conditions. In: *New Developments in EMG and Clinical Neurophysiology*, DESMEDT, J. E. (Ed.), pp. 225–233. Karger, Basel.

HANNERZ, J. (1974) Discharge properties of motor units in relation to recruitment order in voluntary contraction. *Acta physiol. scand.* **91**, 374–384.

HARKER, D. W. (1972) The structure and innervation of sheep superior rectus and levator palpebrae extraocular muscles. I. Extrafusal muscle fibers. *Invest. Ophthal.* **11**, 956–969.

HENN, V. and COHEN, B. (1972) Eye muscle motor neurons with different functional characteristics. *Brain Res.* **45**, 561–568.

HENN, V. and COHEN, B. (1973) Quantitative analysis of activity in eye muscle motoneurons during saccadic eye movements and positions of fixation. *J. Neurophysiol.* **36**, 115–126.

HENNEMAN, E. and OLSON, C. B. (1965) Relations between structure and function in the design of skeletal muscles. *J. Neurophysiol.* **28**, 581–598.

HENNEMAN, E., SOMJEN, G. and CARPENTER, D. O. (1965) Excitability and inhibitibility of motoneurons of different sizes. *J. Neurophysiol.* **28**, 599–620.

HESS, A. (1961) The structure of slow and fast extrafusal muscle fibers in the extraocular muscles and their nerve endings in guinea pigs. *J. Cell. Comp. Physiol.* **58**, 63–80.

HESS, A. (1970) Vertebrate slow muscle fibers. *Physiol. Rev.* **50**, 40–62.

HESS, A. and PILAR, G. (1963) Slow fibers in the extraocular muscles of the cat. *J. Physiol. (Lond.)* **169**, 780–797.

JAMPEL, R. S. (1967) Multiple motor systems in the extraocular muscles of man. *Invest. Ophthal.* **6**, 288–293.

JARCHO, L. W., EYZAGUIRRE, C., BERMAN, B. and LILIENTHAL, J. L., JR. (1952) Spread of excitation in skeletal muscle: some factors contributing to the form of the electromyogram. *Am. J. Physiol.* **168**, 446–457.

KATO, T. (1938) Über histologische Untersuchungen der Augenmuskeln von Menschen und Säugetieren. *Okajimas Folia anat. Jap.* **16**, 131–145.

KATZ, B. and MILEDI, R. (1965) Propagation of electric activity in motor nerve terminals. *Proc. Roy. Soc.*, B, **161**, 453–482.

KELLER, E. L. and ROBINSON, D. A. (1971) Absence of a stretch reflex in extraocular muscles of the monkey. *J. Neurophysiol.* **34**, 908–919.

KELLER, E. L. and ROBINSON, D. A. (1972) Abducens unit behavior in the monkey during vergence movements. *Vision Res.* **12**, 369–382.

KERN, R. (1965) A comparative pharmacologic–histologic study of slow and twitch fibers in the superior rectus muscle of the rabbit. *Invest. Ophthal.* **4**, 901–910.

KEY-ÅBERG, H. (1934) Beitrag zur Kenntnis der Anatomie und Physiologie des Musculus Retractor Bulbi beim Kaninchen. *Svenska Läkaresällskapets Handlingar*, **60**, 117–148.

KOKETSU, K. and NISHI, S. (1957a) Action potentials of single intrafusal muscle fibres of frogs. *J. Physiol. (Lond.)* **137**, 193–209.

KOKETSU, K. and NISHI, S. (1957b) An analysis of junctional potentials of intrafusal muscle fibres in frogs. *J. Physiol. (Lond.)* **139**, 15–26.

KUFFLER, S. W. and VAUGHAN WILLIAMS, E. M. (1953a) Small-nerve junctional potentials. The distribution of small motor nerves to frog skeletal muscle, and the membrane characteristics of the fibres they innervate. *J. Physiol. (Lond.)* **121,** 289–317.

KUFFLER, S. W. and VAUGHAN WILLIAMS, E. M. (1953b) Properties of the "slow" skeletal muscle fibres of the frog. *J. Physiol. (Lond.)* **121,** 318–340.

KUGELBERG, E. (1973) Histochemical composition, contraction speed and fatiguability of rat soleus motor units. *J. Neurol. Sci.* **20,** 177–198.

KUGELBERG, E. (1975) This volume, pp. 85–90.

LÄNNERGREN, J. (1975) This volume, pp. 63–84.

LENNERSTRAND, G. (1972) Fast and slow units in extrinsic eye muscles of cat. *Acta physiol. scand.* **86,** 286–288.

LENNERSTRAND, G. (1974a) Mechanical studies on the retractor bulbi muscle and its motor units in the cat. *J. Physiol. (Lond.)* **236,** 43–55.

LENNERSTRAND, G. (1974b) Electrical activity and isometric tension in motor units of the cat's inferior oblique muscles. *Acta physiol. scand.* **91,** 458–474.

McCOUCH, G. P. and ADLER, F. H. (1932) Extraocula reflexes. *Am. J. Physiol.* **100,** 78–88.

McINTYRE, A. K. (1939) The quick component of nystagmus. *J. Physiol. (Lond.)* **97,** 8–16.

McPHEDRAN, A. M., WUERKER, R. B. and HENNEMAN, E. (1965) Properties of motor units in a homogeneous red muscle (soleus) of the cat. *J. Neurophysiol.* **28,** 71–84.

MATYUSHKIN, D. P. (1961) Phasic and tonic neuromotor units in the oculomotor apparatus of the rabbit. *Fiziol. zh. SSSR,* **47,** 878–883.

MATYUSHKIN, D. P. (1964a) Varieties of tonic muscle fibers in the oculomotor apparatus of the rabbit. *Bull. Exptl Biol. Med.* **55,** 235–238.

MATYUSHKIN, D. P. (1964b) Motor systems in the oculomotor apparatus of higher animals. *Fed. Proc.* **23,** T1103–1106.

MATYUSHKIN, D. P. (1972) Glasodvigatelnii apparat mlekopitayushich. *Isdatectvo "Meditsina",* Leningrad, pp. 1–180.

MATYUSHKIN, D. P. and DRABKINA, T. M. (1970) Electrophysiological characteristics of tonic fibers of the extrinsic ocular muscles. *Fiziol. zh. SSSR,* **56,** 563–569.

MAYR, R. (1971) Structure and distribution of fiber types in the external eye muscles of the rat. *Tissue & Cell,* **3,** 433–462.

MAYR, R. (1975) This volume, pp. 43–45.

MENDELL, L. M. and HENNEMAN, E. (1971) Terminals of single Ia fibers: location, density, and distribution within a pool of 300 homonymous motoneurons. *J. Neurophysiol.* **34,** 171–187.

MILNER-BROWN, H. S., STEIN, R. B. and YEMM, R. (1973) The contractile properties of human motor units during voluntary isometric contractions. *J. Physiol. (Lond.)* **228,** 285–306.

MOTAIS, E. (1885) Recherches sur l'anatomie humaine e l'anatomie comparee de l'appareil moteur de l'oeil (Part 3). *Archs. Ophthal, Paris,* pp. 143–158.

NEMET, P. and MILLER, J. E. (1968) Evoked potentials in cat extraocular muscle. *Invest. Ophthal.* **7,** 592–598.

OLSON, C. B., CARPENTER, D. O. and HENNEMAN, E. (1968) Orderly recruitment of muscle action potentials. *Arch. Neurol.* **19,** 591–597.

ORKAND, R. K. (1963) A further study of electrical responses in slow and twitch muscle fibres of the frog. *J. Physiol. (Lond.)* **167,** 181–191.

OZAWA, T. (1964) Some electrophysiological properties of rabbit extraocular muscle recorded *in vivo* with intracellular electrode. *Jap. J. Ophthal.* **8,** 111–115.

OZAWA, T., CHENG-MINODA, K., DAVIDOWITZ, J. and BREININ, G. M. (1969) Correlation of potential and fiber type in extraocular muscle. *Documenta ophthal.* **26,** 192–201.

PEACHEY, L. D. (1968) Muscle. *Ann. Rev. Physiol.* **30,** 401–440.

PEACHEY, L. (1971) The structure of the extraocular muscle fibers of mammals. In: *The Control of Eye Movements,* BACH-Y-RITA, P. and COLLINS, C. C. (Eds.), pp. 47–66. Academic Press, New York and London.

PILAR, G. (1967) Further study of the electrical and mechanical responses of slow fibers in cat extraocular muscles. *J. Gen. Physiol.* **50,** 2289–2300.

ROBINSON, D. A. (1968) The oculomotor control system: a review. *Proc. IEEE,* **56,** 1032–1049.

ROBINSON, D. A. (1970) Oculomotor unit behavior in the monkey. *J. Neurophysiol.* **33,** 393–404.

SCHILLER, P. H. (1970) The discharge characteristics of single units in the oculomotor and abducens nuclei of the unanesthetized monkey. *Exptl Brain Res.* **10,** 347–362.

SCOTT, A. B. (1971) Extraocular muscle forces in strabismus. In: *The Control of Eye Movements,* BACH-Y-RITA, P. and COLLINS, C. C. (Eds.), pp. 327–342. Academic Press, New York and London.

SCOTT, A. B. and COLLINS, C. C. (1973) Division of labor in human extraocular muscle. *Arch. Ophthal.* **90,** 319–322.

SHERRINGTON, C. S. (1925) Remarks on some aspects of reflex inhibition. *Proc. Roy. Soc.,* B, **97,** 519–545.

SIEBECK, R. and KRÜGER, P. (1955) Die histologische Struktur der äusseren Augenmuskeln als Ausdruck ihrer Funktion. *Albrecht v. Graefes Arch. Ophthal.* **156,** 637–652.

SKAVENSKI, A. A. and ROBINSON, D. A. (1973) Role of abducens neurons in vestibuloocular reflex. *J. Neurophysiol.* **36,** 724–738.

SMITH, R. S. (1964) Activity of intrafusal muscle fibres in muscle spindles of *Xenopus laevis. Acta physiol. scand.* **60,** 223–239.

STEG, G. (1964) Efferent muscle innervation and rigidity. *Acta physiol. scand.* **61,** Suppl. 225.

STEINACKER, A. and BACH-Y-RITA, P. (1968a) A mechanical study of the cat retractor bulbi muscle. *Experientia,* **24,** 1138–1139.

STEINACKER, A. and BACH-Y-RITA, P. (1968b) The fiber spectrum of the cat VI nerve to the lateral rectus and retractor bulbi muscles. *Experientia,* **24,** 1254–1255.

TEIG, E. (1972) Tension and contraction time of motor units of the middle ear muscles in the cat. *Acta physiol. scand.* **84,** 11–21.

TORRE, M. (1953) Nombre et dimensions des unités motrices dans les muscles extrinsiques de l'oeil et, en général, dans les muscles squélettiques reliés à des organes de sens. *Schweizer Arch. Neurol. Psychiat.* **72,** 362–376.

VILIS, T. (1973) Mechanical properties of the extraocular muscles of the cat. Ph.D. Thesis, McGill University, Montreal.

WALLS, G. L. (1962) The evolutionary history of eye movements. *Vision Res.* **2,** 69–80.

WOOTEN, G. F. and REIS, D. J. (1972) Blood flow in extraocular muscle of cat. *Arch. Neurol.* **26,** 350–352.

WUERKER, R. B., McPHEDRAN, A. M. and HENNEMAN, E. (1965) Properties of motor units in a heterogeneous pale muscle (m. gastrocnemius) of the cat. *J. Neurophysiol.* **28,** 85–99.

YAMANAKA, Y. and BACH-Y-RITA, P. (1968) Conduction velocities in the abducens nerve correlated with vestibular nystagmus in cats. *Exptl Neurol.* **20,** 143–155.

ZENKER, W. and ANZENBACHER, H. (1964) On the different forms of myo-neural junction in two types of muscle fiber from the external ocular muscles of the Rhesus monkey. *J. Cell. Comp. Physiol.* **63,** 273–285.

THE HUMAN OCULOMOTOR CONTROL SYSTEM†

Carter Compton Collins

INTRODUCTION

A number of the neural and mechanical factors determining human eye movements have been inaccessible to direct measurement in the past. Gross electromyography (Jampolsky, 1970; Scott, 1968) and single motor unit recordings (Marg *et al.*, 1962; Scott and Collins, 1973) have been the traditional human neurophysiological metric. More recently a quantitatively accurate description of the human eye movement control signal has become available (Collins and Scott, 1973) to be reviewed below. Similarly, oculorotary muscle forces have long been measured indirectly in human subjects by means of a suction contact lens (Robinson, 1964), and lately by means of force transducing eye forceps (Scott *et al.*, 1972). Isometric oculorotary muscle forces have been measured during strabismus surgery (Robinson *et al.* 1969; Collins *et al.*, 1969). Recently continuous, *in vivo*, records of dynamic muscle forces have been obtained during voluntary, unrestricted, natural eye movements (Collins *et al.*, 1972 and 1975 in press).

For a number of years we have addressed ourselves to the problems of strabismus by focusing our attention on the peripheral neuromechanical oculomotor plant and some of the mechanisms of its control. Figure 1 represents a global model summarizing a number of observations on the oculomotor control system and will serve as a road map to indicate the region in which we have been working.

In this model the difference between fovea and target position, ϵ, represents a monocular retinal input to the CNS. The version command signal is taken from one eye or the other by means of the "or" logic block or is derived as the average retinal disparity by means of the summing element. Actually the system is more complex in that parts of the scene from each eye can apparently form a patchwork making it difficult to determine in fact which eye is responsible for control at any given time.

The retinal disparity signals are then operated upon by the higher control processes for fixation, following, saccadic or vergence eye movements. It is then assumed that phase inversion of the processed oculomotor control signal occurs at the supranuclear level resulting in reciprocal innervation of the yoked eye muscles in version. Separate operation of a higher, vergence phase inverter results in both medial rectus muscles contracting simultaneously, thereby producing convergence movements of the eyes.

†This investigation was supported by NIH research grants Nos. P01 EY-01186, P01 EY-00299 and P01 EY-00498 from the National Eye Institute; No. S01 RR-05566 from the Division of Research Resources, and the Smith-Kettlewell Eye Research Foundation.

145

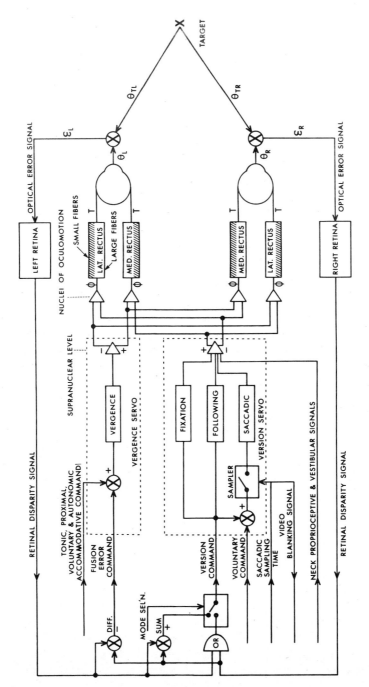

THE BINOCULAR CONTROL SYSTEM

FIG. 1. Holistic model of the human oculomotor control system.

In the area of our current involvement, muscle innervation is labeled ϕ, the resultant muscle tension, T, and I will describe techniques for measuring both *in situ*. The difference between these two tendon forces results in the driving torque which rotates the eye, thus completing the control loop.

In this chapter I will briefly review some of our recent findings in human oculomotion (Scott and Collins, 1973; Collins and Scott, 1973; Collins *et al.*, 1975 in press) and attempt to fit them into a peripheral mechanical model of the human oculomotor control system. Any description or model of the control of eye movements must incorporate both the input and output of the muscle system. The first section below will present recent data on the input control signal, obtained by multiple EMG recordings of single motor units from both large and small muscle fibers in the oculorotary muscles. This will be followed by presentation of material on the output of the muscles in terms of force or tension measured at the muscle tendon. These data, combined with previously established evidence on other components of the oculomotor system, will be utilized in formulating a model of the human eye-movement system which, it is hoped, may be of value in quantitatively assessing pathological deficits of ocular motility and as a possible aid in planning surgery.

THE INPUT SIGNAL AND CONTROL STRATEGIES

To determine the control strategies I have found it necessary to devise a means of measuring the differential innervation of human oculorotary muscles during various types of eye movements. Since there is a one-to-one correspondence of nerve fiber to muscle motor unit, one can effectively sample the activity in a cross-section of human III, IV or VI nerve by monitoring the activity of a large, statistically valid sample of single motor units in an extraocular muscle. This has been done by deploying ten pairs of 25 μm bipolar electrodes every 500 μm down the shaft of a number 30 hypodermic needle inserted obliquely into the muscle (Fig. 2A). Each bipolar electrode pair employed a 25 μm electrode spacing and displayed a recording radius of some 25 μm. This permitted each electrode pair to record up to five single motor units 20 μm in diameter. Thus with ten electrode pairs up to fifty single units could be simultaneously sampled (Collins and Scott, 1973).

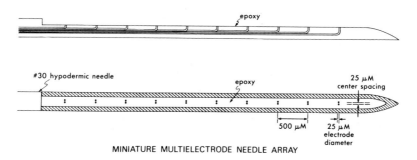

FIG. 2A. Drawing of the 10 pair multiple electrode array assembled in a No. 30 hypodermic needle. A very flexible 20-conductor miniature cable is attached to the needle electrode to isolate external forces from the point of insertion in the muscle.

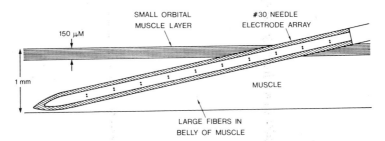

FIG. 2B. Needle electrode array inserted at a shallow angle in order to increase the probability and number of samples from the thin orbital layer.

Innervation data was collected from three informed strabismus patients and one normal, paid volunteer. The needle electrode array was inserted by Dr. Alan Scott into a muscle at an acute angle (approx. 15°) in order to permit more electrodes to sample the very thin (100–200 μm) outer (oribtal) layer of small (slow twitch) fibers (Fig. 2B). Insertion was stopped just as the next to last electrodes picked up a signal and the last electrode pair (closer to the needle hub) was silent. By this means it was known that the next to last electrodes were sampling activity from the small, outer fibers. The remaining electrodes closer to the tip of the needle were then sampling EMG activity from the predominantly large, fast twitch fibers deeper in the central belly or global regions of the muscle.

Figure 3 is a block diagram of the recording and automatic data reduction equipment utilized to individually count and plot single EMG spike recurrence frequencies from the small and large muscle fiber populations respectively.

The innervation signal has been monitored as the subject directed his gaze at a number of preselected targets. The targets were electronically controlled in order to elicit fixation throughout the entire range of eye movements as well as to induce small and large refixation saccades, constant velocity following movements, and asymmetrical fusional and accommodative vergence.

A typical record obtained in these studies is shown in Figure 4 for two fixations and a saccade. At the bottom, six channels of filter-enhanced EMG spike records are shown, the top two from small outer fibers and the bottom four from large inner fibers. Above these are the processed frequencies representing separate control signals of the large and small fibers and their sum, the combined control signal of the muscle as a function of time, $\phi(t)$.

1. Fixation

By recording the electrical activity of both large and small muscle fibers at different positions of fixated gaze and compilation of records such as those of Fig. 4, one can determine the relative contribution of each fiber type at the different positions. Such data are graphically summarized in Fig. 5, in which firing rates are expressed in terms of maximum saccadic activity. It is evident that the large fibers (dashed curve, triangles) are essentially inactive outside the muscle's field of action, then assume an increasing role as the muscle approaches its maximum action (45°R or more).

Their frequency of 200/sec during extreme gaze fixation is about half their maximum capability in saccades. In contrast, the small fibers are active even at extreme gaze outside the field of action, increasing their activity nonlinearly as the eye fixates more and more into its field of action, with maximal discharge frequency at extreme gaze into the field of action.

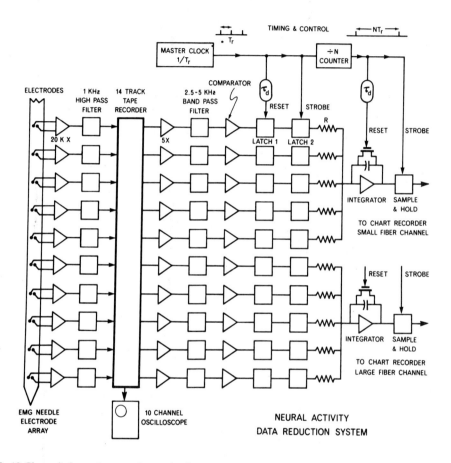

FIG. 3. 10-Channel electrode array data reduction system. The EMG spike information from the 10-channel EMG electrode array is passed in parallel through ten preamplifiers (with gains of up to 20,000) which are automatically set during the first second of the experiment such that the maximum spike amplitudes do not saturate any amplifier. Single unit activity signal-to-noise ratio is enhanced by a 1-kHz high pass filter before recording on analog tape. A gain of 5× during playback makes up losses in the 2.5- to 5-kHz bandpass filter which enhances single unit spike activity. Events selected above threshold of the amplitude comparator trip latch 1 which is loaded into latch 2, typically every 250 μs. The standard output of latch 2 is strobed into the summing node of the channel integrator through resistor R. Every 5 ms the integrated value is strobed into the sample and hold and the integrator reset. Any combination of electrodes can constitute small or large fiber channels. The usual type of EMG integrator suffers from the shortcomings of: (1) a long decay time constant which obscures a rapid rate of decrease of EMG activity and in fact obliterates any fine structure of neural activity lying in the shadow of the long decay time constant; (2) an output which is distorted by the various widths of the individual motor unit spike impulses and thus does not accurately reflect solely the frequency of EMG activity. This digital data reduction system obviates these difficulties.

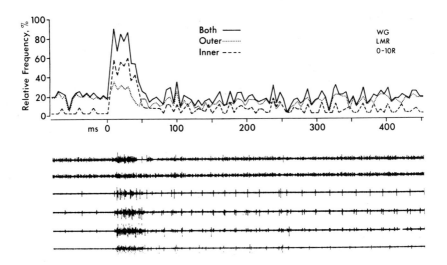

FIG. 4. *Bottom*. A record from six channels of the multiple electrode array. The top two channels are recording from the superficial, small, orbital fibers and the bottom four channels are recording from the predominantly large fibers deeper in the central part of the muscle. *Top*. The instantaneous frequencies of activity of both the large and small fibers and the total muscle activity corresponding to the bottom EMG single-unit records. These represent the eye movement control signal for a 10° "on" saccade.

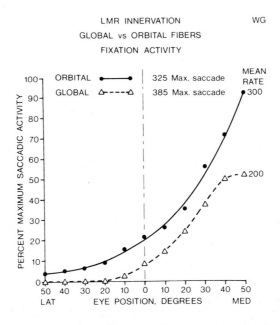

FIG. 5. A quantitative representation of the relative contributions of the large and small oculorotary muscle fibers to fixation and slow tracking movements. It can be seen that the small fibers contribute the greater activity during fixation, progressively increasing their activity across the entire gamut of eye positions. The large fibers appear to saturate at extreme gaze fixation which suggests that they may be fatiguing.

In Fig. 5 it appears that innervation to the central, deeper fibers saturates at extreme gaze fixation in the "on" position. In fixation the CNS utilizes an eye-movement control strategy with a ratio of large to small fiber activity which varies from zero:one (out of the muscle's field of action) to a ratio of one:one at extreme gaze into the field of action (considering that there are twice as many large fibers as small).

The nonlinear relationship of innervation to eye position, $\phi(\theta)$, results from the combination of the outputs of the separate small and large fiber control systems seen in Fig. 5. It will be noted that the shape of the innervation amplitude as a function of eye position is a power function, predominantly parabolic. This observation can be readily understood on the basis of the reported pattern of delayed recruitment of individual fibers as a function of eye position. Since individual fibers are recruited at different points in gaze position (Scott and Collins, 1973; Keller and Robinson, 1972), the total activity of the entire muscle fiber group will summate to yield a progressively increasing curve which experimentally appears essentially parabolic.

The brain thus utilizes a nonlinear pattern of total innervation to the oculorotary muscles as a function of static eye position or fixation, which in terms of muscle force appears as a square-law function. These muscles anatomically function in a reciprocal, class A "push–pull" mode aiding each other. As is well known (Electronic Engineering Staff, MIT, 1943), this mode of operation inherently cancels even harmonic or square-law deviations. This results in a linear static muscle force difference acting on the predominantly linear globe-restraining elasticity (Robinson et al., 1969) while the intermediate individual muscle forces are still grossly nonlinear. Although a small amount of nonlinearity occurs in the globe-restraining tissues at extreme gaze, by far the major nonlinear load on an oculorotary muscle is its opposing nonlinearly innervated antagonist muscle. The detailed nature of the innervation is most important since the muscle viscosity, constituting the major load during saccades, is apparently dependent on contractile element tension developed in proportion to innervation (Hill, 1938; Cook and Stark, 1967; Collins, 1971).

In the static case of fixation, a muscle normally acts as an agonist within its own field of action and therefore its opposing mate can be called an antagonist. It will be noted from Fig. 5 that during fixation our preliminary records show that the small fibers exhibit considerable activity outside of the field of action of the muscle (muscle stretched beyond its primary length). This small fiber activity could be called antagonistic but also appears to serve a tonic function, keeping the muscles on the stretch at all eye positions, thereby removing muscle slack. This permits the oculomotor control system to operate in the linear region of the length–tension characteristics of the muscle at all times (during waking hours).

2. Following Movements

The innervation and force measurements during unrestricted eye movements are quite similar for fixation and slow following movements. There is a slight increase in innervation during following movements to overcome muscle viscosity (and hysteresis). The control strategy for following movements also employs a large to small fiber innervation ratio of from zero:one to one:one; recordings during following movements can also be summarized graphically, and follow the pattern seen in Fig. 5.

3. Saccades

The control mechanism for saccadic eye movements is entirely different from fixation and following movements. Figure 4 shows the nature of the saccadic innervation or input control signal for an agonist muscle. Both large and small fibers are turned on maximally during the first portion of the saccade and decay logarithmically to their new equilibrium value with a time constant of about one-half the saccadic duration (Collins and Scott, 1973). The rise time of the saccadic innervation is about 10 ms.

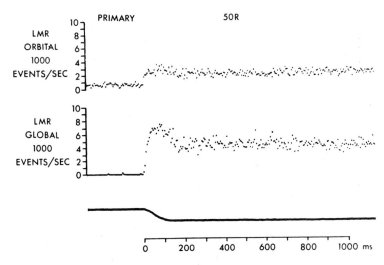

FIG. 6. A typical record of the differential, single unit activity of the outer, orbital fibers and the central or global oculorotary muscle fibers during a primary to 50° right "on" saccade. This record is plotted directly from the electronic data reduction system of Fig. 3.

Figure 6 is a typical recording of the firing frequencies of the orbital and central fibers during a 50° saccade. In this case there is essentially no overshoot in the innervation time course of the orbital fibers since they remain maximally innervated during extreme gaze fixation. However, it can be seen that the central, or global fibers, are maximally innervated during the saccade but decay to about half their saturation value in maintaining the extreme gaze, 50° "on" position. Thus, most of the overshoot activity during saccades is contributed by the large fibers, particularly near extreme gaze.

Figure 7A illustrates the relative amplitude and shape of the innervation signal to the central fibers during a number of different-sized "on" saccades starting from the primary position. (These are hand traced to eliminate sampling noise and to indicate the mean waveshape of a num'er of similar saccades.) It will be noted that both the amplitude and duration of the saccadic innervation signal of the central fibers increases with the magnitude of the saccade.

Figure 7B shows the relationship of the saccadic peak innervation amplitude and duration of these central (global) fibers as a function of the saccadic magnitude. The innervation amplitude increases rapidly at first, and then saturates for very large saccades, following a logarithmic relationship. The saccadic duration, on the other hand,

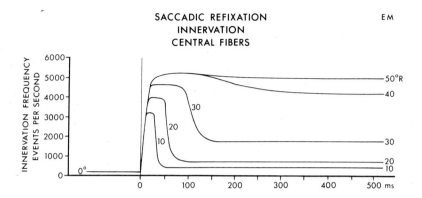

FIG. 7A. The time-varying pattern of summated firing frequencies of the central or global fibers for a number of "on" saccades from the primary position. These pulse shapes represent the agonist oculomotor control signal for saccadic refixation. The antagonist control signal drops to zero for the entire saccadic duration and returns to the new refixation level with a 2-ms time constant.

increases slowly at first and more rapidly for larger saccades, following a power function.

The energy under the saccadic innervation pulse can be expressed as the product of amplitude times duration. From the graph of Fig. 7B this product very closely follows a square law:

$$A \times D = a(\Delta\theta)^2.$$

Thus, it appears that the innervational energy required to move the eye to a given position is proportional to the force required to hold it there (from Figs. 5 and 7C).

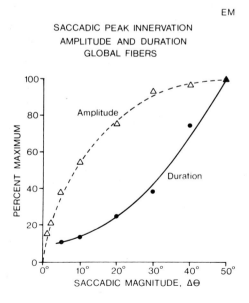

FIG. 7B. The pattern of variation of the amplitude and duration of the saccadic burst of innervation to the agonist as a function of the size of a saccade starting from primary position.

Figure 7C compares saccadic peak innervation activity of the large, central fibers with their fixation activity. It will be noted that the difference between the two increases up to about 20° saccadic amplitude and then decreases once again.

Figure 8 is a recording of the differential activity of the orbital and central fibers for a series of 10° saccades. Here again one can see the division of activity between the two types of fibers both during saccades and during fixation. It will be noted that out of the field of action the large, central fibers contribute predominantly to saccadic innervation, but contribute very little towards holding the eye in fixation.

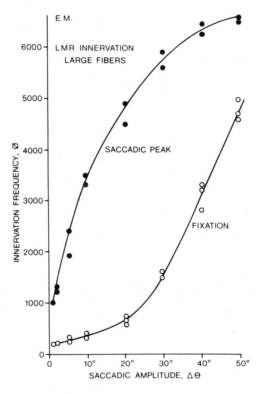

FIG. 7C. A comparison of saccadic peak activity in an agonist oculorotary muscle with the corresponding final steady state activity during fixation.

The smaller, orbital fibers, on the other hand, are active far out of the field of action of the muscle during fixation but contribute less to saccades than do the central fibers.

Supporting this finding, Yamanaka and Bach-y-Rita (1968) report that slow nerve fibers are active during both the slow and fast phases of nystagmus in the cat. Fast nerve fibers are active during the fast phase of nystagmus and towards the latter portion of the slow phase. Although both fiber types contribute to some portion of each type of movement, fast fibers appear to be active principally during phasic movements and slow fibers during tonic activity.

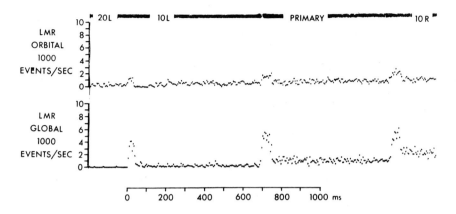

FIG. 8. A recording of the motor unit activity of the small, orbital fibers and predominantly large, central and global fibers of an agonist oculorotary muscle during a series of 10° "on" saccades.

It will be noted in Fig. 8 that the duration of saccadic activity is essentially constant for all of these 10° saccades regardless of the initial position of the eye. However, as indicated in Fig. 9, the amplitude of the saccadic activity and the magnitude of the saccadic overshoot as well as the shape of the saccadic innervational impulses are clearly dependent upon eye position.

Figure 10 shows that the proportion of active orbital and central fibers for these 10° saccades is dependent on the final resting position of the eye, the end point of the saccade. Here again, whether measured from the initial or the final eye position, the peak saccadic overshoot pulse amplitude is maximum at about 20° into the field of action of the muscle. The ratio of central to orbital fiber activity during the saccadic burst dips to a value of approximately 1.4 at primary position, building up to a value of approximately 2.5 at both extreme gaze positions.

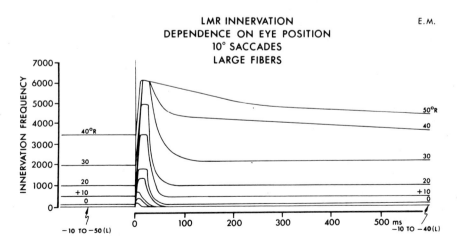

FIG. 9. The pattern of innervation activity as a function of eye position for the complete range of 10° "on" saccades from 50° left to 50° right.

It will be noted from Fig. 10 that the orbital fiber contribution does not change rapidly outside of the field of action of the muscle, in contrast to the rapidly increasing contribution of the deeper fibers. However, in the field of action of the muscle the smaller, outer fibers are increasing their contribution rapidly where the deeper fiber activity saturates and changes very little.

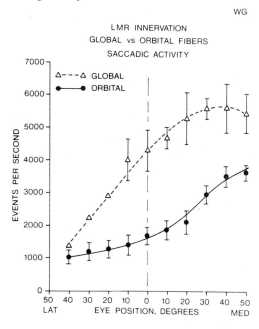

FIG. 10. A comparison of the peak saccadic activity level of the orbital and central (or global) oculorotary muscle fibers as a function of the final eye position for a complete series of 10° "on" saccades. Mean values and standard deviations of the measurements of several saccades at each eye position are shown.

When attempting to define the transfer function of the static oculomotor control system, that is, the fixation innervation as a function of eye position, we find, as illustrated in Fig. 11A, that the innervation level depends upon the direction of approach to that position. At 30° within the field of action of the muscle, there is a two to one ratio of firing rates depending on whether the muscle is acting as an agonist or antagonist. This phenomenon can be described by the term "anti-hysteresis", since the frequency of neural activity *leads* the desired eye position. (Normally, hysteresis is defined as the quality of a phenomenon *lagging* its input.) This finding of hysteresis in human oculorotary muscle innervation confirms previous findings in recording from monkey oculomotor nuclei (Eckmiller, this Symposium.)

It is noteworthy that these characteristics of human neural anti-hysteresis match the mechanical length-tension characteristics of oculorotary muscle as shown in Fig. 11B. The upper curve represents the muscle being stretched to a longer length; the lower curve represents the tension measured as the muscle was allowed to relax to a shorter length. This mechanical characteristic of muscle also exhibits anti-hysteresis since the curve progresses in a clockwise direction, not in the usual counterclockwise direction observed with the common forms of physical hysteresis, backlash, or "dead zone". In this instance, innervation matches and essentially compensates for the mechanical anti-hysteresis of the muscle. When more force is needed to extend an antagonist muscle, more innervation is supplied to the agonist. When less force is needed in permitting the antagonist to become shorter, the agonist is innervated correspondingly less. Thus it appears that this CNS control strategy represents one more jewel in the crown of the master designer.

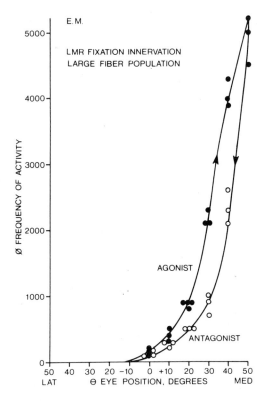

FIG. 11A. A static transfer function of the CNS controlling eye fixation. This is a plot of the large, central fiber population innervation level as a function of the desired eye position. Note the large anti-hysteresis in this control system.

A brief return to the holistic road map of Fig. 1 will serve to review that the above discussion has been of the innervation, ϕ, of the oculorotary muscles. The next section will discuss measurements of tension, T, in the muscle.

MUSCLE FORCES

Only recently have we been able to measure the actual *in vivo* forces resulting from the voluntary innervation of human oculorotary muscles during normal, unimpeded eye movements (Collins *et al.*, 1972 and 1975). The static tension required to maintain fixation at any point of eccentric gaze as well as the dynamic tension patterns responsible for saccadic and following eye movements can now be monitored *in situ* in both the agonist and antagonist muscles simultaneously. These data should prove useful for improving models of the oculomotor system, and particularly for assessing pathological factors relating to strabismus and other oculomotor deficits.

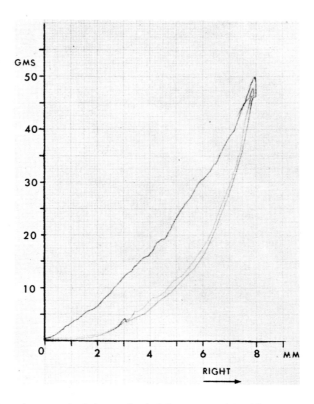

FIG. 11B. A length-tension record of the mechanical force measured while pulling and then releasing a human oculorotary muscle at surgery. The patient was fixing at primary gaze with the unoperated eye.

In order to make these measurements I have found it necessary to devise a special small force transducer. These transducers have been implanted in series with the oculoro-tary muscle tendons and the globe by Dr. Alan Scott during the course of required corrective surgery for strabismus under topical anesthesia. The miniature force trans-ducers consist of an aluminum ring 2 mm in diameter split to form a "C" with suture holes near the slit. A foil strain gauge is cemented to the "C" opposite the slit; flexible insulated No. 36 copper-wire leads are attached and the whole unit is coated with waterproof varnish and baked. Finally, each gauge is dipped in a soft wax coating for further water resistance. "C" gauges maintain a typical sensitivity of 25 μV per gram of applied tension through the entire surgical procedure. The zero point is checked periodically to compensate for small zero drifts which may occur in the transducer or bridge amplifier.

Recordings of muscle tension, eye position (EOG), and the target position (which serves as a self calibration for the EOG) are made on a 14-track tape-recorder and the data is analyzed off-line.

Our tension data has been collected from five informed patients with nonparalytic comitant strabismus. Minimum *in situ* tensions recorded ranged from 8 to 12 g at 15° out of the muscle's field of action and maximum tensions ranged from 28 to 44 g during maximum contraction 45° into the muscle's field of action. Despite the variation between subjects (possibly related to the strabismic conditions) we observe consistent patterns of force during fixation, following and saccadic movements.

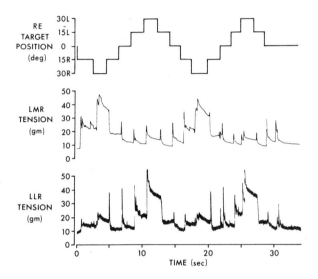

FIG. 12. *In situ* tendon force records with implanted "C" gauge showing reciprocal nature of medial and lateral rectus muscle activity during natural, free and unrestrained eye movements as the eye saccadically refixates the target indicated in the top trace.

1. Fixation

Figure 12 is a typical record of unrestrained medial and lateral rectus muscle tensions, recorded from a patient with 30-prism diopters intermittent exotropia as he performed a series of saccadic refixations. While the reciprocal nature of the force pattern is clearly evident, it will be noted that the tension in the antagonist begins to rise in extreme gaze out of its field of action. Also an unexpected small initial saccadic over-shoot of tension is seen in the antagonist.

It is of interest to compare the reciprocal nature of isometric forces and unrestrained muscle forces by plotting the medial versus lateral rectus muscle forces during fixation across the range of eye positions as shown in Fig. 13. In this figure of isometric forces were measured at primary muscle length (dashed curve) and exhibit a reciprocal, hyperbolic relationship. The solid curve shows that agonist tension due to normal, unrestricted muscle shortening in a freely moving eye is less than in the isometric case. The increased tension in the antagonist is due to passive stretching by the agonist. The shape of this curve is described by a square-law relationship (parabola rotated 45°) more closely than by the reciprocal, hyperbolic relationship observed isometrically. To properly describe the oculomotor control system, a useful mechanical model must match these natural, unrestrained, steady-state eye position–tension relationships.

Previous studies of muscle forces have been largely restricted to measurements of isometric forces during surgery. These can be plotted as a family of length–tension curves shown as dashed lines in Fig. 14A. From these curves one can derive the tension required to hold the eye in fixation at any position of gaze. The resulting static locus of fixation forces is a parabola with its minimum value occurring at 15° out of the field of action of the muscle, as seen in the figure.

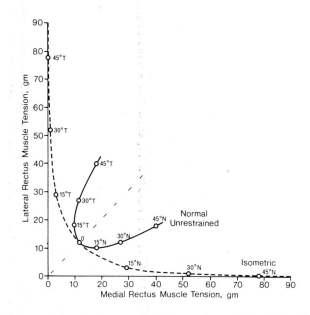

FIG. 13. Reciprocal nature of the simultaneous static isometric medial and lateral rectus muscle forces (plotted one against the other) associated with fixation of the eye at any point of lateral gaze (dashed line). The solid line plots the actual tendon forces measured in each muscle of the antagonistic pair when the eye is free to rotate in its normal unrestricted state. Points above the 45° dashed line represent the LR as an agonist while the LR is an antagonist in points below.

One can define a transfer function relating isometric muscle force to its corresponding innervation (i.e. to the contralateral eye position) as: $F = m(\theta + 50°)^2$ as seen in Fig. 14B. The constant factor, m, assumes an individual value for each person measured (0.011 for the subject data shown). This square-law relationship is closely followed over the entire range of 100 degrees of eye fixation. There also appears a negligible (less than $\pm 5\%$) residual anti-hysteresis as isometric muscle force is measured first with innervation increasing and then with decreasing levels of innervation.

2. Following Movements

Figure 15 is a record of *in vivo*, muscle forces measured during unrestrained following movements at 10°/sec between primary position and extreme gaze positions (cf. legend). Note that the parabolic nature of this curve confirms the calculated fixation values of the static locus in Fig. 14A. Following movements generally require only a small increment of tension greater than the static locus to move the eyes. In Fig. 15 the increment is about ±3 g (mainly within the muscle's field of action; upper left curve compared with lower left curve). This plus or minus 3-g differential at 10°/sec eye-movement velocity would correspond to a viscosity of some 300 mg/degree/sec. During faster following movements a force difference up to 10 g in excess of the static locus of fixation forces overcomes the viscosity of the oculomotor plant, which resides predominantly in the extending antagonist.

On the left side of Fig. 15, the length–tension loop is traced out in a counterclockwise direction, indicating that the muscle is delivering energy to the globe. On the right half of the figure the curve is being traced out in a clockwise direction, indicating that energy is being delivered to the muscle, that is the muscle is absorbing energy from the globe acting as a brake.

Relatively small forces are involved in both fixation and following movements. During both fixation and following the greater proportion of activity is supplied by the small fibers (cf. Fig. 7). According to Alvarado (this Symposium), the small fibers (12.5 μm dia) constitute as many as 56% of the total number of fibers in the muscle and contribute up to 26% of the cross-sectional area of the muscle. It has been determined from succinylcholine experiments that these small fibers develop approximately one-third of the total force of the muscle (Bach-y-Rita and Ito, 1966). From these values of their area and force contribution the small fibers appear to develop a greater force per unit of cross-sectional area than the larger fibers.

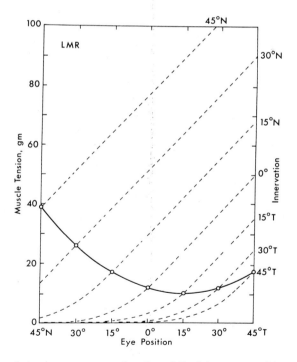

FIG. 14A. Family of length–tension curves as a function of fixed increments of innervation (dashed lines). The open circles are the intersection of a given eye position with the length–tension curve of the corresponding innervation. This intersection establishes the steady-state force utilized to hold the eye at this point of gaze fixation. The solid parabolic line joining these points is the static locus of fixation forces for any point of lateral gaze.

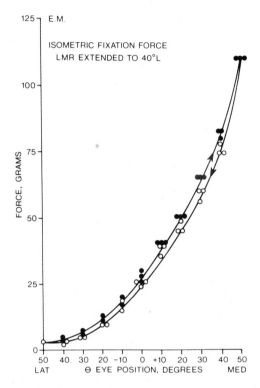

FIG. 14B. A static transfer function for isometric oculorotary muscle force as a function of eye position (of the contralateral eye).

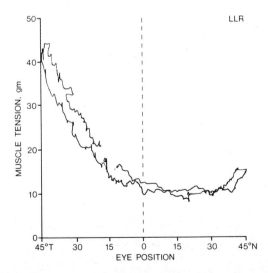

FIG. 15. *In situ* tendon force record obtained with an implanted "C" gauge in the right medial rectus during following movements at 10°/sec. The record starts at primary position, moves to right (45° T), then proceeds to the extreme left (45° N), then returns to primary gaze. Note the agreement with the parabolic nature of fixation forces, Fig. 14A.

3. Accommodative Vergence

Figure 16 is a comparison of isometrically measured saccadic, fixation and accommoda-tive vergence forces measured as a function of contralateral eye position. If we assume an ACA ration of 0.6 in order to make the muscle innervation correspond to the measured eye, then the forces of accommodative vergence fall on top of the isometric fixation forces in version. Our data then indicates that accommodative vergence forces follow the same pattern as those of fixation in version.

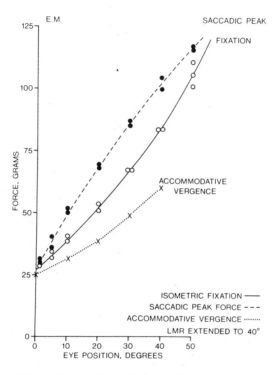

FIG. 16. The relationship of isometric saccadic peak forces, fixation forces and accommodative vergence forces measured as a function of contralateral eye position.

4. Saccades

A comparison of isometric and freely moving muscle forces during a 15° to 30° saccadic eye movement into the field of a left medial rectus is shown in Fig. 17. One will note here that the antagonist RMR muscle tension falls to zero in the isometric case (a) but does not fall when the eye moves (b). In the freely moving eye the agonist LMR reaches a much lower peak tension (b) than that measured in an isometric muscle (a). In fact, the tension increment observed during normal saccadic eye move-ments is only about half that measured isometrically (21 g versus 41 g in this case).

The difference in force between the isometric and freely moving muscle states may be accounted for by foreshortening of both the contractile element (1.2 g/degree) and the series elastic element (2.5 g/degree, or 12.5 g/mm; cf. Fig. 24). For slow movements

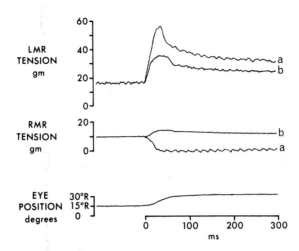

FIG. 17. Isometric tension records (a) compared with unrestrained, freely moving eye movement records of muscle tension (b) for identical 15° to 30° right saccadic refixations.

force effectively slides down the length–tension curve (which has a slope of approximately 0.8 g/degree resulting from these two elasticities in series, cf. Fig. 14A). For fast muscle length changes the mechanical impedence of the muscle viscosity permits essentially only the series elastic element to change length. Thus, for a 10° quick movement we would expect a 25-g drop in muscle tension (compared with isometric).

In Fig. 18 the saccadic peak forces are plotted in comparison with the final, steady-state fixation forces as a function of eye position. The forces in the top dashed curve

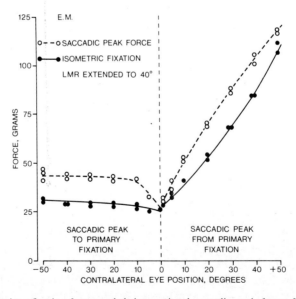

FIG. 18. Isometric agonist refixation forces and their associated saccadic peak forces for concentric saccades (left side of graph) starting from the indicated eye position. Eccentric saccades (right side of graph) starting from primary are shown for the final eye position indicated.

were measured during saccades from primary position to the indicated eye position. The isometric measured force rose from the primary position to the indicated saccadic peak overshoot value and then fell vertically to the corresponding steady-state fixation value of isometric force (solid line). The forces on the right half of the figure were measured during eccentric saccades.

The left curves were measured during "on" saccades moving from the indicated eye position outside of the field of action of the muscle towards the primary position. For these concentric saccades the lower value of isometric fixation force is substantially constant, holding the eye at primary position. It should be noted that the saccadic peak force reached essentially the same value to achieve primary position regardless of the starting-point of these concentric saccades. The saccadic overshoot force remained at a constant 15 g over the entire range from 10° to 50°.

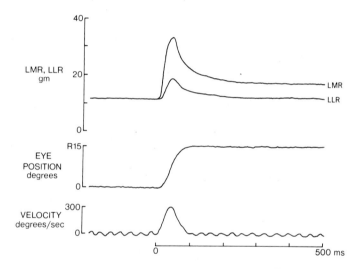

FIG. 19. Comparison of medial and lateral rectus muscle tensions measured during an unrestrained saccadic refixation from primary to 15° right. Note the unexpected *rise* of antagonist LLR tension (lower curve).

This observation affords a clue to the process of eye-movement control. It appears that one strategy of the central nervous system is to employ a fixed saccadic peak force level corresponding to each final eye position regardless of the starting-point or size of the saccade. Although the peak force measured from the starting-point may vary, one measures a constant force increment above the new steady-state fixation tension associated with each eye position.

Figure 19 is a tension record taken from a reciprocally innervated pair of antagonist muscles during a freely moving saccadic movement from primary position to 15° right. The tension in each muscle at primary position is about 12 g and the tension records have been overlapped in order to more easily compare their relative shapes and amplitudes. Note that the peak velocity of eye movement coincides with the peak tension developed by the shortening agonist muscle, which would be expected in a viscous system.

In Fig. 19 one can also see the unexpected tension increase in the relaxing antagonist even though the innervation to this muscle has been completely turned off for the 65-ms duration of this 15° saccade. This rising tension in the relaxing antagonist is due to its being stretched at a rate faster than the viscous element (in parallel with its contractile element) can extend in relaxation. One also notes that the new steady-state fixation level is a few grams greater than that in the primary position since the muscle has been passively stretched to its new steady-state resting length.

As has been noted above, saccades are controlled by a completely separate mechanism inherently different from the continuous control of all of the other types of eye movements. During the saccadic pulse of force all of the fibers, both large and small, are turned on strongly during the first portion of the saccade, settling down to a much lower steady-state value. This type of operation is not employed for fixation, following or vergence movements even in extreme gaze. Our studies show that both the amplitude and the duration of the saccadic control pulse are varied (cf. Fig. 7) such that their product (impulse) matches the final eye position. The magnitude of the saccade is thus determined by impulse modulation. Model studies indicate that saccades provide the most sensitive means for critical determination of the magnitudes of the mechanical parameters of the muscle.

The salient muscle parameter is its developed force. We have seen from multiple electrode array EMG studies that the muscle can be completely depolarized within 10 ms. It appears that the contractile element develops its full tension with a 2-ms rise time, attaining full developed force also within 10 ms. The force which we can measure at the tendon, however, has been filtered through the viscoelastic mechanical elements of the muscle which display roughly a 20-ms time constant; the maximum force at the tendon occurs about 100 ms after maximum sustained innervation. The maximum isometric developed forces which we have measured are over 100 g at the muscle's resting length which, for oculorotary muscle, is apparently about 30° out of its field of action (Robinson et al., 1969), (not at its primary length). However, depending upon the length of the muscle, this static isometric force may be considerably less than that developed at the resting length of the muscle. We measure some 120 g when the muscle is fully extended and fully innervated as seen in the length-tension diagram (Fig. 14A). In contrast, at its fully contracted length a maximally innervated muscle is seen to develop only about 40 g.

During an isometric muscle contraction of 100 g (at resting length and full innervation) the contractile element can change length by as much as 6 mm due to the combined elasticities of its series and parallel elastic elements. This reduces the ultimate developed tension of the contractile element such that we do not measure its full effort even isometrically. Thus, the contractile element probably develops closer to 140 g rather than 120 g as measured at the tendon isometrically in the length-tension graphs of Fig. 14.

The dynamic length-tension characteristics of a freely contracting muscle rotating the globe can be recorded as dynamic saccadic loops as shown in Fig. 20A. This is a dynamic length-tension recording during a number of saccadic refixations of an agonist left medial rectus muscle made with the implanted miniature "C" gauge force transducer plotted against the EOG in a freely moving eye. One can see that the characteristic path described by the muscle force between each pair of fixation points consists of three parts: (a) an initial isometric tension rise (with little change in length),

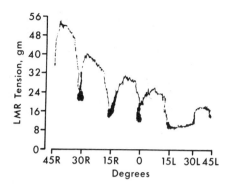

FIG. 20A. A dynamic length–tension record of a sequence of saccadic refixations of an agonist LMR in an unrestrained eye. Note the three-part characteristic path (a) isometric tension rise, (b) isotonic increment 15–25 g above the static locus, and (c) roughly isometric decay to the new steady state tension of refixation.

followed by (b) an essentially isotonic tension increment maintained about 15 to 25 g above the static locus of fixation force (while the eye is moving), and (c) (approaching the new fixation position) a roughly isometric tension decay to the steady-state tension which maintains the eye at its new position of lateral gaze. It will be noted that the steady-state fixation force falls on the parabolic static locus occurring at the bottom of each transient.

Figure 20B shows that these dynamic saccadic length–tension loops do in fact follow a fixed path as illustrated by length–tension recordings during large saccades of 30° and 60°. The 60° saccade (labeled "A") started from the 15° left position (right side of record) with tension rising roughly isometrically, then breaking over to follow the dynamic locus (cf. Fig. 21) with the tension finally rising at a rate of approximately $\frac{1}{2}$ g per degree. The tension rose to 48 g and abruptly fell to the new refixation tension level of approximately 28 g at 45° right. The eye then followed the target

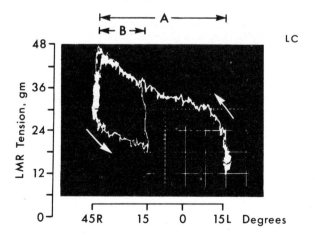

FIG. 20B. Tendon tension in an agonist LMR unrestrained 30° and 60° saccades. Note these two saccadic curves identically retrace each other in the common region of operation. [From Collins, et al., J. Physiol. **245** (1975) (in press).]

back to the 15° right position from which it made a 30° saccade (labeled "B") in which the force again rose isometrically, broke sharply to its $\frac{1}{2}$ g per degree rate of rise to 48 g, and again fell to the new refixation tension of 28 g at 45° right. Here the dynamic tension locus (the upper curve with roughly $\frac{1}{2}$ g per degree slope) is seen to be approximately 20 g greater than, and clearly paralleling, the static locus of fixation tension. Note that the 30° saccadic dynamic tension loop retraces an identical portion of the 60° dynamic saccadic tension curve.

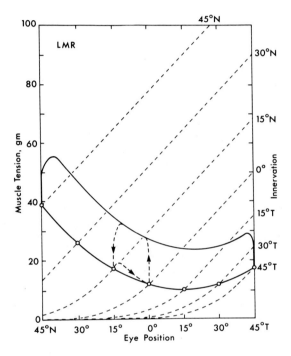

FIG. 21. An operational envelope of the normal working range of oculorotary muscle tensions responsible for fixation, following, vergence and saccadic eye movements (see text for explanation). [From Collins, et al., J. Physiol. **245** (1975) (in press).]

THE OPERATIONAL ENVELOPE

The picture which is now beginning to emerge from all of the *in situ*, unrestrained muscle tension measurements is a length–tension schema which defines the normal ranges of tensions for horizontal eye movements. This schema is presented in Fig. 21 in the form of an operational envelope for the ranges of extraocular muscle tension in normal fixation, following, vergence, and saccadic movements.

A family of length–tension curves is shown as the dashed lines in the background of Fig. 21. The lower heavy line, interrupted by open circles, depicts the static locus of fixation forces, i.e. the tension required to hold the eye in each position of eccentric gaze noted on the abcissa (Collins, 1971). The upper heavy line represents the dynamic locus, or maximum total tension measured at the muscle tendon during saccadic movements.

A typical dynamic length–tension loop for a saccadic movement by the agonist is shown in Fig. 21 as a counterclockwise dashed curve with arrows extending between the open circles on the static locus. This saccadic length–tension loop comprises the three-part dynamic path previously described.

A typical dynamic length–tension loop for the antagonist is shown as the smaller flattened clockwise path moving to the right between the open circles. This was obtained from recordings of antagonists comparable to those of Fig. 20 A and B. The tension in the antagonist never falls below the static locus.

Tensions recorded during smooth following movements lie on or above the lower curve of the operational envelope, the static locus (Fig. 21). Thus, as the muscle contracts within its field of action the tension reaches levels between the lower and upper curves. As it relaxes in movement from extreme gaze toward mid-position, the tension is essentially the same as with fixation at the corresponding eye position (i.e. it matches the lower curve, the static locus).

As seen in Fig. 21, the length–tension curves become parallel straight lines above about 10 g. Since the lower limits of the operational envelope lie above 10 g, the entire operation of the oculorotary muscles occurs on the linear portion of the length–tension characteristics, which greatly simplifies modeling of the oculomotor plant.

As we have seen, under normal physiological conditions all agonist and antagonist muscle forces lie between the upper and lower limits of the operational envelope. This is true even though the innervation to an antagonist is completely shut off during a saccade greater than 10°. The reciprocally innervated and contracting agonist keeps the antagonist on the stretch at levels of tensions associated with fixation. The oculorotary muscles are perpetually kept under some degree of tension, during waking hours, even outside of their field of activity, so that muscle slack is avoided at all times. Recent evidence indicates that this is due to the continuous tonic activity of the small, outer fibers of the muscle (Collins and Scott, 1973) (cf. Fig. 5).

The operational envelope of normal eye-movement forces measured at the tendon is determined by neuromuscular control, the innervational strategy of the CNS operating on the mechanical viscoelastic characteristics of the muscles and globe. The combination of these factors restricts normal muscle activity to a mere 20% of the area of the length–tension diagram. All areas on the length–tension diagram outside the operational envelope are forbidden regions during normal eye movements. Only during abnormal conditions do the muscle forces leave the operational envelope area of the length–tension diagram. Thus the envelope has significance during diagnosis utilizing forced duction techniques; in pathological cases such as contracture, adhesions, or other restrictions; and during surgery where recession or resection will change the shape and location of the operational envelope on the background of the altered family of length–tension curves of the operated muscle.

The static locus and operational envelope are reflections of the innervational strategy chosen by the central nervous system to control eye movements. Since at least two muscles are involved, with a wide range of possible innervation combinations at each eye position, there is an infinite number of possible paths between two eye positions on the length–tension diagram. However, biologically only one path (or strategy) has been chosen. We now know this as *the* static locus.

The shape of the static locus mirrors the isometric innervation–tension transfer function (cf. Fig. 14B). This is a nonlinear innervation–tension relationship which results in tension increments which become larger with equal eye-position increments, resulting in a static locus which is nonlinear, obeys a square law function, and slopes upward into the field of action of the muscle. This relationship matches our physiological measurements (cf. Fig. 14A) and is apparently the correct expression for the innervational strategy utilized by the CNS in controlling eye position in any direction of gaze.

The counterclockwise saccadic loops of Fig. 21 indicate the method of energy release from oculorotary muscle under central control. First, during the isometric tension increase the contractile element stores potential energy. Since little external movement occurs during this phase, negligible external energy is dissipated. Only after the contractile element has locked over does the eye move significantly, thus allowing the passive elastic muscle elements to shorten, delivering their stored potential energy in the form of kinetic energy of movement. Finally, after completion of the eye movement, the contractile element is programmed to relax, but again isometrically with respect to the external world, thus minimizing energy dissipation. This strategy infers the least work demanded from the contractile element. It may be speculated that this process contributes to the eye muscles not getting tired, even though continuously innervated during waking hours.

A MODEL OF THE OCULOMOTOR SYSTEM

Modeling is the method of choice for more complete understanding of the complex interrelationships of oculomotor control. Past models have dealt predominantly with small movements around the primary position. For clinical applicability we must be able to treat larger movements embracing the performance of the oculomotor system over the complete range of eye movements. Pathological ocular deviations are often significantly large, persisting to a great (but variable) degree over the entire range of ocular motility. The variations may point to clinical manifestations of the underlying pathological mechanism. The basic ocular deviation plus the pattern of variation can be plotted to show the differences from normal oculomotor and fixational patterns, and thus can become a potential tool for more quantitative understanding of the faulty (pathological) mechanism and its location (neurological, muscular or simple restrictive).

To fit large ranges of fixation, and large swings of eye movement, we find first that the oculomotor control system embodies basic nonlinearities. Consequently, purely linear modeling will not suffice for realistic clinical application. The fundamental nonlinearity is found in the relationship between the magnitude of innervation and the position of the eye (cf. Fig. 11A). This relationship is more simply expressed in terms of a power function which permits a good fit of muscle forces to eccentric fixation positions of the eyes (cf. Fig. 14B). The length–tension components of the model can be expressed in simple linear terms. However, the muscle viscosity is a function of tension (see below), and the overall control characteristics appear nonlinear.

With the newly recorded data reviewed in this chapter we can now test existing models and update the state of the art of human oculomotor system modeling. To be ultimately useful we should set criteria for a dynamic oculomotor model which would make it of value for clinical diagnostic applications as well as for teaching the basic principles of oculomotor physiology.

Robinson (1964) proposed the first practical model of the human oculomotor plant, based upon measurements of eye movements and forces exerted by the oculorotary muscles upon a suction cup scleral contact lens. His model quite realistically duplicated the time course of eye movements under various conditions. In particular, he pointed out that the major load on an oculorotary muscle is its internal viscosity, which constitutes the greatest impedance to rapid (saccadic) eye movements; and that the rotational inertia of the eyeball can essentially be ignored. He has also determined that the upper mechanical frequency response of the oculomotor system is only one cycle per second and that rapid saccadic movements are made "only under the impetus of a large, briefly applied, excess force delivered by the extraocular muscles" (Robinson, 1964).

Cook and Stark (1964) proposed modifications of Robinson's model, predominantly by imposing A. V. Hill's (1938) concept of an inconstant muscle viscosity which is a function of developed tension and velocity, and Katz's (1939) findings that viscosity depends on the direction of movement of the contractile element. Cook and Stark also separated agonist and antagonist activity, and pointed out that eye-movement velocity is a more sensitive test of model performance than are records of eye position as a function of time.

By means of indwelling "C" gauges we find that unrestrained muscles work at lower tension than past isometric measurements have suggested (Robinson, 1969). The tension in primary gaze is about one-quarter that which Cook and Stark assumed, and the maximum eccentric gaze fixation tension is about half their assumption (1968). Actually, the deduction of primary tension by Robinson (1964) was quite good. The coefficient of viscosity should be increased by about a factor of two over that of Cook and Stark's in light of the latest data on human muscle tensions.

Measurements of viscosity are presented in Fig. 22, compiled from quick-stretch measurements of human oculorotary muscle at surgery. The time constant of recovery of muscle force was determined as the muscle was held fixed at various muscle lengths, tensions, and innervations. The least spread of all data resulted when viscosity was

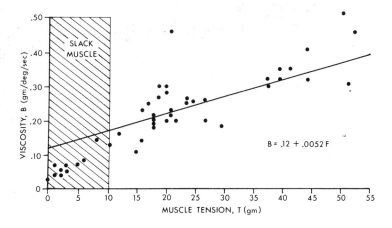

FIG. 22. Human oculorotary muscle viscosity as a function of muscle tension determined by the quick-stretch method at strabismus surgery.

treated as a function of muscle tension (whether derived through innervation or stretch). The analytical expression best fitting these measured human data is:

$$B = 0.12 + 0.0052F(1 - e^{-t/\tau})$$

where B is viscosity, F is developed tension and τ is the time constant of the lag in viscosity change. The variation of viscosity at different constant velocities was determined in our previous studies on cats (Collins, 1971), which revealed that the viscosity of extending muscle remains essentially constant at any given level of innervation for velocities up to 30°/sec, the range of following movements. Beyond this velocity and up to 600°/sec (saccadic velocity) the viscosity fell off by a factor of 5 (Fig. 24, p. 306, op. cit.). An analytical expression relating the variation of viscosity with velocity in this mammalian oculorotary muscle (at 37°C) involves the square of velocity in the denominator, and therefore differs from the inverse linear relationship found for frog sartorius muscle at 0°C by A. V. Hill (1938). Utilizing this data results in the following expression for muscle viscosity (B) as a function of tension (T), velocity ($\dot{X}$) of the contractile element and eye velocity $\dot{\theta}$

$$B = \frac{0.12 + 0.0052F(1 - e^{-t/\tau})}{1 + \left(\dfrac{\dot{X} - \dot{\theta}}{300}\right)^2}$$

Viscosity is observed to transiently increase by an order of magnitude over the average, fixed values determined by Robinson (1964).

Elasticity is probably the most important single element which must be incorporated into any working model of the oculomotor system. At surgery we have measured the physiological values of the series elastic element in human oculorotary muscle by the quick-stretch technique. The value turns out to be approximately 2.5 g/degree. With this measurement one can then calculate the value of the elastic element in parallel with the contractile element, utilizing the slope of the length–tension curve for an oculorotary muscle. The slope of this curve is approximately 0.8 g/degree = K_C, the series combination of K_1 and K_2. The expression relating these variables is:

$$K_C = \frac{K_1 K_2}{K_1 + K_2}$$

where K_1 and K_2 represent the coefficient of elasticity of the series and parallel elastic elements, respectively. Solution of this equation with the measured values of K_C and K_1 gives a value for K_2 of approximately 1.2 g/degree. The elasticity of the globe restraining tissue has been found to be approximately 0.5 g/degree; and with a mean time constant of 120 ms, one can calculate the globe viscosity to be about 0.06 g/degree/sec ($B = K\tau$).

Incorporating elastic, viscous and contractile elements, one can formulate a mechanical model of oculorotary muscle. Figure 23 presents two such models. The upper model conventionally locates the parallel elastic element, K_2, in parallel with the entire muscle, while the lower model places K_2 in parallel only with the contractile element. Length–tension characteristics from each model are plotted in the corresponding graphs. The solid lines represent passive state length–tension characteristics; the dashed lines represent characteristics which would be found with constant levels of developed tension at two constant levels of innervation. With the assumption inherent in the upper model that the contractile element is a constant force generator, we would expect to see a constant force regardless of muscle length until the muscle is stretched to the point where passive forces become additive. This is seen in the upper graph as the dashed lines turn up and parallel the passive curve toward the right. With the lower model, however, the passive length–tension elastic element characteristics in the graph reflect the series combination of K_1 and K_2. Under these conditions, a constant innervation of the contractile element producing a constant tension will shorten K_2 and the length–tension curves will start from a new, shorter length. The resultant length–tension characteristics will then parallel the passive length–tension characteristics but will be simply displaced further and further towards the left in the diagram with increasing innervation. This model more accurately duplicates the physiological measurements made on human oculorotary muscle. Thus if one considers the passive elasticity to be in parallel with the contractile element alone, that is, in series with the series elastic element, we have a simple and convenient mechanism for modeling the inherent characteristics of the muscle length–tension curves as straight, parallel lines throughout the length–tension diagram (above their 10-g slack region).

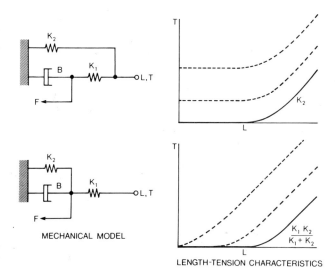

FIG. 23. Conventional (top) and proposed (bottom) mechanical models of human oculorotary muscle. Developed tension, F, is considered to be determined only by innervation. The resulting length–tension relationships are shown for each model with zero and two fixed levels of innervation.

With the advent of more recent quantitative findings in human extraocular muscle and passive globe supporting tissue (Collins and Scott, 1973; Collins et al., 1972; Collins et al., 1975) it is now possible to improve on the neuromechanical model of the oculomotor plant. To be maximally useful to the ophthalmologist in cases of strabismus which involve large deviations of the eyes, an eye-movement model should be capable of faithfully depicting the innervational and mechanical events over the complete range of eye movements from approximately 50° left to 50° right.

With the lower muscle model of Fig. 23 and the evaluation of the viscosities and elasticities in this model, it is possible to outline a mechanical model of the peripheral

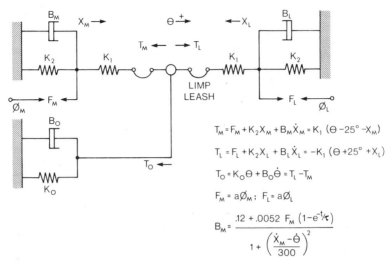

$$T_M = F_M + K_2 X_M + B_M \dot{X}_M = K_1 (\Theta - 25° - X_M)$$

$$T_L = F_L + K_2 X_L + B_L \dot{X}_L = -K_1 (\Theta + 25° + X_L)$$

$$T_0 = K_0 \Theta + B_0 \dot{\Theta} = T_L - T_M$$

$$F_M = a\phi_M ; \quad F_L = a\phi_L$$

$$B_M = \frac{.12 + .0052 \, F_M \left(1 - e^{-t/\tau}\right)}{1 + \left(\dfrac{\dot{X}_M - \dot{\Theta}}{300}\right)^2}$$

FIG. 24. Dynamic mechanical model of the human peripheral oculomotor system and the equations of motion.

ϕ_M, ϕ_L = medial and lateral rectus muscle innervation

F_M, F_L = medial and lateral rectus muscle developed tension

X_M, X_L = displacements of contractile elements

T_M, T_L = muscle tendon forces

T_0, = passive globe restraining force

K_1, K_2 = muscle series and parallel elastic elements

K_0 = elasticity of globe restraining tissue

B_M, B_L = viscosity of medial and lateral rectus muscles

B_0 = viscosity of globe restraining tissue

θ = eye position

oculomotor plant which responds to innervation control signals as shown in Fig. 24. The differential equations of motion for this model also appear in the diagram.

In order to make the model more meaningful both physiologically and anatomically, we have made the configuration of elements correspond with observations on human oculorotary muscles and passive globe restraining tissues. In previous models, the passive elasticities of muscle and globe restraining tissues have been lumped together because adequate measurements on human subjects were not available. We can now separate these elasticities using measurements by Robinson *et al.* (1969). The older models of Robinson (1964) and of Cook and Stark (1968) should be modified to differentiate the elasticities into components associated with the muscles separately from those associated with the globe to facilitate the possibility of application to diagnosis and surgical intervention.

In this model the limp leash simply represents that the muscle can develop tension only, not compression; that is, the muscle can only pull, not push, the globe. It has been found from this model that satisfactory performance is achieved with a single time constant Voigt element representing the passive viscoelastic elements, B_0 and K_0, restraining movement of the globe. These values have been measured with the muscles removed from the globe.

This as yet simplistic analog computer model, involving only one pair of oculorotary muscles, incorporates the physiologically observed nonlinear, innervational, viscous and other properties of the oculomotor plant for large excursions. It performs satisfactorily over the entire range of eye movement up to $\pm 50°$ from the primary position. The model duplicates the observed family of length–tension curves. It traces the static locus, expressing the tension measured physiologically while holding the eyes at any position of eccentric gaze. It properly generates the agonist and antagonist muscle forces which we have measured in freely moving eyes during target tracking movements. It correctly produces dynamic saccadic length–tension loops (which proves to be a more critical test of model performance than matching velocity profiles, since many combinations of muscle force will produce an appropriate force difference, but there is only one, unique combination which will correctly duplicate these dynamic loops that exhibit the three-part isometric, isotonic increment and isometric configuration). It also shows the effect of muscle shortening on the forces derived during an unrestricted saccade, together with the unexpected initial force increase in the relaxing antagonist during a saccade and during fixation out of its field of action. The model-generated eye movements match those observed in both our physiological and clinical studies. Thus, it appears that we are approaching a usable model of the oculomotor system

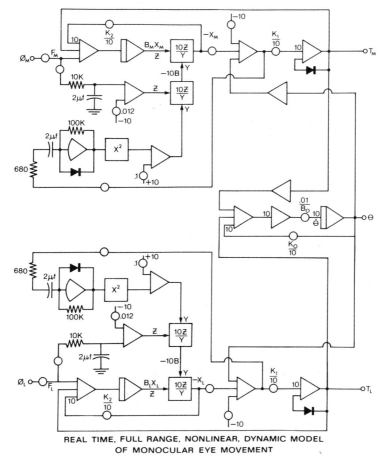

**REAL TIME, FULL RANGE, NONLINEAR, DYNAMIC MODEL
OF MONOCULAR EYE MOVEMENT**

FIG. 25. Analog computer mechanization of human peripheral oculorotary mechanical system model of Fig. 24. Separate upper and lower groups of elements represent the medial and lateral rectus muscle dynamics and the right-central grouping represents the passive globe restraining tissues. Inputs are muscle innervation, ϕ (control signal), and outputs are muscle tendon forces, T_M and T_L, for a freely moving, unrestrained eye with the resultant eye position, Θ.

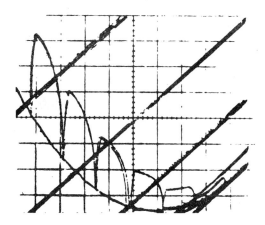

FIG. 26A. Storage oscilloscope record of length–tension model outputs.

under both normal, healthy conditions and under some of its known pathological perturbations. An analog computer mechanization of this model is shown in Fig. 25.

In the model (Fig. 24) the contractile element force consists of three components: the developed force due to innervation, F_L and F_M, the force velocity relationship or viscosity, B_L and B_M, and the force due to the parallel elastic element, K_2, contributing to the length–tension characteristics of the muscle, K_C. In this case the total contractile element force is equal to the force measured at the muscle tendon. However, any one component of this contractile element force cannot be separately measured at the tendon because of the isolating series elastic element, K_1.

Figure 26A shows the model performance characteristics in terms of a family of length–tension curves, the static locus of fixation forces and the dynamic saccadic

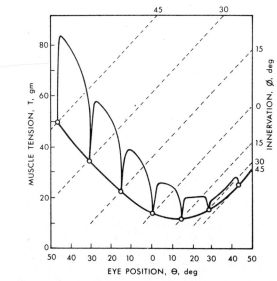

FIG. 26B. Labeled drawing of model outputs showing length–tension characteristics, static locus and dynamic saccadic loops.

force loops on the length–tension diagram as reproduced directly from a storage oscillo-scope. Figure 26B is a hand-traced reproduction of these curves labeled for greater clarity. The length–tension curves exhibit proper nonlinear spacing and agree quite well with those of Fig. 14A and Fig. 21. The static locus of fixation forces is also correctly reproduced in these figures which represent the physiologically measured values of these parameters. Following movements also rather closely duplicate the information shown in Fig. 15. The dynamic saccadic loops agree reasonably well with the physiologi-cally measured values shown in Figs. 20 A and B and 21.

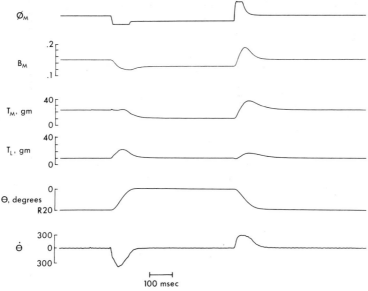

FIG. 27. Oculomotor model performance as a function of time in response to reciprocal innervation (only ϕ_M shown in top trace) for a $20°$ saccade. The responses are respectively: viscosity variation of medial rectus muscle; unrestricted medial and lateral muscle tendon tensions; eye position; and velocity.

Figure 27 is a time-based record of the performance of the model left eye in response to a $20°$R–0–$20°$R input innervation, ϕ_M, of the medial rectus muscle shown on the top channel of the oscillographic record. The lateral rectus was reciprocally inner-vated in accord with the quantitative results of our physiological measurements of innervation. The second channel is a record of the variation of viscosity B_M, of the medial rectus muscle which follows the relationship of Fig. 22 with a 20 ms lagging time constant (equal to the mechanical time constant of the muscle). The details of the variation of viscosity during human saccadic movements have not been heretofore measured. The third and fourth channels are the medial and lateral rectus muscle tendon tensions, respectively, simulating those we measure during an unrestrained eye movement. In the second saccade the 38-g LMR agonist saccadic peak tension at the 22-g fixation tension at $20°$ right agree remarkably well with the human data summarized in Fig. 21, as do the 19-g LLR antagonist saccadic peak tension and the 11-g fixation tension at $20°$ right. The fifth channel is the eye movement record which would be difficult to distinguish from a real one (except for the lack of noise) (cf. Fig. 19). The last channel is velocity which displays reasonable waveforms and correct amplitudes, even to the eccentric saccade being slightly slower.

Another potentially valuable clinical capability offered by this type of model is the ability to examine critically, in quantitative detail, heretofore unobserved parameters of muscle function such as the variation of muscle viscosity during various eye movements (cf. Fig. 27). Further, it affords the opportunity to infer innervational and force imbalances and the intimate nuances of individual muscle innervation patterns and developed forces from noninvasive eye movement measurements.

Correlation of the knowledge of the variation of such specific neuromuscular performance parameters with pathological entities may find application in automated teaching aid devices as well as ultimately prove of clinical value in diagnostic and corrective procedures.

Figure 28A is a record of the normal model left eye responses while performing a 15° right saccade. These essentially duplicate the physiologically measured patient records of Fig. 19 (q.v.) in shape, absolute magnitude and velocity and concur with the human data of Fig. 21.

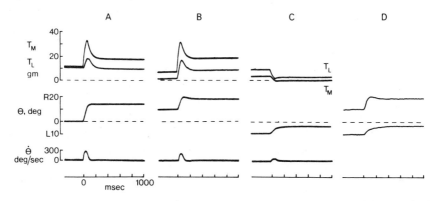

FIG. 28A. Oculomotor model simulation of a *normal* left eye during a 0° to 15° right saccade. (*Top*) The unrestricted medial and lateral rectus muscle tensions, T_M and T_L, shown on the same scale to illustrate comparative performance. (*Next lower trace*) Eye position, θ. (*Bottom trace*) Velocity, $\dot{\theta}$. (Compare these model responses with the measurements during a normal human saccade, Fig. 19.)

FIG. 28B. Model simulation of a *pathological* left eye during a 15° right saccade with a paralysed antagonist LLR muscle. Note the 10° right esotropia, 3° saccadic overshoot, 150°/sec velocity, and 8° final eye movement.

FIG. 28C. Model simulation of pathological left eye during a 15° right saccade with a paralysed agonist LMR muscle. Note the 10° left esotropia, 500 ms saccadic duration, 60°/sec velocity and 7° final eye movement.

FIG. 28D. Eye-movement records of a lateral rectus palsy patient. Top record with palsied antagonist. Note the tropia, overshoot, velocity, and size of eye movement are duplicated by the model in Fig. 28B. Bottom record of movement with the palsied muscle acting as agonist. Note the model duplicates this pathological eye movement in Fig. 28C.

In Fig. 28B the antagonist left lateral rectus muscle has been paralysed (by cutting off its innervation) producing an incomitant strabismus in the model. One can see the accompanying reduction in muscle tensions in the freely moving (covered) left eye which result in a 10° esotropia of this eye (with the right eye fixing in primary gaze). An attempted 15° right saccade (15° saccade by the right eye; left eye covered) results in an 8° final movement of the left eye; a 150°/sec saccade, and a 3° overshoot decaying in 250 ms. Each of these performances is essentially identical with those measured in a lateral rectus palsy patient as shown in the upper curve of Fig. 28D (courtesy of Dr. Alan Scott) and with measurements on volunteer subjects with xylocaine injected into an oculorotary muscle (Scott *et al.*, in prep.). The striking identity of each detail of the model performance with known pathology is indeed remarkable and has important bearing on the possible uses of clinical models.

Figure 28C represents another clinical example of model oculomotor performance with a paralysed agonist left medial rectus muscle. In this case the LMR tension drops below that of the lateral rectus resulting in a 10° exotropia of the covered left eye (right eye fixing primary). A 15° right saccade (of the right eye) results in a 7° slow left eye movement of about 500 ms duration and only 60°/sec maximum velocity. Again, this pathological model performance identically reproduces the clinical observations of a patient making a covered saccadic eye movement with a palsied agonist as illustrated in the lower curve of Fig. 28D (courtesy of Dr. Alan Scott). Here the patient's covered eye moves only 7° (one-half the amplitude of the good fixing eye); with a 60°/sec maximum velocity; a 500-ms saccadic duration, and with a two time-constant waveform identical with that of the model.

These startling examples of pathological model behavior make a strong argument for the real potential clinical utility of individual patient models. Simple clinical quick-stretch measurements with strain gauge forceps (Scott *et al.*, 1972) may be used to evaluate patient viscous and elastic model elements in the surgeon's office; calibrated forceps (Scott *et al.*, 1972) measurement of isometric forces during contralateral eye fixation can determine neuromuscular functional imbalances; and contractures or mechanical restrictions may be quantitatively determined in the office with position monitored forceps measurements of ocular length–tension characteristics.

An individual patient clinical model may be able to quantitatively and possibly even qualitatively aid the ophthalmologist in his diagnosis and choice of surgical treatment plan. An interactive graphic CRT display would provide immediate feedback indicating the results of various combinations of simple surgical techniques on oculomotor performance and alignment. For example, the effects of surgery on comitance could be instantly and directly displayed in graphical form. Operation on the model would permit the surgeon to compare various amounts and types of strabismus surgery and choose as optimum approach from many model responses before going to the OR.

ACKNOWLEDGEMENTS

The author gratefully acknowledges the collaboration of Dr. Alan Scott in collecting the data from which the reported results have been derived. The assistance of Mr. David O'Meara in muscle force studies is also greatly appreciated. I wish to thank Mr. Jules Madey for assistance with instrumentation and electronic design of the EMG data reduction apparatus and Mr. Lee Tate for his assiduous efforts in fabricating the multiple electrode EMG needle and target display apparatus. I thank Mr. Jack Shore and Mr. Elmer Johnson for their mechanical engineering assistance and Mr. Gerald Dittbenner and Mr. Henry Freynick for their design contributions and fabrication of the miniature "C" gauge force transducer.

REFERENCES

ALVARADO, J. Muscle fiber types of the cat inferior oblique (this Symposium).
BACH-Y-RITA, P. and ITO, F. (1966) *In vivo* studies on fast and slow muscle fibers in cat extraocular muscles. *J. Gen. Physiol.* **49**, 1177–1198.

COLLINS, C. C. (1971) Orbital mechanics. In: *The Control of Eye Movements*, BACH-Y-RITA, P. and COLLINS, C. C. (Eds.), pp. 283–325. New York, Academic Press.

COLLINS, C. C. and SCOTT, A. B. (1973) The eye movement control signal. *Proc. Second Bioengineering Conference, Ophthalmology Section, Milan, Italy*, Nov. 1973.

COLLINS, C. C., SCOTT, A. and O'MEARA, D. (1969) Elements of the peripheral oculomotor apparatus. *Am. J. Optom.* **46**, 510–515.

COLLINS, C. C., SCOTT, A. B. and O'MEARA, D. M. (1972) Muscle activity during human eye movements. Paper presented to A.R.V.O., Western Section, Vancouver, B.C. September 11, 1972.

COLLINS, C. C., O'MEARA, D. and SCOTT, A. B. (1975) Muscle tension during unrestrained human eye movements. *J. Physiol.* **245** (in press).

COOK, G. and STARK, L. (1967) Derivation of a model for the human eye positioning mechanism. *Bull. Math. Biophys.* **29**, 153–174.

COOK, G. and STARK, L. (1968) The human eye movement mechanism. *Arch. Ophthal.* **79**, 428–436.

Electronic Engineering Staff, MIT (1943) *Applied Electronics*, COMPTON, K. T. (Ed.), pp. 444–445. New York, John Wiley & Sons, Inc.

HILL, A. V. (1938) Energy liberation and "viscosity" in muscle. *J. Physiol.* **93**, 4.

KATZ, B. (1939) The relation between force and speed in muscular contraction. *J. Physiol.* **96**, 45–64.

KELLER, E. L. and ROBINSON, D. A. (1972) Abducens unit behavior in the monkey during vergence movements. *Vision Res.* **42**, 369–382.

JAMPOLSKY, A. (1970) What can electromyography do for the ophthalmologist? *Invest. Ophthal.* **9**, 570–599.

MARG, E., TAMLER, E. and JAMPOLSKY A. (1962) Activity of a human oculorotary muscle unit. *Electroenceph. Clin. Neurophysiol.* **14**, 754–757.

ROBINSON, D. A. (1964) The mechanics of human saccadic eye movement. *J. Physiol,* **174**, 245–264.

ROBINSON, D. A. O'MEARA, D., SCOTT, A. B. and COLLINS, C. C. (1969) The mechanical components of human eye movements. *J. Appl. Physiol.* **26**, 548–553.

SCOTT, A. B. (1968) A and V patterns in exotropia: an electromyographic study of horizontal rectus muscles. *Am. J. Ophthal.* **65**, 12–19.

SCOTT, A. B. and COLLINS, C. C. (1973) Division of labor in the human extraocular muscle. *Arch. Ophthal.* **90**, 319–322.

SCOTT, A. B., COLLINS, C. C. and O'MEARA, D. M. (1972) A forceps to measure strabismus forces. *Arch. Ophthal.* **88**, 330–333.

SCOTT, A. B. *et al.* (in preparation).

YAMANAKA, Y. and BACH-Y-RITA, P. (1968) Conduction velocities in the abducens nerve correlated with vestibular nystagmus in cats. *Exptl. Neurology,* **20**, 143–155.

STRABISMUS—MUSCLE FORCES AND INNERVATIONS

Alan B. Scott

THE POSITION OF REST

The position of each eye in orthophoric normal adults curarized under complete anesthesia is 2.25° to 6.7° divergent, increasing with age (de Groot *et al.*, 1974). Assuming tension of 12 g for the primary position is reflected in the average cross-section area, the ratio medial/lateral, 17.39/16.73 mm (Volkmann, 1859) would give a slight increase in medial rectus tension over the lateral of 0.66 g. This would not begin to be enough to overcome the globe resistance which is about 1.5 g/degree (the data of Nakagawa, 1965, are similar to Volkmann). Therefore, some innervational differences between the two muscles must be responsible. The medial rectus might achieve this by recruiting more fibers, by giving a higher frequency to the fibers, or by using a larger fiber size than the lateral rectus. The finding that large, stamina-oriented fibers (type III, Alvarado, 1974) were twice as numerous in the medial rectus as compared to the lateral rectus of the cat (which has an exotropic rest position like man) indicates that this third mechanism, larger fibers, is the operating one.

Since our study adults are able to be orthophoric from rest positions which change with age, the nervous system is programming different amounts of convergence tonus to the horizontal muscles, utilizing the disparity in images of the two eyes in the rest position, or the effort needed to overcome this disparity, as a clue to the required asymmetry of activation of the medial and lateral rectus of each eye. This obviates the need to use fusional vergence to gain binocularity. A "tonic" vergence system to correct disharmony between rest eye position and the necessary convergence required to give alignment should act about as the cerebellum is proposed to act to correct disharmony between the labyrinthine stimulus, visual stimulus and the actual motor output in the horizontal gaze system (Jones, 1974). This tonic vergence system would operate to correct the marked exotropia present as the rest position of the normal newborn (Rethy, 1969). Within a few days of birth the eyes are increasingly well aligned with an accuracy of accommodation and AC/A ratio which is nearly mature at 4 months of age (Haynes, *et al.*, 1965). Absence of this tonus, from lack of stimulus, would result in the exotropia usually seen in unilaterally blind eyes at birth (Chavasse, 1939). Further, the exotropia seen with unilaterally blind eyes in older persons indicates a return to the exotropic rest position in the absence of visual feedback to this tonic vergence system. The regaining of parallelism (e.g. after removing a cataract) indicates its reactivation.

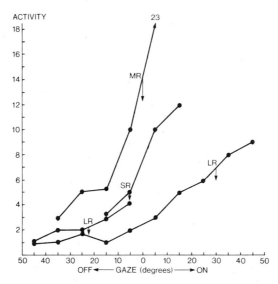

FIG. 1. Individual agonist motor unit activity (ordinate) is the number of discharges in the 40 ms after onset of the innervation increase for each 10° saccade. Notice the marked increase into the field of action. The vertical arrow shows gaze position where the unit begins to participate for fixation.

Intermittent exotropia may be construed as a failure of such a tonic correctional vergence system. Where complete absence of tonus has been obtained in exotropia, the eyes assume the same exotropic position as they do when the patient is awake (de Groot *et al.*, 1974). Thus, fusional convergence is required in order to maintain the eye position in the absence of this corrective tonic convergence.

Both local mechanics in the orbit and the program of binocular cooperation are markedly dependent upon the rest position and its changes with age. Application of control theory and neurophysiologic investigation to the vergence system superimposed upon it should be at least as rewarding as it is for the horizontal gaze system.

SACCADES TO TEST PARALYSIS

Saccadic eye movements are applied to test agonist paralysis in incomitant strabismus where active and passive force tests are not possible because of apprehension, cooperation, etc. Figure 1 shows the rate of discharge of agonist units for saccades is low

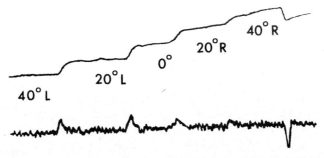

FIG. 2. Eye position (upper trace) and velocity (lower trace) of the right eye with lateral rectus paresis during a set of 20° saccades from 40° left to 40° right (left eye fixing the target).

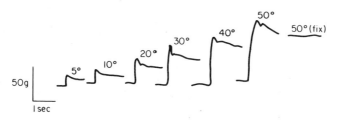

FIG. 3. Saccadic movements of increasing amplitude from the primary position were made by one eye. The force required to hold the other eye still was measured by a gauge.

for movements toward the primary position. It rises rapidly as the saccade moves into the field of action of the muscle. Figure 14A of Collins shows the tension of the medial rectus to be 40 g in adduction. The innervation providing this force is totally inhibited during saccades (10° or greater) back to the primary position. This "sling-shot" effect of the relaxation of the medial rectus against the stretched orbital tissues gives rise to abduction saccadic velocities approaching normal, even when the lateral rectus muscle is paralyzed (Fig. 2). Size of the saccade also markedly influences the force seen on the globe. Figure 3 shows the increasing force with each larger saccade. It is clear that the initial saccades from the off direction into the on direction are driven primarily by antagonist relaxation with increasing participation of the agonist as the eye moves into the on direction, and as the size of the saccade increases. In extremes of saccadic movement into the on direction there is progressively little change between the fixation frequency and force and the saccadic frequency and force (Fig. 3). It will seem that one should study the performance of the agonist muscle in producing high velocity or acceleration in the range from the primary position to the on direction of gaze. However, it is just here where restrictions from the antagonist will usually occur to restrain movement. It is therefore necessary that saccadic eye

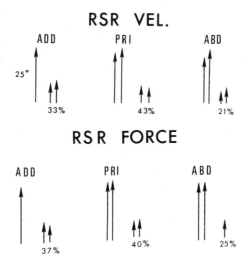

FIG. 4. Isometric force (above) and saccadic velocity (below) of the right eye were measured during 25° upward movements of the left eye from the primary position (PRI) from a position of 25° abduction (ABD) and from a position of 25° adduction (ADD). The small arrows compare the force and velocity after novocaine paralysis of the right superior rectus to the preinjection force and velocity.

movements be studied over a sizable range of gaze and large amplitudes of movement in order to define relative participation of agonist, antagonist, and restriction in the amplitude and peak velocity of saccadic eye movement. Optokinetic movements to drums which give variable or small amplitudes of movement over uncertain ranges of gaze are an imprecise and uncertain way to test such paralysis. The duration of the eye movement is an important parameter reflected, especially, in the deceleration at the end of the movement.

Full paralysis of a horizontal muscle gives a saccadic velocity (for movements of 20–25° from the primary position into the field of action of the muscle) of about 15–20% of normal. By injection of novacaine with EMG guidance we have paralyzed individual vertical eye muscles both for physiologic investigation and as a "therapeutic trial" prior to surgery. There is a very small effect on peak saccadic velocity and isometric force from oblique paralysis, but a quite marked reduction from vertical rectus paralysis (Fig. 4). These contributions to force and velocity are similar to our analysis of the percentage participation of oblique and rectus to amplitude of vertical movement, also.

ANOMALIES OF THE CONTROL SIGNAL

We find human motor units to participate in all the various types of movement, with outer fibers recruiting early in the fixation spectrum from "off" to "on", and deeper fibers participating later (Scott and Collins, 1973).

An interesting clinical finding, then, is disparity between saccadic movement and rotation amplitude. Figure 5 shows a 69-year-old man with a partially healed right lateral rectus palsy several weeks after sudden onset of diplopia without preceding or concomitant symptoms. Note that abduction amplitude of the right eye is only modestly limited, while abduction saccadic velocity is very low (Fig. 6). The EMG (Fig. 7) shows none of the normal pulse of activity at the onset of the saccade, even though the other eye was making normal saccadic movements. We consider this to represent a nerve lesion acting as a filter limiting the high-frequency saccadic burst, but not limiting the lower fixation frequencies. It is a common result of partly healed VI palsy. A supranuclear lesion, reducing the capacity to initiate saccades, gives a similar EMG pattern for the "on" direction (Fig. 8). However, the abrupt "off" saccade response, quite logical for a nerve lesion (Fig. 7), is not seen in saccadic palsies, which have a gradual change for both "on" and "off" saccades. A brainstem lesion causing VI paralysis may create anomalous recruitment, wherein a few units in the lateral rectus increase frequency for adduction rather than abduction. This may even become established enough to produce a Duane's Syndrome (Scott and Wong, 1972). Figure 9 shows that the anomalous connection may extend even to units of the "burst" sort, with increased motor unit frequency occurring before both adduction and abduction saccades.

Rotation Mechanics

The effect of the extraocular muscles considered as single lines joining the origin to the mid-insertion along the shortest great circle path (Krewson, 1950; Boeder, 1961)

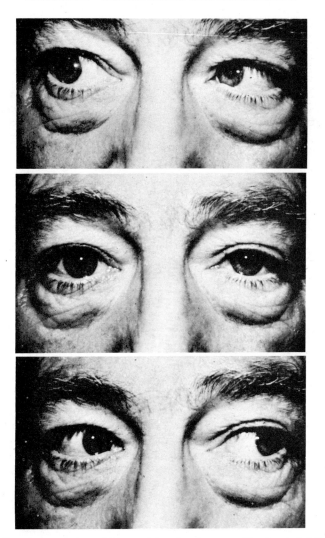

FIG. 5. Right lateral rectus palsy—right gaze (above); primary position (center); left gaze (below).

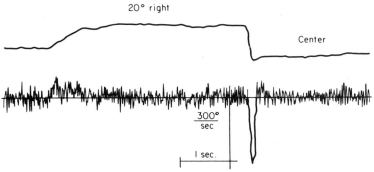

FIG. 6. Right lateral rectus weakness. Eye position (upper trace) and velocity (lower trace) during saccades (with fixation by normal left eye).

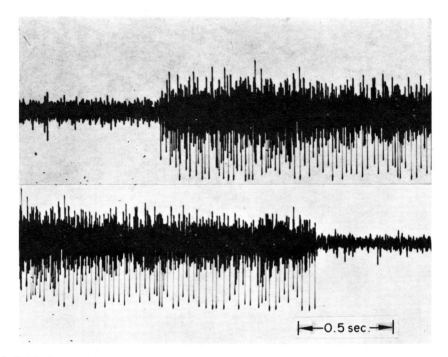

FIG. 7. EMG of paretic lateral rectus. Notice the slow recruitment of units at the beginning of the abduction saccade with absence of the usual "pulse" of activity (upper trace). Reduction of activity for the return saccade is normally abrupt.

gives a vertical lever arm to the lateral rectus during upgaze as shown in Fig. 10. This scheme is capable of being greatly extended by new knowledge of the tension and stiffness characteristics of the muscle and its surrounding tissues. Consider only the upper and lower border muscle fibers of the lateral rectus muscle at 30° upgaze (Fig. 11). If the muscle fibers were exceedingly stiff as tendons, the extension of the lower fibers from 40.0 to 41.5 mm and relaxation of the upper fibers from 40.0 to

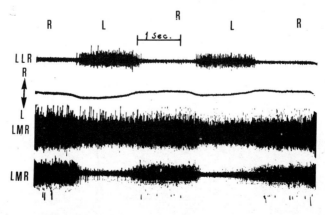

FIG. 8. EMG during attempted saccades. Notice lack of normal abrupt changes in activity. The patient awoke from an alcoholic debauch 3 months before unable to move his eyes normally.

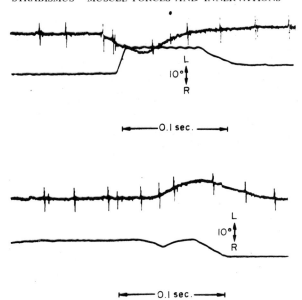

FIG. 9. VI, VII, and VIII, palsy following severe head injury. Notice lateral rectus units change frequency before saccades in either direction, but do not change with altered gaze position (upper trace EMG, lower trace position of fellow eye).

37.1 mm would put the entire strain on the lower muscle fibers. Contrariwise, if stiffness were very low in proportion to tension, then such a twist of insertion would make only a trivial shift of effective force toward the inferior border. We have calculated the effect of stretching and relaxing the muscle by twist, using the stiffness found for human muscle in the primary position (Fig. 14A, Collins current preceding chapter). The result shows the effective insertion, calculated as the center of the sum of moments assigned all along the insertion to be shifted significantly towards the original horizontal line present with gaze in the primary position. This effect differs with various amounts

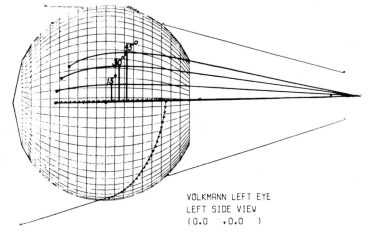

FIG. 10. Vertical lever arm of the lateral rectus in 15°, 30° and 45° upgaze, assuming pull is along a line from center of origin to center of insertion.

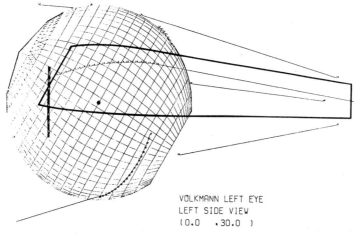

VOLKMANN LEFT EYE
LEFT SIDE VIEW
(0.0   .30.0)

FIG. 11. 30° upgaze.

of gaze, but about a 30% reduction in upward movement of the effective insertion line can be accounted for by this stiffness.

Slip of the lateral rectus muscle over the globe is prevented by two mechanisms. The "footplates" of the muscle attached to underlying sclera 4 to 5 mm posterior to the usual linear insertion, and restrain vertical movement of the muscle to 1–2 mm. The muscle is markedly freed to vertical movement after removing it from its regular insertion, if these attachments are then cut. The intermuscular septum acts in a similar way. In two patients at strabismus surgery the eye was rotated 45° obliquely downward, creating relative stress on the lateral-superior tissues on the globe. The position of the upper border of the muscle and sclera was carefully marked, and the superior intermuscular septum then cut. The upper muscle border immediately moved downward 1 to 2 mm, showing the importance of this membrane in maintaining the muscle insertion at a relatively stable position and preventing vertical movement of the muscle. The intermuscular membrane anteriorly may be looked upon as a mechanism to allow the muscle and tendon to roll on and off the globe in the usual pathway, but which prevent at the same time any sidewise translation around the globe. Effectively, the insertion point of the muscle may thus be considered as moved posteriorly 4–5 mm along its true line, as far as any sideslip is concerned.

Internal restriction on lateral separation of the longitudual muscle fibers is strong just at the tendon–muscle junction. The 9–10-mm width of the muscle here is exceeded only by surgical separation (those who have split the muscle in the O'Conner "Cinch" operation will recall this). A classical great circle path for the upper edge fibers of the muscle would be about 18 mm separated from the lower edge fibers, also going on a great circle path; clearly this is an impossibility, and the muscle is a cohesive unit at this point.

Internal shear. Resistance within the muscle to cross-couple forces concentrates tension on the stretched edge. When a detached muscle in an alert patient fixing straight ahead is held with force measuring gazes at each end of the insertion, a tension of about 7 g is recorded. When one of these is loosened the remaining attachment sees a tension of 11–12 g. The effect of this shear resistance with twisting of the insertion during vertical movements will thus concentrate tension at the lower end of the insertion during upgaze, indeed all tension is slacked off except at the stretched edge for a 45° twist (Fig. 12).

Figure 12 also shows that the angle between the normal center of rotation and each edge of the muscle insertion is very nearly 45°. Thus, the inferior and superior edge of the insertion are brought directly in front of the center of rotation during vertical movements, and create a negligible vertical torque on the globe. Only a proper combination of distance of the insertion in front of the center of rotation, width of the insertion, stiffness of the muscle, and appropriate cross-coupling within the muscle would bring this elegant relationship to pass. An implication of this is that the central nervous system does not have to account to any great degree for the vertical gaze position of the eyes in order to apply horizontal movement, since the entire force of the horizontal rectus muscles will be along the same vector path in the orbit independent of vertical gaze movement. Helmholz's intuition was correct, of course.

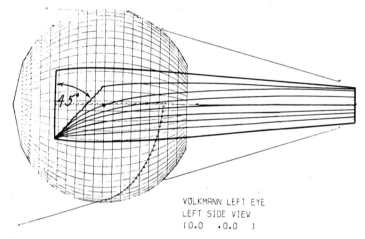

VOLKMANN LEFT EYE
LEFT SIDE VIEW
(0.0 ,0.0)

FIG. 12. Detachment of a rectus muscle except for one end of the insertion transfers 80% of the original tension to the remaining insertion point. 45° twist of the insertion around a point slightly behind the insertion will have a similar effect.

What happens when the tension rises to 40 g as it does in extreme abduction or oblique gaze? Oblique gaze upward and temporally 30° moves the lateral rectus insertion to a position almost on top of the horizontal axis. Thus, even less vertical lever arm is developed than with ordinary vertical gaze through the saggital plane. For oblique gaze upward and medially 30°, the lateral rectus is seen to take a path which is significantly above the center of rotation for the upper fibers (Fig. 13). However, in adduction lateral rectus innervation is reduced and muscle tension is only 17 g. Further, twist of the insertion relaxes these upper fibers, so that little upgaze torque is added. When the eye is restrained from normal adduction the isometric tension in the medial rectus and the tension in the abnormally stiff lateral tissues restraining movement increases to 80 g or more. This creates marked vertical vector components giving rise to the vertical "upshoot and downshoot" which occur in the oblique gaze in exotropia, in tightness of the lateral rectus muscle, and in Duane's syndrome. The finding that the

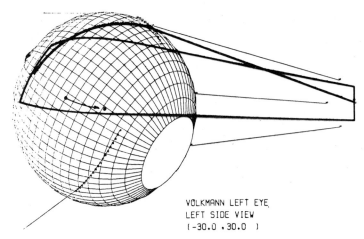

VOLKMANN LEFT EYE
LEFT SIDE VIEW
(-30.0 , 30.0)

FIG. 13. The lateral rectus (heavy lines) viewed from the lateral side with gaze 30° obliquely upward and 30° adduction. The great circle path joining the center of origin and insertion is the upper dashed line. The muscle does not take this position.

intermuscular membrane is loose, thus allowing the muscle to slip vertically upwards in such cases, contributes to the anomaly (Jampolsky, 1968). This high tension cannot be relaxed by the few millimeters' twist of the insertion to restore the effective insertion line to the lower edge of the muscle as happens at normal, lower tensions. Purely horizontal muscle surgery obliterates these vertical effects.

Recession of an extraocular muscle would move the muscle almost over the center of rotation, thus reducing any vertical lever arm created by vertical rotation (Fig. 14). Advancement of the muscle will increase the vertical effects of the horizontal muscles with vertical gaze, quite in contrast with this normalization which occurs from recession. Movement of the muscle superiorly (Fig. 14) will create changes in

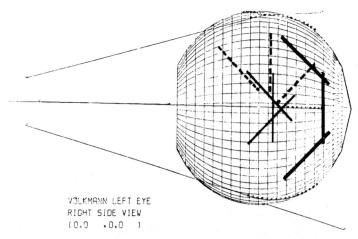

VOLKMANN LEFT EYE
RIGHT SIDE VIEW
(0.0 , 0.0)

FIG. 14. With the muscle insertion recessed (solid line) the horizontal pull remains with 45° vertical gaze up and down. With the insertion advanced (double line) large vertical vectors occur with 45° vertical gaze. With the insertion raised and elevated (dashed line) the insertion is loosened >3.0 mm with upgaze (reducing tension from 12 to 6 g, about) and tightened >3.0 mm with upgaze (increasing tension from 12 to 22 g, about).

horizontal length of the muscle with vertical gaze, with rather little vertical vector change, suitable for the A–V pattern corrections. In such situations bunching the muscle insertion together or keeping it straight will make little difference. In other circumstances, however, attention to the intermuscular membrane and proper reinsertion of the muscle in the globe will be critical in avoiding vertical effects from horizontal muscle surgery.

A similar analysis can be applied to the vertical muscles showing relative stability of vertical muscle effects as the eyes track in horizontal gaze. In particular, the inferior oblique is shown by our experiments to have its effective insertion at the ligament of Lockwood where it is tightly held to the inferior rectus, so it cannot slip forward or posteriorly. This is similar to the intermuscular membrane effect on the lateral rectus in vertical gaze.

ACKNOWLEDGEMENTS

This investigation was supported by NIH Research Grants No. P01 EY-01186 and P01 EY-00299 and by the Smith-Kettlewell Eye Research Foundation.

I gratefully acknowledge the collaboration of Dr. Carter Collins and Mr. David O'Meara in these studies. Mr. Robert Bowen gave important assistance in electromyography.

The computer-drawn figures of the eye after Volkmann's measurements provide a remarkable insight into the local mechanics, and I am grateful to Hellaman Roth Pratt Ferguson, Ph.D., Department of Mathematics, Brigham Young University, Provo, Utah, for their use.

REFERENCES

ALVARADO, G. This volume, pp. 15–43.
BOEDER, P. (1961) The co-operation of extraocular muscles. *Am. J. Opthal.* **51**, 469–481.
CHAVASSE, B. and BLAKESTON, T. (1939) *Worth's Squint*, p. 175. Philadelphia.
DE GROOT, J. A., SCOTT, A. B., SINDON, A. and AUTHIN, L. (1974) The human ocular position of rest. *Proceedings of the Second Congress of the International Strabismus Association, Kingston* (in press).
HAYNES, H., WHITE, B. L. and HELD, R. (1965) *Science*, **148**, 526.
JAMPOLSKY, A. J. (1968) *Strabismus Symposium of The New Orleans Academy of Ophthalmology, Mosby, St. Louis.*
JONES, G. M. This volume, pp. 227–245.
KREWSON, W. E. (1950) The action of the extraocular muscles. *Trans. Am. Ophthal. Soc.* **48**, 433–486.
NAKAGAWA, T. (1965) Topographic anatomical studies on the orbit and its contents. *Acta Soc. Ophthal. Jap.* **69**, 2155–2179.
RETHY, I. (1969) Development of the stimultaneous fixation from the divergent anatomic eye position of the neonate. *J. Ped Opthal* **6**, 92–96.
SCOTT, A. B. and COLLINS, C. C. (1973) Division of labor in human extraocular muscle. *Arch. Ophthal.* **90**, 319–322.
SCOTT, A. B. and WONG, G. Y. (1972) Duane's syndrome. *Arch. Ophthal.* **87**, 140–147.

COORDINATION OF EXTRAOCULAR MUSCLES†

KEN NAKAYAMA

INTRODUCTION

The purpose of this paper will be to describe how some of the elements in the peripheral oculomotor apparatus are coordinated when the eye is not moving. This includes a consideration of how the neural outputs between muscles are interrelated as well as how each motor unit's activity is related to other motor units in the system. This paper takes as a starting-point the conceptual synthesis suggested by Westheimer (1973) relating the kinematic laws of eye movement and modern neurophysiology. It is my aim to further explicate this conceptual link and to describe some experiments of my own which show how the various elements in the oculomotor system are coordinated.

The relevant literature on this subject spans well over a century and is both behavioral and neurophysiological.

I. KINEMATIC LAWS OF EYE POSITION

The geometric/kinematic aspects of eye rotation were thoroughly studied in the nineteenth century and the section on eye movements in Helmholtz's treatise on physiological optics (Helmholtz, 1925) is largely devoted to this subject. For our purposes, two significant generalizations regarding the geometry or kinematics of eye movement are noteworthy; they are Donders' Law and Listing's Law.

Donders' Law states that for every gaze position there exists one and only one orientation of the globe in the head and this is independent of the particular route the eye took to reach that position. Given the visual direction which can be specified in terms of two angles, the angle of twist or cyclorotation about the visual axis is completely determined and cannot vary, indicating that two numbers are sufficient to specify the orientation of the eye in the head. This stands in contrast to the fact that it takes three numbers to describe the orientation of any free body in space. Therefore, one degree of rotational constraint is imposed upon the eye.

An analogy might be useful at this point. Consider a mechanical contrivance such as the movable "type" head of an IBM Selectric Typewriter. The spherical ball or "type sphere" is covered with raised letters and it quickly changes position as the various keys on the keyboard are depressed. This mechanism, like the eye, has one

†This investigation was supported by NIH research grants No. EY-01186 and No. EY-00299 from the National Eye Institute, and by the Smith-Kettlewell Eye Research Foundation.

degree of rotational constraint for if this were not the case, it would be possible for the correct letters to appear on the printed page but they would not necessarily be in the correct upright orientation. For each "letter position" on a useful machine there must exist a particular orientation of the "type sphere" in space. Therefore, this "type sphere" also obeys an analogous law to Donders' Law. If we look at the machine more closely we see that it is the mechanical linkage of the sphere to the typewriter which constrains the sphere to rotate with only two degrees of freedom, there being only two axes of rotation. The "type sphere" is limited in its motion as a simple consequence of its mechanical attachments.

What should be of interest to the neurophysiologist is the fact that such a simple mechanical reason will *not* suffice to explain Donders' Law for the eye, and that one must look *beyond* to the operations of the nervous system. We shall return to this issue shortly.

Listing's Law is more inclusive than Donders' Law as it specifies for each gaze position the particular orientation or cyclorotation of the globe. It says that the eye's orientation for a given gaze position is geometrically equivalent to the situation where the eye has made a single rotation from the primary position to that gaze position about an axis lying in Listing's plane (the frontal plane passing through the center of rotation of the eye). This completely specifies the rotational state of the eye for each gaze position. Such rotational states can be described algebraically by quarternions (Westheimer, 1957) or more conveniently by matrices (Pratt-Ferguson, 1973; Nakayama, 1974; Robinson, 1963). In any case, the expected cyclorotation of an eye marker can be predicted and empirically verified. This has been done on numerous occasions over the past century and the cyclorotations of the globe have been found to be consistent with Listing's Law for selected observers and gaze positions (see Alpern, 1969, for review).

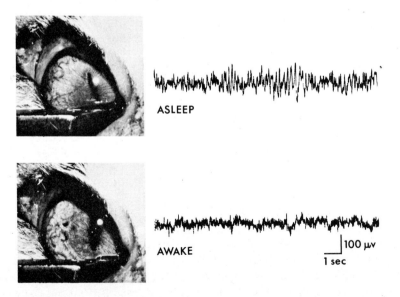

Fig. 1. Photograph of cat slit pupil and associated electroencephalogram during a period of sleeping and waking.

It was stated earlier that this one degree of rotational constraint is entirely neural in origin. There are many reasons to support this conclusion. First, the geometrical arrangement of the origins and insertions of the six extraocular muscles do not oblige the eye to move with only two degrees of freedom. On the contrary, the three pairs of muscles are arranged so that their corresponding axes of rotation are almost mutually perpendicular, ensuring three degrees of rotational freedom over the widest possible range. Second, there are significant examples where Listing's Law is systematically violated. It does not hold during convergence rotations (Hering, 1879; Allen, 1954) and utrically induced countertorsional rotations (Krejcova *et al.*, 1969). Furthermore, I have found in encephale isole cats that, although the cat eye approximates Listing's Law when the animal is awake, it does not do so when the animal is asleep. Figure 1 shows a comparison of the normally intorted slit pupil when the cat is awake as compared to the uncharacteristic extorted orientation of the pupil which can often be seen when the animal is asleep. A distribution of pupil positions (Fig. 2) shows that they are more regular and orderly when the animal is awake and that they are quite disorderly when the animal is asleep. Another way of characterizing the difference between waking and sleeping is to say that in waking the cat eye has two rotational degrees of freedom whereas in sleep the eye has three rotational degrees of freedom.

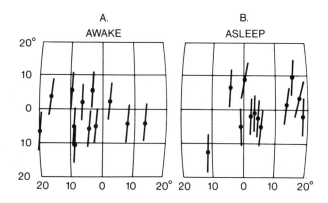

FIG. 2. Superimposition of a series of photographs of pupil positions during waking and sleeping.

All of the above considerations point to the fact that it is the nervous system which must provide the one degree of rotational constraint to the eye and that the kinematic or "behavioral" laws of eye rotation are not the consequence of the mechanical connections to the globe. The constraint must ultimately lie in the manner in which the central nervous system allocates the flow of nerve impulses to the individual motoneurons.

Another obvious and important conclusion which can be derived from the kinematic laws is that these laws rule out a very large set of possible innervational states to the muscles which could point the visual axis in a particular fixation direction. These laws tell us that not only must the sum of the muscles forces point the visual axis in the proper direction, but the innervations to these muscles must be correctly proportioned so the eye is oriented properly in space.

Eye Fixations: Position or Movement Coded

In this section I will argue that the oculomotor system must be a position-coded system. This conclusion was reached by Robinson (1970) from neurophysiological recordings of single oculomotoneurons. The present argument following Westheimer (1973), however, relies on kinematic considerations alone and stands independent of any neurophysiological data. The conclusions of these arguments are that the commands to extraocular muscles must ultimately be expressed in terms of an absolute eyeball position in the head rather than as a relative movement from a previous position, i.e. the coulomotor system must ultimately be referenced with respect to a head-based coordinate system rather than a coordinate system based only on the visual field.

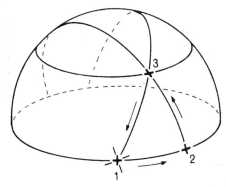

FIG. 3. Pictorial description of the change in cyclorotation of the eye if the visual axis were to move along the shortest path to make fixations. Eye starts by looking at 1 (the primary position) with a vertically oriented cross intersecting the visual axis. Then it rotates to 2, then to 3, then back to 1. After returning to 1, the orientation of the cross is no longer vertical. (Adapted from Boeder, 1957.)

To clarify this point, consider the alternative case where the brain has only visual field information with which to program steady eye fixations. Under these circumstances it can generate eye fixations only as a relative movement from a previous position. Cohen and Henn (1973), for example, suggest that this is indeed how the brain codes the flow of nerve impulses to extraocular motoneurons. The difficulty of this relative movement hypothesis, however, becomes apparent if we imagine a sequence of rotations from the primary position. For example, consider a particular situation where the eye has made a direct rotation to the left of the primary position and then a target appears directly above the fovea in the superior visual field. The relative movement hypothesis assumes that the brain knows only that the target is above the fovea. Given this to be the case, one assumes that it makes the simplest rotation to fixate the target, namely a direct rotation which takes the visual pole along a great circle to that target. If this occurs, however, the result is that the eye is no longer oriented in the head in accordance with Listing's Law, but has an abnormal cyclorotation. Then if a target is presented at the primary position and is fixated by a great circle rotation of the visual pole to this position, the eye will now have a cyclorotation which it did not have at the start of this sequence of rotations (see Figs. 3 and 4).

In order for this sequence of rotations to be consistent with Listing's Law, the visual pole does not necessarily rotate in a manner equivalent to a simple great circle

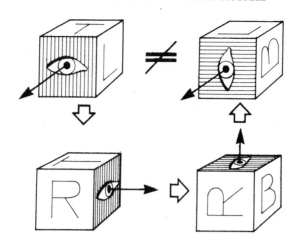

FIG. 4. An extreme example of a sequence of eye rotations which clearly show that direct "great circle" rotations of the visual pole lead to an accumulated torsional error. Eye starts by looking ahead in the primary position (upper left). The eye "sees" a target 90° to its left and the visual axis rotates directly to secure fixation (lower left); then the eye "sees" a target 90° above and the visual axis rotates directly to secure fixation (lower right). Finally the eye "sees" a target 90° to the right and the visual axis again rotates directly to secure fixation (upper right). After this series of rotations, the visual axis is again pointing in the direction of the primary direction of regard but it has accumulated a torsional error of 90°, a clear violation of Donders' Law.

rotation but along a unique circle called a direction circle (Helmholz, 1925; Southall, 1961). This circle passes through the initial and final fixation positions *and* the occipital pole (which is the point lying diametrically opposite to the primary position in the spherical field of fixation).

In essence the brain must know something equivalent to knowing the position of the occipital pole (a head-based reference) in relation to the positions of the fixations. Otherwise the eye could not rotate in accordance with Donders' and Listing's Laws, for without a reference with respect to the head, the brain will have no basis to compute the relative cyclorotation from one fixation to another.

It could be argued, however, that the brain could still generate rotations congruent with Listing's Law by assuming a role for visual cues. For example, this might occur after the eye had fixated the target by using visual cues to determine the layout at the vertical with respect to the retina. This counter-hypothesis, however, predicts correct orientations only for fixations in primary and secondary gaze positions and is therefore rather weak. In order to further deal with this "visual field orientation" hypothesis, the cyclorotation of the eye was measured photographically in the dark where visual cues of orientation were absent. The subject was placed in a bite bar and visible marking pins were placed adjacent to the eye and fixed to the apparatus. By measuring the position of identifiable limbal blood vessels in relation to marking pins it was possible to determine the relative cyclorotation of the eye to better than 0.1°.

In this experiment the subject sat in a completely dark room and successively fixated three dim lamps which were lit only one at a time. First he fixed target 1 (in the primary position), then 2 (10° to the left of 1) and then 3 (10° up from position

2), and then back to the primary position. The sequence of these three fixations is depicted in Fig. 3 (not drawn to scale for this experiment). Each set of these three fixations constitutes a "loop" and photographs of the eye were taken at the primary position after a given number of loops to see if there was a difference in accumulated torsion. If the brain were simply programming a direct rotation from one fixation position to another, as would be predicted from a relative movement hypothesis, we should expect to see an accumulated torsional error of 0.887° in this experiment every time the eye goes around a "loop".

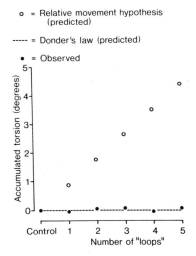

FIG. 5. Accumulated torsion as a function of the number of fixation loops. Eye photographed in dark room with no cues for orientation. Relative movement hypothesis predicts there should be 0.88° of accumulated torsion for each loop (open circles). Position coding hypothesis and Donders' Law (solid line) predict no accumulated torsion. Data obtained plotted as solid points.

Figure 5 shows that after each successive "loop" there is no evidence whatsoever for any accumulated torsion. As one makes successive fixations around the loop and returns to the primary position, there is no difference in the cyclorotation of the eye and this is accurate to better than 0.1° for any number of loops up to five. This indicates that in the dark, the oculomotor system can very accurately program the innervations to the muscles, keeping torsional errors to a very low level. Since there is nothing in the darkened room to act as a cue for spatial orientation the visual system has no information with which to preserve the orientation of the eye in the orbit. This type of data provides another confirmation of Donders' Law and shows that Donders' Law does not rely on visual cues of orientation. Most importantly it affirms the principle that the command signal to the extraocular muscles must be based in terms of an absolute position in the head and not on a relative movement from a previous position.

II. NEUROPHYSIOLOGICAL ASPECTS

Earlier it was argued that the kinematic laws very largely constrain the set of possible innervational states which could point the visual axis in the proper direction. Neurophysiological recordings confirm (Westheimer, 1973) and extend these conclusions. For not only does it appear that the number of innervational states to the muscles for each gaze position is limited, but single unit recordings from oculomotor neurons show that there is essentially one and only one innervational state for each gaze position. The work of Robinson (1970), Schiller (1970), and Fuchs and Luschei (1970) indicates that for a given motoneuron there is a fairly tight linear relationship between motoneuron firing frequency and gaze position in the alert monkey for versions. This has been further confirmed in humans (Scott and Collins, 1973) and other species (Racine, 1972; Gestrin and Sterling, 1973). Furthermore, I have found that this relationship can also be seen between muscle unit firing frequency and isometric tension in a single muscle in an encephale isole cat. Figure 6 shows the relation between firing frequency of two motor units recorded simultaneously with an intra-muscular EMG microelectrode and isometric muscle tension in cat superior oblique muscle. These curves show a close similarity to the ones which relate motoneuron firing frequency and gaze position.

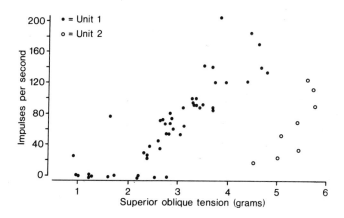

FIG. 6. Relation between isometric tension and firing frequency of two motor units in cat superior oblique muscle recorded simultaneously during steady fixation. Solid points are from unit No. 1, open points from unit No. 2.

These results relating motor unit firing frequency to gaze position and muscle force confirm a clarifying principle of motoneuron organization for oculomotoneurons which has generally been found for skeletal muscle. The principle is that the motoneuron pool to a particular muscle is organized in such a way that there is a determined and orderly recruitment of motoneurons as the muscle is shortened (Henneman, 1965; Davis, 1971). Since the activity of each motor unit is related to the activity of all other motor units in the muscle in a predetermined manner, the whole system of motor units within a muscle has essentially *one* degree of freedom. This implies that the state of an entire motoneuron pool to a muscle can be described by a single parameter. More specifically, work of Collins (reported in this Symposium) very nicely shows that for steady-gaze positions there is very orderly recruitment of motor units as the tension requirements of the muscle increase; with the smaller orbital fibers firing first, followed by the firing of the larger globular fibers as the eye moves further into the field of action of the muscle.

Thus, there appears to be a remarkable simplicity with regard to motoneuron organization within a muscle. Despite the multiplicity of fibers and fiber types (Alvarado and Van Horn, 1974; Peachey, 1971; Lennerstrand, 1974), each fiber appears to have a preordained workload for a given gaze position. In essence, the seeming multiplicity of neural innervation to a single muscle can be described by a single number.

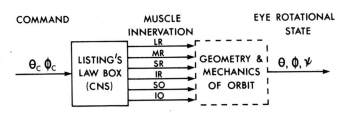

FIG. 7. Overview of oculomotor control system as suggested by considerations of the kinematics of eye rotation (see text).

If we describe the neural activity to a muscle by a single number and call this an "innervation number", we can consider each muscle as having a particular "innervation number" which theoretically can describe the activity of all its elements. Taken together, the six innervational numbers can be considered to be a six component vector. From our previous discussion of eye kinematics and neurophysiology it should be clear that the six terms of this vector have only two degrees of freedom. Thus:

$$
\begin{pmatrix}
\text{lr} \\
\text{mr} \\
\text{sr} \\
\text{ir} \\
\text{so} \\
\text{io}
\end{pmatrix}
= f(\theta, \phi)
$$

where lr, mr, sr, etc., refer to the innervational states to each muscle and θ and ϕ are the two parameters of gaze position. From a machine point of view this is equivalent to saying that a command signal comes down to some sort of mechanism (the Listing's Law Box) and this device determines the innervation to each of the six muscles. These innervations then cause the muscles to pull the globe in a manner whose description will be quite complex, depending on the geometry of the muscle origins and insertions, the mechanical characteristics of the orbital tissues and the length–tension relationship for each individual muscle. Although this mechanical interaction has yet to be satisfactorily described, the end result must be that any eye rotation must be in accordance with Listing's Law.

Figure 7 summarizes this overall view of the relation between command signals, the neurological substrate, and eye kinematics. In essence, I suggest that there is some sort of neural integrating mechanism (Listing's Law Box) which receives the two-dimensional command signal of eye position in the head and then precisely programs an innervation to each muscle. Then given this pattern of innervation to the muscle, the mechanical configuration of muscles in the globe dictates that the eye will rotate in accordance with Listing's Law.

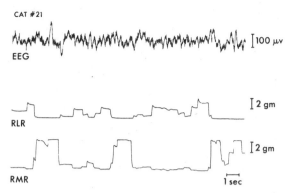

FIG. 8. Simultaneous recordings of EEG and isometric muscle tension of the right lateral rectus (RLR) and the right medial rectus (RMR) in a waking encephale isole cat.

III. EYE MUSCLE RECORDING

As a way to check the above overview and to specify some details more clearly, I recorded the outputs of a number of muscles (up to five simultaneously in the cat). Under halothane anesthesia, the muscles were removed from the globe and isometric strain gauges were attached to the muscles. Then the cats were prepared encephale isole and locally anesthetized with xylocaine. The EEG was also monitored to help determine the state of sleeping and waking. The end tidal CO_2 was monitored by a gas analyzer and was kept within physiological limits by adjusting the rate of artificial respiration. Muscle tensions and EEG were printed on a polygraph.

The most apparent set of relations which can be seen under these circumstances is that of reciprocal innervation within an antagonistic pair of muscles. For example, Fig. 8 shows a sample record of tensions for the lateral rectus and the medial rectus muscles. Note that the tensions are reciprocally directed. If we plot lateral versus medial rectus tension on a single graph we see that the set of tensions fall along the arc of a rectangular hyperbola (Fig. 9A), there being a large set of tensions which are in a sense "forbidden" by the CNS. This result can be also seen for the vertical rectus and the oblique pair of muscles. This is an expected result in that it confirms previous work (Sherrington, 1894; McCouch and Adler, 1932).

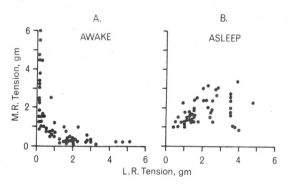

FIG. 9. Relation between isometric tension in the lateral and medial rectus muscle in waking (A) and sleeping (B).

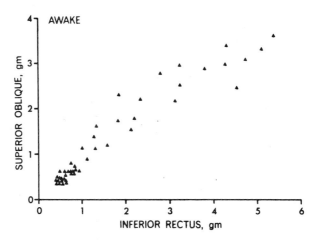

F<small>IG</small>. 10. Relation between isometric tension in superior oblique muscle and inferior rectus muscle for awaking animal.

Another conspicuous relation is the coupling between the oblique muscle system and the vertical rectus system. For example, there is a rather high positive correlation between tensions recorded in the superior oblique and the inferior rectus (Fig. 10), and this is also the case between the inferior oblique and the superior rectus. This yoking of the vertical and the oblique system was postulated many years ago by Hering (1879) mainly on geometrical grounds.

IV. DEGRADATION OF EYE-MUSCLE COORDINATION IN SLEEP

The above results taken together further indicate that the brain proportions the flow of nerve impulses to the muscles in a very orderly manner, permitting only certain patterns of contractions to be generated.

It was mentioned earlier that the rotations of the cat's eye are less ordered in sleep than they are in waking. We should expect therefore to see less orderliness in the pattern of innervational states during sleep as we have argued that kinematic lawfulness (Donders' and Listing's Laws) is the result of innervation lawfulness.

A comparison of Fig. 10 and Fig. 11 shows that the relation between the superior rectus and the inferior oblique is indeed more disordered in sleeping than it is in waking. Characteristically, in sleep the inferior rectus often contracts without concomitant contractions in the superior oblique. A similar breakdown in coupling can also be seen if we compare inferior oblique and superior rectus. Thus the two muscle pairs which are usually coupled in waking appear to be considerably less coupled in sleep. There is in essence less orderliness in the relation between the two muscle pairs.

The breakdown of coordination can also be seen within a muscle pair. Instead of the usual reciprocally related sets of tension normally seen in waking, the tension states are much more randomly distributed. For example, Fig. 9B shows that there is no evidence of the reciprocal relation between lateral and medial rectus normally

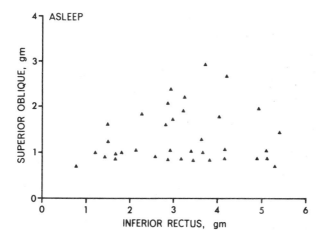

FIG. 11. Relation between superior oblique and inferior rectus tension when animal is asleep.

seen in waking. In sleep the brain no longer "forbids" the set of antagonistic muscles to co-contract.

The concomitant breakdown of rotational lawfulness and innervation lawfulness in sleep further corroborates the view that it is the central nervous system which is responsible for the kinematic laws of eye rotation.

Going beyond this, I believe we should attempt to specify the rules of coordination of muscle innervations since such information may provide clues as to the exact nature of the brain circuitry responsible for the coordination of the muscles. It is of interest to find out whether each reciprocally innervated pair is an independent functional unit such that given any normal set of innervations to the muscles, the relation between muscles within a pair will remain invariant. For example, does the reciprocal relation between the lateral and medial rectus muscle change as a function of what the vertical rectus muscles are doing? To explore this question, I plotted medial rectus tension versus lateral rectus tension when the eye was attempting to make fixations at various elevations. For example, the open triangles of Fig. 12 show the set of tension states where the eye is attempting to make upward fixations (the tension in the superior rectus is greater than 2 g) versus the situation where the eye is programmed to fixate near the horizontal plane (superior and inferior rectus tension both less than 2 g). Comparing the two plots we see that there is no systematic difference in the reciprocal relation between the two conditions. Other plots also show no systematic changes in the reciprocal relations within a pair. Therefore, this data suggests that to a first-order approximation, reciprocal pairs form functional units and these units have an independence from other pairs.

Assuming for the moment that we do have independent reciprocal pairs, I think it is useful to schematize pictorially the type of circuitry we might expect to find inside the hypothetical Listing's Law box. Figure 13 shows that the Listing's Law box consists of three separate sub-systems corresponding to the three sets of antagonistic pairs. The outputs to the three pairs have essentially only two degrees of freedom. This could come about in a number of possible ways and I suggest two. There is

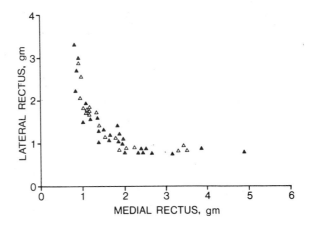

FIG. 12. Plot of lateral rectus versus medial rectus tension as a function of what the vertical rectus is doing. Open symbols are plots when the eye is programmed to look up (superior rectus tension greater than 2 g), filled symbols when eye is looking near the primary plane of regard (superior rectus tension and inferior rectus tension less than 2 g).

the possibility that Listing's and Donders' Law is simply the consequence of the fact that there are three reciprocally innervated pairs and that two of these pairs (the verticals and the obliques) are coupled directly to a vertical gaze system (Possibility A). This implies that Listing's Law was simply the by-product of a simple set of neural connections. At present, too little is known about the exact nature of the mechanical actions of the various muscles to confirm this purely on geometrical and mechanical grounds. Another possibility is that the relations are much more complex with interactions between all the three muscle pair systems (Possibility B). Unfortunately, the data from the muscle's tensions of the encephale isole cat are not sufficiently free from variability to select the alternatives. Hopefully, chronic recordings of motoneuron discharge from intact animals will be more helpful.

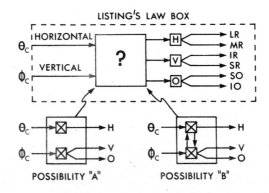

FIG. 13. Descriptive model of the Listing's Law Box. Model suggests that the Listing's Law Box is hierarchically organized such that the three muscle pairs comprise three sub-units.

V. EYE MUSCLE COORDINATION IN TORSION

It was mentioned earlier that under certain circumstances, the eye systematically violates Listing's Law and it is of some interest to examine the pattern of eye muscle coordination under such circumstances. When the head and body are rotated about the anterior–posterior axis, the cat's eye cyclorotates in the opposite direction by an amount less than the tilt of the head. Plotting the relation between the right superior oblique and the right inferior rectus for two head tilt positions, we see that the coupling between the two muscles is altered (Fig. 14). For example, when the head is tilted to the right, the superior oblique muscle is more strongly innervated in relation to the inferior rectus. It seems clear that the alteration of the coordination between the verticals and the obliques is responsible for the differences in torsion observed for the eyeball as a whole. Furthermore, it is of interest to see whether or not there is an alteration of coordination *within* a muscle pair during this change of coordination *between* muscle pairs. Earlier, I suggested that the pair formed an independent unit and if this were the case we should also expect to see no alteration in the relation between an antagonistic pair of muscles during torsion. No systematic alterations of reciprocal coordination have been seen. Figure 15 shows an example of the relation of superior and oblique inferior oblique muscles for two different positions of tilt. Note that there is no apparent difference in the relations between the two antagonistic muscles. This further corroborates the conclusion that one can consider the sets of reciprocal pairs as independent functional units.

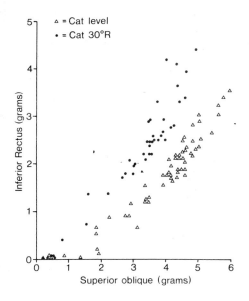

FIG. 14. Relation between right superior rectus tension and right inferior rectus tension during two different positions of body tilt about the anterior–posterior axis. Open triangles: cat level; filled triangles: cat head and body rotated about the anterior–posterior axis by 30° such that the right ear is below the left ear.

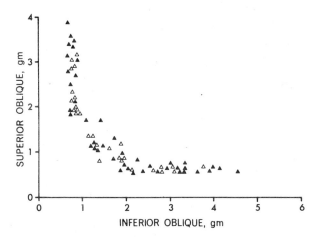

FIG. 15. Relation between tension in superior and inferior oblique muscles under two positions of head tilt. Filled triangles represent cat tilted 30° to the left and open triangles plotted when cat tilted 30° to the right.

VI. COORDINATION OF MUSCLES DURING CONVERGENCE MOVEMENTS

Previously, I mentioned that Listing's Law does not remain invariant during convergence movements. This means that for a given gaze position, there is a different rotational state for the eye depending on the amount of convergence. Such differences in cyclorotations seem to be more pronounced in different positions of gaze (Allen, 1954). It follows, therefore, that during convergence we should see a different set of innervational states to the muscles than during pure versions for given fixation positions. Although Keller and Robinson (1972) saw no change in the relation between gaze position and abducens firing rate during convergence, the above considerations imply that there should be some alteration in the relation between the innervation to the obliques and the superior rectus pair.

REFERENCES

ALLEN, M. J. (1954) The dependence of cyclophoria on convergence elevation and the system of axes. *Am. J. Optom.* **31**, 297–307.

ALPERN, M. (1969) Kinematics of the eye. Chapter 3 In: *The Eye*, III, DAVSON, H. (Ed.). Academic Press.

ALVARADO, J. and VAN HORN, C. Morphology of extraocular muscles (in preparation).

COLLINS. C. C. (1974) The human oculomotor system. In: *Basic Mechanisms of Ocular Motility and Their Clinical Implications*, LENNERSTRAND, G., BACH-Y-RITA, P., COLLINS, C. C. and SCOTT, A. (Eds.). Oxford, England, Pergamon Press Ltd. (in press).

DAVIS, W. J. (1971) Functional significance of motoneuron size and soma position in swimmeret system of the lobster. *J. Neurophysiol.* **34**, 274–288.

FUCHS, A. and LUSCHEI, E. (1970) Firing patterns of abducens neurons of alert monkeys in relationship to horizontal eye movement. *J. Neurophysiol.* **33**, 382–392.

GESTRIN, P. and STERLING, P. (1973) Eye movement related neurons in the goldfish medulla. Paper presented at ARVO Annual Meeting, 1973, Sarasota, Florida, p. 63.

HELMHOLTZ, H. (VON) (1925) *Treatise on Physiological Optics.* SOUTHALL, J. P. C. S. (Ed.). Dover.

HENN, V. and COHEN, B. (1973) Quantitative analysis of activity in eye muscle motoneurons during saccadic eye movements and positions of fixation. *J. Neurophysiol.* **36**, 115–126.

HENNEMAN, E., SOMJEN, G. and CARPENTER, D. O. (1965). Excitability and inhibitibility of motoneurons of different sizes. *J. Neurophysiol.* **28**, 599–620.

HERING, E. (1879) Der Raumsinn und die Bewegungen des Auges. In *Handbuch der Physiologie*, HERMANN, L. (Ed.), vol. III, Teil 1, pp. 343–601. F. C. W. Vogel Leipzig.

KELLER, E. L. and ROBINSON, D. A. (1972) Abducens unit behavior in the monkey during vergence movements. *Vision Res.* **12**, 369–382.

KREJCOVA, H., HIGHSTEIN, S. and COHEN, B. (1969) Labyrinthine and extralabyrinthine effects on ocular counter-rolling. *Acta Otolaryng.* **72**, 165–171.

LENNERSTRAND, G. (1975) Isometric tension and electrical activity in motor units of the cat's inferior oblique muscle. *Acta Physiol. scand.* (in press).

McCOUCH, L. V. and ADLER, F. H. (1932) Extraocular reflexes. *Am. J. Physiol.* **100**, 78–88.

MERGLER-RACINE, DONNA (1973) Neural activity in the efferent limb of the vestibulocular reflex arc. Thesis, McGill University.

NAKAYAMA, K. (1974) Photographic determination of the rotational state of the eye using matrices. *Am. J. Optom. and Physiol. Optics* **51**, 736–742.

PEACHEY, L. (1971) The structure of the extraocular muscle fibers of mammals. In: *The Control of Eye Movements*, BACH-Y-RITA, P. and COLLINS, C. C. (Eds.), pp. 47–66. Academic Press, New York.

PRATT-FERGUSON (1973) In preparation.

ROBINSON, D. A. (1963) A method of measuring eye movement using a scleral search coil in a magnetic field. *IEEE Trans. Biomedical Electronics*, **BME-10**, 137–145.

ROBINSON, D. A. (1970) Oculomotor unit behavior in the monkey. *J. Neurophysiol.* **33**, 393–404.

SCOTT, A. B. and COLLINS, C. C. (1973) Division of labor in human extraocular muscle. *Arch. Ophthal.* **90**, 319–322.

SCHILLER, P. H. (1970) The discharge characteristics of single units in the oculomotor and abducens nuclei of the unanesthetized monkey. *Exptl. Brain Res.* **10**, 347–362.

SHERRINGTON, C. S. (1894) Experimental note on two movements of the eye. *J. Physiol. (Lond.)* **17**, 27–29.

SOUTHALL, JAMES P. C. (1961) *Introduction to Physiological Optics*, Dover Publications.

WESTHEIMER, G. (1957) Kinematics of the eye. *J. Opt. Soc. Am.* **47**, 967–974.

WESTHEIMER, G. and BLAIR, S. M. (1972) Concerning the supranuclear organization of eye movements. *Bibl. Ophthal.* **32**, 28–35.

WESTHEIMER, G. (1973) Saccadic eye movements. In: *The Oculomotor System and Brain Functions*, ZIKMUND, V. (Ed.). Bratislava, Czechoslovakia, Publishing House of the Slovak Academy of Sciences.

COORDINATION OF EXTRAOCULAR MUSCLES; CLINICAL ASPECTS

ARTHUR JAMPOLSKY

INTRODUCTION

Strabismus diagnosis and management problems center around the balance or imbalance of two oculorotary factors: (1) muscle and orbital mechanics, (2) muscle tonus.

The basic deviation is a measure of these two factors in the awake alert state. One makes the determination of the basic deviation (or zero reference point) by eliminating the controllable tonic (retinal) influences of (a) accommodative-convergence and (b) fusion-vergences. What remains are the nonretinally derived (supranuclear) tonic influences, acting together with the mechanical factors, to give the basic deviation. This is a most important clinical determination to make, and is of course the zero reference point for fusion-vergences.

The retinal-tonic factors (accommodative-vergence, and fusion-vergence) are tonic *adjustive* mechanisms.

The nonretinal-tonic factors are derived from a multitude of sources, and constitute a level or substrate of tonic *balance* or imbalance. In the horizontal meridian, there is a difference in mechanical reactivity to the changes in the tonic level or substrate between the medial rectus and the lateral rectus.

One must have a clear understanding of the origins and characteristics of retino-tonic *adjustive* mechanisms, and of the nonretino-tonic mechanical *balance* mechanisms.

Basic to this understanding is what is—and what is not—a fusion-vergence, and how it does, or does not affect the basic deviation. Similarly one must be clear about how and when the nonretino-tonic-mechanical factors affect the basic deviation. In my opinion it is in this area of tonus (retinal and nonretinal) and their characteristics, and modes of action, where there is maximum confusion to clinicians and laboratory scientists alike.

I shall comment on Dr. Nakayama's presentation primarily relative to his remarks on the coordination of muscles during vergence movements, and try to relate this to some practical problems in the clinical management of strabismus. I shall remark especially upon *habitual* fusion-vergence movements in humans.

First, what are some of the clinical problems related to a discussion of muscle tonus and the tonic-mechanical balance or imbalance? What is the basic deviation and how does one measure it? (This is the zero reference point of strabismus diagnosis management.)

Is there a con and divergence *fusion* mechanism or function that "pull against each other", whose balance or imbalance alters the basic mechanical-tonus position?

Is there a supranuclear (nonretinally derived) *specific* con and divergence mechanism or function that similarly may be in or out of balance, thus driving the eyes into esotropia or exotropia?

Does one surgically operate upon the vergence mechanism, or does one surgically alter the basic mechanical deviation?

Is it possible to have a paralysis of convergence and/or divergence, that in one instance does not shift the basic deviation, and in the other instance shifts the basic deviation? Is it possible to have voluntary control of pure convergence and pure divergence, unassociated with a near reflex?

The core problem with all of these questions involves what is and what is not the basic deviation (zero reference point), and how does one determine it. And what is and what is not a fusion-vergence.

I shall state my thesis and biases at the outset. My thesis will be that vergences derived from retinal stimuli (accommodation-vergence and fusion-vergence), which I shall call retino-tonic sources, have well-defined characteristics, are clinically assessable in an acceptable manner for diagnostic purposes, and are manipulateable in management regimes.

Those vergences (supranuclear) derived from other multiple sources and stimuli I shall call nonretino-tonic. These I believe act as increases or decreases in the level or substrate of tonus to *all* the ocular muscles, with differential mechanical effects upon the medial versus lateral rectus muscles. This latter is a statement of my hypothesis. Nonretinal tonus exists as a *balance* of forces, in that changes in the *level* or substrate differentially affect the mechanical action of medial and lateral rectus muscles.

Retino-tonic mechanisms (accommodative-convergence and fusion-vergence) are adjustive mechanisms. There is no balance or imbalance or fight between two opposing forces. There is no permanent effect upon the basic deviation because of increases or decreases in these functions or mechanisms.

There is no fight between con and di, or balance or imbalance of specific vergence mechanisms, either retinal or nonretinal. This is a continuing traditional source of confusion and one to which I shall direct most of my discussion.

My bias is readily admissible. Fusion-vergence mechanisms are preferably studied in humans, measured in real-life situations (with all its usual stimulus parameters), and with adequate controls (of accommodation, fusion, and fixation) in assessing *habitual* fusion-vergence mechanisms.

Prism-induced vergences are highly artificial laboratory circumstances as pointed out by Helmholtz, and again by Linksz (1952). The prism-vergence artifacts are systematically predictable. Adequate controls in prism-induced fusion-vergences are difficult in humans, and in my opinion difficult if not often impossible in animals.

My negative bias is also readily admissible. I believe that investigators sometimes confuse pure accommodative-vergence with pure fusion-vergence, and may mix the two unnecessarily. Or, some may investigate one function, and unhesitatingly make conclusions about the other function. Or speak about a vergence, without appropriately defining what type of vergence.

It is common for the laboratory scientist, when discussing motor control mechanisms, to discuss the vergence system in terms of (1) accommodative-convergence, and (2) fusion-vergences. But the discussion usually concentrates primarily on accommodative-vergence, perhaps because it is more easily accessible in its "natural state" in animals and humans alike. Fusion-vergences are usually observable only in relatively small degrees. The clinician may observe a whole panorama of very large, as well as small amplitudes of fusion-vergences, in their natural state and during habitual use.

So-called normal ranges of fusion-vergence are arbitrary statistical determinants. Extension of this range of fusion-vergence amplitude slightly, moderately, or markedly, should not necessarily be considered different entities. Extension of the range of observation of human habitual fusion-vergences allows one to gain much knowledge about the characteristics of fusion-vergence mechanisms.

Now that we have discussed my thesis and biases, let us turn to a discussion of what is generally agreed upon relative to fusion-vergences in normal individuals and compare this to abnormals.†

TERMINOLOGY

We shall adopt Alpern's (1962) definition: "The stimulus for all of the fusional movements is basically a disparity in the egocentric localization of the visual field (or some part of it) in one eye compared to that of the other."

One of the principal merits of this definition is that it accounts not only for the vergence movements observable in normal patients, but also for those vergence movements observable in patients with manifest strabismus.

TYPES AND CHARACTERISTICS OF FUSION-VERGENCES

There is a function or mechanism of fusion-convergence, divergence, and sursumvergence. We shall be here concerned primarily with con and divergence mechanisms.

One may demonstrate, from the zero-reference point of the basic deviation (or any other fusion-free position), both a fusion-convergence mechanism and a fusion-divergence mechanism. There is, of course, ample evidence that there is a "mechanism", or "function", of fusion-convergence around a fusion-free position, whether it be orthophoria, esophoria, or exophoria, so long as the fusion-amplitudes have been "used", and are available, without having suffered diminution in amplitude from disuse.

It is important to note here that a fusion-vergence mechanism is operable *from* a zero reference position. In the case of strabismus—from the basic deviation.

Fusion-convergence, and fusion-divergence, are not antagonistic in the sense that they are "pulling against" each other. They are not "in balance" or "out of balance," but are purely adjustive reservoir mechanisms, to be used as final adjustments in securing and maintaining bifoveal fixation (fusion) for the normal patient in completing his binocular fixation process.

If the quantity (amplitude) of one fusion-vergence required by habitual demand (or by training) is large, it becomes a large *reservoir*. It is found to be increased at *all*

---

†This paper shall deal only with the rapid-fusion-vergence ending in bifoveal fusion. We will not be able to here discuss the slower vergence movements ending in other than bifoveal fusion. There is a difference in these two circumstances. The fusion-vergences subsystems may be considered relative to (1) initiation of, and (2) completion of, the vergence. I have discussed this elsewhere (Jampolsky, 1971).

fixation distances. Similarly, orthoptic training of one fusion-vergence amplitude may be undertaken at *any* fixation distance, with benefit accruing at all other fixation distances. A large increase in one fusion-vergence, such as divergence, does not permanently affect or shift the basic deviation. Larger reservoirs of fusion-vergences (con or di) are simply to be tapped and made useful *only* when necessarily implemented.

The amplitudes of such fusion-vergence mechanisms may increase enormously when necessitated by habitual increase in the demand to compensate for changing mechanical alignment. I have seen fusion-convergence of as much as 75 prism diopters; fusion-divergence of 50 prism diopters; and vertical fusion amplitude exceed 50 prism diopters. With disuse, i.e. consequent to adult acquired strabismus, the amplitude of fusion-vergence may decrease to almost zero. Routinely, it may be rekindled to normal ranges when fusion is re-established.

Differences exist among the different fusion-vergences. Time does not allow adequate discussion of Dr. Nakayama's interesting presentation of certain torsional fusional movements. I have previously remarked that the clinical measurement of so-called fusion-amplitudes in patients with strabismus are frequently misinterpreted because it is assumed that eye movement responses are proportional to the stimulus parameters. Motor fusion is not always locked to sensory fusion. This is a common misconception (Jampolsky, 1968; Khawam, 1967).

Stewart (1950) found that prism-induced *di*vergence in normal individuals sometimes showed an apparent fusion-divergence unassociated with well-defined movements of the eyes. This is not found with base-out prism-induced convergence. This apparently reflects an inherent difference in the nasal-temporal retinas relative to the sensory-motor fusion process (1958), about which we have previously remarked. There may be more forgiveness in the input system in one direction compared to the other.

Similarly, I have called attention (Pacific Medical Center, 1968) to the upper–lower retinal differences in this regard. The upper retina appears more adaptable than the lower retina, since one may not infrequently find a vertical fusion-disparity in a hyperphoria-tropia, but not in the hypo direction. There is a disproportionate common occurrence of occlusion hyp*er* phoria (dissociated vertical; alternating hyper deviations), and indeed Marlow has shown that occlusion of either eye in normals causes it to go up.†

Lastly, I have called attention (Pacific Medical Center, 1970) to the difference in clinical symptoms resulting from inferior oblique muscle weakening procedures in adults, compared to superior oblique muscle-weakening procedures. Superior oblique alterations invariably produce torsional symptoms, while inferior oblique procedures do not. One should arrest this clinically observable difference and determine its validity and its causes. Several options occur. There may be a difference in the mechanical torsion effect of these two procedures. There may be a difference in the relative localization in these two directions, or some similar "slack" in the system, or forgiveness, or lack of lock between the motor fusion and sensory fusion systems in one direction compared to the other, just as it is in the nasal-temporal differences to which I have so often alluded. Several of us at the Smith-Kettlewell Institute are investigating the causes of this possible clinical difference in subjective vs. objective torsion.

---

†I have previously called attention to the disproportionate frequent occurrence of fixation disparity (fusion-disparity) on the nasal hemiretina in esodeviations, compared with exodeviations (Jampolsky, 1956).

VOLUNTARY CONTROL OF VERGENCES

Apparent voluntary control of pure convergence and divergence invariably is but a manifestation of "letting go" of a compensatory fusion-vergence mechanism, which compensates for an underlying basic deviation, or is but a manipulation of accommodation, with changes in its associated accommodative-vergence.

I do not believe there is such an entity as pure "voluntary convergence" despite its time-honored place in the literature (Jampolsky, 1970). Of course, voluntary control over *accommodation*—and its associated convergence—may be learned, and manipulated positively or negatively, as every schoolchild knows. This is always an accommodative-convergence manipulation. Similarly, in my opinion, so-called pure "voluntary convergence", and "spasm" or "paresis" of convergence will be found to be in association with some aspect of accommodation, if accommodation is critically monitored (by randomly selected letters—not reading print).

In order to claim a voluntary control of pure convergence or divergence, one must obey the rules. One must first establish the zero measure point (the basic deviation) under carefully controlled conditions (by eliminating all retinal-vergences). When this is done, one will find that the so-called voluntary vergences are clearly "letting go of" or implementing fusion-vergences, or manipulation of accommodation-vergence. An orthophore simply cannot "make" an eye diverge, and can only make it converge by initiating accommodation and its associated convergence.

Time does not permit a further discussion of retinally derived vergences† (accommodation and fusion).

FUSION-VERGENCE IN EXODEVIATIONS

Fusion-vergence in exo-deviations are of interest to the clinician because it is an habitual way of life as asymmetric vergence, and pinpoints many of the issues, concepts, and problems. One can examine (both by psychophysical methods and electrophysiological methods) a panorama of degrees of exodeviations from normal to abnormal, with amplitude ranges from normal to large ones.‡

Two crucial clinical and laboratory questions arise in explaining phenomena associated with intermittent exotropia. (1) When such a patient breaks from fusion and parallelism, to manifest exotropia, is this an active process invoking an active divergence mechanism, or is this a relaxation of convergence (as I believe)? What type of vergence is involved? What is the starting point (zero reference point)? (2) Is there a peripheral manifestation of or central integration of the version and vergence mechanisms? The issue is whether or not there is co-contraction of the horizontal muscles of the fixing eye during this habitual asymmetric vergence. Let us discuss the basis for, and the

†There are other retinal-vergences which I have previously discussed (1970). Of especial importance is the continually acting retinal-divergence which I have described as a "competitive binocular interaction" induced by unilateral white noise (overall diffused contours). This is a common clinical situation and a common laboratory situation often misnamed "deprivation". Competitive binocular interaction of unilateral white noise is an *active* retinal-divergence mechanism (examples—unilateral lid closure, or unilateral cataract), and is to be sharply differentiated from occlusion (no light).

‡Asymmetric vergence, i.e. fixation target on the axis of one eye, is a much used laboratory circumstance by which to study vergences, since one eye remains stationary (or relatively so), and one eye does most, or all, of the moving during the vergence, thus simplifying the analysis. Of course, for an intermittent exotrope, pure asymmetric vergence is his real way of life.

clinical importance of opposing laboratory and clinical views, since it very much bears on the question of what is and what is not a fusion-vergence, and its zero reference point.

Observation of the clinical circumstance surrounding the break of fusion in intermittent exotropia reveals that it is often triggered by *in*attention. Alertness and attention are necessary for the maintenance of the psycho-optical fusion-vergence reflex. Which vergence? Convergence, of course! Inattention causes the fusional-convergence to wane and the intermittently exotropic eye may be observed to return slowly, surely, and steadily to the fusion-free exodeviation. Would one seriously believe the notion that *in*attention *activated* divergence? Yet, this is the conclusion by many laboratory and clinical scientists. It is an amazing paradox, and has led to much confusion.

What is the evidence? All the psychophysical data since the time of Hering supports the concept that there is a peripheral mixture of version and vergence in asymmetric vergence. Intermittent exotropia is no different.

It would have been supposed that human ocular electromyography, as an electrophysiologic counterpart to the psychophysical experiments, would have corroborated and complemented the previous laboratory and clinical findings and conclusions. Rather, the electromyograms from several laboratories have been interpreted (on the basis of what we would consider negative evidence) as supporting the "active divergence" notion of intermittent exotropia breaking from fusion into manifest exotropia. Their findings, which depart from the historical flow of psychophysical and electrophysiological evidence, requires a new notion of a central integration of versions and vergences, all on the basis of negative evidence.

Curiously, data obtained from *one* lateral rectus muscle motor unit activity, in one eye, during a binocular divergence movement have been used to *infer* that *both* lateral rectus muscles' EMG's are similar. Several competent investigators have curiously followed the pattern of making conclusions relative to the electrical activity of *both* lateral rectus muscles from evidence based upon the activity of only *one* lateral rectus muscle, during the important and interesting *bi*nocular circumstance of the break from fusion by an intermittent exotrope.

Since Adler, in 1953, first recorded the electromyogram of *a* lateral rectus muscle during "divergence" from a convergent position, it has been clear that *the* lateral rectus has increasing motor unit activity in this situation. This certainly negates views (Scobee, 1972) that this might be a passive phenomenon, i.e. that the elasticity inherent in the orbital structures played a significant role during this abduction movement.

Others (Breinin and Moldaver, 1955) concluded from measurements of one lateral rectus in a patient with intermittent exotropia that "divergence is definitely associated with active innervation of the lateral rect*i*" (italics mine).

Still others (Blodi and Van Allen, 1957) appeared to share this view by stating: "The fact that an active innervation of the lateral muscle*s* [italics mine] occurs at the break point (of convergence) could be another proof for an active divergence mechanism."

My co-workers and I have in no instance found *both* lateral recti increasing their activity during the break of fusion to exotropia. On the contrary, our *bi*nocular electromyograms are similar in every detail to the known instance of diminution of convergence in normal individuals and in exophoria.

This curious inferring of what happens to *both* lateral rectus muscles, from data acquired from *one* lateral rectus muscle, has led to some oft-repeated misinterpretations, in our opinion.

Fusion-vergence assessment by binocular electromyograms must have the following *minimal criteria* in order to avoid unwarranted conclusions from negative evidence: (1) binocular simultaneous electromyograms to record *both* lateral rectus muscles, and preferably all four horizontal rectus muscles (in order to record eye-movement data on each eye); (2) a minimal asymmetric *fusion*-vergence of 15 prism diopters (in order to obviate negative evidence based upon insufficient sensitivity of measurement); and (3) fixation of the dominant eye to be unchanged (and monitored), i.e. on the same target at an unchanged fixation distance (in order to assess the circumstance of pure fusion-vergence disjunctive movement).

When these criteria are followed, electromyographic investigation of the break of fusion from intermittent exotropia to a manifest exotropia reveals (in our laboratory) that the lateral rectus of the *fixing* eye during the break of fusion does not increase its activity (as some *inferred* from monocular EMG's); it rather *decreases* its activity, as it should in any creditable diminution of convergence, or shows no change at all. This may be repeatedly demonstrated for a pure break and diminution of the vergence for any unchanged fixation distance wherein the latent intermittent exotropia is made manifestly. exotropic.

From our electromyograms, a general statement is possible—that will introduce the reader to an interpretation of the electromyograms to be presented: whenever there is a circumstance of *obtaining* bifoveal fixation via a pure and habitual fusion-vergence mechanism, there can be demonstrated co-contraction of the stationary fixing eye's medial and lateral rectus muscles, in the habitually real life asymmetric vergence circumstance. This is a common denominator that we have shown in patients with *eso*deviations, as well as in *exo*deviations (Tamler and Jampolsky, 1967).

When fusion is interrupted and there is a fusion-vergence dissipation, there is co-diminution of the previously co-contracted medial and lateral rectus muscles of the fixing eye.

Figure 1 diagrammatically shows the circumstances of pure fusion-vergences under a variety of conditions, with the appropriate diagrammatic electromyographic changes that are recorded.

Figure 2 shows a binocular eye *movement* recording (eye movement limbal sensing device) during a cover–uncover (dissipation of vergence, and obtaining of fusion-convergence) which shows the fast refusion eye movement of the moving right eye during asymmetric vergence, and also clearly shows the momentary dislodgement from fixation engagement of the usually firmly fixed stationary left eye. Eye-movement recordings have long been shown to support the notion that there is a peripheral (muscular) manifestation of the mixture of fusion-vergence and the version movements, even in the circumstance of asymmetric vergence during such a refusion mechanism. It is of special importance to note that the mixture of vergence-version need not be regarded with a new concept of a neatly packaged *centrally* rearranged innervation flow to the peripheral muscles. Electromyography of pure fusion-vergence circumstance (when observing the minimal criteria stated in order to appropriately assess this, and monitoring of eye movements during this circumstance) gives positive evidence of maintained co-contraction of the fixing eye, and peripheral evidence of a mixture of version-vergence.

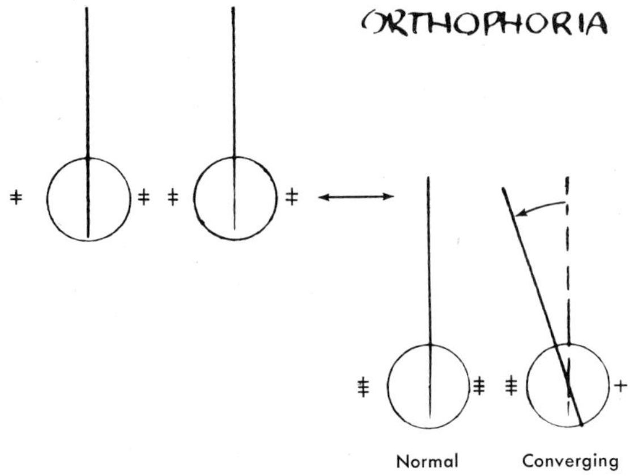

216 A. JAMPOLSKY

ORTHOPHORIA

Normal   Converging

FIG. 1A. Orthophoria, balanced electrical tonus compared with convergence. With an activated vergence, there is co-contraction (increased unit activity in both medial and lateral rectus muscles of the stationary fixing eye), and reciprocity in the moving eye.

ESOPHORIA

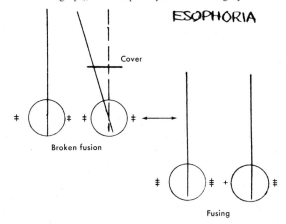

Cover

Broken fusion

Fusing

FIG. 1B. Esophoria, co-contraction in the fixing unmoved left eye during active divergence (to keep the phoria latent during fusion).

INT. EXOTROPIA

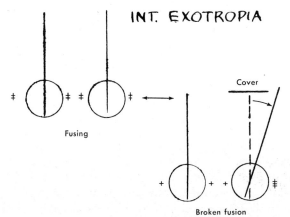

Cover

Fusing

Broken fusion

FIG. 1C. Intermittent exotropia, co-relaxation of fixing unmoved left eye during diminution of a real fusion vergence—in this case, diminished convergence after break of fusion by cover.

This is consistent with all of the previous historical psychophysical and eye-movement evidence. There is no need to postulate a new concept of a central integration, especially since it is based upon what we would consider negative evidence.

Misinterpretations may be avoided if the previously stated minimal criteria are observed, especially the 15 prism diopter amplitude of fusion-vergence. Additionally, in the investigation of fusion-vergences by electrophysiologic techniques (whether by electromyography, or central cell recordings), one should provide, whenever possible, the following information:

Which is the fixing eye? Which is the habitually dominant eye? Whether fusion was present or not, and when it was regained or disrupted. Whether the eye was seen to move or not—and preferably *recorded*. Monitoring of both eyes. The character of the fixation target and its surround. Whether or not normal blinks were allowed to occur.

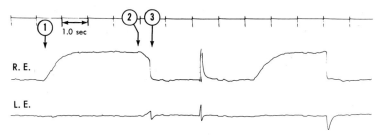

FIG. 2. Eye movements recorded during the break and make of fusion in a patient with a diagnosis of exophoria (16Δ). In the upper tracing the dominant right eye is covered at arrow 1 and a very slow gradual dissipation of fusion-convergence occurs. At arrow 2 the right eye is uncovered and the initial slow movement (convergence) is followed, or masked by a fast version noted by arrow 3. The same maneuver was then repeated (right-hand part of the diagram), this time with only a fast version refusion noted in the moving right eye. Note at arrow 3 that the fixing left eye is momentarily disengaged by the fast-moving right eye. This occurred to a greater extent during the second maneuver when there was a greater velocity of the moving right eye, during the refusion-vergence process.

Thus, the two clinical questions posed at the beginning of this section on fusion-vergences in exodeviations are answered as follows: when an intermittent exotrope breaks from fusion into exotropia, as a real-life asymmetric vergence, there is a relaxation of convergence. And with refusion (bifoveal fixation) there is active convergence from a fusion-free position of exotropia. The basic deviation (starting-point) is, as always, determined by eliminating the retino-tonic factors of accommodative-vergence, and fusion-vergence. And further, there is a maintained co-contraction of the medial and lateral rectus muscles of the fixing eye, as a peripherally manifested mixture of version and vergence.

Others (Keller and Robinson, 1972) have recorded *accommodative*-vergence from cortical cells in animals, which should be sharply differentiated from fusion-vergences under the controls and conditions we have suggested.

The following electromyograms show that in patients with exodeviations there is *never an increase in both lateral rectus muscles* during the *break* of fusion following occlusion of one eye and the resulting manifest exodeviation.

This is in contrast to the situation where real fusional divergence *is* in fact used (as in esophoric patients with habitual vergence compensation), where there is *always* an increase in both lateral rectus muscles when obtaining fusion and parallel alignment, from the fusion-free esodeviation position.

Even in an artificially induced prism-vergence, so often used in clinical and laboratory circumstances, this can be demonstrated. Both lateral rectus muscles increase in the circumstance where a normal patient is subjected to base-in prisms and activates the fusion-vergence process by demonstrating a real fusion-divergence movement. These latter two instances are indeed demonstrations of an actively invoked divergence mechanism, and in *this* circumstance one *does* record both lateral rectus muscles simultaneously increasing their motor unit activity.

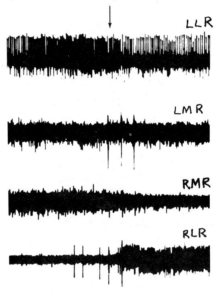

FIG. 3. Arrow shows covering the right eye in a patient with 25Δ of intermittent exotropia. Note the smooth reciprocity of the abducting right eye following the break of fusion. When this movement is free of a blink artifact, as it is here, one clearly sees the usual expected physiologic reciprocity in the moving eye during the break from fusion. Note especially the very clear *decrease* in the lateral rectus of the fixing left eye (at arrow).

In Fig. 3 the arrow indicates covering of the right eye in a patient with intermittent exotropia of 25 prism diopters. The occlusion is followed by a break of fusion and manifest exotropia. As the right eye goes out, the right lateral rectus activity increases, and the right medial rectus activity decreases, as expected. But observe that the left lateral rectus *decreases* in activity at the same time. The fixation is unchanged throughout. Note also that the right lateral rectus does not "pull against" its antagonist medial rectus, as has been reported by others.

Active contraction of *one* lateral rectus muscle, after a break-point of convergence in the eye which abducts, is *not* evidence for the *binocular* function of active divergence. Again, when all four horizontal rectus muscles are recorded simultaneously around the break-point of convergence (note the minimal criteria and controls), it will be seen that the lateral rectus muscle of the "stationary" eye *decreases* in activity as the other eye abducts, rather than the inferred (but never demonstrated) increase reported by others.

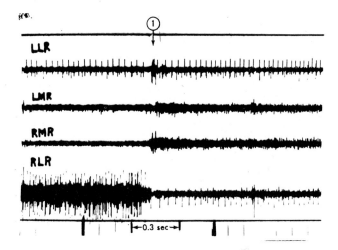

FIG. 4. Arrow 1 shows uncover of the exotropic right eye, followed by a convergence refusion of 40Δ of intermittent exotropia. It clearly shows both the reciprocity of the moving eye, and the maintained co-contraction of the fixing eye. Note the fixation disengagement of the fixing left eye in this brief but "powerful" refusion vergence. This electromyogram clearly shows all the details of refusion in intermittent exotropia.

Figure 4 shows all of the aspects of *refusion* of 40 prism diopters of intermittent exotropia. The reciprocity in the moving right eye is clearly seen during its fast race toward foveal engagement during the refusion vergence. The initial disengagement of fixation of the "stationary" left eye is noted as a brief saccadic electromyographic pattern, a *version* in both eyes, of very short duration with typical saccadic complete inhibition of antagonist muscles. Once the briefly disengaged (and moved) left eye has regained fixation, and fusion is obtained, there is a clear demonstration of *maintained co-contraction* of both horizontal muscles of the fixing left eye (compare before and after arrow 1).† The left lateral rectus recording shows a single motor unit which reflects its increase in activity as an increase in frequency. The left medial rectus recording, of many motor units, reflects its increase in activity by a similarly obvious maintained increase in discharge of many units.‡

Figure 4 alone should cause doubters to accept the view expressed above which has been supported by our laboratory group and few others. This evidence, however, is on the basis of positive evidence, which is in accord with previous psychophysical evidence. A critical examination of these figures allows no other reasonable alternative interpretation of the motor unit events occurring in the eye muscles in the refusion of intermittent exotropia. (1) The version-vergence mechanisms are reflected at the muscle level. (2) When an intermittent exotrope or exophore breaks fusion to manifest tropia, and one eye is seen to abduct in asymmetric divergence, this is a relaxation

†In other subjects, the stationary fixing eye may be truly stationary (when there is good dominance) during the habitual refusion vergence. *All* of the vergence movement occurs via one eye.

‡ Sustained and maintained co-contraction may be characteristic of an exophoric patient during fusion. Non-sustained co-contraction may characterize some asymptomatic intermittent exotropes during fusion. It is speculated that symptoms which may occur in the exophoric patient may be related to the sustained co-contraction, while the often lack of symptoms in intermittent exotropia may be related to the non-sustained co-contraction found in some of these patients.

of fusional convergence, and the zero reference point or starting-point is one of exotropia.

Recent corroboration of this starting-point of intermittent exotropia described above has recently been given by de Groot and Scott (1974). In patients with intermittent exotropia subjected to complete curarization of the ocular muscles, the mechanical resting-point (devoid of all tonus) is one of manifest exotropia, matching the basic deviation as determined by usual clinical rules. This should settle the matter. These experiments given above should clearly elucidate the starting-point, and no new innervation notions are necessary.

RECAPITULATION. THE BASIC DEVIATION
(ZERO REFERENCE POINT)

It was necessary to discuss at some detail the fusion-vergence characteristics in normal people, and extend this into the range of exophorias and intermittent exotropias, as well as other basic deviations which are well compensated for by a fusion-vergence mechanism. These discussions, and the laboratory and clinical evidence presented, re-affirm the fundamental importance of following the rules in clinically determining the basic deviation. It is from this zero reference point that fusion-vergences take place.

At the outset we posed the important clinical problem of clearly defining what is and what is not a fusion-vergence. We will now address ourselves to what is *not* a fusion-vergence, and discuss the non-retinal sources of tonus, their nature, and the effects upon the basic deviation.

The basic deviation is determined by the resultant tonic-mechanical imbalance that exists, and the way in which the *non*-retinal ocular tonus acts upon this mechanical balance.

One should be clear about the notion of the basic deviation, and the controls necessary to determine it, before one can intelligently deal with some of the clinical problems. The basic deviation is the zero reference point of the fusion-vergence mechanisms, and it is important to know where to begin. As will be mentioned, similar specified controls for laboratory investigation in humans and animals, are not always observed in assessing the characteristics of pure fusion-vergences. The rules for the determination are always the same.

THE NON-RETINAL SOURCES OF
OCULAR MUSCLE TONUS

Time does not permit more than a statement of an hypothesis. I do not believe that there is a specific mechanism of convergence or divergence of a supranuclear or nonretinal origin. Nor is there any balance or imbalance, excess or insufficiency of these. I do not feel that there is evidence to support a term of "tonic convergence"[†] (non-retinal, non-proximal).

[†]"Basic tonic convergence" is apparently held to be unleashed when fusion is disrupted, with a resultant esodeviation shift. Yet, as we have noted, acquired bilateral blindness, if immediate and total (important parameters) does *not* result in an unleashed esotropia. Cogan has remarked that congenital total blindness is unassociated with a significant strabismus.

I believe that any change in the *level* of tonic inflow to the orbits from the multiple non-retinal sources will produce a greater mechanical reactive increment, or decrement, of the medial rectus muscles, compared to that of the lateral rectus muscles, with a corresponding disjunctive movement. I believe that the medial rectus muscles have greater mechanical reactivity to *equal* increments, or decrements, of tonic inflow or tonic substrate, than do the lateral rectus muscles.

The clinical support for this hypothesis (to be published elsewhere) is found in the eye-movement patterns in: (a) retraction nystagmus; (b) following death; (c) children with cerebral palsy; and (d) following surgical readjustment of muscles.

The concept of specific non-retinal supranuclear opposing influences of convergence and divergence, which may be in balance or out of balance, has long clouded the basic laboratory and clinical approach to strabismus management. There is neither evidence for, nor need of such views.

PARALYSES OF CONVERGENCE AND DIVERGENCE

Clinical evidence has been given (Jampolsky, 1970) which points out the following paradox: Alleged "divergence paralysis" produces an esodeviation, while alleged "convergence paralysis" does *not* produce an exodeviation. It has been pointed out (Jampolsky, 1970) that so-called divergence paralysis is but a form of VI nerve paresis, and so-called convergence paralyses are anomalies of accommodative-convergence mechanisms, when accommodation is carefully monitored.

There are many dilemmas and unsupportable concepts, and inadequate measurement controls, for the laboratory scientist and the clinical scientist alike, relative to the sources and effects of nonretinaltonus.

The theory here proposed considers that all tonic innervational input to the oculorotary muscles, from the diverse *non-retinal* sources, act upon an unequal horizontal coulorotary mechanical apparatus. For a given increment or decrement of general tonus level, there is more mechanical reaction of the medial rectus muscles compared to the lateral rectus muscles, thus producing a predictable disjunctive movement through changes in the general level of tonic inputs.†

CONCLUSIONS

There are two ways of "looking at" strabismus. The view we have proposed is as follows:

(1) There is a basic deviation (zero reference point) which may be determined with laboratory and clinical accuracy and satisfaction. It is composed of two factors: (a) *mechanical* balance or imbalance *per se*; and (b) non-retinal *tonic* influences that differentially affect the medial versus lateral rectus muscles, with different mechanical effectivity. These two factors are determined for distance fixation by controlled elimination of accommodative-convergence and fusion-vergence (retino-tonic).

---

†Recent work of D. Robinson and others lend support to this notion since the medial rectus muscles are thicker than the lateral rectus muscles, less innervation is required for a medial rectus shortening than for a lateral rectus shortening, of the same amounts.

(2) Fusion-vergences are compensatory vergence mechanisms acting around any zero reference point. These are reservoirs to be tapped when needed. They are not balanced or imbalanced, nor do they have any longterm effect on the basic deviation.

(3) There are no supranuclear specific nonretinal mechanisms of con and divergence. There cannot be voluntary control of, or paralysis of, these nonexisting mechanisms.

(4) A theory is proposed that adequately explains clinical entities. Nonretinal sources of tonus act upon an unequal horizontal oculorotatory mechanical apparatus, with predictable disjunctive effects resulting from increments or decrements of this tonic inflow level.

The alternative view would require a belief in the following points:

(1) Belief that the starting-point in exophoria and intermittent exotropia is one of orthophoria (despite the basic deviation demonstrably otherwise—namely exo).

(2) And one would have to believe that some type of active divergence (certainly not fusion-divergence) actively drives the eye out in the break of fusion (though curare leaves it there in exo).

(3) And that inattention activates the mechanism of divergence.

(4) And that refusion to ortho therefore *must* be a *relaxation* of the activated divergence (though this is a fast movement approaching saccadic velocity).

(5) And that refusion is a neat centrally packaged combination of version-vergence (based upon negative evidence, despite the abundant positive eye movement and electromyographic evidence to the contrary).

This is quite a bundle of unsupportable beliefs to believe.

It is hoped that this presentation and discussion of the evidence and controls, consistency in concepts and conclusions, and comparison of some laboratory and clinical methods, will attend to the goal of mutual awareness of laboratory and clinical problems.

REFERENCES

ALPERN, M. (1962) *The Eye: Muscular Mechanisms*, vol. 3. New York, Academic Press.

BLODI, F. C. and VAN ALLEN, M. W. (1957) Electromyography of the extraocular muscles in fusional movements. *Am. J. Ophthal.* **44**, 136.

BREININ, G. M. (1962) *The Electrophysiology of Extraocular Muscles*, Toronto, University of Toronto Press.

BREININ, G. M. and MOLDAVER, J. (1955) Electromyography of the human extraocular muscles. *Arch. Ophthal.* **54**, 200.

DAVSON, H. (1963) *The Physiology of the Eye*, 2nd ed. Boston, Little, Brown & Co.

DEGROOT, J. A. and SCOTT, A. B. (1974) International Strabismus Association Symposium, May 1974 (in press).

JAMPOLSKY, A. (1956) Esotropia and convergent fixation disparity. *Am. J. Ophthal.* **41**, (5), 830 (May 1956).

JAMPOLSKY, A. (1968) Some anomalies of binocular vision. In: *The First International Congress of Orthoptists*, pp. 1–31. Transactions of a Congress held at the Royal College of Surgeons of England, July 3, 4, 5, 1967. The C. V. Mosby Co., St. Louis.

JAMPOLSKY, A. (1970) Ocular divergence mechanisms. *Trans. Am. Ophthal Soc.* **68**, 770.

JAMPOLSKY, A. (1971) American Academy of Ophthalmology Orthoptic Symposium on Prisms. Dallas, Texas (unpublished).

KELLER, E. L. and ROBINSON, D. A. (1972) Abducens unit behavior in the monkey during vergence movements. *Vision Res.* **12**, 369–382.

KESTENBAUM, A. (1961) *Clinical Methods of Neuro-ophthalmologic Examination*, 2nd ed. New York, Grune & Stratton, Inc.

KHAWAM, E., SCOTT, A. B. and JAMPOLSKY, A. (1967) Acquired superior oblique palsy. *Arch. Ophthal.* **77**, 761–768.

LINKSZ, A. (1952) *Physiology of the Eye*. vol. 2: *Vision*. New York, Grune & Stratton.

NAWRATSKI, I. and JAMPOLSKY, Z. (1958) A regional hemiretinal difference in amblyopia. *Am. J. Ophthal.* **46**, 339–344.

Pacific Medical Center Strabismus Conference, 1968 (unpublished).
Pacific Medical Center Strabismus Conference, 1970 (unpublished).
SCOBEE, R. G. (1952) *The Oculorotary Muscles.* St. Louis, The C. V. Mosby Co.
STEWART, C. R. (1950) Thesis: An investigation of the time characteristics of lateral fusional movements
    of the eye. Ohio State University.
TAMLER E. and JAMPOLSKY, A. (1967) Is divergence active? An electromyographic study. *Am. J. Ophthal.*
    63, 452.

Panel Discussion. Synopsis prepared by Björn Tengroth

This part of the symposium concerning the fine structures of the extra-ocular muscles has been most interesting. Unfortunately, as pointed out by Mr. Peter Fells, it may give the clinician a feeling that the gulf between the scientist and the practising doctor is growing wider instead of more narrow. What astonishes the strabismus surgeons, a point made by both Mr. Fells and Dr. Souza-Dias, is that one can, very crudely, excise large portions of the extraocular muscles without doing an immense harm to its function as one would expect, but instead do some good to the patient. The detailed separation in to five different muscle fibres presented by Dr. Alvarado was supported by Dr. Mayr (see Discussion Remarks, pp. 44–45). The separation into an orbital and global muscle layer is well established and should by first sight suggest the development of different surgical techniques. Unfortunately, the results of the work presented by Durston at the Third Cambridge Ophthalmological Symposium on Strabismus make such speculations rather unacceptable (*Brit. J. Ophth.* 74, **58,** no. 3,193) as it was shown that neither in baboons nor in man are the orbital and global muscles layers similarly situated throughout the whole muscle length. The global fibres were centrally situated in the posterior portion of the muscles, surrounded by the orbital layer. As a clinician one would hope for a labelling technique of the different fibres into slow and fast ones, perhaps by vital staining, that would give the surgeon a new approach to eye-muscle surgery.

A question brought up as to whether branching of muscle fibres takes place, was answered by Dr. Alvarado who said that the better technique the less evidence there was of fibre branching. If the fibres do not travel the entire muscle length, that is from tendon to tendon, how then is the force transmitted that moves the eyeball? Dr. Alvarado pointed out that there are similar connections in the zonule fibres transmitting the forces from the ciliary muscle to the lens. These fibres are built up by short collagen filaments, which are attached to each other by some mucopolysaccharide. This has been proven, as non-collagenolytic enzymes disrupt the zonular fibres. This is a good and parallel example of such force-transmitting connections.

For the clinician different ophthalmological symptoms suggest that there are a number of different ocularmotor functions that might be related to dysfunction of different fibre types. However, there are still so many questions to be answered until we can draw the right conclusions from our morphological findings that a confirmation of the clinical importance of the fibre types will have to wait.

In ageing, the eye muscles change their content of collagen and elastic tissue. The collagen contents hypertrophy immensely in the aged muscle. Dr. Miller was, however, unable to demonstrate any elastic tissue increase, a result that was contradictory to earlier studies and that only could be explained by a different interpretation of what should be considered elastic tissue.

To summarize the first part of the discussion one can say that in spite of the fact that we can separate five different fibre types at least in animals both on a morphological and physiological basis, we do not know enough to be able to start any clinical applications based on this knowledge. There is no doubt, however, that these great advances will in many ways give the clinicians an incentive to start a more physiological approach, especially in the field of strabismus therapy. It seems to be of the greatest importance for the future understanding in clinical practice of the muscle morphology and physiology that clinicians and scientists work together in order to narrow the present gap. The separation into a global and an orbital layer of the extraocular muscles is, as we mentioned before, a well-established concept. However, the difference in fibre pattern in the layers seem from the discussion to be different in different species. The question whether the fibres have a tendon-to-tendon construction and if they are singly or multiply innervated was brought up by Dr. Vossius. When considering the graded contraction of the muscles the graded force necessary, he said it would be difficult to explain some of the presented data where single innervated fibres were found.

The question on proprioceptive arrangements in the eye muscles has since a long time been of great interest. In a separate paper Dr. Manni has presented his experiences in the field of eye-muscle proprioception. The relationship between head position, head and body movement, and eye position has been dealt with in a number of animal experiments and there is no doubt that we have here a regulatory system of the greatest importance. This is known to the clinicians through a number of obscure and unclear symptoms, one of them being so-called blocked nystagmus. However, as pointed out both by Dr. Souza-Diaz and Dr. Bach-y-Rita we do not know enough about the proprioceptive systems in the eye and neck muscles to get the right explanation, but as was suggested this must be a very interesting field for the scientists and the clinicians to solve in collaboration.

CENTRAL MECHANISMS

GOAL-DIRECTED FLEXIBILITY IN THE VESTIBULO-OCULAR REFLEX ARC

G. Melvill Jones and A. Gonshor

THE functional goal of vestibular control of eye movement can be readily appreciated using the disc with radial lines illustrated in Fig. 1. When such a disc is oscillated in front of the stationary head at a frequency higher than about 1 Hz, radial lines having components oriented at right angles to the direction of motion appear blurred, whether the disc is oscillated from side to side in a horizontal plane or up and down in a sagittal (vertical) plane. Indeed, even when the disc is oscillated in the third orthogonal plane (frontal = oscillatory rotation in its own plane) the radial lines appear blurred. In marked contrast to this, if the disc is held stationary and the head oscillated relative to it, in any of the three orthogonal planes, even at frequencies up to 5–7 Hz, the perceived image of the radial line disc remains strikingly clear (Melvill Jones and Drazin, 1961; Melvill Jones, 1968).

This phenomenon reflects two primary features, namely: (a) the frequency response of purely optokinetic tracking of a moving visual target is severely limited by an upper "cut-off" frequency around 1 Hz (Mevill Jones and Drazin, 1961; Fender and

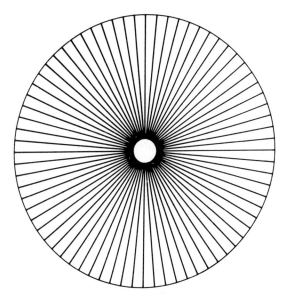

FIG. 1. The radial-line disc. (Reproduced from Melvill Jones and Drazin, 1961.)

Nye, 1961; Michael and Melvill Jones, 1966; Young, 1962), whereas, (b) the vestibulo-ocular reflex, although active over a wide range of frequencies, becomes particularly effective at frequencies in the region of 1 Hz and above (Benson, 1969). Consequently, since the head is exposed to frequencies well above 1 Hz during normal locomotor movement, for example in running (Steindler, 1955; Melvill Jones *et al.*, 1973), the vestibulo-ocular stabilizing reflex becomes a prerequisite for fine discriminatory vision in these circumstances. A knowledge of functional capabilities and limitations in both mechanical and neural components of the vestibulo-ocular reflex system therefore becomes of considerable practical interest.

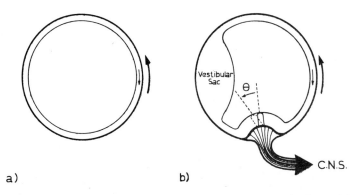

FIG. 2. Diagrammatic representation of essential mechanical components in the semicircular canal.

MECHANICAL VESTIBULAR RESPONSE

It is important to appreciate that the spherical eyeballs are only capable of angular (rotational) movements relative to the skull. Consequently, it is entirely appropriate that the main vestibular source of reflex drive to the extra-ocular muscles originates in the rotation-sensing semicircular canals of the vestibular mechanical end organs. Figure 2 illustrates the essential physical characteristics of relevant hydrodynamic components in a semicircular canal. Simplified to its limit (Fig. 2a), a canal comprises a circular tube containing fluid which, on account of its inertia, tends to be left behind *relative* to the tube when the whole system is angularly accelerated. However, the initiation of fluid flow immediately generates opposing viscous forces which, due to the laminar nature of flow in a tube so small as the endolymphatic canal (0.3 mm internal diameter), must be strictly proportional to the relative velocity of flow. Furthermore, the driving force due to inertia of the endolymph must be proportional to the absolute angular acceleration of the endolymphatic fluid. This in turn closely approximates the actual angular acceleration of the canal itself due to the high ratio of viscous to inertial forces acting on the fluid in a tube so small as this (i.e. due to the very low Reynolds number of the system). Indeed, except for the very short time required to reach steady state flow (time constant determined by the ratio of inertial to viscous coefficients is in the order of 0.005 sec (Melvill Jones and Milsum, 1965; Oman and Young, 1972)) it turns out that the absolute angular acceleration of the endolymph is strictly proportional to that of the canal itself and hence also the head. Since inertial and viscous forces must balance in the simple system of Fig. 2a it follows that the velocity of relative flow must be strictly proportional to the angular acceleration of the whole system, i.e. the skull. If the velocity of relative flow is proportional to head angular acceleration, then at any instant the relative *displacement* of fluid must be directly related to the *rate* of head rotation in the plane of that canal. This conclusion states that the hydrodynamic response of such a system as that in Fig. 2a performs an accurate integration on the angular acceleration of the head and hence acts as an integrating angular accelerometer, or in other words as an angular speedometer for the skull. The conclusion is readily supported by more rigorous analytical treatment of the physical system (Steinhausen, 1933; Van Egmond *et al.*, 1949; Melvill Jones, 1972).

In reality the circular tube of the so-called semicircular canal contains a measuring device, or transducer, comprising a watertight cupula in the expanded ampulla, acting so that the cupula is apparently hinged at its base, deflecting through an angle (θ in Fig. 2b) proportional to the displacement of fluid round the circular tube. As already indicated the fluid displacement round the tube provides a measure of instantaneous head angular velocity relative to space, and hence so does the angular deflection of the watertight cupula. It has been shown that in most normal circumstances the cupula does probably faithfully follow the instantaneous angular velocity of the head and, as indicated below, feeds angular velocity modulated neural information to the central nervous system (Groen *et al.*, 1952; Melvill Jones and Milsum, 1970; Melvill Jones and Milsum, 1971; Fernandez and Goldberg, 1971), although in all probability with very small actual displacement of the cupula (Melvill Jones and Milsum, 1971; Oman and Young, 1972).

However, it is well known that with prolonged turning movements, and on suddenly stopping such prolonged turning movements, the neural message received by the brain may become grossly different from that of head angular velocity. A major contribution to this effect is probably introduced by the elasticity of the cupula structure itself. Thus, on initiating a rotational movement of constant angular velocity, the cupula initially deflects through the proper angle, but thereafter is exponentially restored towards its zero position by means of its own elasticity. Then on suddenly arresting the angular motion, deceleration deflects the cupula in the opposite direction, by an equal but opposite amount, with subsequent exponential return again to the original zero position. This phenomenon is thought to be largely responsible for the familiar patterns of "pre-rotational" and "post-rotational" stimulation of the semicircular canals which have been used in clinical testing of the rotation sensing elements in the vestibular system (Van Egmond *et al.*, 1948).

NEURAL RESPONSE OF THE
CANAL SYSTEM

From a functional viewpoint the next question is, with what fidelity of informational transfer does the peripheral nervous system carry the mechanical response of the end organ into the central nervous system? The micro-anatomical structure of the transducing mechanism, namely the ciliated sensory epithelium of the crista ampullaris (Wersäll, 1972), modulates trains of action potentials in primary vestibular afferent neurones,

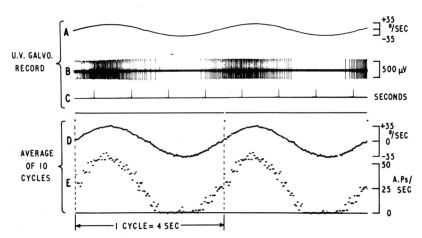

FIG. 3. Original (A and B) and computer-averaged (D and E) records of rotational stimulus and central neural response recorded from a single canal-dependent neural unit in the vestibular nucleus of cat. (Reproduced from Benson *et al.*, 1970.)

many of which closely follow the expected mechanical response of the end organ (Groen *et al.*, 1952; Fernandez and Goldberg, 1971). Moreover, this primary afferent signal generates secondary vestibular afferent neurone activity in the vestibular nuclei having a similarly faithful representation of the expected mechanical response of the end organ (Melvill Jones and Milsum, 1970; Melvill Jones and Milsum, 1971; Shimazu and Precht, 1965).

Figure 3 illustrates original and computer-averaged responses from a single second-order vestibular neuron in the medial vestibular nucleus of the cat (Benson *et al.*, 1970). From above down the traces show (A) horizontal head angular velocity, (B) an extract from the original train of action potentials generated by this sinusoidal pattern of head angular velocity, (C) time in sec, (D) the averaged head angular velocity generated throughout ten consecutive cycles of sinusoidal stimulation at $\frac{1}{4}$ Hz, and

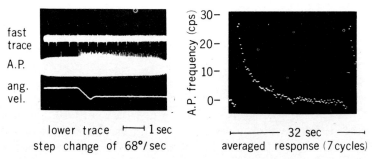

FIG. 4. Original (left) and averaged (right) response of a canal-dependent central vestibular unit to sudden change of steady-state angular velocity (Reproduced from Melvill Jones, 1968.)

(E) the averaged action potential frequency in this neuron, correctly phase related to the averaged head angular velocity in (D). Evidently under these circumstances a neuronal response such as this remains closely tied to the angular velocity signal resulting from integrative transduction of head angular acceleration performed by mechanical components of the canal.

Again, Fig. 4 shows that in accordance with the erroneus patterns of mechanical end-organ response due to cupula elasticity, a sudden stepwise change in angular *velocity* of the head generates a burst of action potentials the frequency of which subsequently declines along an exponential time course shown in the averaged pattern of response depicted on the right side of the figure.

PATTERNS OF REFLEXLY INDUCED
EYE MOVEMENT

What patterns of eye movement are induced by central vestibular neural activity of the kinds depicted in Figs. 3 and 4? The functionally useful goal would appear to be generation of compensatory ocular rotation in such a direction and speed as to cause stabilization of the eye relative to space. In practice, the compensatory pattern of response is often complicated by the inclusion of intermittent quick-phase repositioning eye flicks which together with the slow-phase compensatory movements constitutes vestibular nystagmus.

Figure 5 helps to clarify the functional significance of these phenomena (Melvill Jones and Milsum, 1965). Each of the three sets of curves read from above downwards (I) angular movement of the skull relative to space, (II) angular eye movement relative to the skull, and (III) angular eye movement relative to space, the latter being the sum of the former two variables. In Fig. 5a the head is held still relative to space whilst the eye scans backwards and forwards across the prevailing visual scene. The straight line depicts zero angular head movement. The intermittent displacement of eye relative to skull represents purely saccadic shifts of gaze from one point of interest to the next. Indeed, it is usually not possible for an individual to make smooth movements across a well-defined visual scene under voluntary control in the absence of either a moving target or a moving head. Summing the first two records one obtains the trace of eye movements relative to space seen in the third curve. With proper calibration this curve would tell the experimenter where the subject was looking relative to space throughout the experiment.

In Fig. 5b the subject fixates upon a single point in space and then rotationally oscillates his head backwards and forwards in a horizontal plane. Compensatory eye movement, driven by both optokinetic and vestibular stimulation, then occurs relative to the skull such that when these movements are added to movements of the skull relative to space, a straight line is achieved in the record of eye movement relative to space. In this case the eye continues to retain a stationary image of a stationary object in the outside world upon the retina, despite more or less violent head movement.

Figure 5c depicts the more usual case when a subject moves his head to left and right whilst scanning a general visual scene in front of him. Under these circumstances a nystagmoid pattern of interspersed slow and quick-phase eye movements, nystagmus, is induced, but with the particular feature that when this trace of eye movement

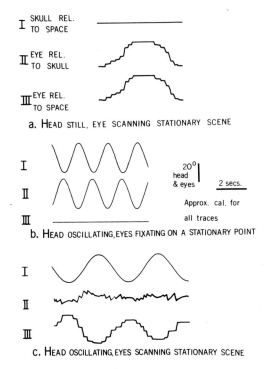

FIG. 5. The functional goal of the vestibulo-ocular reflex is to achieve stabilization of the retinal image of a stationary outside world during angular head movement. (Reproduced from Melvill Jones and Milsum, 1965.)

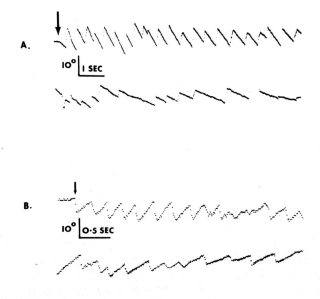

FIG. 6. Ocular nystagmus in (A) horizontal and (B) frontal planes of the skull, induced by sudden change of steady state rotation. (Reproduced from Melvill Jones et al., 1964.)

relative to the skull is algebraically added to the skull movement relative to space, the bottom trace in Fig. 5c emerges. Comparing this with the corresponding trace in Fig. 5a one sees that the functionally useful achievement in these circumstances is reestablishment of the simple sequences of successive visual fixations on points of interest in the outside world, despite the introduction of disturbing angular head movements. As might be expected from the patterns of oculomotor response seen in Fig. 5, unnatural patterns of vestibular neural drive of the kind illustrated in Fig. 4 generate correspondingly unnatural patterns of compensatory nystagmus with exponentially declining angular velocity of slow-phase eye movements. Figure 6 shows records of "post-rotational" nystagmus recorded in man (A) after sudden initiation of a steady angular velocity in the horizontal plane and (B) in the frontal plane.

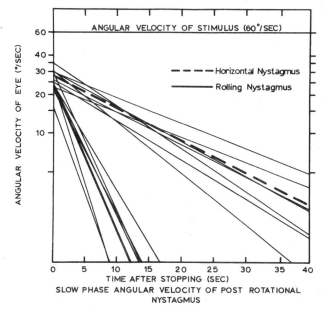

FIG. 7. Log-linear plots of calculated regression lines depicting the exponential patterns of decay in slow-phase angular velocity of nystagmus induced as in Fig. 6.

Here the records are of eye angular displacement relative to skull, and hence the slopes of the slow-phase sweeps of resulting nystagmus provide a quantitative measure of angular velocity of the eye relative to the skull. Log-linear plots of the slopes of these lines measured in each of these two planes from a number of different subjects are shown in Fig. 7. The exponential patterns of decay indicated by these approximately straightline plots reflects the general form of mechanical response to be expected from the end-organ, as well as the neural response at the first central relay station in the vestibular nuclei of the central nervous system. A significant additional feature is the difference of mean slopes (heavy lines) for the two sets of data, probably reflecting different canal time constants for horizontal and vertical canals (Melvill Jones et al., 1964). The tortional eye movements illustrated in Fig. 6b were recorded by a semi-automated movie-photographic technique capable of measuring eye movements in al three degrees of freedom (Melvill Jones, 1963).

Such records provide a means of measuring the penalty incurred by man due to misleading vestibular signals generated by the unnatural movements of manmade vehicles. The three-dimensional records of eye-movement shown in Fig. 8 were obtained from the pilot of a jet-trainer aircraft during an eight-turn aerodynamic spin (Melvill Jones, 1965a). The segment of record shown includes the moment of recovery from the spin. Thus, whilst spinning, the aircraft performs rotational movements in all three degrees of rotational freedom (yaw, pitch, and roll). This generates what are initially appropriate compensatory nystagmoid eye movements in those three degrees of freedom

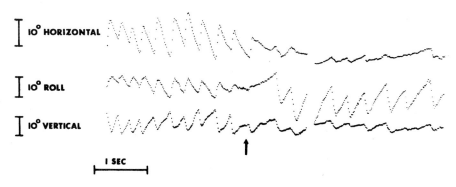

Fig. 8. 3-D records of nystagmus recorded from the pilot of an aircraft during recovery (arrow) from an eight-turn aerodynamic spin. (Reproduced from Melvill Jones, 1965a.)

(i.e. "horizontal", sagittal, and frontal planes of the skull). However, as the spin proceeds, elastic restoration of the cupulae as well as neural adaptation (Goldberg and Fernandez, 1971; Malcolm and Mevill Jones, 1970) leads to reduction in the respective compensatory eye angular velocities and consequent generation of increasing velocities of image slip on the retina of the pilot during his spin. At the moment of recovery, indicated by the arrow in Fig. 8, there was evidently generation of post-rotational nystagmus, most marked in the frontal (roll) plane. In practice, this would necessarily generate rapid rotational movement of the image of the horizon upon the pilot's retina, at the very moment when, for successful recovery, he most needs to make a valid assessment of his movement relative to that horizon. Evidently physiological dynamics of the vestibulo-ocular reflex can materially complicate the inherent aerodynamic problems of spin recovery.

CENTRAL NEURAL CONNECTIONS

The previous sections have examined characteristics of the mechanical and neural afferent response of relevant components in the vestibular system and the functionally useful response of the effector organ, namely rotation of the eyes relative to the skull. At the time of writing there is a rapidly growing body of knowledge about the central interconnections between the afferent and efferent components of the vestibulo-ocular reflex system. Before describing these, however, it is helpful to examine two important physical principles which apply to the whole system.

First, the vestibular end-organ is encased in the skull and consequently responds specifically to accelerative movement of the head relative to space. In addition, although the eyeball is free to rotate relative to the skull the origins of all extra-colour muscles are fixed to the skull itself. Consequently, at least to a first approximation, dependent upon instantaneous eye position in the skull, there must always be a unique relationship between the vestibular afferent signal (head movement relative to space) and the required extra-ocular muscular response for stabilization of the eye relative to space.

Secondly, pairs of semicircular canals are arranged in the skull in planes which approximately parallel corresponding pairs of extra-ocular muscles. Thus in the simplest case, the horizontal semicircular canals parallel the planes of action of the medial and lateral rectus muscles in both eyes. Geometrically an equally simple physical arrangement applies to the vertical canals. However, the detailed anatomical arrangement of parallel pairs of canals and muscles makes it somewhat more difficult to appreciate the simplicity of the system in these degrees of freedom. First, it is necessary to appreciate that the vertical semicircular canals are all oriented diagonally relative to the sagittal plane of the skull. Correspondingly, the superior and inferior recti, and the superior and inferior oblique muscles predominantly rotate the eyes in planes diagonal to the sagittal plane of the skull. For example, the left anterior canal approximately parallels the right posterior canal and these two canals operate in a differential (reciprocal) manner similar to the more familiar pair of horizontal canals. As explained in more detail below it is appropriate therefore that the influences of these canals bear predominantly upon the superior and inferior rectus muscles in the left eye and the superior and inferior oblique muscles in the right eye. A similar geometric relationship obtains for the pair of vertical canals denoted by the right anterior and left posterior canals.

These two physical principles, namely the uniqueness of required stimulus-response relationships and approximate paralleling of pairs of canals with respective pairs of extra-ocular muscles, would appear to call for relatively direct and "hard-wired" interconnections between the afferent and efferent systems in the vestibulo-ocular reflex arc.

This does indeed prove to be so for the elementary pathways which are represented diagrammatically in Fig. 9 by connections between the horizontal canals and the medial and lateral rectus muscles of the right eye. Despite a somewhat incomplete picture of connections determined by neuroanatomical methods (Tarlov, 1972), neurophysiological evidence has clearly indicated the essential connections illustrated in this figure. First, there are inhibitory commissural connections between right and left vestibular nuclei in the brainstem (Shimazu and Precht, 1966). To appreciate the significance of these connections it is important to realize that in any parallel pair of canals a particular direction of head rotation in that plane generates an increase in the primary afferent discharge above its spontaneous level in one canal and a decrease in the other. Thus turning to the left excites the left and suppresses the right horizontal canals. Pairs of afferent inputs act reciprocally and it is apparently the difference between the opposite inputs which constitutes the relevant neural signal (Groen et al., 1952; Melvill Jones and Milsum, 1970; Shimazu and Precht; 1965; Melvill Jones, 1965b). Thus an inhibitory commissural relationship ensures the potential for maintenance of this reciprocal characteristic, even though, for example, there may be damage to one peripheral end-organ or its primary afferent innervation.

Next, since leftward rotation excites the left horizontal canal, it is appropriate that

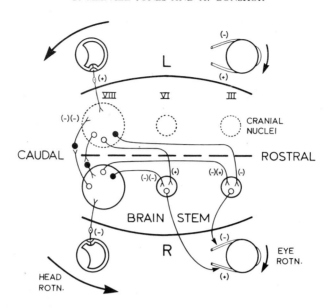

FIG. 9. Diagrammatic representation of neural connections comprising the elementary vestibulo-ocular reflex arc.

there should be an excitatory interneuronal connection between that input and the oculomotor neurones arising in the right sixth nerve nucleus (abducens) since these activate specifically the right lateral rectus muscle, causing compensatory eye rotation to the right (Szentágothai, 1950). Similarly, it is appropriate for an inhibitory interneuron to act as a reciprocal input to motoneurons from the third nerve nucleus innervating the right medial rectus muscle. Again, correspondingly appropriate excitatory and inhibitory interconnections from the right and left vestibular nuclei respectively are called for. From extensive and elegant neurophysiological investigations on this matter by several different teams of investigators it is now known that such connections are indeed made by single interneurons, not only in the horizontal plane (Precht et al., 1967) as depicted in Fig. 9, but also appropriately for all parallel pairs of canals and extra-ocular muscles (Baker et al., 1969; Highstein et al., 1971; Precht and Baker, 1972; Highstein, 1973; Ito et al., 1973; Precht, 1972). Consequently, stimulus-response relationships appear to be carried through the shortest possible neuronal pathways, bearing in mind the necessity of at least one interneuron for the generation of inhibitory post-synaptic influence.

Table 1 lays out the specific relations between excitatory and inhibitory influences on ipsi- and contralateral muscles and the semicircular canals. This table is a modification of that presented by Ito et al. (1973). When interpreting the table it is essential to refer to the earlier statement that in the vertical canals the left anterior canal parallels the right posterior one and correspondingly the right anterior canal parallels the left posterior one. Furthermore, the afferent discharge from the anterior canals is excited by nose-down angular movements in the planes of those canals, whilst the posterior ones are excited by nose-up components of angular movements.

Thus, to follow through one example, consider the relationships which obtained when the head is rotated in a nose-down direction in a plane parallel to the left

TABLE 1. EXCITATORY AND INHIBITORY INFLUENCES OF THE SEMICIRCULAR CANALS UPON THE EXTRAOCULAR MUSCLES

MR, LR, SR, IR denote medial, lateral, superior and inferior rectus muscles; SO, IO denote superior and inferior oblique muscles (Modified from Ito, 1973)

| | Ipsilat. muscles | | Contralat. muscles | |
	+	−	+	−
Horizontal	M.R.	L.R.	L.R.	M.R.
Anterior vertical	S.R.	I.R.	I.O.	S.O.
Posterior vertical	S.O.	I.O.	I.R.	S.R.

anterior and right posterior canals. Excitation of left anterior primary afferents then cause excitation of superior rectus and inhibition of inferior rectus muscles of the left eye. Correspondingly, the right posterior canal has its spontaneous afferent discharge suppressed and this will reduce an inhibitory influence on the left eyes superior rectus leading to its increased contraction, whilst suppressing the excitatory interneuronal influence on the inferior rectus of that eye. Thus, a reciprocal action of afferent inputs produces commensurate reciprocal influences on superior and inferior rectus muscles in the left eye, in such a way as to generate the appropriate upwards diagonal angular movement of the eyeball in the skull for stabilization of the eye relative to space.

It is incidentally noteworthy that if the eye is looking to the left during such a movement, the pupil will appear to move up and down; but if looking to the right then the *same* plane of ocular rotation relative to the skull produces a *torsional* eye movement, i.e. rotation about the visual axis. The geometric and neurophysiological features described above thus account for this apparent anomaly. Using Table 1, the reader may exercise his understanding of the system by deriving the proper relationships between the outputs of the right anterior and left posterior canals in these circumstances and the generation of excitatory and inhibitory, disfacilitatory and disinhibitory, influences on the superior and inferior oblique muscles of the left eye. From the details of Table 1 it will be found that a corresponding compensatory angular movement of the eye will be generated in the appropriate diagonal plane relative to the skull.

FLEXIBILITY OF CENTRAL NEURAL INFLUENCES

In view of the direct geometrical relations between canals and extra-ocular muscles emphasized above it might be thought that direct interneuronal relays as depicted in Fig. 9 and Table 1 would suffice. Apparently, however, this is not the case. At least two additional and substantially influential central neural systems are now known to play an integral part in the formulation of the final oculomotor response to a given vestibular stimulus, namely the Reticular Formation of the brainstem, and the Vestibular Cerebellum (flocculo-nodular lobes and paraflocculus).

RECTICULAR FORMATION

It has been known for many years that proper vestibulo-ocular reflex function cannot take place in the absence of the reticular formation. Indeed, as Lorente de Nó showed in the early 1930s (Lorente de Nó, 1933), ascending reticular projections onto oculomo-toneuron cell bodies appear to be more numerous than direct vestibulo-oculomotor projections mediated through the medial longitudinal fasciculus (MLF). The deductive reasoning of Robinson and his colleagues (Skavenski and Robinson, 1973) has led to the plausible inference that one important function of the reticular network feeding synaptic influence upon oculomotoneurons may be to serve a mathematical integrative function on the angular velocity modulated neural signal received in the vestibular nuclei of the brainstem. This conclusion is drawn from the observed fact that the actual eye movement induced by oculomotoneurons requires that there should be both a positional and velocity component in the informational content of motoneuronal

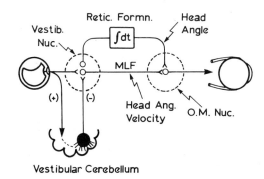

FIG. 10. Additional neural components acting on the vestibulo-ocular reflex arc.

firing frequency. Consequently, there is a necessary requirement for integration of at least a component of the velocity modulated message received from the primary afferents of the semicircular canals in the brainstem. This could well be effected in the reticular formation, from which the time integral of the vestibular signal (i.e. head angular position) could then in the simplest case be fed forward to sum algebraically at a synaptic level with the direct angular velocity modulated MLF neural message, at the level of the oculomotoneuron (Fig. 10).

THE VESTIBULAR CEREBELLUM

It has recently been shown that primary afferent vestibular neurones project directly into the cortex of the vestibular cerebellum (Precht and Llinás, 1969; Llinás and Precht, 1972). Furthermore, Purkinje cell modulation induced by this projection through granule cell responses, projects an inhibitory influence upon second-order vestibular neurones which are themselves projecting to oculomotor nuclei (Baker et al., 1973; Fukuda et al., 1972). This influence, depicted diagrammatically in Fig. 10, would seem to account for the tonic inhibitory influence of cerebellar control upon vestibulo-ocular projections. As with the reticular formation, we may inquire what kind of function could such an inhibitory "feed forward" influence play in the response of the whole vestibulo-ocular reflex system? Retrospectively, we may find some hints in the clear observation that removal of the vestibular cerebellum prevents the induction of motion sickness in previously susceptible dogs exposed to the normally nausea-inducing stimulus of a pendula swing (Bard, 1945; Wang and Chinn, 1956). Of more direct relevance is the fact that removal of the cerebellum substantially modifies the transfer function relating rotational eye response to rotational stimulation of the canals (Carpenter, 1972). Very recently a further clue is to be found in the novel observation that, at least in the rabbit, retinal stimulation by a moving visual object causes modulation of vestibular cerebellar Purkinje cell activity (Maekawa and Simpson, 1972). This influence, acting through the accessory optic tract and climbing fibers from the contralateral olive, has since been shown to be capable of a modulation of central vestibular neuronal activity in a goal-directed sense such that the induced "vestibulo-ocular" response would tend to reduce image slip upon the retina (Ito *et al.*, 1973; Ito *et al.*, 1974 a and b). Thus, it now appears plausible that the vestibulo-ocular reflex system can be driven by purely retinal optokinetic stimuli to facilitate what amounts to optokinetic tracking behaviour! Similar neurophysiological observations in alert monkeys have now been observed by Henn *et al.* (1974), and these effects presumably account for a psychophysical phenomenon experienced by man described as "circular vection" (Dichgans and Brandt, 1972). Thus several authors have observed that human perceptual impressions of real rotational motion of the body are systematically generated by purely *optokinetic* rotational stimuli, even in the absence of any real rotation of the body relative to inertial space.

Similarly current observations from our own laboratory (Canadian Defence Research Board, Aviation Medical Research Unit Reports, 1973) have demonstrated that not only can the vestibulo-ocular reflex be excited or suppressed by appropriate retinal stimuli, but the influence can be so versatile as to bring about effectively complete reversal of the vestibulo-ocular reflex of man as a retained response consequent upon long-term optical reversal of vision.

An initial experimental approach examined the gain of the vestibulo-ocular reflex (ratio of induced slow-phase eye angular velocity to head angular velocity, measured with eyes open in complete darkness) in subjects who had been sinusoidally oscillated on a rotating chair whilst looking at the surroundings via a plane mirror (Gonshor, 1970; Gonshor and Melvill Jones, 1969, 1971a). The plane mirror exactly reverses the visually perceived movement of the outside world, which therefore provides an optokinetic drive to the oculomotor system which exactly opposes that of the simultaneous vestibulo-ocular drive. The results from eight subjects, each exposed to 16 min of horizontal rotational oscillation at $\frac{1}{6}$ Hz and 60°/sec angular velocity amplitude on each of three successive days, showed a highly significant mean attenuation of gain per day of approximately 25%. In addition there was a highly significant, though small, cumulative retention of attenuation between days. The attenuation was shown to be dependent on the reversed optokinetic stimulus, since the same subjects exposed to the same vestibular stimulus, but *without vision* showed no significant attenuation, either within days or from beginning to end of the 3-day period (Gonshor and Melvill Jones, 1969). Arousal was continually maintained by mental arithmetic in both sets of experiments.

In order to examine longer-term effects of reversed vision on the vestibulo-ocular reflex, four subjects were fitted with optically reversing goggles equipped with dove prisms (Gonshor and Melvill Jones, 1971b; Melvill Jones and Gonshor, 1972; Gonshor and Melvill Jones, 1973; Canadian Defence Research Board Aviation Medical Research Unit Reports, 1973). The goggles were worn continuously for periods extending up to 4 weeks. Vestibulo-ocular gain was intermittently measured in the dark using exactly the same sinusoidal rotational test procedure as before. Figure 11 illustrates a subject wearing the prism-goggles, seated on the servo-controlled turntable.

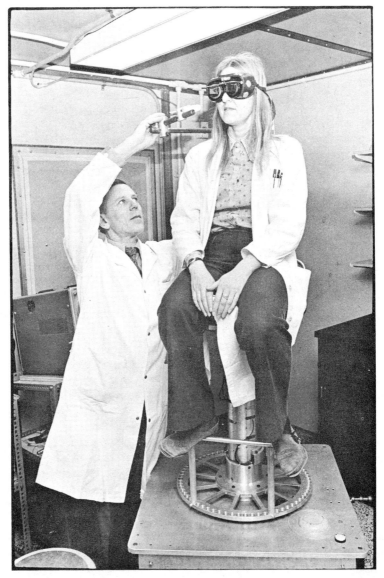

FIG. 11. The reversing prism goggles worn by a subject seated on the servo-controlled turntable.

All subjects showed rapid and substantial attenuation of "horizontal" vestibulo-ocular gain amounting to about 65% in the first 2 to 3 days. Figure 12 compares the nystagmoid responses obtained from the same subject on (a) the control day and (b) 3 days after donning the prisms respectively. Again the attenuation could not have been due to simple loss of arousal since vestibulo-ocular gain in the sagittal plane (in which there was no vision reversal) remained unchanged at its control value throughout. Moreover, there was presumably also no attenuation due to vestibular stimulation *per se* since this comprised natural head movement throughout the subjects' daily life.

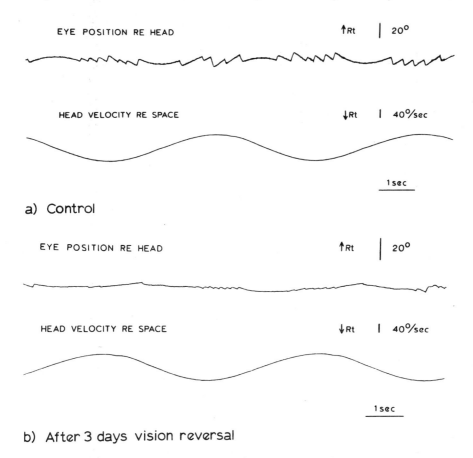

a) Control

b) After 3 days vision reversal

FIG. 12. Vestibulo-ocular reflex response to sinusoidal rotation recorded in the dark (a) before and (b) 3 days after donning the reversing prisms.

After about 2 weeks of continuous vision reversal the vestibulo-ocular response recorded in the dark was not merely attenuated, but had become effectively completely reversed! The phenomenon is exemplified in Fig. 13, which compares a control response (top trace) with that obtained 14 days after donning the prisms (middle trace). The bottom trace gives turntable angular velocity. When the eyes are open the reversed response seen in the middle trace would, of course, act to assist, rather than oppose, the reversed optokinetic tracking task. One may guess that the goal towards which plastic change was driven amounted here to reacquisition of automatic retinal image stabilization by means of the vestibulo-ocular reflex. Of very considerable added interest is the fact that on removal of the prism-goggles the time required for restoration to a normal pattern of vestibulo-ocular response was in all subjects approximately the same as the preceding duration of maintained vision reversal.

Subsequently, although unable to achieve the reversal of response seen in Fig. 13, Robinson has shown that the attenuation of normal vestibulo-ocular response induced in cat by vision reversal is apparently abolished by removal of the vestibular cerebellum (this volume, pp. 337–374). The strong implication of vestibular cerebellum participation, in particular the flocculus, in visual modification of vestibulo-ocular reflex, has similarly very recently been demonstrated in rabbits (Ito *et al.*, 1974 a and b).

Thus, although at the time of writing it is still early to draw firm conclusions, there is currently strong evidence from several different experimental approaches in different laboratories to support the view that a vestibulo-cerebellar component, such as that illustrated diagrammatically in Fig. 10, plays an important, if not essential, part in the plastic modulation of vestibulo-ocular reflex responses induced by normal and abnormal patterns of retinal image movement.

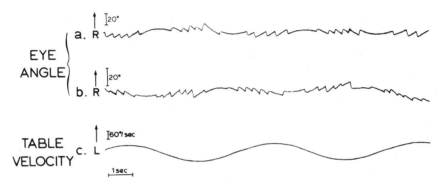

FIG. 13. Comparison of (a) control and (b) reversed vestibulo-ocular reflex, recorded from the same subject as in Fig. 12. The reversed response was recorded in the dark 14 days after donning the reversing prisms. The slight phase advancement of (b) relative to true reversal was characteristic at this stimulus frequency of $\frac{1}{6}$th Hz, and was consistently maintained from the 14th day until removal of the prisms.

No doubt, due to the current intensive application of research interest in this field, views expressed in this article will rapidly come to represent an insufficient statement of the complexity of neuronal mechanisms which tie the vestibular afferent input to the reflexly induced oculomotor response. However, at this time it is abundantly clear that despite the proven presence of short "hard-wired" neuronal connections of the kind exemplified in Fig. 9, additional central elements such as those indicated in Fig. 10 permit substantial levels of goal-directed plastic change when such change is functionally called for. It seems highly probable that the vestibular cerebellum plays an important role in the organization of such plastic change. Indeed it is tempting to conclude that perhaps we see here a quantitative example of the cerebellum acting as the central neural source of adaptive control in sensory-motor mechanisms.

REFERENCES

BAKER, R. G., MANO, N. and SHIMAZU, H. (1969) Post-synaptic potentials in abducens motoneurones induced by vestibular stimulation. *Brain Res.* **15**, 577.

BAKER, R. G., PRECHT, W. and LLINÁS, R. (1973) Cerebellar modulatory action on the vestibulo-trochlear pathway in the cat. *Exptl Brain Res.* **15**, 364.

BARD, P. (1945) Physiological investigation of courses and nature of motion sickness. National Research Council Committee on Aviation Medicine; Report No. 485.

BENSON, A. J. (1969) Interactions between semicircular canals and gravireceptors. In: *Recent Advances in Aerospace Medicine*, BUSBY, D. E. (Ed.). Pub. D. Reidel Publishing Co., Dordrecht, Holland.

BENSON, A. J., GUEDRY, F. E. and MELVILL JONES, G. (1970) Responses of semicircular canal dependent units in vestibular nuclei to rotation of a linear acceleration vector without angular acceleration. *J. Physiol. (Lond.)* **210**, 475.

Canadian Defence Research Board Aviation Medical Research Unit Reports (1973), Vol. III, Report No. DR 220, pp. 56–65.

CARPENTER, R. H. S. (1972) Cerebellectomy and the transfer function of the vestibulo-ocular reflex in the decerebrate cat. *Proc. R. Soc. Lond. B*, **181**, 353.

DALLOS, P. J. and JONES, R. W. (1963) Learning behaviour of the eye fixation control system. *IEEE Trans. Autom. Control*, AC-**8**, 218.

DICHGANS, J. and BRANDT, TH. (1972) Visual-vestibular interactions and motor perception. In: *Cerebral Control of Eye Movements and Motion Perception. Bibl. Ophthal.* **82**, pp. 327–328. Publ. S. Karger, Basel.

FENDER, D. H. and NYE, P. W. (1961) An investigation of the mechanisms of eye movement control. *Kybernetik* **1**, 81.

FERNANDEZ, C. and GOLDBERG, J. M. (1971). Physiology of peripheral neurones innervating the semicircular canals of the squirrel monkey. II. Response to sinusoidal stimulation and the dynamics of the peripheral vestibular system. *J. Neurophysiol.* **34**, 661.

FUKUDA, J., HIGHSTEIN, S. M. and ITO, M. (1972) Cerebellar inhibitory control of the vestibulo-ocular reflex investigated in rabbit IIIrd nucleus. *Exptl Brain Res.* **14**, 511.

GOLDBERG, J. M. and FERNANDEZ, C. (1971) Physiology of peripheral neurones innervating semicircular canals of the squirrel monkey. III Variations among units in their discharge properties. *J. Neurophysiol.* **34**, 676.

GONSHOR, A. (1970) Vestibular habituation induced in man by reversing the visual field during rotational stimulation. *Proc. Can. Fed. Biol. Sci.* **13**, 46.

GONSHOR, A. (1974) An investigation of plasticity in the human vestibulo-ocular reflex arc. Ph.D. Thesis, Department of Physiology, McGill University Montreal, Quebec, Canada.

GONSHOR, A. and MELVILL JONES, G. (1969) Investigation of habituation to rotational stimulation within the range of natural movement. *Proc. Aerospace Med. Sci. Meeting, San Francisco*, pp. 94.

GONSHOR, A. and MELVILL JONES, G. (1971a) Vestibular habituation induced by mirror-vision: an optimising process? *Proc. Aerospace Med. Sci. Meeting, Houston*, pp. 253.

GONSHOR, A. and MELVILL JONES, G. (1971b) Plasticity in the adult human vestibulo-ocular reflex arc. *Proc. Can. Fed. Biol. Sci.* **14**, 11.

GONSHOR, A. and MELVILL JONES, G. (1973) Changes of human vestibulo-ocular response induced by vision-reversal during head rotation. *J. Physiol.* **234**, 102 P.

GROEN, J. J., LOWENSTEIN, O. and VENDRICK, A. J. H. (1952) The mechanical analysis of the responses from the end organs of the horizontal semicircular canal in the isolated elasmobranch labyrinth. *J. Physiol.* **117**, 329–346.

HENN, V., YOUNG, L. R. and FINLEY, C. (1974) Vestibular nucleus units in alert monkeys are also influenced by moving visual fields *Brain Res.* **71**, 144.

HIGHSTEIN, S. M. (1973) Synaptic linkage in the vestibulo-ocular and cerebello-vestibular pathways to the VI nucleus in the rabbit. *Exptl Brain Res.* **17**, 301.

HIGHSTEIN, S. M., ITO, M. and TSUCHIYA, T. (1971) Synaptic linkage in the vestibulo-ocular reflex pathway of rabbit. *Exptl Brain Res.* **13**, 306.

ITO, M., NISIMARU, N. and YAMAMOTO, M. (1973) The neural pathways relaying reflex inhibition from semicircular canals to extra-ocular muscles of rabbits. *Brain Res.* **55**, 189.

ITO, M., SHIIDA, T., YAGI, N. and YAMAMOTO, M. (1974a) Visual influence on rabbit horizontal vestibulo-ocular reflex presumably effected via the cerebellar flocculus. *Brain Res.* **65**, 170.

ITO, M., SHIIDA, T., YAGI, N. and YAMAMOTO, M. (1974b) The cerebellar modification of rabbit's horizontal vestibulo-ocular reflex induced by sustained head rotation combined with visual stimulation. *Proc. Japan Acad.* **50**.

LLINÁS, R. and PRECHT, W. (1972) Vestibular cerebellar input: physiology. In: *Basic Aspects of Central Vestibular Mechanisms*, BRODAL, A. and POMPEIANO, O. (Eds.), pp. 341–359. Elsevier Pub. Co., Amsterdam-London-New York.

LORENTE DE NÓ, R. (1933) Vestibulo-ocular reflex arc. *Arch. Neurol. Psychiat. (Chicago)*, **30**, 245.

MAEKAWA, K. and SIMPSON, J. I. (1972) Climbing fiber activation of Purkinje cells in the flocculus by impulses transferred through the visual pathway. *Brain Res.* **39**, 245.

MALCOLM, R. C. and MELVILL JONES, G. (1970) A quantitative study of vestibular adaptation in humans. *Acta Otolaryng. (Stockh.)* **70**, 126.

MELVILL JONES, G. (1963) Ocular nystagmus recorded simultaneously in three orthogonal planes. *Acta Otolaryng.* **56,** 619.

MELVILL JONES, G. (1965a) Vestibulo-ocular disorganisation in the aerodynamic spin. *Aersopace Med.* **36,** 976.

MELVILL JONES, G. (1965b) The vestibular contribution to stabilisation of the retinal image. NASA Symposium on the role of the vestibular organ in the exploration of space. Pensacola, Florida Jan. 20–22. NASA SP-77, pp. 163–172.

MELVILL JONES, G. (1968) From land to space in a generation: an evolutionary challenge. *Aerospace Med.* **39,** 1271.

MELVILL JONES, G. (1972) Transfer function of labyrinthine volleys through the vestibular nuclei. In: *Basic Aspects of Central Vestibular Mechanisms,* BRODAL, A. and POMPEIANO, O. (Eds.), pp. 139–156. Elsevier Publishing Co., Amsterdam–London–New York.

MELVILL JONES, G., BARRY, W. and KOWALSKY, N. (1964) Dynamics of the semicircular canals compared in yaw, pitch and roll. *Aerospace Med.* **35,** 984.

MELVILL JONES, G. and DRAZIN, D. H. (1961) Oscillatory motion in flight. In: *Human Problems of Supersonic and Hypersonic Flight,* BARBOUR, A. B. and WHITTINGHAM, H. E. (Eds.), pp. 134–151. Pub. Pergamon Press, London, England.

MELVILL JONES, G. and GONSHOR, A. (1972) Extreme vestibular habituation to long-term reversal of vision during natural head movements. *Proc. Aerospace Med. Assn. Ann. Sci. Meeting, Bal Harbour Florida,* 1972, *Proc.* p. 22.

MELVILL JONES, G. and MILSUM, J. H. (1965) Spatial and dynamic aspects of visual fixation. *IEEE Trans. Biomed. Engng,* BME-**12,** 54.

MELVILL JONES, G. and MILSUM, J. H. (1970) Characteristics of neural transmission from the semicircular canal to the vestibular nuclei of cats. *J. Physiol. (Lond.)* **209,** 295.

MELVILL JONES, G. and MILSUM, J. H. (1971) Frequency response analysis of central vestibular unit activity resulting from rotational stimulation of the semicircular canals. *J. Physiol. (Lond.)* **219,** 191.

MELVILL JONES, G., WATT, D. G. D. and ROSSIGNOL, S. (1973) Eighth nerve contributions to the synthesis of locomotor control. In: *Control of Posture and Locomotion,* STEIN, R. B., PEARSON, K. G., SMITH, R. S. and REDFORD, J. B. (Eds.), pp. 579–598. Plenum Press, New York–London.

MICHAEL, J. A. and MELVILL JONES, G. (1966) Dependence of visual tracking capability upon stimulus predictability. *Vision Res.* **6,** 707.

OMAN, C. M. and YOUNG, L. R. (1972) Physiological range of pressure difference and cupula deflections in the human semicircular canal: Theoretical considerations. In: *Basic Aspects of Central Vestibular Mechanisms,* BRODAL, A. and POMPEIANO, O. (Eds.), p. 529. Elsevier Pub. Co., Amsterdam–London–New York.

PRECHT, W. (1972) Vestibular and cerebellar control of oculomotor functions. In: *Cerebellar Control of Eye Movements and Motion Perception. Bibl. Ophthal.* **82,** 71. Pub. S. Karger, Basel.

PRECHT, W. and BAKER, R. (1972) Synaptic organisation of the vestibulo-trochlear pathway. *Exptl Brain Res.* **14,** 158.

PRECHT, W., GRIPPO, J. and RICHTER, A. (1967) Effects of horizontal angular acceleration on neurones in the abducens nucleus. *Brain Res.* **5,** 527.

PRECHT, W. and LLINÁS, R. (1969) Functional organisation of the vestibular afferents to the cerebellar cortex of frog and cat. *Exptl Brain Res.* **9,** 30.

SHIMAZU, H. and PRECHT, W. (1965) Tonic and kinetic response of cat's vestibular neurones to horizontal angular acceleration. *J. Neurophysiol.* **28,** 991.

SHIMAZU, H. and PRECHT, W. (1966) Inhibition of central vestibular neurones from the contralateral labyrinth and its mediating pathway. *J. Neurophysiol.* **29,** 467.

SKAVENSKI, A. A. and ROBINSON, D. A. (1973) Role of abducens neurones in vestibulo-ocular reflex. *J. Neurophysiol.* **36,** 724.

STEINDLER, A. (1955) *Kinesiology of the Human Body under Normal and Pathological Conditions.* Charles C. Thomas, Springfield, Illinois.

STEINHAUSEN, W. (1933) Uber die Beobachtung der Cupula in den Bogengangsampullen des Labyrinths des lebenden Hechts. *Pflüg. Arch. Ges. Physiol.* **232,** 500.

SZENTÁGOTHAI, J. (1950) The elementary vestibulo-ocular reflex arc. *J. Neurophysiol.* **13,** 395.

TARLOV, E. (1972) Anatomy of the two vestibulo-oculomotor projection systems: In: *Basic Aspects of Central Vestibular Mechanisms,* BRODAL, A. and POMPEIANO, O. (Eds.), p. 471. Elsevier Pub. Co., Amsterdam–London–New York.

VAN EGMOND, A. A. J., GROEN, J. J. and JONGKEES, L. B. W. (1948) The turning test with small regulable stimuli. I. Method of examination: cupulometrics. *J. Laryng. Otol.* **62,** 63–69.

VAN EGMOND, A. A. J., GROEN, J. J. and JONGKEES L. B. W. (1949) The mechanics of the semicircular canals. *J. Physiol.* **110,** 1–17.

WANG, S. C. and CHINN, H. I. (1956) Experimental motion sickness in dogs: Importance of labyrinth and vestibular cerebellum. *Am. J. Physiol.* **185,** 617.

WERSÄLL, J. (1972) Morphology of the vestibular receptors in mammals. In: *Basic Aspects of Central Vestibular Mechanisms*, BRODAL, A. and POMPEIANO, O. (Eds.), pp. 3–17. Elsevier Publishing Co., Amsterdam–London–New York.
YOUNG, L. R. (1962) A sampled data model for eye tracking movements. M.I.T. D.Sc. Thesis.

PLASTICITY—DYNAMIC PROPERTIES OF THE VESTIBULO-OCULAR ARC

Nils G. Henriksson and Alf Nilsson

Identical vestibular stimulation may provoke varying nystagmus responses for many various reasons.

Vestibular responses are frequently severely influenced by variations in position of the subject.

When vestibular impulses make false and to the optic and proprioceptive systems contradictory information, central integration mechanisms seem to build up an increasing disregard, an increasing disbelief in vestibular impulses. The effect of this is a suppression of vestibular responses.

Between the vestibular and the three other eye-motor systems, the optic, the voluntary, and the vergence systems, there is a continuous interaction, facilitating or inhibiting. Variations in this interaction may also cause changes in vestibular response. Further, the vestibular responses may also vary as effects of changes in the central integrating mechanisms due to such factors as variations in alertness, effects of tobacco, eye-closure, etc. All of these expressions of the dynamic properties in the vestibulo-ocular arc have also been conceived as expressions of plasticity in the vestibular system.

In practical clinical work the different types of these dynamic properties of the vestibulo-ocular arc have to be considered for two reasons. First, they may obscure the information of the vestibular reflex arc and must then be considered and calculated for when the resulting nystagmus curve is interpreted. Secondly, the characteristics of these dynamic properties may themselves also furnish valuable information about normal or pathological conditions in the vestibulo-ocular arc. It will therefore be the aim of this paper to give a survey of different clinical implications of variations in vestibular responses.

The presentation of the dynamics of the vestibulo-ocular arc will be based on the working model presented in Fig. 1A. The reflex arc is built up by five different components:

1. The mechano-receptors in the labyrinth.
2. The peripheral neuron.
3. The vestibular nuclei.
4. "Slow" or "fast" eye-movement selector.
5. The eye-motor unit.

In the selector mechanism a constant competence between the "slow" or "fast" systems seems to take place. A fast eye movement can never coexist with a slow eye movement —one of the types must always be in full control of the movements of the eyes.

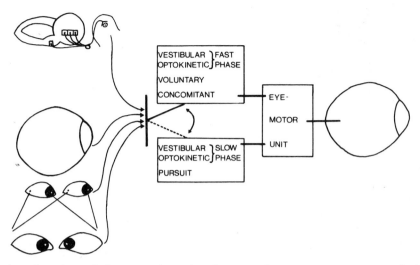

FIG. 1A. Apart from the vestibular system also optic, voluntary, and vergence eye-motor systems feed impulses into the selector for fast and slow eye-movements. The vestibulo-ocular arc can then be divided in a first part for vestibular impulses only and a latter part shared with the other eye-motor systems.

A vestibular stimulation will then provoke via the vestibular nucleus a stimulation of a slow phase center resulting in a slow phase; after a certain time elapse the fast phase center will take over and provoke a fast-phase movement in opposite direction. Apart from the vestibular system also optic, voluntary and vergence systems feed impulses into the brainstem for control of eye movement. There is clinical evidence (Fox and Holmes, 1926; Dix *et al.*, 1971; Henriksson, 1973) that all types of slow eye movements—vestibular slow phase, optokinetic slow phase as well as pursuit eye movements—are transmitted through the same system, the slow phase system. On

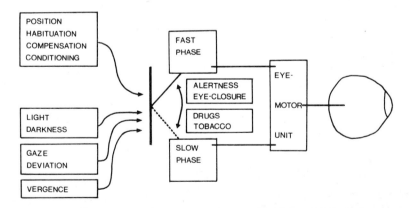

FIG. 1B. Anticipated and hypothetic locations of different processes responsible for plasticity in the vestibulo-ocular arc. Effects of position but possibly also of habituation, compensation, and conditioning may take place in the former part of the vestibular reflex arc. Variations in light, in gaze deviation, and in convergence provoked changes in the vestibular nystagmus output and these interactions may take place in the latter part of the vestibulo-ocular arc. Spontaneous variations in alertness or caused by eye-closure, drugs, or tobacco cause a variation in vestibular nystagmus as effects of changes in the central integrating mechanisms.

the other hand, do all fast movements—the voluntary, the concomitant (Henriksson *et al.*, 1974), and the fast phase of vestibular and of optic nystagmus—employ the other, the so-called saccadic system.

From this it follows that the vestibular reflex arc may be divided into two parts. The first part, comprising the receptor, the vestibular neuron, and the vestibular nuclei, is mainly transmitting vestibular impulses. The second part of the vestibulo-ocular arc is engaged also by the other eye-motor systems—the optic, voluntary and the vergence systems. An extra-vestibular system controlling and related to alertness affects severely transmission in vestibular and oculo-motor synapses and pathways (Collins and Guedry, 1961; Collins, 1970; Blegvad, 1962; Nathanson *et al.*, 1957).

The dynamic properties of the vestibular system can then be related to the first or the second part of the vestibular arc but also to a third system related to alertness and affected by such factors as eye-closure, drugs, or tobacco (Fig. 1 B).

I. MODULATIONS RELATED TO PROCESSES IN THE FIRST AND EXCLUSIVELY VESTIBULAR PART OF THE ARC

1. Effect of Position

Changing position frequently modulates spontaneous nystagmus of peripheral type, e.g. nystagmus caused by vestibular neuronitis or by labyrinth destruction.

The vestibular nuclei of the two sides are normally bombarded by an equal amount of action potentials from the right and from the left vestibular nerve. The lack of impulses or the decrease of the number of impulses from one nerve causes a vestibular imbalance resulting in a nystagmus with the fast component directed towards the healthy ear. Such nystagmus is in otologic literature referred to as destruction nystagmus and the concomitant vertigo referred to as a destruction type of vertigo. Patients in such situations spontaneously put their healthy ear undermost which results in a decrease of vertigo and a decrease of nystagmus (Fig. 2). This modification of the vestibular nystagmus response is well known and described by Simpson (1967), Scott-Brown (1971), and Ballenger (1969). Fluur (1973) discussed the mechanisms for this phenomenon and related the decrease of nystagmus output to an inhibiting effect from the utricular macula of the healthy ear when placed undermost. With the healthy ear uppermost this macula would facilitate the nystagmus and vertigo. In cases with nystagmus for other reasons and with normal labyrinthine activity the facilitatory and inhibitory effects from the maculae of the two labyrinths are expected to cancel each other. The lateral position in such cases will then not cause a change of either vertigo or of nystagmus.

2. Habituation

Habituation may be defined as a suppression of response as an effect of repetition of stimulus. Vestibular habituation seems to take place only if the vestibular stimulus is in disagreement with other postural impulses. Further, the process of habituation

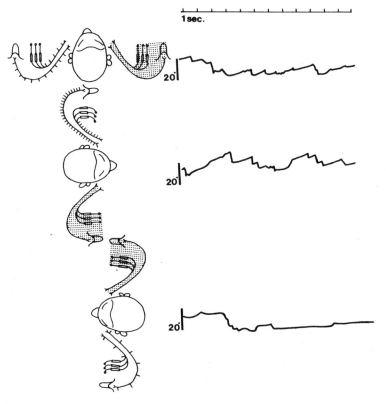

Fig. 2. Modulation of peripheral spontaneous nystagmus by position of the head. The effect could be attributed to different direction of stimulation of the gravity receptors of the remaining labyrinth.

is more effective the more pronounced this disagreement is (Guedry, 1965; Gonshor and Melvill Jones, 1974). The phenomenon of habituation has also been extensively studied by Graybiel *et al.* (1960, 1961) in a number of reports. Their ultimate goal was to find procedures to habituate a crew of a planned rotating spacecraft in order to make it capable of working also in a rotating environment.

Although habituation by definition takes place as an effect of repetition in healthy subjects it still has to be considered also by the clinician. Intense sensation of rotation induced in vestibular disorders as in Menière cases must be expected to provoke habituation. Such mechanisms must also be expected to reduce nystagmus and vertigo in repeated attacks.

There have also been efforts to reduce vertigo and concomitant nystagmus by exposing Menière cases between the attacks to repeated rotations or caloric stimulations (Fig. 3). Such procedures have been claimed to improve the ability of the patients to suppress inadequate vestibular impulses during attacks (Gramowski, 1964).

3. Compensation

Spontaneous nystagmus initiated by a sudden labyrinthine inactivity is known to be slowly compensated for by means of central compensation mechanisms. These

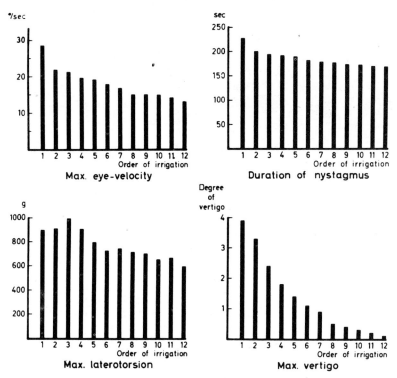

FIG. 3. Diagrammatic representation of maximum eye-velocity, duration of nystagmus, maximum laterotorsion and maximum vertigo following repeated calorizations. Mean values from fifteen normals, all irrigated twelve consecutive times in darkness for 40 sec with water of 30°C in the right ear (From Forssman *et al.*, 1963.)

mechanisms may be of two kinds. One is an accommodation process made up by efferent activity inhibiting impulses from the healthy side (Pfaltz *et al.*, 1973). The other part of compensation is made up by somato-sensory regulation in which proprioceptive and optic impulses take part (Henriksson *et al.*, 1973).

McCabe and Ryu (1969) have studied compensation mechanisms by recording electrical activity in the two vestibular nuclei in cats after one-sided labyrinthectomy. After operation there was immediate decrease of activity in both vestibular nuclei. In the nucleus of the healthy side impulses soon reappeared while on the unhealthy side gradual recovery of the animal was reflected by gradual returning of impulses (Fig. 4). There was also evidence produced indicating a cerebellar role in modifying these processes.

In cases of vestibular neuronitis clinical findings indicate a sudden abolishment of vestibular activity from one nerve. The effect of this loss of activity is diminished by the same kind of central compensation as in cases with labyrinth destruction. In some instances the vestibular neuronitis will heal and the vestibular activity in the nerve slowly return. If this returning takes place after some amount of central compensation has occurred the impulses from the recovering labyrinth will create a vestibular imbalance. In such cases more vestibular impulses reach the diseased side than the healthy side and that will result in a nystagmus directed towards the diseased side—a recovery nystagmus according to Stenger (1959).

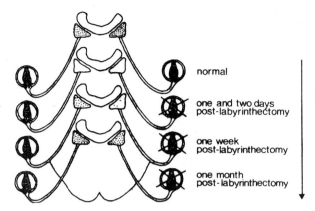

FIG. 4. Activity in the vestibular nuclei before and after one-sided labyrinth-ectomy according to McCabe (1969). Immediately after labyrinth-ectomy there is abolishment of vestibular activity in both vestibular nuclei. The activity reappears, however, much more rapidly on the healthy side than on the diseased side.

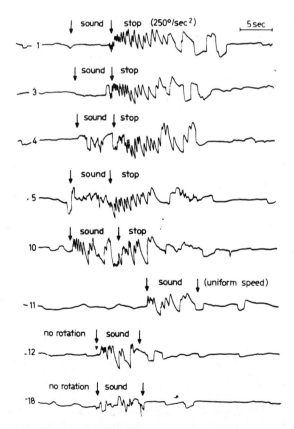

FIG. 5. Vestibular stimulation by rotation simultaneous with sound provokes a conditioned vestibular reflex. After repetition of the combination of vestibular stimulation and sound for 10 times the sound only is enough to provoke nystagmus. (From Arslan et al., 1970.)

Compensation processes seem to be modified by pathological disturbances in the central nervous system. A lack of compensation resulting in a slow recovery is frequently found in patients with central disturbances of different kinds. Patients exposed to previous head trauma (Pfaltz *et al.*, 1973) as well as patients with depression (Henriksson, 1974) seem to compensate less rapidly than patients with a healthy central nervous system.

4. Conditioning

Mechanisms very closely related to habituation may be responsible for conditioning of vestibular nystagmus. After repetition of vestibular stimuli with consistent and simultaneous non-vestibular impulses these non-vestibular impulses may provoke vestibular nystagmus (Fig. 5) (Arslan *et al.*, 1970). It may be assumed that conditioning of vestibular nystagmus has a clinical implication; however, the clinical importance has up till now been very moderate and will therefore no more be discussed in this paper.

II. MODULATION RELATED TO PROCESSES IN THE LATTER, COMMON PART OF THE EYE-MOTOR SYSTEM. EFFECTS OF VARYING INTERFERENCE FROM THE OPTIC FIXATION, GAZE DEVIATION AND VERGENCE SYSTEMS

1. Optic Fixation

Increase of vestibular nystagmus by lack of fixation and inhibition by fixation in light is well documented (Frenzel, 1955). Some authors apply in clinical work only eye-closure to exclude fixation (Aschan *et al.*, 1956). Demanez and Ledoux (1970) exploited for clinical purposes variations in inhibition of vestibular nystagmus by fixation. They measured in caloric nystagmus the quotient between intensity in light and that behind closed eyes and found in cases with labyrinthine disorders or in normals a ratio rarely exceeding 25%, while a ratio about 25% often indicated a central disturbance. As Tjernström (1973) has pointed out, eye-closure in itself frequently modifies nystagmus. This will make it difficult to differ in the Demanez–Ledoux-test effects of eye-closure from the effect from lack of fixation. It must therefore be recommended to have the eyes of the patient open both in light and darkness and to determine the relation between nystagmus in light with fixation and nystagmus in darkness with eyes open. In Fig. 6 is presented a normal amount of inhibition of nystagmus by fixation and in a case with a central disturbance, lack of such inhibition.

2. Gaze Deviation

The modulation of vestibular nystagmus by engagement of the voluntary system has been exploited in the clinic for grading intensity of vestibular nystagmus (Alexander, quoted from Brunner, 1924). According to this classification a first-degree nystagmus (weak nystagmus) is present only when the patient looks in the direction of the fast

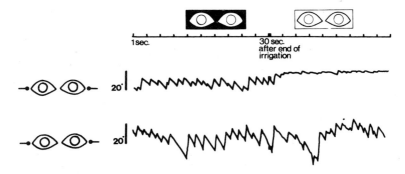

FIG. 6. Normal inhibition of caloric nystagmus by fixation in light (upper curve) and lack of such inhibition in a case with central disorder.

phase. Second-degree nystagmus (moderate nystagmus) occurs when the patient is look-ing straight ahead. Third-degree nystagmus (intense nystagmus) persists when the patient looks in the direction of the slow component (Fig. 7). When this classification is used normal fixation should be allowed (Henriksson et al., 1972).

The mechanism behind this interference between the voluntary and vestibular system has been very little studied. As was pointed out above when the model of the vestibular arc was described, the fast phase of nystagmus and voluntary eye movements at brain-stem level may be conveyed through at least partially the same pathways. Neurons engaged in provoking fast eye movements may be stimulated simultaneously by the vestibular system provoking a fast phase as well as by the voluntary system provoking a voluntary saccade. We may assume some kind of summation in transmittance resulting in an intensification of at least the fast component of nystagmus.

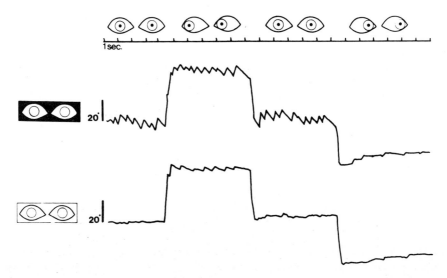

FIG. 7. Modulation of spontaneous nystagmus by gaze deviation, upper curve in darkness, bottom curve in light.

3. Convergence

During convergence in light a pronounced inhibition of vestibular nystagmus takes place. This is most likely an effect of intensified fixation. An effect of convergence in darkness is presented in Fig. 8. This is a recording from a subject who when calorically stimulated is converging on an imaginary object in darkness. Vestibular nystagmus is severely inhibited also by convergence in darkness. We may assume an inhibiting effect by convergence in the latter part of the vestibulo-ocular arc.

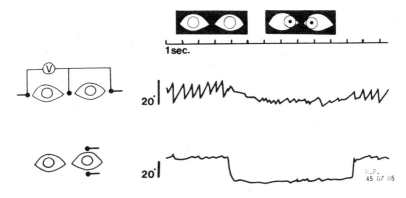

FIG. 8. Effect of convergence on caloric nystagmus.

III. MODULATIONS AS EFFECTS OF VARIATIONS IN ALERTNESS AND OF EYE-CLOSURE

1. Alertness

A decrease of alertness frequently diminishes the nystagmus output (Wendt, 1951; Collins *et al.*, 1961). There is often a disintegration of the normal rhythmic pattern of nystagmus, frequently in combination with a decrease in amplitude and in frequency of the nystagmus beats. These changes are also combined with deviation of the eyes in the direction of the slow component of nystagmus (Nathanson *et al.*, 1957; Nathanson and Bergman, 1958). In sleep there is a total abolishment of nystagmus together with a deviation of the eyes. At still lower levels of alertness, as in deep sleep or unconsciousness, the eyes will return to their mid-positions (Blegvad, 1962).

The mechanisms for the changes of nystagmus patterns are largely unknown but can, however, well be explained according to the model presented in the beginning in this paper (see Fig. 1 A). We must then add the assumption that sleepiness decreases the activity in the fast-phase system more than in the slow-phase system. This will tend to make the initiation of the fast phases irregular and will also tend to allow the slow-phase system to dominate, making the eyes deviate in the direction of the slow component.

The clinical interpretation of dysrhythmia and deviation of the eyes in the direction of slow component is not always simple. The findings may be effects of normal sleepiness in healthy subjects. They may also express a lowered level of alertness in patients with central disorders. They may again express pathology in subjects with a normal level of alertness and then the dysrhythmia is frequently interpreted as an expression of an ischeamic condition of the brainstem.

In practical clinical work it is very rewarding to expose patients with dysrhythmia and deviation of the eyes with a short period of light. The light usually infers enough arousal to make the eyes return to their mid-positions, sometimes with and sometimes without reappearance of nystagmus (Fig. 9).

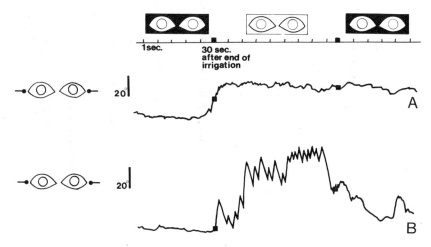

FIG. 9. Two cases with brainstem disturbances affecting alertness. (A) Caloric stimulation with eyes open in darkness does not provoke nystagmus but deviation of the eyes towards the left in the direction of the expected slow component. At exposure to light the eyes return to mid-position but nystagmus does not appear. (B) In this case the altering effect of light is enough to bring the eyes back to mid-position and to allow the appearance of normal caloric nystagmus.

2. Eye-closure

Weak spontaneous nystagmus is frequently enhanced by eye-closure, an intense spontaneous nystagmus often inhibited (Henriksson, 1974). Nystagmus induced by caloric stimulation or rotation is on the other hand most frequently severely inhibited by eye-closure. The mechanism behind this inhibition is unknown. An explanation by mechanical factors is shown unlikely by Tjernström (1973). He discussed the possibility that upward rotation of the bulbs simultaneous with the eye-closure could change the mechanical situation much enough to severely inhibit nystagmus. He regarded such mechanisms unlikely and attributed the inhibition of nystagmus to central processes.

The variation in inhibition of vestibular nystagmus by eye-closure has been exploited also for clinical purposes (Naito et al., 1963). Henriksson and Afzelius (1974) found a less pronounced inhibition in nervous vertiginous subjects than in vertiginous subjects without nervousness or in normals (Fig. 10). This finding contributing clinical information by eye-closure together with the clinical information given by variations in inhibition of nystagmus in light has made us introduce in caloric routine tests a short period of eye-closure as well as a period of exposition to light (Fig. 11). By this

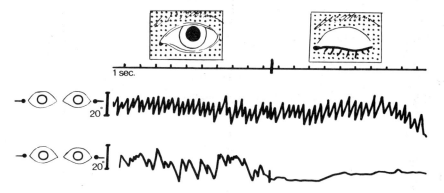

FIG. 10. Effect of eye-closure on caloric nystagmus. *Upper curve*: No effect by eye-closure. *Curve below*: Abolishment of nystagmus by eye-closure. (From Henriksson and Afzelius, 1974.)

technique variation in the dynamic properties of the vestibular reflex arc are providing important information on the condition of the central nervous system.

3. Drugs and Tobacco

The vestibular reflex arc is severely interfered with by different drugs (Jongkees and Philipszoon, 1960; Bergmann and Gutman, 1962). Sedatives seem to decrease the nystagmus output by causing sleepiness, first disturbing the function of the fast-phase system causing a deviation of the eyes in the direction of slow component and also dysrhythmia. The effect of antihistaminics on vestibular nystagmus is also well known (Philipszoon, 1959). A patient exposed to cinnarazine shows a decrease in the speed of slow component abolishing all nystagmus.

In late years it has also been shown that tobacco changes the nystagmus pattern in a unique way (Tibbling and Henriksson, 1968). Tobacco seems to infer a stimulation of the fast phase resulting in frequent interruptions of slow phases increasing the

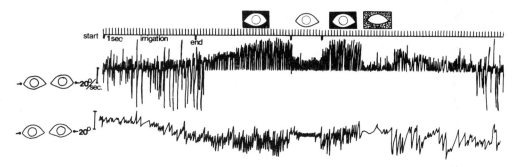

FIG. 11. Recording of eye-movements during and after caloric stimulation. Recordings from above: (1) Time in sec. (2) Horizontal eye-speed recording, time constant 0.01 sec, rectification of the potentials make possible a recording of slow phase velocity only. (3) Conventional DC-recording was made with the eyes of the patient open in darkness, except for one period with the patient exposed to light for 10 sec and one period during which he was allowed to close his eyes for another 10 sec.

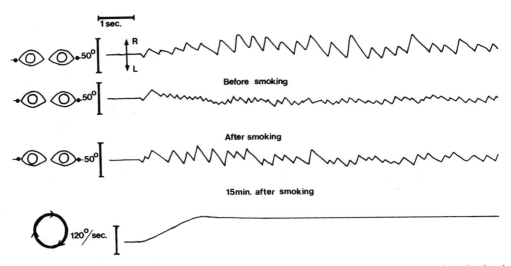

FIG. 12. Effect of tobacco smoking on post-rotatory nystagmus. The fast phases seem to be stimulated by tobacco and interrupt the slow phases earlier than before tobacco smoking resulting in a nystagmus curve of high frequency and low amplitude but with preservation of the original speed of slow components. (From Tibbling and Henriksson, 1969.)

frequency and decreasing the amplitude but with a preservation of the speed of slow component in the nystagmus (Fig. 12).

CONCLUSION

The necessity of continuous optic information in terrestrial life is reflected by the existence of four different eye-motor systems. Each situation seems to demand specific combination of impulses from the different systems.

In some situations vestibular impulses control eye-movements completely, in others vestibular impulses are meaningless or provide even misleading information. There

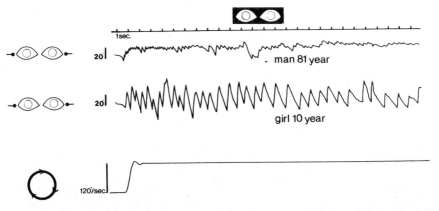

FIG. 13. Horizontal nystagmus response as effect of rotation in one old man and a girl of 10 years. A continuous change of nystagmus response seems to take place through years—younger people have larger nystagmus amplitudes and smaller frequency than older people. (Courtesy Dr. Tibbling.)

are at least three different modes in which the vestibular reflex arc is reorganized to meet different demands. An immediate change of the nystagmus response results as an effect of changes of position, of sudden exposure to light allowing fixation, at eye-closure and at engagement of the voluntary eye-motor system. Immediate changes do also take place as results from disturbance of the level of alertness.

A slower reorganization in the vestibulo-ocular arc results by habituation, compensation, or conditioning from repetition of or continuous vestibular impulses in conflict with optic or proprioceptive information.

An extremely slow change of the pattern of vestibular responses seems to take place during the course of normal life as a purely physiological process (Fig. 13). It has been pointed out that young people have much larger nystagmus amplitudes with a corresponding decrease of frequency of nystagmus than grown ups and elderly people (Tibbling, 1969).

REFERENCES

ARSLAN, M., MEGIGHIAN, D. and MARCHIORI, C. (1970) Evocation of vestibular nystagmus with the technique of conditioned reflexes. Interference between specific and nonspecific vestibular stimulations. *Adv. Oto-Rhino-Laryng.* **17,** 63.

ASCHAN, G., BERGSTEDT, M. and STAHLE, J. (1956) Nystagmography. *Acta Otolaryng.,* Suppl 128.

BALLENGER, J. J. (1969) *Disease of the Ear, Nose and Throat,* Lea & Febiger, Philadelphia.

BERGMAN, F. and GUTMAN, J. (1962) Effect of Largactil on various forms of nystagmus. *Psychopharmacol. Serv. Cent. Bull.* **2,** 57.

BLEGVAD, B. (1962) Caloric vestibular reaction in unconscious patients. *Arch. Otolaryng.* **75,** 506.

BRUNNER, H. (1924) Allgemeine Symptomatologie der Erkrankungen des Nervus vestibularis, seines peripheren und centralen Ausbreitungsgebietes. III. Der spontane Nystagmus. *Handbuch der Neurologie des Ohres,* I. Band, p. 959.

COLLINS, W. E. and GUEDRY, F. E. (1961) Arousal effects and nystagmus during prolonged constant angular acceleration, US Army Medical Research Laboratory, Fort Knox, Kentucky, Report no. 5000.

COLLINS, W. E., CRAMPTON, G. H. and POSNER, J. B. (1961) Effects of mental activity upon vestibular nystagmus and the electroencephalogram. *Nature,* **190,** 194.

COLLINS, W. E. (1970) Habituation of vestibular responses: an overview. *Fifth Symposium on the Role of the Vestibular Organs in Space Exploration, Pensacola, Florida, August 19–21.* NASA SP-314, p. 157.

DEMANEZ, J.-P. and LEDOUX, A. (1970) Automatic fixation mechanisms and vestibular stimulation. Their study in central pathology with ocular fixation index during caloric tests. *Adv. Oto-Rhino-Laryng.* **17,** 90.

DIX, M. R., HARRISON, M. J. G. and LEWIS, P. D. (1971) Progressive supranuclear palsy (The Steel–Richardson–Olszewski Syndrome). *J. Neurol. Sci.* **13,** 237.

FLUUR, E. (1973) The reason why the patient with acute labyrinthine destruction lies on his sound ear. *ORL* **35,** 253.

FORSSMAN, B., HENRIKSSON, N. G. and DOLOWITZ, D. A. (1963) Studies on habituation of vestibular reflexes. VI. Habituation in darkness of calorically induced nystagmus, laterotorsion and vertigo in man. *Acta Otolaryng.* **56,** 1.

FOX, J. D. and HOMES, G. (1926) Optic nystagmus and its value in the localization of cerebral lesions. *Brain,* **49,** 333.

FRENZEL, H. (1955) *Spontan- und Provokations-Nystagmus als Krankheits-symptom.* Springer-Verlag, Berlin–Göttingen–Heidelberg.

GONSHOR, A. and MELVILL JONES, G. (1974) Habituation of the human vestibulo-ocular reflex induced by reversal of the retinal image during sinusoidal rotation of the head, DRB Aviation Medical Research Unit, Dept. of Physiology, McGill University, Montreal, Canada.

GRAMOWSKI, K.-H. (1964) Das trainierte Labyrinth. Vorläufige Mitteilung über die therapeutische Anwendung vestibulärer Habituation bei Vestibularisstörungen. *HNO,* **12,** 105.

GRAYBIEL, A., GUEDRY, F. E., JOHNSON, W. and KENNEDY, R. (1961) Adaptation to bizarre stimulation of the semicircular canals as indicated by the oculogyral illusion. *Aerospace Med.* **32,** 321.

GUEDRY, F. E. (1965) Psychophysiological studies of vestibular function. *Contributions to Sensory Physiology,* NEFF, W. D. (Ed.), p. 63. New York and London: Academic Press.

HENRIKSSON, N. G., PFALTZ, C. R., TOROK, N. and RUBIN, W. (1972) *A Synopsis of the Vestibular System. An effort to standardize vestibular conceptions, tests, and their evaluation.* Gasser & Cie, AG, Basle, Switzerland.

HENRIKSSON, N. G. (1973) Conjugated eyemotor disturbances reflecting brain stem lesions. *Equil. Res.* **22**, 148.

HENRIKSSON, N. G., NOVOTNY, M. and TJERNSTRÖM Ö. (1974) Eye movements as a function of active headturnings. *Acta Otolaryng.* **77**, 86.

HENRIKSSON, N. G. and AFZELIUS, L.-E. (1974) Effect of eye-closure on caloric nystagmus in nervous subjects and normals. (In preparation.)

HENRIKSSON, N. G. (1974) Unpublished observations.

JONGKEES, L. B. W. and PHILIPSZOON, A. J. (1960) Some nystagmographical methods for the investigation of the effect of drugs upon labyrinth. *Acta Physiol. Pharmacol. Neerl.* **9**, 240.

MCCABE, B. F. and RYU, J. H. (1969) Experiments on vestibular compensation. *Laryngoscope*, **79**, 1728.

MCCABE, B. F., RYU, J. H. and SEKITANI, T. (1972) Further experiments on vestibular compensation. *Laryngoscope*, **82**, 3, 381.

NAITO, T., TATSUMI, T., MATSUNAGA, T. and MATSUNAGA, T. (1963) The effect of eye-closure upon nystagmus. *Acta Otolaryng.*, Suppl. 179, 72.

NATHANSON, M., BERGMAN, P. S. and ANDERSSON, P. J. (1957) Significance of oculocephalic and caloric responses in the unconscious patient. *Neurology*, **7**, 829.

NATHANSON, M. and BERGMAN, P. (1958) New methods of evaluation of patients with altered states of consciousness. *Med. Clin. N. Amer.*

PFALTZ, C. R., PIFFKO, P. and MISHRA, S. (1973) Central compensation of vestibular dysfunction. Neuronal and central lesions. *Equil. Res.* **3**, 86.

PHILIPSZOON, A. J. (1959) *The Effect of some Drugs upon the Labyrinth. A Nystagmographical Study.* Over de Linden—Enkhulzen, Netherlands.

SCOTT-BROWN, W. G. (1971) in Ballantyne and Grove's *Diseases of the Ear and Throat,* 3rd ed., vol. 2. Butterworths, London.

SIMPSON, J. F. and ROBÉN, J. (1967) *A Synopsis of Otolaryngology.* Wright, Bristol.

STENGER, H. H. (1959) "Erholungsnystagmus" nach einseitigem Vestibularisaus-fall, ein dem Becterew-Nystagmus verwandter Vorgang. *Arch. Ohr-, Nas-Kehlk.-Heilk.* **175**, 545.

TIBBLING, L. and HENRIKSSON, N. G. (1968) Effect of cigarette smoking on the vestibular nystagmus pattern. *Acta Otolaryng.* **65**, 518.

TIBBLING, L. (1969) The rotatory nystagmus response in children. *Acta Otolaryng.* **68**, 459.

TJERNSTRÖM, Ö. (1973) Nystagmus inhibition as an effect of eye-closure. *Acta Otolaryng.* **75**, 408.

WENDT, G. R. (1951) Vestibular functions. *Handbook of Experimental Psychology,* STEVENS, S. S. (Ed.), p. 1191. Wiley.

CEREBELLAR INFLUENCES ON EYE MOVEMENTS

Wolfgang Precht

THE classical notion that the cerebellum is involved in the control of movement generally refers to lesion-evoked disturbances of limb and trunk rather than eye movements. It has long been known, however, that stimulation of the cerebellum also evokes eye movements. (Ferrier, 1876; Hitzig, 1874), and that cerebellar lesions, particularly of the vestibulo-cerebellum, alter oculomotor performance. In fact if one were to review all the numerous stimulation studies of the past 100 years (for review see Dow and Manni, 1964; Ron and Robinson, 1973) one would come to the conclusion that practically any part of the cerebellar cortex may evoke eye movements. Obviously, this is very unlikely! It must be assumed that differences in the stimulating electrodes, intensities of stimulation, level of anesthesia, and recording procedures have been responsible for this confusing picture. Fortunately, in recent years well-controlled stimulation studies employing precise recording of eye movements have been performed in different species which allow us to present a much clearer picture of this subject. It should be emphasized, however, that it is very difficult if not impossible to infer cerebellar motor-control function from stimulation experiments only. Even if one carefully avoids current spread to the brainstem (particularly when deep cerebellar structures are stimulated), the correlation of a given stimulation effect with a structural element in the cerebellum is practically impossible. To appreciate this difficulty one has to realize that any cerebellar cortical region not only contains Purkinje cells which are the only output element of the cortex but also receives mossy and climbing fiber afferents many of which supply the cerebellar and brainstem nuclei as well. Furthermore, mossy fiber afferents branch profusely, so that a given mossy fiber may reach several cortical regions through its various branches. Since electrical stimulation of the cerebellar cortex excites both efferent and afferent elements, it is impossible to tell whether a given effect is due to Purkinje cell excitation and/or axon reflex excitation of brain stem and cerebellar nuclear neurons via the antidromic activation of mossy and climbing fiber afferents. The finding that stimulation of the cortex and the corresponding cerebellar nuclei causes similar and not the expected opposite eye movements may suggest that cerebellar cortical motor maps are not based on the effects of Purkinje cell activation and the resulting inhibition of target neurons but rather on the excitation of cerebellar and/or brainstem nuclei through axon reflexes of cerebellar afferents.

Even if stimulation experiments do not yield true output motor maps of the cerebellar cortex their results may still serve as useful guidelines in the further exploration of cerebellar control of eye movements by means of microelectrode recording techniques, lesion procedures, and morphological methods. Recent well-controlled stimulation studies of the cat (Cohen *et al.,* 1965) and monkey (Ron and Robinson, 1973) have shown that there are four main regions in the cerebellum (Fig. 1) the stimulation of which produce eye movements: (1) the vermis, lobulus V–VII; (2) crus I and II and lobulus simplex; (3) the vestibulo-cerebellum; (4) the cerebellar nuclei. In the following a review will be given of the present knowledge of the importance of these cerebellar regions in the control of eye movements. Emphasis will be placed on the experimental side, and the reader interested in details of clinical or control systems aspects is referred to the papers by Dichgans (1975) and Robinson (1975).

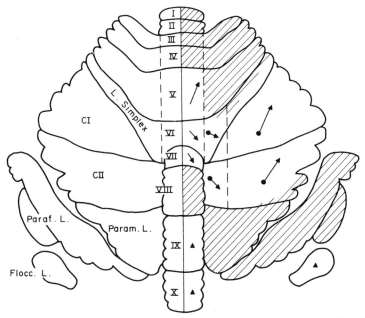

FIG. 1. Summary of results of cerebellar stimulation. Arrows indicate lobes where stimulation elicited saccades. The angle of the saccade above or below the horizontal is shown by the tilt of the arrow; ● indicates lobes where stimulation evoked smooth movements. A dot and an arrow represent a structure where stimulation evoked both saccades and smooth movements. The direction of the movements was the same as that of the evoked saccades (the direction of the arrow); ▲ indicates lobes where stimulation evoked nystagmus; shaded areas indicate structures where stimulation did not evoke eye movements (from Ron and Robinson, 1973).

CEREBELLAR VERMIS AND EYE-MOVEMENTS

Stimulation Experiments

There is general agreement among various authors that electrical stimulation of the vermis, lob. VI–VII, evokes ipsilateral, horizontal eye movements in different species (Hitzig, 1874; Hoshino, 1921; Hare *et al.,* 1936; Cohen *et al.,* 1965; Ron and Robinson, 1973). As for the rest of the vermis the results vary considerably, e.g. up movements have been reported to occur after stimulation of lob. II–V by some authors (Mussen,

1927; Cohen *et al.*, 1965) and not by others (Ron and Robinson, 1973), and down movements from lob. VII have only been reported by Cohen *et al.* (1965) and Ron and Robinson (1973). Some of the discrepancies are certainly due to differences in stimulus intensities. Unfortunately, the stimulus current was not monitored in earlier studies, so that a comparison between different stimulation points and/or different studies is difficult.

In a recent study of the alert monkey (Ron and Robinson, 1973) evoked eye movements were recorded so that a description of the direction *and* type of evoked eye movements could be given. They reported that conjugate eye-movements, mainly of the saccadic type, were evoked by stimulation of lob. V–VII only (Fig. 1). There was no difference between the amplitude-duration relationship of evoked and spontaneous saccades. Saccades required a threshold current of *ca.* 0.5 mA and occurred with latencies of 15–35 ms. The directions of saccades were spatially coded in that they varied with electrode location from horizontal (ipsilateral) in lob. VI to straight upward and downward in the midline of lob. V and VII respectively. Saccade amplitudes were independent of frequency, pulse width and duration of stimulation but depended on stimulus intensity. These findings indicate that saccade amplitudes are neither spatially nor temporally coded. In general amplitudes and directions of evoked saccades depended on the eye position prior to the stimulus onset and were often goal-directed.

In addition to saccades stimulation of the lateral edge of the vermis evoked smooth eye movements whose thresholds, however, were higher than those of the smooth eye movements evoked from the adjacent paravermis. Since the smooth movements may be attributed to current spread to paravermal regions, saccades are probably the characteristic type of eye movements evoked by stimulation of the vermis.

Lesion Experiments

Given the great difficulties that exist in the interpretation of cerebellar stimulation experiments (see above), lesion studies are of considerable importance for the further elucidation of the eye movement related function of a particular cerebellar region. The effects of unilateral lesions of lob. VI–VII and the adjacent paravermis on saccadic eye movements of the monkey have been studied (Aschoff and Cohen, 1971). With these lesions the eyes moved often from midposition to the contralateral side, and there were few saccades into the ipsilateral hemifield. Furthermore, saccades to the side contralateral to the lesion tended to be larger and of the single type whereas those to the ipsilateral side were smaller and composed of several smaller saccades. Smooth pursuit movements were affected very little by these lesions. Unfortunately in this study saccades were not made to calibrated targets, so it is impossible to compare pre- and post-operative data or to determine whether the animal did not or could not perform certain saccades, i.e. dysmetria may or may not be present.

In more recent experiments by Ritchie (personal communication) which incorporated a calibrated target control, a lesion of the vermis did indeed cause dysmetria which was usually less than 30% of the intended amplitude. Saccades were hypometric for movements from midline position to lateral (e.g. 0–30°) and hypermetric in the opposite direction (30–0°). Thus patterns of cerebellar saccadic dysmetria cannot be simply the result of impaired central processing of a retinal error since the error is the same for movements in either direction. What is different is the resistance of the orbital tissue to movement in the center and in the periphery. This finding suggests that the disturbance of saccadic eye-movements by vermal lesions is caused by the inability of the animal to take into proper account the eye position prior to the onset of saccades. Based on these results one would have to postulate extraocular proprioceptive input to the vermis (V-VII). That this is, indeed, the case will be illustrated in the next section.

Although the disturbances of eye-movements resulting after total cerebellectomy are of limited value for the evaluation of the functional properties of the oculomotor region of the vermis, a few interesting observations regarding the comparative aspects of the saccadic system should be mentioned (for more details see below). While cerebellectomy in the rabbit severely affected the quick phase of the optokinetic nystagmus but did not disturb the slow phases (optokinetic following reaction) cerebellectomy in the cat interfered with neither (Collewijn, 1970; Robinson, 1974). In untrained cerebellectomized monkeys an apparently normal saccadic system and a severely impaired smooth pursuit eye-movement system were reported (Westheimer and Blair, 1973). As for the apparent lack of effects of cerebellectomy on saccades it should again be emphasized that without calibrated targets it is impossible to exclude the presence of dysmetria. A critical evaluation of the disturbances of saccadic eye movements in patients with vermal lesions can be found in the paper by Dichgans (1975).

Input to the "Oculomotor" Vermis

Stimulation and lesion experiments suggest that the oculomotor vermis is in some way involved in the control of saccadic eye movements. One of the interesting findings was that this control function depended on the information of eye position. In the

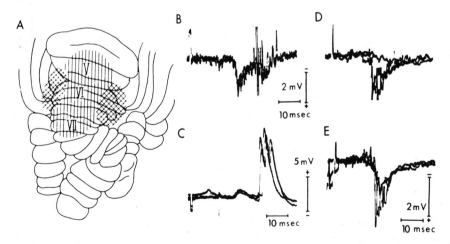

FIG. 2. Projections of extraocular muscle afferents to the cerebellum. (A) Diagram of the distribution of the potentials recorded in the cerebellum (lob. V, VI, VII) and evoked by electrical stimulation of the sensory fibers (a branch of the Vth nerve) from the sup. oblique muscle. Vertical hatching corresponds to a short latency mossy fiber input followed by climbing fiber input which are illustrated in (B) (extracellular) and (C) (intracellular recording). Note that in (C) stimulation caused an early EPSP–IPSP sequence through mossy fiber afferents followed by climbing fiber all-or-none EPSPs. Cross-hatching indicates climbing fiber input exclusively which is illustrated in (D) and (E) at different intensities of stimulation (from Baker et al., 1972a).

light of these lesion studies, it is not surprising that the vermis lob. V–VII receives an input from extraocular muscle proprioception (Fuchs and Kornhuber, 1969; Baker et al., 1972a). In Fig. 2A the distribution of the proprioceptive projection onto the cerebellar vermis of the cat is shown as determined by recording field and unitary potentials following electrical activation of extraocular afferents in the orbit (Baker et al., 1972a). The region marked with vertical hatching was characterized by the early mossy fiber activation of Purkinje cells (latency 5–6 ms) which was followed by a climbing fiber activation (latency ca. 18 ms) of the same population of neurons (Fig. 2 B, C). Although the exact pathway from the eye to the vermis is not known at present it is clear that only a few synapses can be involved in the fast mossy fiber path. Bilaterally at the junction between lob. VI and paravermal zone (Fig. 2A, cross-hatching area) pure climbing fiber evoked field potentials were recorded (Fig. 2 D, E).

Even before the proprioceptive input from eye muscles to the oculomotor vermis was described it was found that this region received visual, tactile and auditory inputs (Snider and Stowell, 1944). Recently proprioceptive afferent information from the neck (Berthoz and Llinás, 1974) has also been recorded in this region. Although it is tempting to speculate that these other sensory inputs are somehow also related to the role of the vermis in the control of saccadic eye movements it should be emphasized that at present there is no experimental evidence which indicates that this is the case.

Purkinje Cell Activity in the Oculomotor Vermis

If the cerebellar vermis were involved in the saccadic eye-movement system in a corrective mode of operation one would expect Purkinje cell activity (the only output neurons of the cerebellar cortex) to precede the onset of saccades. Such a postulate seems reasonable since saccades are movements of the ballistic (preprogrammed) type and are not altered much by feedback once they are initiated. Recent experiments by Wolfe (1971) in the alert cat have shown that field potentials can be observed in the vermis which precede the onset of saccades. These observations have been substantiated and extended by Llinás and Wolfe (1972) and Llinás (1974) who showed that these field potentials corresponded to the activation of Purkinje cells located primarily in lob. VIa, VIb and VII via mossy fiber afferents. As shown in Fig. 3 Purkinje cell firing begins to increase prior to the onset of saccades by as much as 25 ms. The maximum Purkinje cell activity slightly precedes or coincides with the onset of the saccade. Given that the delay between the onset of the firing of ocular motoneurons and the initiation of eye movement is ca. 7 ms (Robinson, 1968) increased Purkinje cell firing would be expected to precede motoneuron firing by ca. 18 ms. It was also shown that the firing of some units correlated with the direction of the saccades but that others did not. Furthermore, an inverse relationship between the amplitude of the saccades and the presaccadic number of Purkinje cell spikes was observed, i.e. the smaller the saccades the larger the peak of Purkinje cell firing. The total duration of increased, individual Purkinje cell firing was not related to the amplitude of the saccades. It is not clear at present what functional meaning may be ascribed to the inverse relationship between Purkinje cell firing and saccade size. With electrical stimulation the amplitudes of saccades were independent of pulse rate, at least between 200–1000 Hz (Ron and Robinson, 1973). However, a direct comparison between the two kinds of cerebellar activation may not be possible. Nothing is known about the specific pathways by which vermal Purkinje cells exert their influences on ocular motoneurons. It may be assumed, however, that for the most part effects are mediated to the brainstem indirectly through the cerebellar nuclei (see also last section).

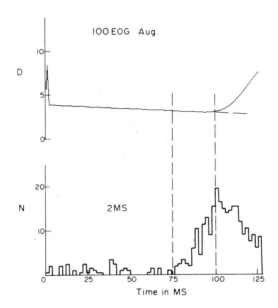

FIG. 3. Histogram of the time relationship between Purkinje cell firing and the initiation of eye-movement. One hundred EOGs of the same size were averaged, from taped material, in the upper record. The onset of the eye-movements is marked by the second vertical line. The histogram gives a Purkinje cell spike count accompanying the same 100 eye-movements (N) against time (ms). The computation is initiated 100 ms prior to the commencement of the saccade. The first vertical line denotes onset of the increase in Purkinje cell activity over the background level (from Llinás, 1974).

In concluding this section on the oculomotor vermis it may be asked what we have learned about the role of the cerebellar vermis in the control of eye-movements. The findings that (1) low intensity electrical stimulation produced direction coded saccades and that (2) Purkinje cells of this very region started firing prior to the onset of spontaneous saccades strongly suggest that the vermis is intimately involved in the saccadic eye-movement system. Lesion experiments allow us to qualify this general statement a little further since they indicate that the eye-position signal is of particular importance for the vermal control of saccades. These results are in complete agreement with the electrophysiological data showing the arrival of extraocular muscle proprioceptive input at the vermis. So far, the functional importance of other sensory inputs to the vermis has no experimental basis and needs further elaboration.

Finally, a few speculations regarding the function of the cerebellar vermis may be discussed in the light of the following experimental data. Based on morphological (Braitenberg, 1961) and clinical (Kornhuber, 1971) observations it has been suggested that the cerebellar cortex may convert spatial information (e.g. angle to be moved) into temporal patterns (duration of neuronal firing). For the control of saccadic eye movements (ballistic movement) which are too fast to be controlled continuously by feedback the cerebellum, of course, must perform the space into time conversion prior to the actual onset of movement. This means that the duration of the saccade-related firing of ocular motoneurons (which alone determines the amplitude of the saccade) is controlled by the cerebellar vermis which computes the proper setting of saccade size from spatial data. As described above, this attractive "spatio-temporal translator" theory has been tested experimentally and all of the evidence collected so far tends to be negative. Clearly more work is needed to evaluate such overall functional concepts.

CEREBELLAR HEMISPHERES AND EYE MOVEMENTS

Compared to the vermis very little is known about the role of the cerebellar hemispheres in eye-movement control. Our knowledge is primarily based on the following stimulation studies which will be briefly summarized. Low-intensity tetanic stimulation of crus I and II and lob. simplex in the monkey (Fig. 1) produced saccades whose characteristics were similar to those evoked from the vermis (Ron and Robinson, 1973), i.e. their directions were spatially coded, and their amplitudes were neither spatially nor temporally coded, but rather depended upon stimulus intensity, i.e. they were population-size coded. In addition to saccades smooth eye movements have been obtained by the stimulation of the same hemispherical areas (Fig. 1). In fact saccades and smooth movements generally occurred together. They had the same directions: ipsilateral and down in the paravermis, horizontal in the medial hemisphere and upward and ipsilateral in the lateral hemisphere. Smooth movements started after latencies of ca. 10–15 ms, and their velocity increased with an increase in all stimulus parameters.

As pointed out by Ron and Robinson (1973), the occurrence of smooth movements after constant frequency stimulation indicates that the evoked spike activity is integrated by a neural integrator which is most likely outside the cerebellar cortex since smooth movements were also evoked by stimulation of the cerebellar nuclei and brachium conjunctivum. Since the function of the smooth pursuit system seems to be related to the optimalization of the relation between eye velocity and target velocity (Collewijn, 1972) it is not surprising that cerebellar evoked smooth movements show a slower velocity in the presence of the visual texture (Ron and Robinson, 1973). Evoked eye movements present a disturbance to the stationary visual field and attempts are made to counteract the evoked movement thereby reducing its velocity.

Lesion experiments in rabbits and cats tend to suggest that the cerebellum is not in the direct pathway of the smooth pursuit system since smooth eye movements were not altered by total cerebellectomy (Collewijn, 1970; Robinson, 1974). However, recent cerebellectomy studies in the monkey showing the absence of all smooth pursuit movements suggest an intimate relationship between the cerebellum and the smooth pursuit system (Westheimer and Blair, 1973). In conjunction with the above stimulation studies it may be assumed that the smooth pursuit failure is mainly due to the removal of crus I, II and lob. simplex. This notion is also supported by the finding that selective lesion of the oculomotor vermis did not impair the smooth pursuit system (Ritchie, pers. comm.).

It has been pointed out that one of the functional implications of the presence of smooth pursuit as well as saccade control in the hemispheres might be that hand–eye coordination occurs in these regions (Ron and Robinson, 1973) which are indeed quite large in species with highly developed hand and finger movements. In support of this notion experiments have shown that pursuit eye movements are much better when a subject actively moves an object with his hands as compared to passive observation and passive movement (Steinbach, 1969).

THE VESTIBULO-CEREBELLUM AND EYE MOVEMENTS

It has been known for a long time that the vestibulo-cerebellum is intimately related to control of eye movements, particularly the vestibular evoked ocular reflexes (for summary of much of the earlier studies see Dow and Manni, 1964). Given the close anatomical relationship between this region of the cerebellum and the vestibular system such a finding is not so surprising. In recent years much progress has been made in the study of the anatomical and functional organization of the vestibulo–cerebello–oculomotor interrelationship so that at the present time this region is perhaps the most promising for experimental studies of the function of the cerebellum in motor control. In the following a brief description of both the anatomy and physiology of the neuronal circuitry of the system will be given. Based on this data an attempt will be made to interpret stimulation and lesion experiments which have been undertaken to elucidate the functional role of the flocculo-nodular lobe. The reader interested in this field is also referred to the articles by Dichgans (1975), Melvill Jones (1975), and Robinson (1975) appearing in this book.

Anatomical and Functional Properties of the Vestibulo–oculo–cerebellar Circuitry

In recent years anatomical (Tarlov, 1970; Gazek, 1971) and physiological studies (Baker *et al.*, 1969; Precht, 1972; Precht and Baker, 1972; Highstein, 1973; Ito *et al.*, 1973 a, b, c) have greatly advanced our knowledge of the circuitry of the short-latency vestibulo-ocular reflex and its anatomical (for review see Walberg, 1972) and functional relationship to the vestibulo-cerebellum (Baker *et al.*, 1972b; Fukuda *et al.*, 1972). The main findings of the above studies will be summarized briefly.

In Fig. 4 are shown the disynaptic excitatory and inhibitory vestibulo–ocular reflexes connecting the horizontal semicircular canals with the motoneurons of the lateral and medial recti muscles. Also shown is the commissural path which inhibits the type I vestibular neurons on the other side by means of an intercalated type II neuron (Shimazu and Precht, 1966). As may be deduced from this diagram, a counterclockwise rotation increases the activity of type I vestibular neurons on the left side, while the type I neurons in the right nucleus decrease their firing. These changes are brought about by a combination of peripheral and commissural effects. As a result of this modulation of vestibular neurons the right lateral and left medial rectus motoneurons will be excited by activation and disinhibition, and the motoneurons of the left lateral and right medial rectus will be inhibited by inhibition and disfacilitation. This innervation pattern will result in a conjugate slow eye movement to the right which compensates for the equal and opposite head movement. As a result the visual axis remains stationary

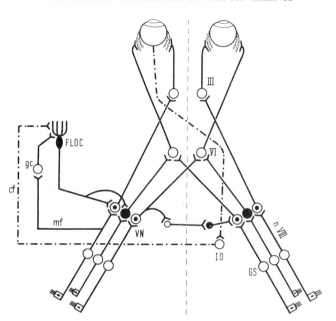

Fig. 4. Diagram of the short latency vestibulo-ocular reflexes originating from horizontal canals and their relation to the cerebellum. Open and filled circles represent excitatory and inhibitory neurons respectively. Dotted circles show second-order excitatory vestibular neurons. Small filled circle indicates type II inhibitory neuron mediating commissural inhibition. Broken line denotes the visual path from the eye to the flocculus. For explanation see text. Abbrevs.: cf, climbing fiber; Floc, flocculus; gc, granule cell; GS, ganglion scarpae; IO, inferior olive; mf, mossy fiber; VN, vestibular nucleus; III, motoneurons of medial rectus; VI, abducens nucleus; n. VIII, nerve fibers from horizontal canal.

with respect to the environment and the image of the latter on the retina does not move when the head is turned. As illustrated in Fig. 4 for the horizontal canals, the vertical canals have similar short latency connections with their corresponding eye muscles so that vestibulo–ocular compensatory reflexes may be evoked in all directions. To avoid a lengthy description Fig. 7 gives a summary of the circuit organization of all the known short-latency vestibulo-ocular canal reflexes. It should be pointed out that the polysynaptic vestibulo-ocular pathways through the reticular formation have been omitted in the diagrams since their organization is far from being known at present. Their possible functional contribution, however, has been recognized long ago (Lorente de Nó, 1933) and its alleged neural integrator role will be discussed in Robinson's (1975) contribution in this book.

As shown in Figs. 4 and 5, the elementary vestibulo-ocular reflex has a parallel connection through the cerebellum: primary and secondary (not shown) vestibular fiber project as mossy fibers to the vestibulo-cerebellum (Brodal and Hoivik, 1964) and activate Purkinje cells via the mossy fiber granule cell pathways (Precht and Llinás, 1969). Purkinje cells send their inhibitory axons to vestibular neurons which project to ocular motoneurons (Baker *et al.*, 1972b; Fukuda *et al.*, 1972; Precht, 1972; Ito *et al.*, 1973 a, b, c). Anatomical studies (Angaut and Brodal, 1967) have shown that the flocculus projection to the vestibular nuclei overlaps with the projection of labyrinthine afferents whereas the nodulus/uvula region supplies areas which receive projections from the contralateral fastigial nuclei (Fig. 5) but few primary afferents. This differential

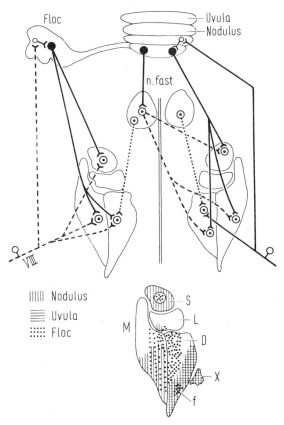

FIG. 5. Diagrammatic representation of the major fiber connections of the vestibulo-cerebellum and vestibular nuclei. Open and filled circles represent excitatory and inhibitory neurons. On the left and right connections of flocculus and nodulus are shown respectively. In the lower diagram the differential projections of flocculus, nodulus, and uvula on the vestibular nuclei are shown. Note that floccular Purkinje cells project to those regions which receive primary afferents whereas nod/uvula projects to regions free of vestibular afferents but receiving projections from the caudal contralateral fastigial nucleus (n. fast.). In addition nod/uvula project to n. fast. whereas floc. appears to lack this projection. Ipsilateral fastigio-vestibular projection originates from rostral nucleus. Not shown are connection from vestibular nucl. to cerebellum, and reticular projections of cerebellum. D, L, M, S, descending, lateral, medial and sup. vestib. nucl.; x, f, vestibular cell groups. For details see text and Walberg (1972).

organization may explain the weak inhibitory effects on vestibulo-ocular transmission exerted by the nodulus as compared to the flocculus (Precht and Giretti, unpublished observation).

Also the flocculus does not appear to affect all vestibulo-ocular reflexes in the same way (Fig. 7). For example, in the horizontal vestibulo-ocular reflex of the rabbit only the motoneurons of the ipsilateral eye are affected (Figs. 4 and 7). Whether this finding holds also in animals with frontal eyes remains to be seen. It is clear, however, that stimulation of the flocculus in cats and rabbits inhibits transmission in certain vestibulo-ocular reflex paths, i.e. the cerebellum can influence the gain of this reflex. Preliminary experiments indicate that the otolith reflexes to the ipsilateral abducens (Schwindt et al., 1973) are likewise under inhibitory cerebellar control (Precht and Giretti, unpubl. observ.).

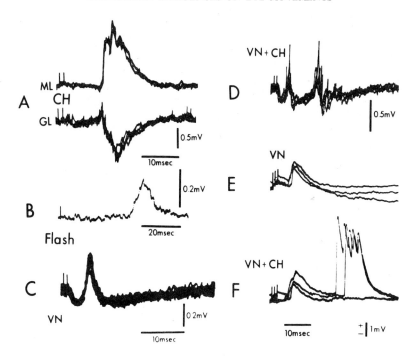

FIG. 6. Vestibular-visual convergence in the vestibulo-cerebellum of the cat. (A) Climbing fiber field potentials evoked by electrical stimulation of the optic chiasm (CH) and recorded in the molecular layer (ML) and granular layer (GL) of the flocculus. (B) Climbing fiber field potential evoked by strobe flash stimulation (64 presentations) in the molecular layer of the flocculus. (C) Mossy fiber field potential evoked by ipsilateral VIIIth nerve stimulation (VN) in the nodulus. (D) Field potential sequence evoked by simultaneous VN/CH stimulation. (E) VN evoked EPSP–IPSP sequence recorded from nodular Purkinje cell. (F) Same as (E) but with combined VN/CH stimulation. Note appearance of visual evoked all-or-none climbing fiber EPSPs. Negativity upwards in all records but (E and F). (From Simpson *et al.*, 1974a.)

In addition to the vestibular mossy fiber input Purkinje cells of the vestibulo-cerebellum in rabbit and cat receive a visual climbing fiber input through a pathway which consists of the accessory optic tract, central tegmental tract and inferior olive (Maekawa and Simpson, 1972; Simpson *et al.*, 1974a). As shown in Fig. 4 this pathway connects the eye with the ipsilateral vestibulo-cerebellum, and it has been shown that its activation in the rabbit inhibits the vestibulo-ocular transmission in certain reflex paths (Ito *et al.*, 1973c, Fig. 7). Vestibular-visual convergence occurs in Purkinje cells of the flocculo-nodular lobe, and the two sensory systems use separate channels, namely the mossy and climbing fiber pathways (Fig. 6). In the monkey, however, both inputs appear to arrive via mossy fibers (Lisberger and Fuchs, 1974).

Experiments using natural vestibular and visual stimulation have indicated some of the functional characteristics of the circuit shown in Fig. 4. Rotatory stimulation of the horizontal canals in frog (Llinás *et al.*, 1971) and rabbit (Simpson *et al.*, 1974b) have demonstrated type I and type II Purkinje cell responses in the vestibulo-cerebellum. The dynamics of the responses gave no indication of an integration of the velocity signal arriving from the canals. In the presence of vestibular or optokinetic nystagmus Purkinje cells showed a distinct reversal of the ongoing firing pattern during the fast phase thereby reflecting the modulation also found in the mossy fiber input under

Semicircular canal	extraocular	muscle	motor nucl.+relay nucl.		flocc.+AOT inhib.of	
	contracting	relaxing	activ.	inhib.	excit.reflex	inhib.reflex
					flocc. AOT	flocc. AOT
Horizontal	c—lat.rect.	i—lat.rect.	c—n.VI medial	i—n.VI medial	− −	+ +
	i—med.rect.	c—med.rect.	i—n.III medial	c—n.III superior	+ +	− −
Anterior	c—inf.obl.	c—sup.obl.	c—n.III y—group	i—n.IV superior	+ −	+ −
	i—sup.rect.	i—inf.rect.	C—n.III y—group	i—n.III superior	+ −	+ −
Posterior	i—sup. obl.	i—inf. obl.	c—n.IV medial	i—n.III superior	(+) −	− −
	c—inf. rect.	c—sup.rect.	c—n.III medial	i—n.III superior	− −	− −

FIG. 7. Summary of vestibulo-ocular reflex paths and their relation to the cerebellar flocculus. Abbrevs.: AOT, accessory optic tract; C, contralateral; i, ipsilateral; flocc., flocculus; relay nucl., denotes subdivision of vestibular complex involved in a given reflex path. Example: stimulation of horizontal canal makes c. lat. rect. contract by activating c.n.VI through relay cells in medial vestibular nucleus. Both stimulation of flocc. and AOT do not inhibit this reflex (for details and ref. see text).

the same conditions (Simpson et al., 1974b). In the monkey modulation of firing frequency appeared to be weaker as compared to the rabbit and particularly the frog (Lisberger and Fuchs, 1974). This difference may be due to a different cerebellar circuit organization regarding inhibitory control of cerebellar inputs (Precht and Llinás, 1969). Presentation of a variety of visual stimuli to one eye revealed that the trigger features for the predominant visual climbing fiber input to the cerebellum in rabbit are On and Direction-Selective (Simpson and Alley, 1973). Step changes in light level evoked climbing fiber bursts and field activation at On but not at Off throughout large receptive fields. Movement (maximum sensitivity 0.5–0.8°/sec) of a large field target resulted in an increase of climbing fiber activity when the pattern was moved from posterior to anterior and a decrease on the reverse movement.

In short it may be stated that the Purkinje cells of the flocculo-nodular lobe exert a tonic inhibitory influence on some vestibulo-ocular relay cells in the vestibular nuclei. This tonic action, mainly supported by mossy fiber input, may be increased or decreased depending on the direction of rotation and on the type of Purkinje cells projecting to a given target neuron. In the presence of vision Purkinje cells receive additional information regarding the direction of movement of the image on the retina. Thus the latter input may help to stabilize vision during head movements (see below).

Besides the cerebellar cortex some of the deep cerebellar nuclei are also involved in the control of the vestibulo-ocular circuitry. The fastigial nuclei receive vestibular input (not shown) and project to the vestibular nuclei (Fig. 5). The latter projection consists of the crossed hook-bundle originating in the caudal part of the nucleus and the uncrossed connection which originates primarily in the rostral fastigial nucleus (see for ref. Walberg, 1972). These projections go to different regions of the vestibular nuclei (Fig. 5). Not shown in the diagram are the connections to the reticular formation which may also be of importance for eye-movement control. Stimulation experiments have demonstrated that type I vestibular neurons are monosynaptically excited following ipsilateral and disynaptically inhibited on contralateral fastigial stimulation via the activation of the type II inhibitory neurons (Shimazu and Smith, 1971). These findings are in good agreement with the anatomy (Fig. 5). Furthermore, rotational stimulation revealed that the majority of fastigial neurons responding to rotation showed a type II response while type I was found less frequently (Gardner and Fuchs, unpubl. observ.). Since the frequency distribution of the types I and II tended to be the reverse in the Purkinje cell population it may be assumed either that caudal fastigial neurons are under control of the inhibitory output of the nodulus (Fig. 5), or that they receive their input mainly from the contralateral labyrinth. In both cases predominantly type II responses may be expected. The dynamic response character of fastigial neurons was similar to Purkinje cells, i.e. no integration of the canal signal occurred in most of the fastigial neurons. A few type I neurons, however, showed signs of eye position related response dynamics. Assuming that Purkinje and fastigial neurons project to similar target neurons the effects of type I Purkinje cell and type II fastigial response will add at the site of the target neurons and decrease their excitability by inhibition and disfacilitation respectively.

Finally it should be mentioned that parts of the dentate nucleus receive primary vestibular afferents (Brodal and Hoivik, 1964; Precht and Llinás, 1968), and that there is evidence that this projection is involved in a disynaptic vestibulo-ocular reflex to the superior and inferior recti muscles (Highstein, 1971). The dentate projection to the IIIrd nucleus is the only direct cerebellar projection to ocular motoneurons.

Stimulation Experiments

Stimulation of the vestibulo-cerebellum (nodulus, ventral uvula, flocculus) in the alert monkey produced nystagmus the quick phase of which was directed contralaterally upon weak electrical stimulation and reversed to the ipsilateral upon strong stimulation (Ron and Robinson, 1973). The reversal of the direction of nystagmus upon strong stimulation may readily be explained by assuming current spread to the VIIIth nerve and/or nuclei, since stimulation of these regions is known to generate ipsilateral nystagmus (Tokumaso et al., 1969). Thus it may be assumed that weak cerebellar stimulation activates Purkinje cells in the vestibulo-cerebellum which exert their monosynaptic inhibitory action on vestibular and cerebellar nuclei (Fig. 4). This unilateral inhibition causes an unequal distribution of activity between the bilateral vestibular nuclei resulting in ocular nystagmus. Following ncar-threshold stimulation (0.08 mA) of the vestibulo-cerebellum, slow-phase movements appeared first and quick phases were added on stronger stimulation. Afternystagmus followed cessation of stimulation. As with slow movements evoked from the hemispheres, the velocity of the slow movements initiated from the vestibulo-cerebellum was increased when any of the stimulus parameters were increased. The distribution of the directions of eye-movements over the vestibulo-cerebellum shows a tendency for upward slow movements in the dorsal uvula and ventral nodulus and downward movements in the ventral uvula and dorsal nodulus (Ron and

Robinson, 1973). Downward eye movements were also observed on nodulus stimulation in the cat (Cohen et al., 1965). Furthermore, stimulation of the nodulus quickly inhibited both rotatory and caloric nystagmus. During stimulation the eyes remained in a conjugate deviation toward the side of the slow component (Fernández and Fredrickson, 1963). This finding also suggests an interaction of excitatory vestibular and inhibitory cerebellar inputs at the level of the brainstem which is able to reset the balance between the bilateral vestibular and recticular centers.

Lesion Experiments

Effects of lesions of the vestibulo-cerebellum on eye movements have been studied by numerous investigators (for summary see Dow and Manni, 1964; Cohen and Highstein, 1972). On the basis of the above stimulation data one might expect spontaneous nystagmus to occur following unilateral lesions of the vestibulo-cerebellar cortex. That this is indeed the case has been shown in the monkey (Dow, 1938; Carrea and Mettler, 1947; Takemori and Cohen, 1974), guinea pig (Manni, 1950b), cat (Allen and Fernández, 1960; Fernández and Fredrickson, 1963), and rabbit (Lorente de Nó, 1931; Grant et al., 1964). In all cases, however, the nystagmus disappeared after some days. In darkness it persisted over longer periods of time (Takemori and Cohen, 1974). Long-term positional nystagmus can be observed after flocculo-nodular lesions (Spiegel and Scala, 1941, 1942; Carrea and Mettler, 1947; Allen and Fernández, 1960; Takemori and Cohen, 1974). With floccular lesions in the monkey positional nystagmus was horizontal rotatory, and direction fixed in type (Takemori and Cohen, 1974). Apparently otolith-evoked central imbalance caused by changing the position of the head can no longer be controlled in lesioned animals. Evoked caloric and post-rotatory nystagmus was also affected by cerebellar lesions in various species at least for a week or so following the lesion (Bauer and Leidler, 1912; Hoshino, 1921; Lorente de Nó, 1931; Ferraro and Barrera, 1938; Fernández and Fredrickson, 1963; Takemori and Cohen, 1974). Generally only a transient directional preponderance to the lesioned side was noted which may be interpreted as an inhibitory release phenomenon of brainstem centers. The transient nature of the lesion effects may explain the negative results obtained by other investigators (Rademaker, 1931; Dow, 1938). Neither slow-phase velocity nor duration of caloric nystagmus showed longterm changes after bilateral flocculectomy (Takemori and Cohen, 1974).

The above findings may give the impression that the vestibulo-ocular reflex is very little affected by cerebellar lesions. This is unexpected on morphological and physiological grounds (see above). Recent cerebellectomy studies in the cat (Carpenter, 1972; Robinson, 1974) have shown, however, that certain changes may be noted on closer inspection of rotation-induced eye movements. Slow and fast phases of vestibular nystagmus showed a curvilinear distortion of their time course which has been interpreted as a deficiency in the neural integrator (Robinson, 1974, 1975). A neural integrator must be postulated, since an integration of the velocity information contained in the afferent inflow is required to obtain the eye position related firing found in the ocular motoneurons (see Robinson, 1974, 1975). Since the integrating capacity of the neural integrator was only altered and not destroyed, Robinson (1974) suggested that the cerebellum may not actually perform the neural integration but may rather assure the quality of the integration. The above-described single-unit experiments support this assumption (Llinás *et al.*, 1971). Carpenter (1972), however, favored the hypothesis that integration was performed by the cerebellum. The gain changes of the vestibulo-ocular reflex (ratio between eye and head velocity) which he found in the decerebrate, cerebellectomized cat were compatible with this assumption. It should be noted, however, that in the decerebrate animals quick phases are missing which may in itself introduce a severe disturbance of the integrator. In fact, in the otherwise intact animal cerebellectomy produced no consistent gain changes (Robinson, 1974). Single unit recordings from abducens motoneurons in the decerebrate, cerebellectomized cat during rotation also indicated that the second integration was missing, so that the dynamic response of the neurons appeared to be related to velocity rather than position (Precht *et al.*, 1969). It should be pointed out, however, that the above described cerebellectomy studies do not necessarily imply that selective lesion of the flocculo-nodular lobe shows the same results. Further experimentation is needed to clarify this point.

Otolith reflexes on the eyes, i.e. oculocompensatory eye position changes, are increased on tilting to the lesioned side and decreased in the opposite direction. Lesions may extend over half of the cerebellum (Di Giorgio and Giulio, 1949) or may be restricted to the unilateral flocculo-nodular lobe (Manni, 1950a,b). As shown above there is experimental evidence indicating that some static vestibulo-ocular reflexes are likewise inhibited by flocculo-nodular stimulation. These findings may explain the above flocculo-nodular lesion results.

Recent studies in the cat (Robinson, 1974) and monkey (Westheimer and Blair, 1973) confirmed previous studies by Ferraro and Barrera (1938) which revealed that the most striking long-term oculomotor disturbance after cerebellectomy was the inability of the animals to maintain an eccentric gaze particularly in the dark. As a result gaze nystagmus was observed. The tendency of the eyes to slip back after a saccade *ca.* 20 times faster than normal (Robinson, 1974) also indicates that without the cerebellum the integrator function has become extremely poor. In view of the proposal that gaze nystagmus is caused by lesion of cerebellar nuclei (Kornhuber, 1971), it is interesting to note that floccular lesions alone can produce gaze nystagmus in the monkey (Takemori and Cohen, 1974). Since the flocculus projects directly to the brainstem probably bypassing the cerebellar nuclei (see above), this finding may indicate a direct cerebellar cortical control of the neural integrator. The absence of eye-muscle proprioceptive input to the flocculus suggests that length signals from spindle organs are not essential for its alleged post-saccadic hold function.

Let us now consider some of the functional aspects of the above described vestibulo-visual projection to the vestibulo-cerebellum. If one compares the gain of the vestibulo-ocular reflex in man in light and darkness one finds that the absence of vision reduces the gain (Meiry, 1971). Similar findings have been obtained by Ito *et al.* (1974 a,b) in the rabbit. In the dark the gain was 0.3 which increased to 0.7 when a stationary light slit was presented which by itself was subthreshold for following eye movements. The fact that flocculectomy abolished this effect suggested that vision added eye velocity to the canal-induced compensatory eye movement by way of the climbing fiber path through the flocculus. Can this effect be explained on the basis of the above single-unit studies? As shown in Figs. 4 and 7 in the rabbit the visual input to one eye goes only to the ipsilateral eye muscles. Consequently if we want the left eye to move faster to the right during left rotation of the head the climbing fiber–Purkinje cell pathway would have to generate disinhibition of both the excitatory path to the medial rectus and the inhibitory one to the lateral rectus at the level of the vestibular nuclei, i.e. climbing fiber firing of the left flocculus should be reduced. According to the results of Simpson and Alley (1973) this does not seem to occur (see above). Instead the climbing fiber path seems to increase Purkinje cell firing under this condition. Similar difficulties arise if one attempts to explain the finding that following cerebellectomy and/or flocculectomy (Ito et al., 1974; Robinson, 1974) there is no consistent change in gain of the vestibulo-ocular reflex. The discrepancies between single-unit data and behavioral experiments should serve to instigate further investigations particularly of the details of the Purkinje cell response to natural stimulation and the connections from these cells to the target neurons. Thus it may well be that the above described type I and type II Purkinje cells project to functionally different brainstem neurons. Such a differential projection could explain some of the above findings.

Further evidence for visual control of eye velocity through the flocculus was given by Takemori and Cohen (1974). They showed that the visual suppression of the velocity of the slow phase of caloric nystagmus was abolished after flocculectomy. After unilateral lesions visual suppression of slow-phase velocity was lost when the quick phases were directed to the ipsilateral side, and after bilateral lesions visual suppression was lost in both directions. These findings are in agreement with the predominantly ipsilateral projection of the flocculus to the brainstem. In this artificial experimental situation a large retinal motion is created by the vestibular-evoked nystagmus and is reduced by the retino-floccular pathway. Single unit studies in the flocculus showed that in the monkey the climbing fiber system does not carry visual information to Purkinje cells (Lisberger and Fuchs, 1974). The latter were, however, strongly modulated via the mossy fiber system when a sinusoidally rotating animal was fixating a target which moved with the chair. It is reasonable to assume that the increased Purkinje cell response during fixation was at least partially responsible for the suppression of the vestibulo-ocular reflex. The same Purkinje cells exhibited little response to pure vestibular stimuli in the darkness which indicates that the vestibular contribution to the cerebellar control of the gain of the vestibulo-ocular reflex is small in the monkey. The loss of the visual pathway through the flocculus also affected the optokinetic nystagmus in monkeys (Takemori and Cohen, 1974). They were unable to follow optokinetic stimulus velocities faster than 45°/sec. Smooth pursuit failure has also been observed in the monkey after cerebellectomy (Westheimer and Blair, 1973). Part of the failure was due possibly to the removal of the vestibulo-cerebellum.

Long-term effects have been observed in addition to the above described short-term changes of the vestibulo-ocular reflex through the flocculo-nodular lobe. It has been postulated (Ito et al., 1974 a,b; Melvill Jones, 1975) that the vestibulo-cerebellum must be able to learn to respond to an error signal from the retina by changing the gain of the vestibulo-ocular reflex in a plastic way. Thus in the rabbit gain changes were found when certain conflicting or non-conflicting visual stimuli were presented while the animals were sinusoidally rotating for 12 hr (Ito et al., 1974b). In their studies of the same species which used somewhat different stimulus parameters, Collewijn and Kleinschmidt (1975) were unable to confirm the long-term gain changes. On the other hand, considerable functional adaptation of the system was observed partly by improving the optokinetic response. Dramatic changes in the vestibulo-ocular reflex were found by Gonshor and Melville Jones (1971), and Melville Jones (1975) when they studied subjects wearing left–right reversing prisms. In this situation the reflex nearly reverses. Robinson (1974; 1975) did similar experiments in cats and found a drastic drop in gain in about 2 days. When he removed the cerebellum no such gain decrease of the vestibulo-ocular reflex was seen. At present no neurophysiological data is available that can explain these long-term plastic changes. Learning capability of cerebellar circuits has been postulated theoretically (Marr, 1969) but it awaits experimental proof.

Possibly related to the above described long-term changes of ocular function are the findings concerning the role of the cerebellum, particularly the vermal areas (lob. VII–VIII), in habituation of ocular responses to vestibular stimulation (Halstead *et al.*, 1937; Di Giorgio and Pestelli, 1948, Wolfe, 1968). Apparently, vestibulo-ocular habituation occurred unidirectionally after folium-tubervermis lesions.

Cerebellar Nuclei and Eye Movements

Since the Purkinje cells project onto the deep cerebellar nuclei in an orderly fashion extending rostrocaudally as well as mediolaterally (Jansen and Brodal, 1954) it is not surprising that eye-movements may be evoked by stimulation of the cerebellar nuclei as well. In fact stimulation results obtained from the cerebellar nuclei of the alert monkey for the most part reflected the eye-movement responses that one would obtain by stimulation of the corresponding part of the cerebellar cortex (Ron and Robinson, 1973). All evoked eye movements had an ipsilateral horizontal component. Specifically, stimulation of the fastigial nuclei evoked saccades with up and down components except for its inferior part from which slow phases of nystagmus were elicited. This latter region receives its cortical input from the nodulus, from which nystagmus is also elicited. Interpositus and dentate nucleus stimulation evoked saccades and smooth movements with down and up components respectively. The similarity in *direction* of cortical and nuclear-evoked eye movements is unexpected on physiological grounds since Purkinje cells are inhibitory to the excitatory cerebellar nuclear cells (Ito *et al.*, 1970). However, as pointed out in the Introduction, these results may have been caused predominantly by excitation of nuclear cells in either stimulus condition.

In contrast to the relatively long latency (15–30 ms) eye-movements obtained from stimulation of most cortical and cerebellar nuclear sites, short latency (5–6 ms) vertical saccades with horizontal components of slightly longer latencies were obtained from stimulation of some regions of the dentate nucleus (Ron and Robinson, 1973). The vertical saccades are probably caused monosynaptically by the activation of the only direct cerebello-oculomotor pathway running from dentate nucleus to contralateral superior and inferior rectus motoneurons which is a part of the vestibulo-ocular reflex (Carpenter and Strominger, 1964; Azzena and Giretti, 1967; Highstein, 1971). No monosynaptic cerebellar connections exist to motoneurons involved in horizontal eye movements, a finding which explains their longer latencies. The exact anatomical pathways which mediate the multisynaptic, long-latency cerebellar evoked eye-movements or unitary responses (Azzena and Giretti, 1967) are not known. Projections from the fastigial nuclei to the vestibular nuclei and pontine reticular formation, both of which project to eye motoneurons (see above), are probably important (for ref. see Brodal *et al.*, 1962; Angaut and Brodal, 1967). Lesion studies are inconclusive regarding the function of the cerebellar nuclei in eye movements, since in most cases the overlying cortex or its connection with the nuclei has been severed too (for clinical aspects see Dichgans, 1975).

Single-unit studies do not yet support a reasonable functional concept for the cerebellar nuclei. Although the participation of nuclear neurons in the control of vestibular evoked eye movements appears very likely on the basis of the data described in the previous section, their role in the saccadic system remains to be determined.

REFERENCES

ALLEN, G. and FERNÁNDEZ, C. (1960) Experimental observations in postural nystagmus. I. Extensive lesions in posterior vermis of the cerebellum. *Acta Oto-laryng.* (*Stockh.*) **51**, 2.

ANGAUT, P. and BRODAL, A. (1967) The projection of the "vestibulocerebellum" onto the vestibular nuclei in the cat. *Arch. Ital. Biol.* **105**, 441.

ASCHOFF, J. C. and COHEN, B. (1971) Changes in saccadic eye movements produced by cerebellar cortical lesions. *Exptl Neurol.* **32**, 123.

AZZENA, G. B. and GIRETTI, M. L. (1967) Responses of the oculomotor units to deep cerebellar stimulation. *Brain Res.* **6**, 523.

BAKER, R. G., MANO, N. and SHIMAZU, H. (1969) Postsynaptic potentials in abducens motoneurons induced by vestibular stimulation. *Brain Res.* **15**, 577.

BAKER, R. G., PRECHT, W. and LLINÁS, R. (1972a) Mossy and climbing fiber projections of extraocular muscle afferents to the cerebellum. *Brain Res.* **38**, 440.

BAKER, R. G., PRECHT, W. and LLINÁS, R. (1972b) Cerebellar modulatory action on the vestibulo-trochlear pathway in the cat. *Exptl Brain Res.* **15**, 364.

BAUER, J. and LEIDLER, R. (1912) Über den Einfluss der Ausschaltung verschiedener Hirnabschnitte auf die vestibulären Augenreflexe. *Arb. a. d. neurol. Inst. a.d. Wien. Univ.* **19**, 155.

BERTHOZ, A. and LLINÁS, R. (1974) Afferent neck projection to the cat cerebellar cortex. *Exptl Brain Res.* **20**, 385–401.

BRAITENBERG, V. (1961) Functional interpretation of cerebellar histology. *Nature* (*Lond.*) **190**, 539.

BRODAL, A. and HOIVIK, B. (1964) Site and mode of termination of primary vestibulo-cerebellar fibres in the cat. An experimental study with silver impregnation methods. *Arch. ital. Biol.* **102**, 1.

BRODAL, A., POMPEIANO, O. and WALBERG, F. (1962) *The Vestibular Nuclei and Their Connections: Anatomy and Functional Correlations.* London: Oliver & Boyd.

CARPENTER, R. H. S. (1972) Cerebellectomy and the transfer function of the vestibulo-ocular reflex in the decerebrate cat. *Proc. R. Soc. Lond.* B, **181**, 353.

CARPENTER, M. B. and STROMINGER, N. L. (1964) Cerebello-oculomotor fibres in the rhesus monkey. *J. Comp. Neurol.* **123**, 211.

CARREA, R. M. E. and METTLER, F. A. (1947) Physiologic consequences following extensive removal of the cerebellar cortex and deep cerebellar nuclei and effect of secondary cerebral ablations in the primate. *J. Comp. Neurol.* **87**, 169.

COHEN, B., GOTO, K., SHANZER, S. and WEISS, A. H. (1965) Eye movements induced by electrical stimulation of the cerebellum in the alert cat. *Exptl Neurol.* **13**, 145.

COHEN, B. and HIGHSTEIN, S. M. (1972) Cerebellar control of the vestibular pathways to oculomotor neurons. In: *Progress in Brain Res.* **37**, 411, BRODAL, A. and POMPEIANO, O. (Eds.). Elsevier, Amsterdam.

COLLEWIJN, H. (1970) Dysmetria of fast phase of optokinetic nystagmus in cerebellectomized rabbits. *Exptl Neurol.* **28**, 144.

COLLEWIJN, H. (1972) An analog model of the rabbit's optokinetic system. *Brain Res.* **36**, 71.

COLLEWIJN, H. and KLEINSCHMIDT, H. J. (1975) Vestibulo-ocular and optokinetic reactions in the rabbit: changes during 24 hrs of normal and abnormal interaction. This volume, p. 477.

DICHGANS, J. (1975) Spinal afferents to the oculomotor system: physiological and clinical aspects. This volume, p. 299.

DI GIORGIO, A. M. and GIULIO, L. (1949) Riflessi oculari di origine otolitica ed influenza del cervelletto. *Boll. Soc. Ital. Biol. Sper.* **25**, 145.

DI GIORGIO, A. M. and PESTELLINI, G. (1948) Inibizione acquista dei riflessi vestibolari: Significato degli emisferi cerebrali e del cervelletto. *Arch. Fisiol.* **48**, 86.

DOW, R. S. (1938) Effect of lesions in the vestibular part of the cerebellum in primates. *Arch. Neurol. Psychiat.* **40**, 500.

DOW, R. S. and MANNI, E. (1964) The relationship of the cerebellum to extraocular movements. In: *The Oculomotor System*, BENDER, M. B. (Ed.), pp. 280. New York: Hoeber.

FERNÁNDEZ, C. and FREDRICKSON, J. M. (1963) Experimental cerebellar lesions and their effect on vestibular function. *Acta Oto-laryng.* (*Stockh.*) **192**, 52.

FERRARO, A. and BARRERA, S. E. (1938) Differential features of "cerebellar" and "vestibular" phenomena in macacus rhesus: Preliminary report based on experiments on 300 monkeys. *Arch. Neurol. Psychiat.* **39**, 902.

FERRIER, D. (1876) *The Function of the Brain.* London, Smith-Elder & Co.

FUCHS, A. F. and KORNHUBER, H. H. (1969) Extraocular muscle afferents to the cerebellum of the cat. *J. Physiol. (Lond.)* **200**, 713.

FUKUDA, J., HIGHSTEIN, S. M. and ITO, M. (1972) Cerebellar inhibitory control of the vestibulo-ocular reflex investigated in rabbit IIIrd nucleus. *Exptl Brain Res.* **14**, 511.

GACEK, R. R. (1971) Anatomical demonstration of the vestibulo-ocular projections in the cat. *Acta Oto-laryng.* **293**, 1.

GONSHOR, A. and MELVILL JONES, G. (1971) Plasticity in the adult human vestibulo-ocular reflex arc. *Proc. Can. Fed. Biol. Soc.* **14**, 14, 25.

GRANT, G., ASCHAN, G. and EKVALL, L. (1964) Nystagmus produced by localized cerebellar lesions. *Acta Oto-laryng. (Stockh.)* **58**, 192, 78.

HALSTEAD, W. C., YACORZYNSKI, G. and FEARING, F. (1937) Further evidence of cerebellar influence in the habituation of after-nystagmus in pigeons. *Am. J. Physiol.* **120**, 350.

HARE, W. K., MAGOUN, H. W. and RANSON, S. W. (1936) Electrical stimulation of the interior of the cerebellum in the decerebrate cat. *Am. J. Physiol.* **117**, 261.

HIGHSTEIN, S. M. (1971) Organization of the inhibitory and excitatory vestibulo-ocular reflex pathways to the third and fourth nuclei in rabbit. *Brain Res.* **32**, 218.

HIGHSTEIN, S. M. (1973) The organization of the vestibulo-oculomotor and trochlear reflex pathways in the rabbit. *Exptl Brain Res.* **17**, 285.

HITZIG, E. (1874) *Physiologische und klinische Untersuchungen über das Gehirn,* Ed. 1. Berlin, A. Hirschwald, see also ed. 2, 1904.

HOSHINO, T. (1921) Beiträge zur Funktion des Kleinhirnwurnes beim Kaninchen. *Acta Oto-laryng.* **2**, 1.

ITO, M., NISIMARU, N. and YAMAMOTO, M. (1973a) The neural pathways mediating reflex contraction of extraocular muscles during semicircular canal stimulation in rabbits. *Brain Res.* **22**, 183.

ITO, M., NISIMARU, N. and YAMAMOTO, M. (1973b) The neural pathways relaying reflex inhibition from semicircular canals to extraocular muscles of rabbits. *Brain Res.* **55**, 189.

ITO, M., NISIMARU, N. and YAMAMOTO, M. (1973c) Specific neural connections for the cerebellar control of vestibulo-ocular reflexes. *Brain Res.* **60**, 238.

ITO, M., SHIIDA, T., YAGI, N. and YAMAMOTO, M. (1974a) Visual influence on rabbit's horizontal vestibulo-ocular reflex that presumably is effected via the cerebellar flocculus. *Brain Res.* **65**, 170.

ITO, M., SHIIDA, T., YAGI, N. and YAMAMOTO, M. (1974b) The cerebellar modification of rabbit's horizontal vestibulo-ocular reflex induced by sustained head rotation combined with visual stimulation. *Proc. Japan Acad.* **50**, 85.

ITO, M., YOSHIDA, M., OBATA, K., KAWAI, N. and UDO, M. (1970) Inhibitory control of intracerebellar nuclei by the Purkinje cell axons. *Exptl Brain Res.* **10**, 64.

JANSEN, J. and BRODAL, A. (1954) *Aspects of Cerebellar Anatomy.* Oslo: Johan Grundt Tanum.

KORNHUBER, H. H. (1971) Motor functions of cerebellum und basal ganglia: the cerebellocortical saccadic (ballistic) clock, the cerebellonuclear hold regulator, and the basal ganglia ramp (voluntary speed smooth movement) generator. *Kybernetik,* **8**, 157.

LISBERGER, S. G. and FUCHS, A. F. (1974) Response of flocculus Purkinje cells to adequate vestibular stimulation in the alert monkey: fixation vs. compensatory eye movements. *Brain Res.* **69**, 347.

LLINÁS, R. (1974) Motor aspects of cerebellar control. *The Physiologist,* **17**, 19.

LLINÁS, R., PRECHT, W. and CLARKE, M. (1971) Cerebellar Purkinje cell responses to physiological stimulation of the vestibular system in the frog. *Exptl Brain Res.* **13**, 408.

LLINÁS, R. and WOLFE, J. W. (1972) Single cell responses from the cerebellum of rhesus preceding voluntary, vestibular and optokinetic saccadic eye movements. *Soc. for Neuroscience,* **2**, 201.

LORENTE DE NÓ, R. (1931) Ausgewählte Kapitel aus der vergleichenden Physiologie des Labyrinths. Die Augenmuskelreflexe beim Kaninchen und ihre Grundlagen. *Ergebn. Physiol.* **32**, 71.

LORENTE DE NÓ, R. (1933) Vestibulo-ocular reflex arc. *Arch. Neurol. Psychiat.* **30**, 245.

MAEKAWA, K. and SIMPSON, J. I. (1972) Climbing fiber activation of Purkinje cell in the flocculus by impulses transferred through the visual pathway. *Brain Res.* **39**, 245.

MANNI, E. (1950a) Localizzazioni cerebellari corticali nella cavia. I. Il corpus cerebelli. *Arch Fisiol.* **49**, 213.

MANNI, E. (1950b) Localizzazioni cerebellari corticali nella cavia. II. Effeti di lesioni delle parti vestibolari del cervelletto. *Arch Fisiol.* **50**, 110.

MARR, D. (1969) A theory of cerebellar cortex. *J. Physiol. (Lond.),* **202**, 437.

MEIRY, J. L. (1971) Vestibular and proprioceptive stabilization of eye movements. In: *The Control of Eye Movements,* BACH-Y-RITA, P. and COLLINS, C. C. (Eds.). N.Y. Academic Press.

MELVILL JONES, G. and GONSHOR, A. (1975) Goal-directed flexibility in the vestibulo-ocular reflex arc. This volume, p. 227.

MUSSEN, A. T. (1927) Experimental investigations on the cerebellum. *Brain,* **50,** 313.

PRECHT, W. (1972) Vestibular and cerebellar control of oculomotor functions. *Bibl. Ophthal.* **82,** 71. Karger Basel.

PRECHT, W. and BAKER, R. (1972) Synaptic organization of the vestibulo-trochlear pathway. *Exptl Brain Res.* **14,** 158.

PRECHT, W. and LLINÁS, R. (1968) Direct vestibular afferents to cat cerebellar nuclei. *Proc. of the XXIV Int. Cong. Physiological Sciences,* Washington.

PRECHT, W. and LLINÁS, R. (1969) Functional organization of the vestibular afferents to the cerebellar cortex of frog and cat. *Exptl Brain Res.* **9,** 30.

PRECHT, W., RICHTER, A. and GRIPPO, J. (1969) Responses of neurones in cat's abducens nuclei to horizontal angular acceleration. *Pflügers Arch.* **309,** 285.

RADEMAKER, G. G. J. (1931) *Das Stehen: Statische Reaktionen, Gleichgewichtsreaktionen und Muskeltonus unter besonderer Berücksichtigung ihres Verhaltens bei kleinhirnlosen Tieren.* Berlin, Springer Verlag.

ROBINSON, D. A. (1968) Eye movement control in primates. *Science,* **161,** 1219.

ROBINSON, D. A. (1974) The effect of cerebellectomy on the cat's vestibulo-ocular integrator. *Brain Res.* **71,** 195.

ROBINSON, D. A. (1975) This volume, pp. 337–374.

RON, S. and ROBINSON, D. A. (1973) Eye movements evoked by cerebellar stimulation in alert monkey. *J. Neurophysiol.* **36,** 1004.

SCHWINDT, P. C., RICHTER, A. and PRECHT, W. (1973) Short latency utricular and canal input to ipsilateral abducens motoneurons. *Brain Res.* **60,** 259.

SHIMAZU, H. and PRECHT, W. (1966) Inhibition of central vestibular neurons from the contralateral labyrinth and its mediating pathway. *J. Neurophysiol.* **29,** 467.

SHIMAZU, H. and SMITH, C. M. (1971) Cerebellar and labyrinthine influence on single vestibular neurons identified by natural stimuli. *J. Neurophysiol.* **34,** 493.

SIMPSON, J. I. and ALLEY, K. E. (1973) Trigger features for the visual climbing fiber input to rabbit vestibulocerebellum. *Soc. for Neuroscience,* **3,** 152.

SIMPSON, J. I., PRECHT, W. and LLINÁS, R. (1974a) Sensory separation in climbing and mossy fiber inputs to cat vestibulocerebellum. *Pflügers Arch.* **351,** 183–193.

SIMPSON, J. I., LLINÁS, R. and PRECHT, W. (1974b) Unit activity in the cerebellar flocculus of alert rabbit evoked by physiological vestibular and visual stimulation. *Proc. Int. Union Physiol. Sci. New Delhi,* Vol. XI, p. 299.

SNIDER, R. S. and STOWELL, A. (1944) Receiving areas of the tactile, auditory and visual system in the cerebellum. *J. Neurophysiol.* **7,** 331.

SPIEGEL, E. A. and SCALA, N. P. (1941) Vertical nystagmus following lesions of the cerebellar vermis. *Arch Ophthal.* **26,** 661.

SPIEGEL, E. A. and SCALA, N. P. (1942) Positional nystagmus in cerebellar lesions. *J. Neurophysiol.* **5,** 247.

STEINBACH, M. J. (1969) Eye tracking of self-moved targets: the role of efference. *J. Exptl Psychol.* **82,** 366.

TAKEMORI, S. and COHEN, B. (1974) Loss of visual suppression of vestibular nystagmus after flocculus lesions. *Brain Res.* **72,** 213.

TARLOV, E. (1970) Organization of the vestibulo–oculo–motor projections in the cat. *Brain Res.* **20,** 159.

TOKUMASO, K., GOTO, K. and COHEN, B. (1969) Eye movements from vestibular nuclei stimulation in monkeys. *Ann. Otal. Rhinol. Laryngol.* **78,** 1105.

WALBERG, F. (1972) Cerebellovestibular relations: Anatomy. In: *Progress in Brain Res.* **37,** 361, BRODAL, A. and POMPEIANO, O. (Eds.). Elsevier, Amsterdam.

WESTHEIMER, G. and BLAIR, M. (1973) Oculomotor defects in cerebellectomized monkeys. *Invest. Ophthal.* **12,** 618.

WOLFE, J. W. (1968) Evidence for control of nystagmic habituation by folium-tuber vermis and fastigial nuclei. *Acta Oto-laryng.* **231,** 5.

WOLFE, J. W. (1971) Relationship of cerebellar potentials to saccadic eye movements. *Brain Res.* **30,** 204.

OCULOMOTOR ABNORMALITIES DUE TO CEREBELLAR LESIONS

JOHANNES DICHGANS and RICHARD JUNG

SUMMARY

1. Cerebellar diseases may cause eye-movement disturbances, but exclusive cerebellar lesions, not involving the brainstem and proven by autopsy, are rare. Hence, the contribution of clinical studies to the knowledge of cerebellar oculomotor functions is limited.
2. Impaired stability of eye position in cerebellar diseases is demonstrated by spontaneous and gaze nystagmus. These are, however, unspecific symptoms occurring more often in brainstem lesions.
3. Characteristic but relatively rare cerebellar symptoms are opsoclonus in myoclonic encephalopathy and pendular nystagmus in multiple sclerosis. More common but less specific cerebellar oculomotor disturbances are large Gegenrucke (opposite jerks).
4. Horizontal positional nystagmus to the upper ear or downward nystagmus with the head reclined may occur in lesions of the lower vermis.
5. Smooth pursuit deficits can be caused by cerebellar lesions and are of particular diagnostic value when associated with normal or increased vestibulo-ocular excitability. Severe pursuit and OKN deficiency with relatively undisturbed saccades are most common in advanced cerebellar cortical atrophies.
6. Kornhuber's theory of cerebellar control of eye movements neurologically can only be supported with respect to eye position control by the cerebellar nuclei. Neurological evidence for a "saccadic clock" in the cerebellar cortex is lacking.
7. The diagnostic value of eye-movement disturbances for cerebellar diseases is smaller than that of symptoms of impaired body motility such as ataxia of trunk and limbs.

The clinician who attempts to define oculomotor syndromes indicative of cerebellar lesions is confronted with the fact that cerebellar diseases often also involve brainstem structures. This hampers all conclusions drawn from cerebellar lesions in tumors, abscesses, hematomas and vascular diseases. (All cerebellar branches of the vertebral and basilar arteries also supply brainstem structures by their proximal ramifications.) Even the systematic cerebellar atrophies and toxic degenerations of the cerebellar cortex may involve brainstem nuclei, at least in their later stages. It should be noted that practically no cases in which eye-movement disorders have been carefully studied and recorded showed a lesion restricted to the cerebellum exclusively.

Thus the clinician must also rely on ablation studies in animals (see Precht, this volume) and must draw his conclusions by analogy. Therefore, in this report the results of animal experiments reported so far will be discussed conjointly with some clinical symptoms observed in patients. We shall try to answer the following questions in the light of clinical and experimental evidence:

1. Does the cerebellum exert *tonic influences* on neutral eye position, saccade amplitude or gaze range?
2. Is the cerebellum responsible for *holding gaze position*?
3. Does the cerebellum contribute to *ocular pursuit* and optokinetic nystagmus?
4. Is the *vestibulo-ocular reflex gain* altered in patients with cerebellar lesions?
5. Is the cerebellum necessary to *program saccades*?

The old German literature from Bárány onwards contains several references to the influence of the cerebellum on nystagmus and vestibular functions. They are mostly based on observations of a few cases using the classical Bárány tests of calorization and short rotation without eye-movement recordings. The cases of the early otologists were often cerebellar abscesses and their quantification does not approach modern standards. Bárány (1907, 1910), Grahe (1930) and other otologists have already described some of the main clinical syndromes. The postulate that different parts of the cerebellum cause different kinds of nystagmus, based mainly on clinical findings, however, was conjectural. But Bárány (1914) also carried out animal experiments to elucidate the role of the flocculus.

Comprehensive reviews on disturbances of eye movements in patients and animals with cerebellar lesions were presented by Dow and Moruzzi (1958), Dow and Manni (1964), Kornhuber (1966) and Hoyt and Daroff (1971).

TONIC INFLUENCES

In patients with an acute lesion of a cerebellar hemisphere *conjugate ocular deviation towards the opposite side* (simulating homolateral "gaze paresis") and eventually gaze nystagmus towards the side of the lesion may be observed in the early stages of the disease (Spiller, 1910; Holmes, 1917; Meyers, 1931; Fisher *et al.*, 1965; Nashold *et al.*, 1969). The large amplitude gaze nystagmus resembling gaze paretic nystagmus in pontine lesions is provoked by fixation of any point except that to which the eyes, when at rest, tend to deviate—the "rest point" (Holmes, 1917). Both gaze deviation and large amplitude nystagmus are *transient*. These contralateral deviations are similar to those occurring after brainstem lesions of the pontine tegmentum, mainly the reticular nuclei. In cerebellar lesions recovery occurs within weeks, whereas gaze paresis may perpetuate in brainstem lesions.

Although in most of the clinical cases brainstem lesions cannot be excluded, the assumption of a cerebellar origin of the gaze deviation is supported by evidence from lesion experiments in animals. Contralateral gaze deviation and ipsiversive gaze nystagmus have been found in hemicerebellectomized dogs (Luciani, 1891; Lewandowski, 1903) and monkeys (Botterell and Fulton, 1938; Westheimer and Blair, 1974).

In man, Nashold and Slaughter (1969) observed a transient ipsilateral gaze paresis following a stereotactic lesion of cerebellar nuclei involving the nucleus interpositus and the medial portion of the dentate and obtained conjugate ipsilateral gaze deviation through stereotaxic stimulation of the brachium conjunctivum, the nucleus interpositus or the dentate nucleus. Similar results in the monkey were obtained in stimulation experiments by Magoun *et al.* (1935), who observed ipsiversive conjugate deviations of the eyes and (not consistently) the head, when stimulating any one of the deep cerebellar nuclei and the adjacent white matter.

The gaze deviation may be explained as the result of contralateral removal of the archicerebellar inhibitory control (Fukuda *et al.*, 1972) balancing between the steady-state output of the vestibular nuclei on both sides. The functional gaze paralysis towards the side of the lesion may be the result of this imbalance biasing the oculomotor nuclei via the vestibulo-ocular connections.

An analogous interpretation may be given for the *spontaneous nystagmus* beating towards the side of the lesion. Spontaneous nystagmus is often seen in cerebellar patients. Unilateral or at least asymmetrical cerebellar lesions involving the lower parts of the caudal vermis, primarily flocculus and nodulus and the fastigial nuclei as well as the "supramedullary portion of the iuxta-restiform system", cause spontaneous nystagmus in different animals (Bauer and Leidler, 1911; Lorente de No, 1931, 1933; Ferraro and Barrera 1936 a, b, 1938; Carrea and Mettler, 1947; Manni, 1950; Cranmer, 1951; Allen and Fernandez, 1960; Grant et al., 1964).

Since vision may interfere with the tonic influences exerted by the cerebellar lesion, the shift in neutral position must be measured in the dark, viewing a homogenous *Ganzfeld* in the light, or most suitable for clinical observations, during exclusion of fixation by high plus (+20D) Frenzel glasses.

Disconjugate Skew-deviation

This, or the *Magendie–Hertwig syndrome*, may be observed in patients with acute cerebellar gunshot wounds (Holmes, 1917) but also in patients with Wallenberg's disease (Kommerell and Hoyt, 1973; Hagström et al., 1969) and cerebellar tumors (Walsh and Hoyt, 1969). Skew-deviation refers to a vertical or oblique divergence of the eyes with the homolateral eye turned downward and inward while the contralateral eye deviates upward and outward. Hunnius (1881) and Smith et al. (1964) presented cases in which an infarction in the *middle cerebellar peduncle* was evident and examination of the mesencephalon revealed no lesions at autopsy. The anatomical evidence in man so far is not sufficient to exclude brainstem lesions in the lower pons and the medulla as additional or alternative causes. Luciani (1891) observed skew-deviation after hemicerebellectomy in dogs and monkeys, but in the monkey this was not reported by Westheimer and Blair (1974). In man, Nashold and Slaughter (1969) observed an inverse skew-deviation (homolateral eye up and outward) during stimulation of the *brachium conjunctivum*.

Lateropulsion of Saccades

Tonic influences on *saccade amplitude* so far have been observed in a few patients with Wallenberg's syndrome (Hagström et al., 1969; Kommerell and Hoyt, 1973). Since the thrombosis of the posterior inferior artery involves mainly the posterolateral oblongata with the vestibular nuclei it may be possibly explained by these brain stem lesions rather than by the inferior cerebellar lesion. But caloric excitability of the inner ear was symmetrical. The authors found *lateropulsion* of saccadic eye movements combined with lateropulsion of limb and body movements. The patient of Kommerell and Hoyt, besides the typical neurological syndrome, exhibited the following oculomotor disturbances: all saccades to the side *ipsilateral* (left) to the lesion were too large, thus *overshooting* a visual target, while all saccades to the *opposite* side were *too small* (undershoot). Saccades upward or downward deviated ipsilaterally along an oblique rather than a vertical line. A tonic bias on eye position was demonstrated during eye closure (ipsilateral gaze deviation of 20°). Other abnormalities included gaze nystagmus as well as left beating positioning nystagmus with the ipsilateral ear down. It may be noted that the tonic bias of saccades in these patients, contrary to the tonic eye deviation described in the first paragraph of this section, was not directed towards the side contralateral to the lesion but to the *ipsilateral* side.

Lateropulsion of saccades has not been investigated in animals with lesions of the lower parts of the cerebellar vermis or hemispheres. The abnormality produced in monkeys after ablation parts of the middle vermis and adjacent paravermis including the Larsell area VI and VII (Aschoff and Cohen, 1971) shows some similarity to the above cases. But the lesion was not in the supply area of the Wallenberg artery and these animals moved their eyes most often from the mid-position to the *contralateral* hemifield of movement and saccades towards the contralateral side were significantly larger.

DEFICIENCIES OF EYE POSITIONING

For holding the eye in a certain position, the oculomotor nuclei have to be tonically influenced by some cerebral structure which in turn is controlled by visual and vestibular signals. So far it is undecided whether this function is shared by the pontine tegmentum and the cerebellum. Kornhuber (1971) proposed the deep cerebellar nuclei as the probable site of position control. The ablation studies by Carpenter (1972) and Robinson (1974) in the cat and by Westheimer and Blair (1973, 1974) in the monkey support the assumption that the cerebellum is involved in holding eye positions but do not contribute to a more precise localization of this function within the cerebellum. Robinson (1974) presented evidence that the position integrator is shared by the cerebellum and the brainstem.

Gaze Nystagmus

A deficiency in stabile positioning of the eyes by itself causes gaze nystagmus, because the eyes will tend to slip back towards the neutral position each time a gaze direction away from this position is intended. Small saccades then will be executed in an attempt to refixate on the target. The resulting pattern may be classified as gaze nystagmus or gaze paretic nystagmus if of large amplitude (and eventually exponentially deformed slow phases: see Kommerell, this volume). Thus gaze nystagmus may not only be due to an imbalance of the oculomotor system caused by asymmetrical vestibulo-cerebellar lesions but may also be the consequence of a lack of ability to hold excentric gaze (leaking integrator).

In patients with chronic cerebellar atrophies, bilateral gaze nystagmus may be observed permanently in about one-half of the cases (Jung and Kornhuber, 1964), whereas the gaze paretic nystagmus in acute unilateral cerebellar lesions is transitory. Bilateral gaze nystagmus has also been found in completely cerebellectomized monkeys (Ferraro and Barrera, 1938; Westheimer and Blair, 1973) and in the cat (Robinson, 1974). It has, however, been shown by Westheimer and Blair (1974) that if cerebellectomy is performed in very young animals oculomotor functions recover within a few days, whereas the defects persist in the adult.

A special form of gaze nystagmus, *rebound nystagmus*, was found in patients with cerebellar and in some cases additional brainstem lesions by Hood *et al.* (1973). It is characterized as follows: with commanded gaze deviation, say to the right, a brisk ipsiversive nystagmus appears. After some 20 sec it fatigues and may even reverse its direction. If at this time the eyes are returned to the primary position, nystagmus to the left, not present initially, occurs and this too fatigues with time.

Instability of fixation with more or less conjugate oscillations of the eyes also *in the neutral position* may be observed in two special diseases involving the cerebellum: opsoclonus in myoclonic encephalopathy and pendular nystagmus in multiple sclerosis.

Opsoclonus†

This rare but impressive oculomotor disorder consists of rapid bursts of involuntary mostly conjugate to-and-fro jerks of the two eyes at frequencies from 6 to 12 per sec that irregularly occur in series of variable amplitude and cause oscillopsia. The direction is *primarily horizontal*, but rotating or vertical jerks occur also. Synchronous lid flutter is frequently observed. Eye closure facilitates opsoclonus (Fig. 2, upper record).

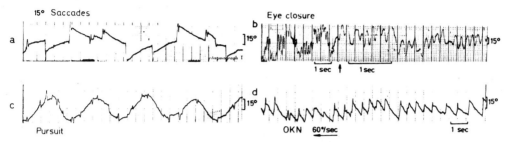

FIG. 1. Opsoclonus and myoclonic saccadic dysmetria (horizontal motion component only, AC recording, $t = 1$ sec) in a 19-year-old male during myoclonic encephalitis with severe ataxia and later recovery. Overshooting oscillations terminate each goal directed saccade (a) and some rapid phases of OKN (d). 7/sec oscillations appear during eye closure, recorded at two different paper speeds (b). Rather normal sinusoidal tracking with interspersed gaze myoclonies (c).

Opsoclonus persists during sleep (Smith and Walsh, 1960) where it is somewhat activated during arousal periods (Kuhlo and Dichgans, 1971). More specific correlations between opsoclonus and single EEG phenomena were not found. Figure 1 shows an electronystagmographic recording of spontaneous opsoclonus with the eyes closed (b). An additional abnormality—not invariably found in these cases—is *myoclonic saccadic dysmetria* causing an overshoot that is immediately followed by a second jerk without intersaccadic interval (a). This phenomenon may even be present in the rapid phases of OKN (d). Otherwise the pursuit function upon gross inspection seems usually normal, although disrupted by myoclonic oscillations superimposed on the tracking of, for example, a swinging pendulum (c). Figure 2 illustrates that horizontal myoclonic saccadic dysmetria may occur with both horizontal and vertical eye movements, e.g. with horizontal optokinetic nystagmus (middle record) and also simultaneously with rapid phases of vertical optokinetic nystagmus (bottom record). Reliable signs of brainstem involvement are rare. *Signs of cerebellar involvement,* however, ataxia of the trunk, more than the extremities, speech disturbance and myoclonic jerks of face, head, trunk, and extremities—the latter being also facilitated by eyelid closure—are invariably present, although to a variable degree. Opsoclonus and the non-synchronous myoclonies of the body may be precipitated by the intention to move or during the frequent periods of increased irritation.

The rather rare syndrome termed "myoclonic encephalopathy" (Kinsbourne, 1962) or "infantile polymyoclonia" (Dyken and Kolar, 1968) does not represent a nosological entity. The majority of cases are children below the age of 4 in whom the syndrome may show a protracted course with frequent remissions and exacerbations over several

---

†The original term "opsoclonus" (Orzechowski, 1928) is synonymous to "ataxic conjugate movements of the eyes" of Walsh (1947), "gaze myoclonus" (Jung and Kornhuber, 1964), the "dancing eye syndrome" of Ford (1966), and the "saccadomania" of Hoyt and Daroff (1971).

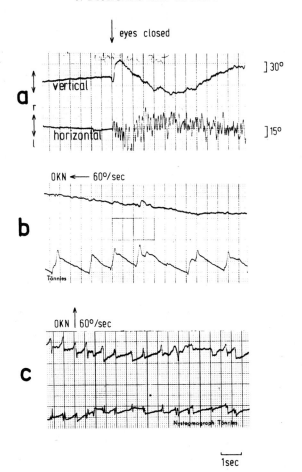

FiG. 2. Opsoclonus in the same patient as in Fig. 1. (a) Immature provocation of high-frequency oscillations —exclusively horizontal in direction—by eye closure. (b) Saccadic overshoots terminate most rapid phases of horizontal OKN. (c) Also during vertical OKN marked horizontal myoclonies occur at each rapid phase downward.

years. The most probable cause is an auto-immune reaction (Baringer *et al.*, 1968; Dyken and Kolar, 1968) sometimes "unspecifically started" by viral infection (Arthuis, 1960; Curnen and Chamberlin, 1961; Baringer *et al.*, 1968) or as an immune reaction in cases with simultaneous occurrence of neuroblastoma (Hellström *et al.*, 1968; Bray *et al.*, 1969; Förster and Weinmann, 1971).

The frequent efficacy of adrenal corticoids and ACTH may also indicate an immune process. The syndrome also occurs in adults (McLean, 1970), in a few cases in conjunction with carcinoma of epithelial-cell origin (Alessi, 1940; Ross and Zeman, 1967; Ellenberger *et al.*, 1968).

The *anatomical evidence* for cerebellar origin of the disease may be taken as suggestive, but is far from being conclusive and certainly does not allow the ascription of the syndrome to any particular area within the cerebellum. Alessi (1940) and Ellenberger *et al.* (1968) found a *diminished number of Purkinje cells, demyelinization of the dentate nucleus* and cerebral as well as diffuse white matter gliosis. Histochemical studies of

Ross and Zeman (1967) suggested abnormalities of oxidative enzymes in the dentate. In Bray's case (1969) associated with neuroblastoma there was a mild degree of peridentate demyelinization. Moe and Nellhaus (1970) found marked loss of Purkinje cells and depletion in the internal granular layer of the cerebellar folia but no abnormalities of the dentate. Only Lemerle *et al.* (1969) found no cerebellar changes, neither in number nor in appearance of Purkinje cells or the dentate neurons.

In summary, opsoclonus occurs in conjunction with symptoms indicative of a cerebellar disease. Additional signs of brainstem damage are rare. The few autopsies reported mostly show involvement of the *cerebellar cortex* and of the *dentate*, but discrete brainstem lesions are not completely excluded. One may be tempted, therefore, to attribute the disease to a high instability of the cerebello-pontine oculomotor integrator, proposed by Kornhuber (1971), Carpenter (1972), and Robinson (1974).

Pendular Nystagmus in Multiple Sclerosis

In the late course of multiple sclerosis pendular nystagmus may be observed in about 4% of the cases and was described as the result of a disturbance of cerebellar nuclei (Aschoff *et al.,* 1970). This nystagmus is of lower frequency than in opsoclonus and more often may be disconjugate and vertical. As a rule this pendular nystagmus is *associated with other signs of cerebellar damage* (predominantly head tremor and trunk ataxia), but additional brainstem lesions are common. Thus the localization

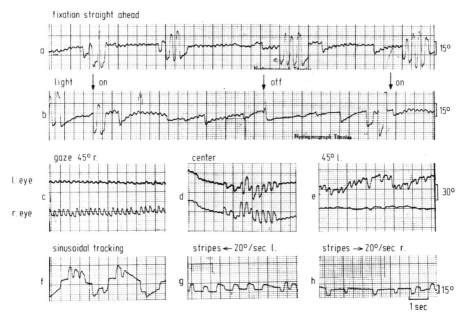

FIG. 3. Pendular nystagmus in multiple sclerosis: 26-year-old-female with severe ataxia, head tremor and spastic tetraparesis. (a) Small amplitude pendular nystagmus and interspersed bursts of large opposite saccades (Gegenrucke) during fixation in the light. (b) In the dark (light off) pendular nystagmus disappears while intending to fixate on an acoustic target, spontaneous nystagmus continues to the left (down). Besides possible lesions in the cerebellar nuclei additional brainstem lesions are ascertained by internuclear ophthalmoplegia (shown in c-e) and severe disturbance of sinusoidal tracking (f) and OKN (g, k) which, in this case, is combined with marked vestibular *hypo*excitability.

of the causal lesion in the cerebellar nuclei (the nucleus fastigii or its efferent pathways were suggested by Aschoff and Cohen, 1971, and Kornhuber, 1971) appears less certain than in opsoclonus.

Nevertheless, *autopsies* in patients with acquired pendular nystagmus—associated with palatal nystagmus—of other origin than multiple sclerosis (Alajouanine, 1935; Guillain, 1938; Nathanson, 1956) have always shown lesions in the cerebellar nuclei and/or the brachium conjunctivum (in addition to lesions in the inferior olive). Moreover, Nashold *et al.* (1969) produced oscillating eye movements by stimulating the fastigeal nuclei in man, and Ron and Robinson (1973) evoked nystagmus by stimulating the caudal part of the fastigial nucleus and the adjacent white matter in the monkey.

Clear-cut *differences between opsoclonus and pendular nystagmus in multiple sclerosis* are to be noted. Figure 3 depicts the oculomotor syndrome in a 26-year-old female with severe multiple sclerosis and marked involvement of brainstem, cerebellum, and spinal cord as well. In contrast to opsoclonus, the small amplitude pendular nystagmus is relatively slow (4/sec) and occurs only with the eyes open and in the presence of light. But the nystagmus is not dependent upon fixation since it also occurs under high plus Frenzel glasses and it is not invariably combined with severely impaired vision due to neuritis of the optic nerve.† Interspersed bursts of large saccades alternating in direction as well as spontaneous nystagmus to the left are additional signs of fixation instability (a, b, d). In this case, as in several others, lesions of internuclear and probably supranuclear oculomotor brainstem structures are demonstrated by the simultaneous occurrence of dissociated gaze nystagmus (c, e) and disturbance of sinusoidal tracking (f). Slow phases of optokinetic nystagmus may be severely impaired (g, h).

Congenital Nystagmus

Fixation instability is a characteristic disturbance in congenital nystagmus which nearly always beats in the horizontal plane. This horizontal conjugate fixation nystagmus may be pendular (29%), arcaded (48%) or jerky in form. Only exceptionally vertical nystagmus is found in special families with hereditary nystagmus (Dichgans and Kornhuber, 1964). Congenital nystagmus is invariably associated with severe impairment of horizontal optokinetic nystagmus (OKN), whereas vertical OKN may be normal. Most often horizontal OKN is inverted (67%) (Dichgans, 1969), the rapid phases moving towards the direction of the moving stimulus as first described by Brunner (1921). The origin of the syndrome is unknown. Autopsies are not reported in the literature. Signs of cerebellar involvement such as ataxia or speech disorders are usually lacking. Developmental brainstem lesions are the most probable but not yet proven cause and cerebellar lesions may be present in the rare cases with ataxia.

Large Amplitude Saccades Alternating in Direction

Square wave opposite jerks or *Gegenrucke*—have earlier been claimed to be due to cerebellar lesions. Jung and Kornhuber (1964) observed these sometimes extremely enlarged fixation saccades in different kinds of cerebellar atrophies. Potthoff and Haustein (1970) found large *Gegenrucke* in 65% of operated tumors of the cerebellum, when

---

†Vestibulo-ocular reflexes elicited by the head tremor were excluded as the cause of the pendular nystagmus in this case.

examined some years after the operation. It must, however, be mentioned that frequent small opposite jerks can also be observed in normals and that the distinction from the large "Gegenrucke" in cerebellar lesions is sometimes difficult to make.

IMPAIRED SMOOTH PURSUIT AND OPTOKINETIC NYSTAGMUS

Ocular pursuit may be impaired by brain damage of different location, in brainstem, cerebral and cerebellar cortex. The cerebellum appears to be more essential for eye tracking in man and monkey than in lower mammals. The following conflicting results of the experimental studies may originate from species differences (rabbit, cat, monkey). Robinson (1974) found in cerebellectomized *cats* only a slight impairment of optokinetic nystagmus with exponential decay of slow phases at lower stimulus velocities which he explained as being due to the leaking integrator whose decay-time was determined to be in the order of 1.3 sec. Collewijn (1970) in the *rabbit* found the optokinetic response to sinusoidal movements of a surrounding drum unchanged. These rabbits were cerebellectomized with the exception of the flocculus. Westheimer and Blair (1973), however, in completely cerebellectomized *monkeys* found ocular tracking to be practically absent when the animal was presented with a sinusoidally moving target and maximal slow phase velocity of OKN was markedly reduced. The same was found after exclusive removal of the monkey's *flocculus* by Takemori and Cohen (1974). In Westheimer's cerebellectomized monkeys, however, the vestibulo-ocular reflex response was normal. Ocular pursuit was shown to be impaired towards the side of hemicerebellectomy while optokinetic and vestibular nystagmus showed a directional preponderance towards the side of the lesion, i.e. slow phase velocity was diminished to the lesioned side. The bias of Magnus (1924) against the role of the cerebellum in the oculomotor regulation may perhaps be explained by his preference for rabbits as experimental animals.

Clinical observations of impaired smooth pursuit mainly concern *optokinetic nystagmus* (OKN). In unilateral cerebellar lesions and VIIIth nerve neurinomas which mainly damage the *flocculus* disturbances of OKN to the contralateral side may occur. Among patients with cerebellar atrophies, Jung and Kornhuber (1964) found an impaired optokinetic nystagmus in the upward direction and/or in both horizontal directions in most advanced cases of adult *cerebellar cortical atrophy* and in 28% of all cases of cerebellar atrophy. We found later that optokinetic nystagmus may be impaired in all directions in cerebellar cortical atrophies (see Fig. 4). Kornhuber (1966) conceded that concurrent atrophy of brainstem structures in the later stages might at least in part be responsible for the deficiency. The severe oculomotor disorders of pursuit- and saccadic functions consistently observed in *olivo-pontine cerebellar degenerations* are obviously caused by brainstem lesions. Additional brainstem involvement may also explain the marked oculomotor disorders in the Louis-Bar syndrome although cerebellar cortical lesions prevail. Similar interpretations might be given to Potthoff and Haustein's (1970) results in patients operated for cerebellar tumors describing severe oculomotor disorders only in cases with additional brainstem lesions. They observed impaired sinusoidal tracking in about 50% of these tumors located in different parts of the cerebellum but never saw exclusive optokinetic disturbances without other nystagmic syndromes in their forty-one patients. Thus, lesion experiments in the monkey supply better arguments

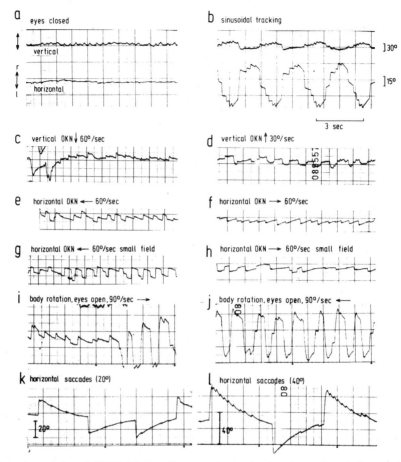

Fig. 4. Smooth pursuit and OKN deficits with normal saccades in advanced cerebellar cortical atrophy. 67-year-old male with severe ataxia of trunk and gait, more than in arms and legs. During closed eyes only weak spontaneous nystagmus to the left and lid flutter (a). Severe impairment of sinusoidal tracking (b) and of OKN in all directions (c-h). Even full field stimulation by constant velocity body rotation with eyes open does not elicit OKN but large amplitude *Gegenrucke* (opposite jerks) with saccades (i, j). (k, i) Normal horizontal saccades to and from targets 20° and 40° lateral from mid-position (as also to all other positions not shown). Horizontal gaze nystagmus is more marked at 40° (l) than at 20° displacements (k). Condensor coupled amplifier with time constant of 1.8 sec.

for the cerebellar role in smooth pursuit than clinical data, which, however, are consistent with those results.

VESTIBULAR HYPEREXCITABILITY AND POSITIONAL NYSTAGMUS

Hyperresponsiveness

The intimate anatomical connections between the vestibular nuclei and the vestibular cerebellum (nodulus, flocculus, uvula, ventral paraflocculus) and back to the vestibular nuclei (in part indirectly via the fastigial nucleus) suggest a very intensive cerebellar control of vestibulo-oculomotor and vestibulo-spinal functions (see Precht, this volume).

This control is proved by many authors showing that Purkinje cells have inhibitory synapses at neurones of the vestibular nuclei (Baker *et al.*, 1972; Fukuda *et al.*, 1972; Ito, 1972 a, b) and at fastigial nucleus neurones. The release of this inhibition by cerebellar lesions consequently should result in hyperresponsiveness in these neurones. This *vestibular neuronal disinhibition* may be quantified in terms of the vestibulo-ocular gain (Zee *et al.*, 1974), vestibular thresholds, or duration and angular velocity as well as total amplitude of caloric and post-rotatory nystagmus (Jung and Kornhuber, 1964; Kornhuber, 1966).

Ablation experiments in animals may support this interpretation. Hemicerebellectomy may result in directional preponderance of post-rotatory nystagmus towards the side ipsilateral to the lesion (Simonelli and Di Giorgio, 1931; Di Giorgio, 1950; Westheimer and Blair, 1974). Most specifically vestibulo-ocular hyperresponsiveness has been found after ablation of the vestibular cerebellar cortex and/or fastigial and interpositus nuclei (Bauer and Leidler, 1911; Hoshino, 1921; Spiegel and Scala, 1942; Chambers and Sprague, 1955; Fernandez and Fredrickson, 1964).

In *human cerebellar lesions*, however, hyperresponsiveness appears to be rare. Most cerebellar atrophies show normal vestibular responses. But the vestibulo-ocular gain has only been thoroughly measured in one study. Zee *et al.* (1974) in quantitative tests on patients with downbeat nystagmus (Arnold–Chiari malformation) found a vertical vestibulo-ocular reflex gain of five which they suggested to be due to flocculo-nodular involvement. However, the gain for horizontal eye head coordination was normal.

In animals, the gain of the vestibulo-ocular reflex is *not* permanently increased in totally cerebellectomized monkeys (Westheimer and Blair, 1973, 1974) and cats (Robinson, 1974). The ability to re-adjust the gain after visual re-arrangement by prisms (Melvill Jones, this volume) is abolished after flocculectomy (Ito *et al.*, 1974; Robinson, this volume).

In man the *combination of vestibulo-ocular hyperresponsiveness* or normal vestibulo-ocular response *and an impaired eye tracking* as well as impaired optokinetic nystagmus illustrated in Fig. 5 seems indicative of cerebellar lesions. Similar cases were presented by Hood *et al.* (1973). The combination of *reduced optokinetic nystagmus and reduced vestibular nystagmus* in an awake patient, however, is invariably due to *tegmental lesions in the pons*. To complicate matters, it should be noted that *tegmental* brainstem lesions may also cause *vestibular hyperexcitability* but in those cases OKN is less impaired than in cerebellar atrophies. After small brainstem lesions of the region of the vestibular nuclei and the adjacent reticular formation, vestibular hyperexcitability was described in rabbits by Lorente de Nó (1931), in cats by Spiegel and Scala (1942) and in monkeys by Fernandez and Fredrickson (1964). In man, it may be observed in patients with multiple sclerosis and with syringobulbia in which brainstem lesions prevail.

Positional Nystagmus

Positional nystagmus (*Lagenystagmus*) of central origin contrasts to transitory positioning nystagmus (Lagerungsnystagmus) due to peripheral labyrinthine lesions. Positional nystagmus, spontaneous nystagmus, and vestibular hyperexcitability are mentioned as symptoms of the vestibular cerebellum (flocculus and nodulus) by Jung (1953). The usefulness of positional nystagmus in diagnosis of a cerebellar lesion has been debated. Whereas Salmon (1969) and Hoyt and Daroff (1971) negate any localizing significance for the cerebellum, *positional nystagmus of alternating direction* has been found to be indicative of lesions of the *vestibulo-cerebellum* by others (Nylen, 1939; Kirstein, 1949;

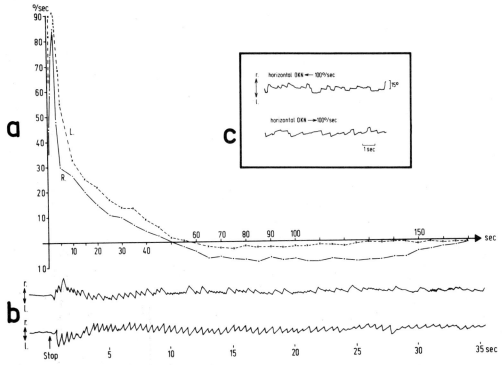

FIG. 5. Normal vestibulo-ocular responsiveness in cerebellar cortical atrophy (same patient as in Fig. 4).
(a) The time course of slow phase velocity of post-rotatory vestibular nystagmus following a 90°/sec constant
velocity body rotation, (b) in the original records below, only preponderance to the left appears. The long
duration of second post-rotatory nystagmus may indicate slight hyperexcitability. (c) In contrast to vestibular
nystagmus, the optokinetic responses are severely impaired.

Aubry, *et al.*, 1954; Riesco MacClure, 1955; Kornhuber, 1969). Upon inspection with
Frenzel glasses one may find down-beating nystagmus in patients with lesions that
involve the lower vermis—in particular the nodulus—as a relatively specific symptom,†
when the patient's head is maximally reclined in a supine position. Sometimes direction-
changing horizontal nystagmus, mostly towards the upper ear, appears when the patient
lies side-down (Kornhuber, 1966). Dizziness accompanies this nystagmus only in the
early stages of the disease. Positional nystagmus has been observed in animals with
lesions of the lower vermis and the fastigial nuclei by Spiegel and Scala (1942), Carrea
and Mettler (1947), Di Giorgio (1950), Allen and Fernandez (1959), Fernandez *et al.*
(1960 a, b), Grant *et al.* (1964). Down-beating nystagmus was observed after lesions
of the nodulus (Allen and Fernandez, 1960; Fernandez *et al.*, 1960b; Singleton, 1967).

POSSIBLE ROLE OF THE CEREBELLUM FOR
SACCADE PROGRAMMING

Kornhuber (1971), after observing dysmetric saccades in patients with atrophy of
the cerebellar cortex (1969), postulated that the cerebellum is "necessary to properly

†Permanent down-beating nystagmus, maximal on down and lateral gaze has also been observed in
patients with lesions of the lower brainstem and/or the cerebellum (Cogan, 1968; Mahaley, 1968; Hart
and Sanders, 1970; Zee *et al.*, 1974), e.g. in patients with the Arnold–Chiari malformation.

translate the spatial concept of movement (existing in the cerebral cortex) into time (duration of innervation)" which latter determines the amplitude of saccades. His patients showed during horizontal eye movements (fig. 3 in Kornhuber, 1974) a series of small hypometric saccades successively executed to reach a distant target on one side. The same record, however, shows normal saccades to the other side on return. In view of Kornhuber's interpretation the question arises: *Is the cerebellum necessary to program saccades?*

Up to now Kornhuber's interpretation has not been supported by any investigation of a larger group of cerebellar atrophies. Moreover, the majority of cortical cerebellar atrophies even in their later stages do *not* exhibit marked saccadic hypometria while severe alterations of optokinetic nystagmus are present (see Fig. 4). In these cases the velocity of the rapid nystagmic phase appears normal.† Adequate experiments recording eye movements in monkeys trained to saccade between targets of variable angular distance before and after cerebellar cortical lesions so far have not been performed. Aschoff and Cohen (1971) who ablated the cortex in area VI and VII where Fuchs and Kornhuber (1969) found a cerebellar projection of eye muscle proprioceptors are not directly to be analogized with Kornhuber's finding in his patient. The evidence available from studies in which the total cerebellum (Carpenter, 1972; Westheimer and Blair, 1973 in monkeys; Robinson in cats, 1974) was removed does exclude that the intact cerebellum is necessary to program saccades. It may, however, contribute to the proper adjustment of force in relation to the starting eye position. Defects of this function may result in saccadic dysmetria. Westheimer and Blair—who recorded from untrained monkeys—expressively stated that saccades were undisturbed; but quantitative data on accuracy of saccades were not presented. A detailed investigation of saccade accuracy in trained monkeys is currently undertaken by Ritchie and Bizzi (personal communication). Animal experiments of Ron and Robinson (1973) lead to the conclusion that saccades are neither spatially nor temporally coded in the cerebellum (see Precht's preceding report).

Thus neurological observations and experimental results do not support the existence of a "saccadic clock" of the cerebellar cortex, postulated by Kornhuber (1971). Only some influence of eye muscle proprioceptors projecting to the vermis remains possible but the main connections of these proprioceptors are located in the brainstem (Whitteridge, 1960) and their function is unknown.

CLINICAL COMMENTS

Cerebellar diseases may cause disturbances of eye movements. However, in view of the frequency of coincident brainstem lesions in cerebellar diseases and the lack of detailed autopsies one should accept only those syndromes as characteristic for cerebellar lesions that have also been demonstrated in cerebellar ablation experiments in animals. The combined evidence allows the following statements: valuable signs (exclusively seen in cerebellar patients) are: (1) *the coincidence of normal or increased vestibulo-ocular responses with impaired ocular pursuit and optokinetic nystagmus* (in contrast to nearly equal disturbances of both visuo-ocular and vestibulo-ocular responses and gaze impairment in pontine lesions); (2) *opsoclonus*, i.e. irregular but conjugate

---

†Aschoff's interesting proposal (1974) that the supranuclear decussation of oculomotor pathways for saccades uses the pontine nuclei and cerebellum, is not yet supported by clinical observations.

high frequency myoclonic ocular oscillations (indicative of lesions of the deep *cerebellar nuclei*). Both syndromes usually are combined with severe trunk ataxia. Pendular nystagmus may also be caused by lesions of the cerebellar nuclei in multiple sclerosis.

Transient symptoms that in addition to brainstem lesions may also be caused by cerebellar lesions are: down-beating positional nystagmus with head reclination, horizontal positional nystagmus (to the upper ear), ipsiversive gaze paretic nystagmus with contralateral gaze deviation, "rebound gaze nystagmus" and spontaneous nystagmus.

It is an open question whether *skew deviation* is due to lesion of the pontine cerebellar peduncle and/or of the lower pons and medulla. Gross disturbances of *saccade performance* are not found to be a valuable sign of lesions of the oculomotor cerebellar cortex. But saccadic dysmetria, dependent on the starting position in the orbit, might result from cerebellar lesions, involving the eye muscle proprioceptor projection area described by Fuchs and Kornhuber (1969).

All this shows that oculomotor impairment alone cannot supply sufficient diagnostic criteria for cerebellar lesions. Ataxia and other disturbances of body motility are more reliable signs of cerebellar deficiency than nystagmus, and gaze disorders.

CONCLUSIONS

The five questions posed in the introduction, on the basis of clinical evidence, can only be answered provisionally and partially as follows:

1. Neutral eye position is influenced by the cerebellum since transient gaze deviations and gaze paretic nystagmus may occur after acute cerebellar lesions. Tonic influences on saccade amplitudes are found in combined brainstem and cerebellar lesions.

2. The cerebellum stabilizes eye position. This is demonstrated by gaze nystagmus and large "Gegenrucke" in cerebellar atrophies. This may also be inferred from opsoclonus in myoclonic encephalopathy and pendular nystagmus in multiple sclerosis.

3. A substantial contribution of the cerebellum to smooth pursuit and optokinetic nystagmus (OKN) is suggested by the frequent smooth pursuit- and OKN-deficits in cerebellar atrophies.

4. Damage of the vestibulo-cerebellum may cause vestibulo-ocular hyperresponsiveness and more frequently positional nystagmus.

5. The cerebellum, in man, is not necessary to program goal directed saccades. But, as a minor collateral loop it may assist the fine adjustment of saccades according to starting eye positions.

REFERENCES

ALAJOUANINE, TH., THUREL, R. and HORNET, TH. (1935) Un cas anatomo-clinique de myoclonies vélopharyngées et oculaires, *Rev. Neurol.* **64,** 853.

ALESSI, D. (1940) Lesioni parenchimatose del cervelleto da carcinoma uterino (gliosis carcinotossica?). *Riv. Pat. Nerv. Ment.* **55,** 148.

ALLEN, G. and FERNANDEZ, C. (1960) Experimental observations in postural nystagmus. I. Extensive lesions in posterior vermis of the cerebellum. *Acta oto-laryng. (Stockh.)* **51,** 2.

ARTHUIS, M., LYON, G. and THIERFERY, S. (1960) La forme ataxique de la maladie de Heine-Medin. *Rev. Neurol.* **103,** 329.

ASCHOFF, J. C. (1974) Reconsideration of the oculomotor pathway. In: *The Neurosciences,* III. SCHMIDT, F. O. and WORDEN, F. G. (Eds.), p. 305. M.I.T. Press, Cambridge/Mass., London, England.

ASCHOFF, J. C. and COHEN, B. (1971) Changes in saccadic eye movements produced by cerebellar cortical lesions. *Exptl Neurol.* **32**, 123.

ASCHOFF, J. C., CONRAD, B. and KORNHUBER, H. H. (1970) Acquired pendular nystagmus in multiple sclerosis. *Amsterdam, Proc. Bárány Soc.* 127.

AUBRY, M., PIALOUX, P. and BOUCHET, J. (1954) Le nystagmus de position en oto-neurologie. *Ann. Oto-laryng. (Paris)*, **71**, 531.

BAKER, R., PRECHT, W. and LLINAS, R. (1972) Cerebellar modulatory action on the vestibulo-trochlear pathway in the cat. *Exptl Brain Res.* **15**, 364.

BÁRÁNY, R. (1907) *Physiologie und Pathologie (Funktionsprüfung) des Bogengang-Apparates beim Menschen. Klinische Studien.* Deuticke, Leipzig, Wien.

BÁRÁNY, R. (1910) Neue Untersuchungsmethoden, die Beziehungen zwischen Vestibularapparat, Kleinhirn, Großhirn und Rückenmark betreffend. *Wien. med. Wschr.* **60**, 2033.

BÁRÁNY, R. (1914) Untersuchungen über die Funktion des Flocculus am Kaninchen. *Jb. Psychiat. Neurol.* **26**, 631.

BARINGER, J. R., SWEENEY, V. P. and WINKLER, G. F. (1968) An acute syndrome of ocular oscillations and truncal myoclonus. *Brain*, **91**, 473.

BAUER, J. and LEIDLER, R. (1912) Über den Einfluß der Ausschaltung verschiedener Hirnabschnitte auf die vestibulären Augenreflexe, *Arb. a.d. Neurol. Inst. a.d. Wien. Univ.* **19**, 155.

BOTTERELL, E. H. and FULTON, J. F. (1938) Functional localization in the cerebellum of primates. I. Unilateral section of the peduncles. *J. Comp. Neurol.* **69**, 31.

BRAY, P. F., ZITER, F. A., LAHEY, M. E. and MYERS, G. G. (1969) The coincidence of neuroblastoma and acute cerebellar neuropathy. *J. Pediat.* **75**, 983.

BRUNNER, H. (1921) Über Inversion des experimentellen optokinetischen Nystagmus. *Wschr. Ohrenhk.* **55**, 574.

CARPENTER, R. H. S. (1972) Cerebellectomy and the transfer function of the vestibulo-ocular reflex in the decerebrate cat. *Proc. Roy. Soc. (Lond)* B, **181**, 353.

CARREA, R. M. E. and METTLER, F. A. (1947) Physiologic consequences following extensive removal of the cerebellar cortex and deep cerebellar nuclei and effect of secondary cerebral ablations in the primate. *J. Comp. Neurol.* **87**, 169.

CHAMBERS, W. W. and SPRAGUE, J. M. (1955) Functional localization in the cerebellum. II. Somatotopic organization in cortex and nuclei. *Arch. Neurol. Psychiat.* **74**, 653.

COGAN, D. G. (1968) Down-beat nystagmus. *Arch. Ophthalmol.* **80**, 757.

COLLEWIJN, H. (1970) Dysmetria of fast phase of optokinetic nystagmus in cerebellectomized rabbits. *Exptl Neurol.* **28**, 144.

CRANMER, R. (1951) Nystagmus related to lesions of the central vestibular apparatus and the cerebellum. *Ann. Otol. Rhin. Laryng.* **60**, 186.

CURNEN, E. C. and CHAMBERLIN, H. R. (1961) Acute cerebellar ataxia associated with poliovirus infection. *Yale J. Biol. Med.* **34**, 219.

DICHGANS, J. (1969) *Congenitaler und früherworbener Nystagmus: Nystagmographische, statistische und genetische Untersuchungen.* Habilitationsschrift, Freiburg.

DICHGANS, J. and KORNHUBER, H. H. (1964) Eine seltene Art des hereditären Nystagmus mit autosomal-dominantem Erbgang und besonderem Erscheinungsbild: vertikale Nystagmuskomponente und Störung des vertikalen und horizontalen optokinetischen Nystagmus. *Acta genet. (Basel)* **14**, 240.

DI GIORGIO, A. M. (1950) Reflexes vestibulaires et cervelet. *Acta Oto-rhino-laryng. Belg.* **4**, 282.

DOW, R. S. (1938) Effect of lesions in the vestibular part of the cerebellum in primates. *Arch. Neurol. Psychiat.* **40**, 500.

DOW, R. S. and MANNI, E. (1964) The relationship of the cerebellum to extraocular movements. In: *The Oculomotor System*, BENDER, M. B. (Ed.), p. 280. New York, Evanston, London, Hoeber.

DOW, R. S. and MORUZZI, G. (1958) *The Physiology and Pathology of the Cerebellum.* The University of Minnesota Press, Minneapolis.

DYKEN, P. and KOLAR, D. (1968) Dancing eyes, dancing feet: infantile polymyoclonia, *Brain*, **91**, 305.

ELLENBERGER, C., CAMPA, J. F. and NETSKY, M. G. (1968) Opsoclonus and parenchymatous degeneration of the cerebellum. The cerebellar origin of an abnormal ocular movement. *Neurology*, **18**, 1041.

FERNANDEZ, C., ALZATE, R. and LINDSAY, J. R. (1960a) Interrelations between flocculonodular lobe and vestibular system. In: *Neural Mechanisms of the Auditory and Vestibular Systems*, RASMUSSEN, G. L. and WINDLE, W. F. (Eds.), p. 285. Charles C. Thomas, Springfield, Ill.

FERNANDEZ, C., ALZATE, R. and LINDSAY, J. R. (1960b) Experimental observations on postural nystagmus. II. Lesions of nodulus. *Ann. Otol. Rhinol. Lar.* **69**, 94.

FERNANDEZ, C. and FREDRICKSON, J. M. (1964) Experimental cerebellar lesions and their effect on vestibular function. *Acta Oto-laryng. (Stockh.)*, Suppl. **192**, 52.

FERRARO, A. and BARRERA, S. E. (1936) Effects of lesions of the juxtarestiform body (I.A.K. bundle) in Macacus Rhesus monkeys. *Arch. Neurol. Psychiat.* **35**, 13.

FERRARO, A. and BARRERA, S. E. (1938) Differential features of "cerebellar" and "vestibular" phenomena in Macacus Rhesus: Preliminary report based on experiments on 300 monkeys. *Arch. Neurol. Psychiat.* **39**, 902.

FERRARO, A., BARRERA, S. E. and BLAKESLEE, G. A. (1936) Vestibular phenomena of central origin. An experimental study in Macacus Rhesus. *Brain,* **59**, 466.

FISHER, C. M., PICARD, F. H., POLAK, A., DALAL, P. and OJEMAN, R. G. (1965) Acute hypertensive cerebellar hemorrhage, diagnosis and surgical treatment. *J. Nerv. Ment. Dis.* **140**, 38.

FÖRSTER, C. and WEINMANN, H. (1971) Symptomatische infantile Polymyoklonie. *Z. Kinderheilk.* **111**, 240.

FORD, F. R. (1966) *Diseases of the Nervous System in Infancy, Childhood and Adolescence,* 5th ed. Charles C. Thomas, Springfield, Ill.

FUCHS, A. F. and KORNHUBER, H. H. (1969) Extraocular muscle afferents to the cerebellum of the cat. *J. Physiol. (Lond.)* **200**, 713.

FUKUDA, J., HIGHSTEIN, S. M. and ITO, M. (1972) Cerebellar inhibitory control of the vestibulo-ocular reflex investigated in rabbit IIIrd nucleus. *Exptl Brain Res.* **14**, 511.

GRAHE, K. (1930) Das Verhalten der Haltungs- und Bewegungsreaktionen (der Vestibularapparate) bei zentralen Erkrankungen. In: *Handbuch der Normalen und Pathologischen Physiologie,* BETHE, A. G., BERGMANN, G. V., EMBDEN, G. and ELLINGER, A. (Eds.), p. 411. Springer, Berlin.

GRANT, G., ASCHAN, G. and EKVALL, L. (1964) Nystagmus produced by localized cerebellar lesions. *Acta Oto-laryng. (Stockh.),* Suppl. **192**, 78.

GUILLAIN, G. (1938) The syndrome of synchronous and rhythmic palatopharyngolaryngo-diaphragmatic myoclonus. *Proc. Roy. Soc. Med.* **31**, 41.

HAGSTRÖM, L., HÖRNOTEN, G. and SILFVERSKIÖLD, B. P. (1969) Oculostatic and visual phenomena occurring in association with Wallenberg's syndrome. *Acta Neurol. Scand.* **45**, 568.

HART, J. D. and SANDERS, M. D. (1970) Down-beat nystagmus. *Trans. Ophthal. Soc. UK,* **90**, 483.

HELLSTRÖM, I. E., HELLSTRÖM, K. E., PIERCE, G. E. and BELL, A. E. (1968) Demonstration of cell-bound and humeral antibodies against neuroblastoma cells. *Proc. Nat. Acad. Sci. (Wash.)* **60**, 1231.

HOLMES, G. (1917) The symptoms of acute cerebellar injuries, due to gunshot injuries. *Brain,* **40**, 461.

HOOD, J. D., KAYAN, A. and LEECH, J. (1973) Rebound nystagmus. *Brain,* **96**, 507.

HOSHINO, T. (1921) Beiträge zur Funktion des Kleinhirnwurmes beim Kaninchen. *Acta Oto-laryng. (Stockh.),* Suppl. **2**, 1.

HOYT, W. F. and DAROFF, R. B. (1971) Supranuclear disorders of ocular control systems in man. In: *The Control of Eye Movements,* BACH-Y-RITA, P., COLLINS, C. and HYDE, J. E. (Eds.), p. 175. Academic Press, New York, London.

HUNNIUS, (1881) Zur Symptomatologie der Brückenerkrankungen, Bonn (Zit. n. Tschermak in Nagels *Handbuch der Physiologie des Menschen* IV), p. 201. Braunschweig, Vieweg.

ITO, M. (1972a) Neural design of the cerebellar motor control system. *Brain Res.* **40**, 81.

ITO, M. (1972b) Cerebellar control of the vestibular neurons: physiology and pharmacology. In: *Basic Aspects of Central Vestibular Mechanisms,* BRODAL, A. and POMPEIANO, O. (Eds.), p. 377. Elsevier, Amsterdam, London, New York.

ITO, M., SHIIDA, T., YAGI, N. and YAMAMOTO, M. (1974) The cerebellar modification of the rabbit's horizontal vestibulo-ocular reflex induced by sustained head rotation combined with visual stimulation. *Proc. Japan. Acad.* **50**, 85.

JUNG, R. (1953) Nystagmographie. Zur Physiologie und Pathologie des optisch-vestibulären Systems beim Menschen. In: *Handbuch der inneren Medizin,* 4. Aufl., Band V/1, pp. 1325–1379, BERGMANN, G. V., FREY, W. and SCHWIEGK, H. (Eds.). Berlin, Göttingen, Heidelberg, Springer.

JUNG, R. and KORNHUBER, H. H. (1964) Results of electronystagmography in man: the value of optokinetic, vestibular and spontaneous nystagmus for neurologic diagnosis and research. In: *The Oculomotor System,* BENDER, M. (Ed.). Hoeber, New York.

KINSBOURNE, M. (1962) Myoclonic encephalopathy of infants. *J. Neurol. Neurosurg. Psychiat.* **25**, 271.

KIRSTEIN, R. (1949) Nystagmustypen bei Kleinhirntumoren. *HNO-Wegweiser (Berlin)* **1**, 443.

KOMMERELL, G. and HOYT, F. (1973) Lateropulsion of saccadic eye movements. *Arch. Neurol.* **28**, 313.

KORNHUBER, H. H. (1966) Physiologie und Klinik des zentralvestibulären Systems (Blick- und Stützmotorik). In: *Handbuch für Hals-Nasen-Ohrenheilkunde,* Bd. III, 3, BERENDES, J., LINK, R. and ZÖLLNER, F. (Eds.), p. 2150. Thieme, Stuttgart.

KORNHUBER, H. H. (1969) Physiologie und Klinik des vestibulären Systems. *Arch. Klin. exp. Ohr.-Kehlk. Heilk.* **194**, 110.

KORNHUBER, H. H. (1971) Motor functions of the cerebellum and basal ganglia: the cerebello-cortical saccadic (ballistic) clock, the cerebello-nuclear hold-regulator, and the basal ganglia ramp (voluntary speed smooth movement) generator, *Kybernetik,* **8**, 157.

KORNHUBER, H. H. (1974) Cerebral cortex, cerebellum, and basal ganglia: an introduction to their motor functions. In: *The Neurosciences,* III, SCHMIDT, F. O. and WORDEN, G. (Eds.), p. 267. M.I.T. Press, Cambridge/Mass. London, England.

KUHLO, W. and DICHGANS, J. (1970) Troubles oculo-moteurs observés au cours de polymyoclonies infantiles. *Rev. Neurol.* **123,** 327.

LEMERLE, J., LEMERLE, M., AICARDI, J., MESSICA, C. and SCHWEINSGUTH, O. (1969) Trois cas d'association à un neuroblastome d'un syndrome oculo-cérébello-myoclonique. *Arch. franç. Pediat.* **26,** 547.

LEWANDOWSKI, M. (1903) Über die Verrichtungen des Kleinhirns. *Arch. Anat. Physiol.* **27,** 129.

LORENTE DE NÓ, R. (1931) Ausgewählte Kapitel aus der vergleichenden Physiologie des Labyrinthes. Die Augenmuskelreflexe beim Kaninchen und ihre Grundlagen. *Ergebn. Physiol.* **32,** 73.

LORENTE DE NÓ, R. (1933) Vestibulo-ocular reflex arc. *Arch. Neurol. Psychiat.* **30,** 245.

LUICIANI, L. (1904) Das Kleinhirn. *Ergbn. Physiol.* **3,** 259.

MAGNUS, R. (1924) *Körperstellung.* Berlin, Springer.

MAGOUN, H. W., HARE, W. K. and RANSON, S. W. (1935) Electrical stimulation of the interior of the cerebellum in the monkey. *Am. J. Physiol.* **112,** 329.

MAHALEY, M. S. (1968) Ocular motility with foramen magnum syndromes. In: *Neuroophthalmology,* SMITH, J. L. (Ed.), IV, p. 110. CV Mosby Co., St. Louis.

McLEAN, D. R. (1970) Polymyoclonia with opsoclonus. *Neurology* **20,** 508.

MANNI, E. (1950) Localizzazioni cerebellari corticali nella cavia. Nota Ia: Il "corpus cerebelli". *Arch. Fisiol. Fir.* **49,** 213.

MEYERS, I. L. (1931) Conjugate deviation of the head and eyes. Its value in the diagnosis and localization of abscess of the brain. *Arch. Otol.* **13,** 683.

MOE, P. G. and NELLHAUS, G. (1970) Infantile polymyoclonia-opsoclonus syndrome and neural crest tumors. *Neurology,* **20,** 756.

NASHOLD, B. S. and SLAUGHTER, D. G. (1969) Effects of stimulating or destroying the deep cerebellar regions in man. *J. Neurosurg.* **31,** 172.

NASHOLD, B. S., SLAUGHTER, D. G. and GILLS, J. (1969) Ocular reactions in man from deep cerebellar stimulation and lesions. *Arch. Ophthal.* **81,** 538.

NATHANSON, M. (1956) Palatal myoclonus. *Arch. Neurol. Psychiat.* **75,** 285.

NYLEN, C. O. (1939) Oto-neurological diagnosis of tumours of the brain. *Acta Oto-laryng. (Stockh.),* Suppl. **33,** 1.

NYLEN, C. O. (1943) Einiges über die Entwicklung der klinischen Vestibularforschung während der letzten 25 Jahre, besonders bezüglich des Labyrinthfistelsymptoms und des Lagenystagmus. *Acta Oto-laryng. (Stockh.),* **31,** 223.

ORZECHOWSKI, C. (1927) De l'ataxie dysmétrique des yeux: remarques sur l'ataxie des yeux dite myoclonique (opsoclonie, opsochorie). *J. Psychol. Neurol. (Leipzig),* **35,** 1.

POTTHOFF, P. C. and HAUSTEIN, M. (1970) Nystagmus und Elektro-nystagmogramm nach Kleinhirntumoroperationen. *Neurochirurgia,* **13,** 174.

RIESCO, MacCLURE, J. S. (1955) Sindromes vestibulares en las lesiones de la fosa cerebral posterior. *Rev. Otolar., Santiago,* **15,** 1.

ROBINSON, D. A. (1974) The effect of cerebellectomy on the cat's vestibulo-ocular integrator. *Brain Res.* **71,** 195.

RON, S. and ROBINSON, D. (1973) Eye movements evoked by cerebellar stimulation in the alert monkey. *J. Neurophysiol.* **36,** 1004.

ROSS, A. T. and ZEMAN, W. (1967) Opsoclonus, occult carcinoma and chemical pathology in dentate nuclei. *Arch. Neurol. (Chic.)* **17,** 546.

SALMON, S. D. (1969) Positional nystagmus. Critical review and personal experiences. *Arch. Otolar.* **90,** 58.

SIMONELLI, G. and DI GIORGIO, A. M. (1931) Il compartamento del nistagmo spontaneo e provocato nelle lesioni asimmetriche del cervelletto. *Boll. Soc. Ital. Biol. Sper.* **6,** 206.

SINGLETON, G. T. (1967) Relationships of the cerebellar nodulus to vestibular function: a study of the effects of nodulectomy on habituation. *Laryngoscope,* **77,** 1579.

SMITH, J. L., DAVID, N. J. and KLINTWORTH, G. (1964) Skew deviation. *Neurology,* **14,** 96.

SMITH, J. L. and WALSH, F. B. (1960) Opsoclonus-ataxic conjugate movements of the eyes. *Arch. Ophthal.* **64,** 244.

SPIEGEL, E. A. and SCALA, N. P. (1942) Positional nystagmus in cerebellar lesions. *J. Neurophysiol.* **5,** 247.

SPILLER, W. G. (1910) Conjugate deviation of the head and eyes in paralysing or irritative lesions of the cerebellum. *Rev. Neurol. Psychiat.* 1.

TAKEMORI, S. and COHEN, B. (1974) Loss of visual suppression of vestibular nystagmus after flocculus lesions. *Brain,* **72,** 213.

WALSH, F. B. (1947) *Clinical Neuro-ophthalmology,* p. 310. Williams & Wilkins Co., Baltimore.

WALSH, F. B. and HOYT, W. F. (1969) *Clinical Neuro-ophthalmology,* 3rd ed. Williams & Wilkins Co., Baltimore.

WESTHEIMER, G. and BLAIR, S. M. (1973) Oculomotor defect in cerebellectomized monkeys. *Invest. Ophthal.* **12,** 618.

WESTHEIMER, G. and BLAIR, S. M. (1974) Functional organization of primate oculomotor system revealed by cerebellectomy. *Exptl. Brain Res.* **21**, 463.

WITTERIDGE, D. (1960) Central control of eye movements. In: *Handbook of Physiology*, Sec. 1, Neurophysiology, Vol. II, FIELD, J., MAGOUN, H. W. and HALL, V. E. (Eds.), p. 1089. Am. Physiol. Soc., Washington.

ZEE, D. S., FRIENDLICH, A. R. and ROBINSON, D. A. (1974) The mechanism of downbeat nystagmus. *Arch. Neurol.* **30**, 227.

SPINAL AFFERENCES TO THE OCULOMOTOR SYSTEM: PHYSIOLOGICAL AND CLINICAL ASPECTS

Johannes Dichgans

The existence of spinal afferents to the oculomotor system was first demonstrated behaviourally by Bárány (1906) who was able to elicit a coordinated deviation of the eyes towards the direction of trunk movement with respect to the head, that was held stationary in space. Behavioural investigations on the neck to eye reflex were carried further by De Kleyn (1918, 1921), Grahe (1922), Magnus (1924), Frenzel (1928), Phillipszoon and Bos (1963) and Takemori and Suzuki (1971). From these results it seems to be certain that neck to eye afferents co-operate with the vestibulo-ocular reflex loop to stabilize the eyes on visual targets during active or passive head on trunk movements. Functional significance of the neck to eye loop is also suggested by the observation of at least partially preserved compensatory eye-movements in people with a non-functioning labyrinth such as deaf mutes or people with streptomycin lesions.

The *phasic neck reflexes* active during movement may be distinguished from *tonic neck reflexes* responding to posture in gravitational space (Magnus, 1924, and his school). The latter interact with otolith inputs at the level of the brainstem, whereas the former in addition depend on vestibular canal afferents. Tonic neck reflexes on the eyes are relatively small and, even with the contribution of vestibular afferents, never fully compensate for head tilt.

PHYSIOLOGY

The receptive area responsible for neck-induced oculomotor activity has been located in the region of the upper *neck joints* and possibly the ligaments, especially at the atlanto-axial and atlanto-occipital joints (McCouch *et al.*, 1951; Biemond and de Jong, 1969). The afferent information enters the spinal cord via the *dorsal roots* C1 *to* C3 and possibly C4. Dorsal rhizotomy C1 to C3 has been shown to eliminate the neck–ocular reflex in the rabbit (De Kleyn, 1918). Analogous results have been obtained in the cat through stimulation of the dorsal roots by Hikosaka and Maeda (1973). According to Hikosaka and Maeda (1973) the afferent spinal signals *reach the contralateral vestibular nuclei* where they impinge upon vestibulo-oculomotor relay neurons. These results are in agreement with earlier findings of Fredrickson *et al.* (1966) and anatomical data from Corbin and Hinsey (1935) and Brodal *et al.* (1962) who showed that cervical afferents project to the vestibular nuclei. More specifically, Hikosaka and Maeda found that the test reflex elicited in the *abducens nerve* by electrical stimulation of the contralateral vestibular nerve was *inhibited by contralateral and facilitated by ipsilateral cervical dorsal root or neck joint stimulation.* Corresponding interactions were demonstrated for the inhibitory vestibulo-oculomotor relay neurons (Hikosaka and Maeda, 1973). Spinal influences on oculomotor neurons originating from the more caudal segments of the cord have not been demonstrated, although spinal ascending effects (bilateral excitation) on Deiter's neurons have been found by Wilson *et al.* (1966) and it has been demonstrated that even inputs from the proximal joints of the hindlimbs are capable of modulating unit activity in the vestibular nuclei (Fredrickson *et al.*, 1966).

The effects of neck and labyrinth stimulation on the oculomotor system have been shown to summate by measuring the amplitude of compensatory eye movements (De Kleyn, 1921; Grahe, 1922; Meiry, 1971). Using passive trunk movements the gain of the neck to eye loop in humans was shown to be on the order of 30% at frequencies below 0.6 rad/sec and 8% at frequencies exceeding 2.4 rad/sec (Meiry, 1971; Suzuki, 1972). In the rabbit the neck to eye gain seems to be rather high (De Kleyn, 1918; Phillipszoon, 1962; Suzuki, 1972), whereas in the intact monkey the neck to eye reflex has been shown to be functionally inactive during passive body movements about the stationary head (Dichgans *et al.*, 1974).

The *clinical evidence* about the possible spinal influence on oculomotor activity in patients is very limited. The existence of "cervical positional nystagmus" in patients with upper cervical cord lesions or damage of the cervical roots, claimed mainly by Biemond, has not generally been accepted. Biemond and De Jong (1969) who reviewed the entire clinical literature on this subject were cautious enough to point to the fact that mostly the involvement of the lower parts of the brainstem, be it by invasion, indirect pressure, oedema, circulatory disregulation or irritation of the sympathetic vertebral plexus cannot be completely excluded. There remain, however, a few patients in which long-lasting positional nystagmus may have been caused exclusively by unilateral damage of afferent fibres to the upper cervical spinal cord, i.e. patients in whom the upper cervical roots were severed for treatment of spastic torticollis (Biemond, 1939, 1940). Biemond and De Jong (1969) supplemented the clinical evidence by lesion studies in rabbits yielding results consistent with the clinical findings.

Recent investigations suggest that the neck to eye afferences may become very significant in the process of *recovery from vestibular lesions.* In man partial recovery of eye head coordination has been observed after inflammatory and streptomycin lesions of the labyrinth and in deaf mutes. Frenzel (1930) described a marked "cervical nystagmus" in patients with bilateral labyrinthine lesions evoked by stimulating the neck receptors through turning the body in relation to the stationary head in the dark. Anaesthesia of neck muscles and joints reduced this nystagmus. The quantitative data on recovery, however, besides the work of Atkin and Bender (1968) who found partial recovery in a few patients with permanent bilateral labyrinthine damage so far stem from experiments in monkeys (Dichgans *et al.*, 1973). These animals show a marked plasticity of the gain of the loop, which, supplemented by central mechanisms, allows for recovery of gaze stabilization after bilateral labyrinthectomy. In the monkey the recovery process with respect to neck afferents entails two mechanisms: *tonic potentiation* of the neck to eye loop gain reaching a steady state of about 30% in passive movements 1–2 months after labyrinthectomy and a *phasic enhancement* concurrent only with active initiation of head turning. The latter ultimately amounts to an estimated additional gain of about 45%. Thus after labyrinthectomy the monkey manages to increase the gain from almost zero to about 75% during active head turning. It remains to be shown in future investigations how the gain potentiation is achieved by the central nervous system. Three possible mechanisms seem particularly conspicuous: (1) denervation hypersensitivity of the vestibular nuclei; (2) synaptic sprouting after degeneration of terminals from primary vestibular afferents; (3) cerebellar facilitation by way of disinhibition of vestibulo-ocular connections (Baker *et al.*, 1972; Fukuda *et al.*, 1972; Ito, 1972; and Precht as well as Robinson, this Symposium). The directionally selective visual input necessary to properly readjust the gain of the loop in the rabbit reaches the Purkinje cells of the flocculus via climbing fibres (Maekawa and Simpson, 1972; Simpson and Alley, 1973). The supposed cerebellar gain control may be particularly active in the phasic gain increase occurring with the active initiation of head movements.

Additional mechanisms like central programming of compensatory movements and recalibration of the spatial sensory motor coordination of eye and head system play a minor role in the recovery process, but are of theoretical interest. These have been described by Dichgans *et al.* (1973). The latter two mechanisms become particularly effective after an additional neck deafferentation. Comparable data from man are still lacking.

REFERENCES

ATKIN, A. and BENDER, M. B. (1968) Ocular stabilization during oscillatory head movements. *Arch. Neurol. (Chic.)* **19**, 559.

BAKER, R., PRECHT, W. and LLINAS, R. (1972) Cerebellar modulatory action on the vestibulo-trochlear pathway in the cat. *Exptl. Brain Res.* **15**, 364.

BÁRÁNY, R. (1906) Augenbewegungen durch Thoraxbewegungen ausgelöst. *Zbl. Physiol.* **20**, 298.

BIEMOND, A. (1939) On a new form of experimental position nystagmus in the rabbit and its clinical value. *Proc. kon. ned. Akad. Wet.* **42**, 370.

BIEMOND, A. (1940) Further observations about the cervical form of positional-nystagmus and its anatomical base. *Proc. kon. ned. Akad. Wet.* **43**, 901.

BIEMOND, A. and DE JONG, J. M. B. V. (1961) On cervical nystagmus and related disorders. *Brain,* **92**, 437.

BRODAL, A., POMPEIANO, O. and WALBERG, F. (1962) *The Vestibular Nuclei and their Connections. Anatomy and Functional Correlations.* London: Oliver & Boyd.

CORBIN, K. B. and HINSEY, J. C. (1935) Intramedullary course of the dorsal root fibers of each of the first four cervical nerves. *J. Comp. Neurol.* **63**, 119.

DICHGANS, J., BIZZI, E., MORASSO, P. and TAGLIASCO, V. (1974) The role of vestibular and neck afferents during eye head coordination in the monkey. *Brain Res.* **71**, 225.

DICHGANS, J., BIZZI, E., MORASSO, P. and TAGLIASCO, V. (1973) Mechanisms underlying recovery of eye-head coordination following bilateral labyrinthectomy in monkeys. *Exptl Brain Res.* **18**, 548.

DE KLEYN, A. (1918) Actions réflexes du labyrinthe et du cou sur les muscles de l'œil. *Arch. néerl. Physiol.* **2**, 644.

DE KLEYN, A. (1921) Tonische Labyrinth- und Halsreflexe auf die Augen. *Pflügers Arch. ges. Physiol.* **186**, 82.

FREDRICKSON, J. M., SCHWARZ, D. and KORNHUBER, H. H. (1966) Convergence and interaction of vestibular and deep somatic afferents upon neurons in the vestibular nuclei of the cat. *Acta Oto-laryng. (Stockh.)* **61**, 168.

FRENZEL, H. (1928) Rucknystagmus als Halsreflex und Schlagfeldverlagerung des labyrinthären Drehnystagmus durch Halsreflexe. *Z. Hals-, Nas.-u. Ohrenheilk.* **21**, 177.

FRENZEL, H. (1930) Halsreflektorisches Augenrucken von vestibulärer Schlagform, ein typisches Vorkommnis bei vollständig oder nahezu vollständig Unerregbaren. *Passow-Schäfers Beitrg.* **28**, 305.

FUKUDA, J., HIGHSTEIN, S. U. and ITO, M. (1972) Cerebellar inhibitory control of the vestibulo-ocular reflex investigated in rabbit IIIrd nucleus. *Exptl Brain Res.* **14**, 511.

GRAHE, K. (1922) Über Halsreflexe und Vestibularreaktion beim Menschen. *Zeitschr. f. Hals-, Nasen- u. Ohrenheilk.* **3**, 550.

HIKOSAKA, O., MAEDA, M. (1973) Cervical effects on abducens motoneurons and their interaction with vestibulo-ocular reflex. *Exptl. Brain Res.* **18,** 512.

ITO, M. (1972) Neural design of the cerebellar motor control system. *Brain Res.* **40,** 81.

MAEKAWA, K. and SIMPSON, J. I. (1972) Climbing fiber activation of Purkinje cells in the flocculus by impulses transferred through the visual pathway. *Brain Res.* **39,** 245.

MAGNUS, R. (1924) *Körperstellung,* Berlin, Springer.

MCCOUCH, G. P., DEERING, I. D. and LING, T. H. (1951) Location of receptors for tonic neck reflexes. *J. Neurophysiol.* **14,** 191.

MEIRY, J. L. (1971) Vestibular and proprioceptive stabilization of eye movement. In: *The Control of Eye Movements,* BACH-Y-RITA, P., COLLING, S. and HYDE, J. R. (Eds.). New York, London, Academic Press.

PHILLIPSZOON, A. J. (1962) Compensatory eye movements and nystagmus provoked by stimulation of the vestibular organ and the cervical nerve roots. *Pract. Oto-rhino-laryng.* **24,** 193.

PHILLIPSZOON, A. J. and BOS, J. H. (1963) Neck torsion nystagmus. *Pract. Oto-rhino-laryng.* **24,** 193.

SIMPSON, J. I. and ALLEY, K. R. (1973) Trigger features for the visual climbing fiber input to rabbit vestibulo cerebellum. *Proc. Third Ann. Meeting of the Soc. for Neuroscience, San Diego,* 152.

SUZUKI, J. I. (1972) Vestibular and spinal control of eye movements. In: *Cerebral Control of Eye Movements and Motion Perception,* DICHGANS, J. and BIZZI, E. (Eds.). Basel, S. Karger.

TAKEMORI, S. and SUZUKI, J. (1971) Eye deviations from neck torsion in humans. *Ann. Otol.* **80,** 439.

WILSON, V. J., KATO, M., THOMAS, R. C. and PETERSON, R. W. (1966) Excitation of lateral vestibular neurons by peripheral afferent fibres. *J. Neurophysiol.* **29,** 508.

ACTIVITY IN EYE MUSCLE MOTONEURONS AND BRAINSTEM UNITS DURING EYE MOVEMENTS†

V. Henn and B. Cohen

INTRODUCTION

Units whose activity is related to eye movements are present at many sites in the brainstem. In this paper we will review data on recordings from these neurons in order to show what parameters they might code. Results from lesion or stimulation studies will be compared with data from unit studies to determine what areas play a necessary part in generating eye movements, and what areas receive information about eye movements without being necessarily involved in generating eye movements.

Probably the oldest method for exploring supranuclear oculomotor pathways is to study changes in eye movements after destroying parts of the brain. Used first by Flourens (1842), this technique was improved with the introduction of stereotaxis and electrolytic lesions, and there is an extensive literature on this subject. When specific functions have been lost or impaired, lesion studies have been helpful in understanding the organization of the central oculomotor system (Bender and Shanzer, 1964). However, if gaze defects are only transient after lesions, there is often considerable ambiguity in interpretation of results.

An alternate method for studying oculomotor organization is by electrical stimulation. Fritsch and Hitzig (1870) discovered that the central nervous system can be excited by electrical currents, and observed bodily reactions during electrical stimulation of small areas of the brain. With this method Ferrier (1876) and Schäfer (1888) explored the areas of the cerebral and cerebellar cortex from which eye movements can be evoked. Adamük (1870) discovered that stimulation of the superior colliculus also reliably elicits eye movements.

Recently the range of physiological methods has been extended by intracellular and extracellular recordings from single neurons. Intracellular recordings are usually done in immobilized animals, and generally focus attention on direct or monosynaptic rather than polysynaptic connections. With this technique the synaptic physiology and pathways of direct vestibulo-oculomotor reflexes have been considerably clarified. This subject is reviewed in detail elsewhere (Wilson, 1972; Brodal and Pompeiano, 1972; Cohen, 1974).

In extracellular recordings, on the other hand, it is possible to precisely determine how brainstem neurons change activity before and during quick eye movements in alert animals. The emphasis in this paper is on how activity patterns of motoneurons

†This work was supported by the City of New York Research Foundation Grant No. 10730E, National Science Foundation Grant No. 74-00938 and the National Institute of Neurological Diseases and Stroke Grant No. 00294.

and of neurons from the pontine reticular formation are related to saccadic eye movements and positions of fixation. Although a statistical relationship between eye movements and unit firing has been shown for neurons in several brainstem areas, the question of causality still remains an open one. This includes consideration of which parameters are meaningful for correlation with eye movements and what level of statistical significance would be acceptable for causality, bearing in mind the exactness of the oculomotor system. It seems that definite answers as to causality can be obtained only when single unit studies are evaluated together with the results of stimulation and lesion experiments.

Data considered in this review comes primarily from alert monkeys (usually *Macaca mulatta*). Techniques of recording extracellular unit activity in these animals are more or less standard and will only be summarized here. Generally, a plug which serves as a receptacle for a micromanipulator is permanently implanted on the skull. Extracellular unit activity is recorded with tungsten microelectrodes of 2–10 megohms resistance. The monkey's head is firmly fixed. Eye movements are recorded either by electrooculography with needle electrodes or with silver–silver chloride electrodes permanently implanted around the orbit (Bond and Ho, 1970) or electromagnetically (Fuchs and Robinson, 1966). In the alert monkey saccades occur at frequencies of up to 3 to 4 per second interspersed between pursuit movements and periods of fixation. Nystagmus is induced by optokinetic or vestibular stimulation, or the monkeys can be trained to make specific movements.

MOTONEURONS

Sasaki (1963) was the first to record intracellularly from motoneurons. He showed that motoneurons receive powerful EPSPs and IPSPs when the vestibular system is stimulated and are hyperpolarized after an action potential. Intracellular studies of the vestibulo-ocular reflexes by Precht, Shimazu, Baker, Ito and Highstein and co-workers are summarized in Brodal and Pompeiano (1972). Horcholle and Tyč-Dumont (1969) demonstrated that motoneurons are actively inhibited during eye movements in the off-direction. Similar results were obtained by Maeda *et al.* (1971 and 1972) and by Baker and Precht (1972) recording from abducens and trochlear motoneurons respectively during vestibular nystagmus. Baker and Precht (1972) found that the prominent after-hyperpolarization in trochlear motoneurons is produced by increased membrane conductance which effectively shunts the excitatory current of the preceding EPSPs. That makes it possible for motoneurons to fire at high rates without the spike mechanism being inactivated. Therefore continuous firing at high rates seen during positions of fixation are most likely due to continuous excitatory input from premotor cells on motoneurons, and probably are not generated by a self-regenerating mechanism of the motoneurons themselves.

Extracellular studies of single units of extraocular motoneurons concentrate on three questions:

1. Are there different types of motoneurons?
2. What is the quantitative relationship between their firing rate and eye movements?
3. What information would motoneurons need from premotor structures in order to move the eyes and hold them in certain positions during fixation?

DIFFERENT TYPES OF MOTONEURONS

Motoneurons serve three different functions: they produce slow movements (pursuit and convergence movements and slow phases of nystagmus), fast eye movements (saccades and quick phases of nystagmus), and hold the eyes in position during periods of fixation. It is well known that there are motoneurons and eye muscle fibers of different sizes (Tsuchida, 1906; Cheng and Breinin, 1966; Mayr *et al.*, 1966; Alvarado, Lennerstrand, this volume) and axons in the motor nerves have different conduction velocities (Yamanaka and Bach-y-Rita, 1968; Baker and Precht, 1972). The question is: Can different physiological functions be attributed to different morphological types of fibers and to the motoneurons which innervate them?

Schubert and Bornschein (1962) recorded from the third nerve of the cat and induced vestibular nystagmus by caloric stimulation. All motoneurons were active during most fast and slow phases of nystagmus. Schaefer (1965) found abducens motoneurons to be either predominantly tonic or phasic in their behavior, although both types participated in quick and slow movements during nystagmus. Yamanaka and Bach-y-Rita (1968) found that some motoneurons fired only during quick phases, others during both slow and quick phases of nystagmus. Units firing only during the fast phases had high conduction velocities (between 41 and 83 m/s), and units firing during the slow phases or in periods when the eyes did not move at all had considerably lower conduction velocities (6 to 40 m/s).

Our results indicate that motoneurons can be classified according to their behavior during saccades and periods of fixation (Henn and Cohen, 1972). Phasic activity is the sudden activation of a motoneuron during a quick eye movement if that activation is higher than during the subsequent period of fixation. A tonic response is the firing of a motoneuron during a period of fixation. In this restricted definition the term phasic–tonic does not directly refer to slow phases of nystagmus. A large range of velocities are possible during slow phases of nystagmus (slightly above 0°/sec to greater than 100°/sec), thresholds for individual units are often crossed, and nystagmus in normal animals tends to beat in a rather restricted field of possible eye movements. Therefore unit behavior during nystagmus is not an entirely satisfactory parameter for characterizing motoneurons.

Robinson (1970) recorded from neurons in the oculomotor nucleus of alert monkeys. He found that the same units participated in all kinds of movements, although their thresholds varied. Several units had thresholds which were markedly higher for fast than for slow movements or for holding the eyes in certain positions. However, the patterns of activity were the same in all units he encountered. Similar reports were given by Schiller (1970) and Fuchs and Luschei (1970). Finally, Fuchs and Luschei (1971) and Keller and Robinson (1972) concluded that there is only one type of motoneuron which subserves all different functions.

Our own experiments on a large (more than 200) sample of motoneurons in alert monkeys gave different results. All motoneurons had clear on–off directions. (The on-direction is the movement direction of the eyes in which the motoneurons fire maximally. The off-direction is just the reverse.) On–off directions for medial rectus and abducens units lay strictly in the horizontal plane; on–off directions for the other muscles were tilted 10° to 20° off the vertical plane.

During spontaneous eye movements most units were active during periods of fixation as well as during saccades (Fig. 1 A–D). Included were units which were designated as tonic units (Fig. 1 A,B). These units were active during periods of fixation and increased their firing frequencies in a stepwise fashion with hardly any overshoot during saccades in the on-direction. That is, the firing during saccadic eye movements was not substantially higher than during the subsequent period of fixation, although the firing level was below the highest frequency these units could reach. A smaller percentage of units was active only during saccades (Fig. 1F), and these units were designated as phasic units. Such units did not fire during periods of fixation even when the eyes were strongly deviated in the on-direction.

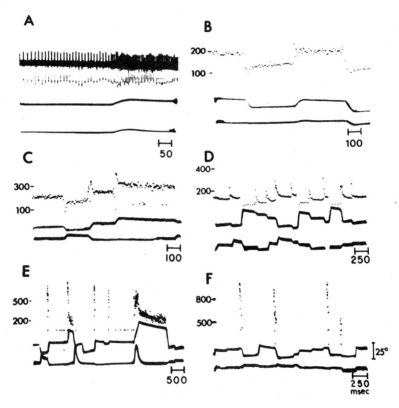

Fig. 1. Medial rectus units with different characteristics. In A the top trace is spike activity, in B–F the dot displays represent instantaneous frequency. The height of each dot is the reciprocal of the last spike interval. Numbers on the left refer to frequencies in hertz. The middle and bottom traces are the horizontal and vertical EOG respectively. Up corresponds to right or upward movements. A and B are samples of the same tonic unit; C and D are two predominantly tonic units; E a predominantly phasic unit, and F a phasic unit. Note that from C to F the phasic part of the unit activity becomes more prominent until in F the unit fires only during quick eye movements in the on-direction.

The different types of units formed a continuum with the tonic and phasic types at the ends and the predominantly tonic, tonic–phasic and predominantly phasic types in the middle (Fig. 1). Boundaries between types were arbitrary although there were distinct differences across two or more groups. Tonic units tended to have a low threshold, although several exceptions were noted. Similarly many phasic units were active over nearly the entire range of eye movements, firing a burst of spikes whenever the eye moved in the on-direction. Tonic units tended to have lower maximum frequencies than phasic units and often were not completely inhibited during movements in the off-direction. Results were similar whether recording from neurons in the third nucleus or from axons in the third nerve confirming that the phasic or tonic units actually were motoneurons.

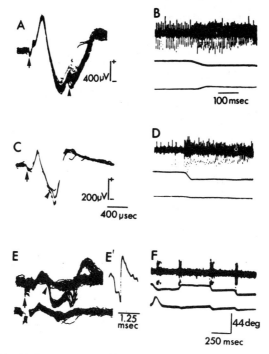

FIG. 2. Antidromically identified motoneurons (A, C, E) and their activity patterns during saccades and positions of fixation (B, D, F). The IIIrd nerve was stimulated with 1–2-volt pulses of 100 μs duration (1st arrow). This evoked characteristic positive–negative field potentials in the IIIrd nucleus and activated motoneurons at varying latencies (2nd arrow). The complex waveform associated with activation of the unit in E is the same as the spontaneously occurring firing shown in E′ at a slower time base. The IIIrd nerve evoked field potential without the unit is shown in the bottom trace of E. Time base for A, C, E is 400 μs shown under C, for E′ is 1.25 ms, for B, D is 100 ms shown under B, and for F is 250 ms. The 2nd and 3rd traces in B, D, F are the horizontal and vertical EOG. Their calibration is 44° shown under F. Vertical calibration of C, E and E′ is 200 μV shown by the vertical bar beside C. (From Matsuo and Cohen, unpublished data.)

Only a few units were tested during slow movements, i.e. during visually guided movements or slow phases of nystagmus. All tonic units became active as soon as their threshold was reached regardless of whether the movement was a pursuit movement or a slow or quick phase of nystagmus. In general, findings in monkeys were similar to those of others in cats, that is, some neurons were continuously active during slow phases, while others fired during every rapid eye movement and were only activated during the fastest slow phases or when the eyes were far in the on-direction. From these data it seems fair to conclude that while specific eye movements are not specifically produced by one cell or muscle fiber type, nevertheless, there is a functional differentiation with the more tonic motoneurons being mainly responsible for holding the eyes steady or for moving them slowly, and the more phasic motoneurons being mainly responsible for moving the eyes more rapidly (Henn and Cohen, 1972).

Proof that different types of cells were actually motoneurons was also obtained recently in experiments of Matsuo and Cohen on alert monkeys (unpublished data). The third nerves were electrically stimulated intracranially, and motoneurons were identified by antidromic activation. Three such units are shown in Fig. 2. The unit potentials were superimposed on the characteristic field potential evoked in the motor nucleus by motor nerve stimulation (Fig. 2 A, C, E lower trace) (Baker *et al.*, 1969; Baker and Precht, 1972). Activity patterns for each of these units during spontaneous eye movements are shown on the right (Fig. 2 B, D, F). The first (Fig. 2 A, B) is a tonic neuron, the second (Fig. 2 C, D) a predominantly tonic neuron, and the third (Fig. 2 E, E', F) a predominantly phasic cell. Cells with more phasic activity tended to have faster conduction velocities than those with more tonic activity. This indicates that the more phasic neurons have larger axons (Gasser and Grundfest, 1939) and therefore can be identified as the larger motoneurons which singly innervate the larger eye muscle twitch fibers (Yamanaka and Bach-y-Rita, 1968; Lennerstrand, this volume).

QUANTITATIVE ANALYSIS OF MOTONEURONS

Positions of fixation during which the units exhibit a regular tonic discharge will be considered first. During periods of fixation the frequency (independent variable) of a neuron can be plotted against eye position (dependent variable) as in Fig. 3A. Data points in this figure were derived from frequency measurements of consecutive periods of fixation from a single medial rectus unit. It can be seen that the higher the frequency, the farther the eyes tended to be positioned in the on-direction. It can also be seen that a single frequency would not predict an eye position closer than $\pm 5°$ to $\pm 10°$, although average frequencies would tend to lie on a straight line.

In Fig. 3B the same data points are replotted. On the abscissa is plotted changes of frequency, i.e. the difference in frequency between the current fixation period and the previous one. On the ordinate is plotted the corresponding change in eye position. The reduction in scatter is evident. The points can be described by a linear line of regression of the following form:

$$P2 - P1 = k.(F3 - F1) \tag{1}$$

(symbols are explained in Figure 4). The activity of all units which exhibited a tonic response is described by this equation, and the correlation factor for the linear line of regression was consistently greater than 0.9 in each instance.

Considering the phasic response of motoneurons (Fig. 5), a linear relationship was found between change of frequency times the duration of the phasic response and change of position. Again these data points which were derived from subsequent eye movements of a single unit can be described by a linear line of regression:

$$P2 - P1 = k.(F2 - F1).D. \tag{2}$$

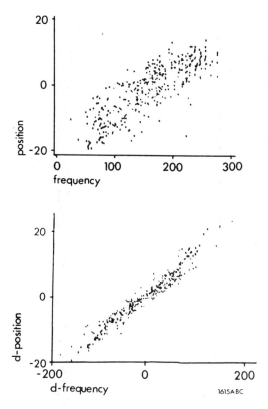

FIG. 3. Left medial rectus unit. *Upper graph*: frequency during periods of fixation (abscissa) is plotted against the position of the eyes in the horizontal plane (ordinate). *Lower graph*: same data points as above, except that changes in frequency are plotted against changes in position. Note the reduction in scatter. The linear line of regression is: $Y = -0.069 + 0.194X$. The correlation factor is 0.954.

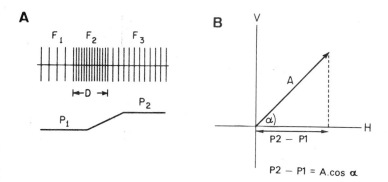

FIG. 4A. Scheme of frequencies used for the different calculations. $F1$ and $F3$ are average frequencies during periods of fixation. $F2$ is the average frequency during a phasic response. $P1$ and $P2$ are the respective positions of the eyes. D is the duration of the phasic response.

FIG. 4B. Arrow (A) represents an oblique eye movement. Its vector projection onto the horizontal plane is $P2 - P1$. The enclosed angle is α.

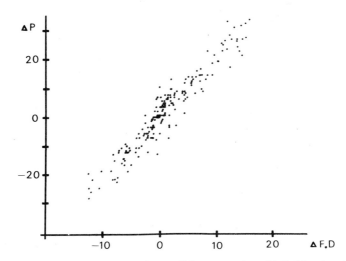

Fɪɢ. 5. Abscissa, phasic change of frequency of a medial rectus unit multiplied by duration of the phasic burst ($(F2 - F1).D$). Ordinate, position change $P2 - P1$ during that movement. The equation for the linear line of regression in this case is: $Y = 2.585 + 3.086X$. The correlation factor is 0.943.

All units which exhibited phasic behavior could be described by this equation, and the correlation factors were consistently greater than 0.85.

One point should be emphasized: the position changes which are related to frequency changes in medial or lateral rectus units are not restricted to eye movement in the horizontal plane. These equations are valid for eye movements in any direction, as long as the vector projection in the pulling direction of that particular muscle is used as the parameter for position change. This is shown in Fig. 4B. For example, the horizontal position change during a movement can be described:

$$P2 - P1 = A.cos\, \alpha. \tag{3}$$

In other words, only position changes along the respective pulling direction of a muscle can be related to frequency changes in its motoneurons. For a medial or lateral rectus unit, this is the horizontal plane. Consequently, firing in medial rectus or abducens motoneurons is independent of the vertical position of the eyes.

These equations can be generalized further to describe the behavior of motoneurons of all extraocular muscles if frequency changes are related to eye position changes along their respective pulling directions. The average pulling direction of vertical or oblique eye muscles was found to be tilted by 10° to 20° from the vertical. This implies that motoneurons for these muscles exhibit a small change in activity during every horizontal eye movement. Or, in other words, each muscle participates in each movement save those movements which are perpendicular to its respective on–off direction.

As the left sides of equations (1) and (2) are equal, the right sides can be combined into the following equation:

$$F3 - F1 = k/k.(F2 - F1).D \tag{4}$$

or

$$F3 = k/k.(F2 - F1).D + F1. \tag{5}$$

Equation (5) shows that the frequency during a period of fixation is entirely determined by parameters of the preceding quick eye movement. This means, that the frequency of a motoneuron during a position of fixation can be predicted from the frequency change which occurred during the preceding phasic response. It should be stressed that such frequency predictions depend only on knowledge of the behavior of the motoneuron and are independent of measurements of eye position. More details about quantitative description of motoneurons can be found in Henn and Cohen (1973).

This approach toward quantitative characterizing motoneurons differs in some respects from other descriptions given in the literature (Robinson, 1970; Schiller, 1970; Fuchs and Luschei, 1970). The main differences are: (1) we consider it essential to regard causal relationships in these equations, i.e. frequency is the independent variable and the eye position is the dependent variable. Standard deviations for these two variables might be considerably different and are not comparable. (2) In order to get a valid and complete description of motoneuron behavior, it is essential or at least desirable to have unselected data points available for the independent variable. That is, to quantitatively characterize motoneurons, it is necessary to consider every frequency change and not only those which are associated with eye movements of specific amplitude and direction. These differences in data acquisition, description of raw values, and subsequent statistical treatment eventually lead to very different interpretations of the organization of the oculomotor system. Another more pragmatic point is the criterion of predictability. The equations offered here can predict the behavior of motoneurons. Moreover, from this behavior they can also predict eye movements in any direction and of any amplitude.

What Information is Needed by Motoneurons to Move the Eyes and to Hold Them in Position During Periods of Fixation?

Experimental evidence showed that frequency changes in motoneurons which lead to quick eye movements are equivalent to a vector representing amplitude and direction of movement. One should therefore expect to find neurons at levels prior to the motoneurons, i.e. at prenuclear levels which code either or both of these parameters. Moreover, one would expect to find the direction of eye movement coded as the cosine function, since motoneurons themselves make use of that function. This means, however, that the units should be active over a wide range of different movement directions and should not just fire to movements in a single direction. It is not clear whether amplitude and duration are separately represented. Since in monkey as in man there is a linear relationship between amplitude and duration of quick eye movements, the coding of either amplitude or duration could be achieved by having a unit fire over a certain time.

It was shown above that all information required to move the eyes and hold them during a period of fixation is already present in the information that produces a saccade.

The equation describing the quick movement can be transformed to

$$P2 - P1 = k \cdot (F2 - F1) \cdot D \tag{2}$$

$$P2 - P1 = k \cdot \frac{\text{number of spikes}}{\text{time}} \cdot D. \tag{6}$$

In this transformation one can see that it is the number of "extra" spikes added to a preceding frequency which moves the eyes. To hold the eyes in certain positions and have the motoneurons continue to discharge at relatively high sustained rates, however, would require pulse integration. A pulse integrator converts a burst of pulses at the input to a constant frequency of pulses at the output. This output level remains unchanged until the next input modifies it by adding or subtracting pulses. Such a mechanism could explain how motoneurons can discharge at unchanging levels during periods of fixation, although the level of this discharge had been determined during the preceding quick movement.

Aside from the logical need for such integration, evidence for this mechanism is still relatively meager. If this integrator were located in the vicinity of the motoneurons, then at prenuclear levels one should expect to find units whose activity is related mainly to eye movement. However, if this integrator were located more proximally in the PRF or in the vestibular nuclei, for example, then frequency of those units should be closely related to firing frequencies of motoneurons during periods of fixation. This will be considered subsequently.

INTERNEURONS

Experimental evidence is in conflict as to whether or not there are interneurons in the eye muscle motor nuclei. Anatomical studies in the monkey showed a variety of cell sizes in the oculomotor nucleus (Tsuchida, 1906), but it is not clear whether these are all motoneurons. Warwick found no neurons in the motor nuclei which did not show chromatolytic changes after motor nerve section (1953).

In electrophysiological studies only motoneurons have been encountered within the confines of eye muscle motor nuclei (Precht et al., 1969; Baker and Precht, 1972; Highstein et al., 1974). However, Tyč-Dumont (this volume) and Goldberg et al. (1974) using intracellular recordings and Tyč-Dumont (this volume) using cell-marking techniques found evidence for the existence of interneurons. Whether or not the cell bodies lie exactly within the motor nuclei probably depends to some extent on the definition of the borders. It seems certain, however, that such cells lie within close proximity of motoneurons, and that their processes coexist in the same area with those of motoneurons.

In our own studies about one-third of units in the oculomotor nuclei of the alert monkey were not motoneurons as judged by their activity patterns, and there is indication that some of these units might be cells. Most of these units resembled neurons found in the pontine reticular formation or in certain parts of the vestibular nuclei. Most of the recordings probably were from fibers projecting to the oculomotor nuclei from these areas. Additional work is necessary to provide a more complete description of activity patterns of interneurons and to characterize their activity quantitatively during spontaneous eye movements in alert animals.

PONTINE RETICULAR FORMATION

Evidence which suggests that the immediate supranuclear generator for quick phases of nystagmus and saccades in the horizontal plane lies in the pontine reticular formation

(PRF) comes from clinical and lesion studies, from stimulation studies and from single unit studies. PRF participation in horizontal gaze mechanisms has been postulated on the basis of clinical evidence for many years (for reviews see Freeman, 1922, and Jung and Kornhuber, 1964). Lorente de Nó (1933) first demonstrated that quick phases of nystagmus were lost in rabbits after PRF lesions, and Teng et al. (1956), and Bender and Shanzer (1964) that small lesions of the pontine tegmentum caused paralysis of ipsilateral conjugate gaze in monkeys. Portions of the pontine tegmentum which cause conjugate paralysis of gaze when destroyed are limited to medial parts of nucleus reticularis magnocellularis in the pons (Goebel et al., 1971). This region has been designated as the paramedian zone of the pontine reticular formation (Bender and Shanzer, 1964; Cohen et al., 1968). Ipsilateral rapid eye movements and positions of fixation in the ipsilateral hemifield are preferentially affected during conjugate gaze paralysis produced by PRF lesions.

Some information about reticulo-ocular pathways has been provided in stimulation studies. Supranuclear oculomotor pathways converge in the PRF (Shanzer and Bender, 1964), and all types of slow and rapid horizontal eye movements and positions of fixation can be induced by PRF stimulation (Cohen and Komatsuzaki, 1972). Integration of stimulating pulses was also shown to occur either in the PRF or in reticulo-oculomotor pathways (Cohen and Komatsuzaki, 1972).

Gross potentials changes in the PRF precede each rapid eye movement (Cohen and Feldman, 1968). The PRF potential changes are present in association with every eye movement and blink, but are larger and more complex when the eyes move to the ipsilateral side. There is no qualitative difference in the potential changes whether the rapid eye movement is a saccade or quick phase of nystagmus. These and other data suggest that saccades and quick phases are generated by the same mechanism (Cohen and Henn, 1972b).

Reticulo-ocular projections have been reported by Lorente de Nó (1933), Scheibel and Scheibel (1958), and Szentágothai (1964), but their origin and ending has not been studied systematically. Intracellular recordings provide additional evidence for their existence (Highstein et al., 1974). In cats stimulating electrodes were placed on both IIIrd and both VIIIth nerves, in the rostral PRF and in the MLF at the level of the abducens nuclei. Intracellular potentials were recorded from IIIrd nucleus motoneurons which were identified by their antidromic responses to IIIrd nerve stimulation. Field potentials in and around IIIrd nucleus were also recorded. PRF stimulation produced EPSPs (Fig. 6A), EP-IPSPs, and IPSPs all with latencies within the monosynaptic range (0.5–1 ms). EPSPs were capable of firing motoneurons (Fig. 6B). PSPs evoked by PRF stimulation (Fig. 6D) were not a part of the disynaptic vestibulo-ocular reflex as they did not occlude with PSPs produced by VIIIth nerve stimulation (Fig. 6E-H). This shows that activity responsible for the vestibular and PRF-induced PSPs was travelling over separate pathways.

MLF and PRF stimulation could produce PSPs of the same or of opposite sign. Results of occlusion testing in cells in which both MLF and PRF stimulation produced EPSPs indicate that at least part of the excitatory projection from the PRF to IIIrd nucleus lies outside the MLF. Field potentials analysis was consistent with this. In addition PRF stimulating sites which produced maximum short latency field potentials in the IIIrd nucleus lay several millimeters below the MLF. These data indicate that there are direct, i.e. monosynaptic, projections from the PRF to motoneurons in the ·

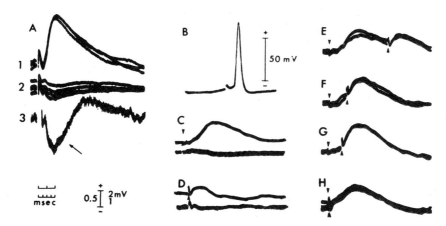

FIG. 6. Intracellular potentials from identified IIIrd nucleus motoneurons (upper traces); lower traces are extracellular controls. (A) EPSPs evoked by PRF stimulation. Upward arrow under A_3 indicates PRF-induced extracellular negativity. (B) Action potential induced by PRF stimulation. (C) EPSP evoked by VIIIth nerve (downward arrow). (D) PRF stimulation (upward arrow). (E–H) combined VIII and PRF stimulation. Upper time calibration is millisecond for A and B, lower calibration is millisecond for C–H. Voltage calibration is 1 mV for A_1 and A_2, 0.5 mV for A_3, and 2 mV for C–H. (From Highstein, Cohen, and Matsunami, *Brain Res.* **75**, 340–344 (1974).)

IIIrd nucleus. Similarly, direct projections from the PRF to the abducens nucleus have also been found.

EXTRACELLULAR RECORDINGS FROM THE PONTINE RETICULAR FORMATION

Unit activity preceding eye movements in the PRF has been demonstrated by a number of workers (Duensing and Schaefer, 1957, 1960; Sparks and Travis, 1971; Luschei and Fuchs, 1972; Cohen and Henn, 1972b; Keller, 1974). The density of units whose activity can be related to eye movements is high in this region, some neurons being activated and other neurons inhibited during quick eye movements. Just outside this area very few units are encountered whose activity can be related to eye movements.

Samples of unit activity found in the PRF are shown in Figs. 7 and 8. Types of units most frequently encountered are:

1. *Burst units* (Fig. 7). These units fire with a burst of spikes before and during quick eye movements. Peak frequencies in different neurons vary between 100 and 1200 impulses/sec; likewise the number of spikes per burst also varies from one to about 50 spikes per burst. Some burst units fire before movements in any direction, but many show a directional selectivity, i.e. they only fire, or fire maximally, before and during movements in one direction. In other units, the frequency during bursts varies with the amplitude of eye movements. Between movements these units are either silent or exhibit some low-frequency discharge which cannot be related to the position of the eyes.

2. *Pause units* (Fig. 8). Activity in these neurons is relatively constant during periods of fixation at rates between 100 and 150 Hz, but prior to and during quick eye movements, they are completely inhibited. Most of these units show no change in frequency during slow phases of nystagmus. A few of them change frequency when

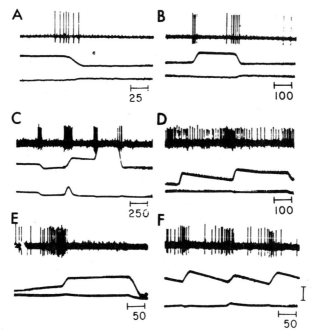

FIG. 7. Different burst units from the PRF; 2nd and 3rd traces are the horizontal and vertical EOG. The vertical bar beside F shows 25° of deviation. Time base is in msec. Each of these units had a frequency change prior to onset of quick eye movements.

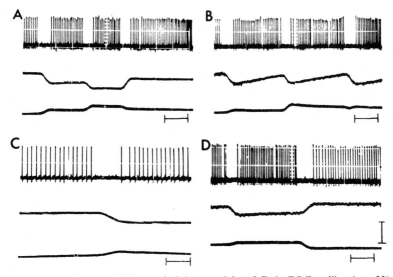

FIG. 8. Pause units from the PRF. The vertical bar at right of D is EOG calibration, 25°. Horizontal bars are time calibrations, being 100 ms for A, B, D, and 25 ms for C. Firing in these cells is interrupted prior to and during quick eye movements. A, B, C, Same unit. Note that firing is also constant during slow phases of nystagmus (B). D, Unit which tended to reduce its frequency when the eye was to the right and down. However, overall frequency modulation even for extreme positions were not more than ±20%.

the eyes are in different positions, but the modulation of frequency is small so that the position of the eyes could not have been predicted solely from this information.

3. *Other units.* There are several types of units with more complex behavior (for details see Luschei and Fuchs, 1972; Cohen and Henn, 1972b; Keller, 1974). However, these units as well as the burst and pause units have the following characteristics in common:

(a) Activity changes occur prior to quick eye movements at latencies usually of 12 to 20 ms. Occasionally, however, the latencies are much longer.

(b) If a change in activity occurs before a quick eye movement, it is the same whether the quick eye movement is a saccade or a quick phase of vestibular or optokinetic nystagmus. Moreover, it is independent of whether the eye movements are made in the light or the dark.

(c) The parameters mainly coded by these activity changes seem to be amplitude and direction of eye movements. Although a few units exhibit activity during periods of fixation, efforts to correlate activity to eye position during periods of fixation have not given reliable results. That is, from the frequencies encountered in these units, one can usually give an estimate of whether the eyes are in the left or right hemifield, but exact eye position cannot be predicted with any accuracy.

For the pause units a relationship can be established between pause length and amplitude of eye movement. An example is shown in Fig. 8. More than 300 consecutive spontaneous eye movements in every direction were used for this plot. Mean values for data points could be connected by a straight line on a log–log plot which can be described by a power function. The line, $y = 0.004X^2$, drawn in Fig. 9, is the average value for five such units.

Burst units were also found in the rostral PRF in which the number of spikes encountered during the burst could be related to the amplitude of eye movement. Similar data are given by Luschei and Fuchs (1972) and by Keller (1974), who found linear relations between these parameters. The surprising thing is that there are units which independently code just one of the several parameters which would be necessary to execute eye movements. For example: in some units amplitude is coded independent of direction. Contrariwise, several burst units were found which coded direction of eye movements exclusive of amplitude or duration. Most of the direction-specific burst units had an on-direction which was not sharply defined and often they also fired with small bursts during eye movements in the off-direction. Figure 10 shows such a unit. The direction of consecutive eye movements, independent of amplitude, is plotted on the ordinate. The abscissa gives values for the frequency during each burst. Peak frequencies for this unit occurred around 250°, but relatively high frequencies were still encountered at directions of 200° or 300°. Again it should be stressed that these values are independent of the amplitude of the respective eye movement, i.e. the frequency of the burst was the same for two eye movements in the same direction, regardless of whether one was 5° and the other 20°.

For many such units a cosine function closely described the distribution of data points (Fig. 10). In Fig. 10B the same data points used in Fig. 10A are replotted. The abscissas are identical (frequency of burst), but the ordinate in Fig. 10B is now the cosine of the respective angle of movement (relative to the peak value at 250°). The correlation factor for the linear line of regression connecting these points is 0.85.

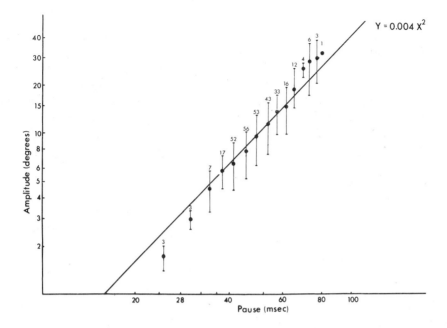

FIG. 9. Relation between duration of cessation of firing (abscissa) in a pause unit from the PRF and amplitude of eye movement (ordinate) independent of its direction. Means and standard deviations are given. Number above standard deviation gives the size of the sample for each bin. The line which represents a power function, $Y = 0.004X^2$, gives average values for five such units.

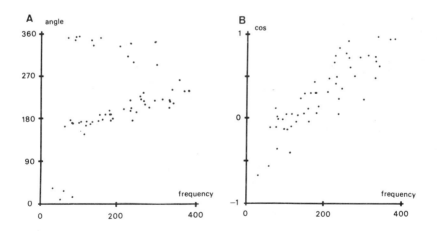

FIG. 10. Unit from the PRF which codes direction of eye movement independent of amplitude. A, Frequencies of consecutive bursts are plotted against direction of respective eye movements. 0° and 180° are right and left, 90° and 270° up and down, respectively. Peak frequency for this unit occurs around 250°, which is down and to the left. B, The data points of A are replotted. The abscissa is still frequency, but the ordinate is now the cosine of the angle of movement (relative to peak frequency value at 250°). The correlation factor for the linear line of regression for these points is $r = 0.85$.

All units which have been analyzed so far have had their on-directions either in the horizontal plane or tilted about 15° from the vertical. These are all directions which coincide with pulling directions of extraocular muscles.

This quantitative analysis differs in several aspects from data given in the literature (Luschei and Fuchs, 1972; Keller, 1974). Essentially all of the arguments which have been raised in connection with analysis of motoneurons (see above) would also apply when trying to evaluate and compare results of analysis of these premotor units.

Comment: What Information is Processed in the Pontine Reticular Formation?

Results of unit analysis, including parameters coded and latencies to onset of eye movement as well as the results of stimulation and lesion studies, are consistent with the hypothesis that PRF units are part of the system which produces quick eye movements. It was shown in our previous work that the information motoneurons need to execute eye movements and hold the eyes in certain positions during periods of fixation can be described by the amplitude and direction of a vector. Both of these parameters are found in the PRF.

It was surprising to find that these two parameters seem to be coded separately in most units. Of special interest are the units which code the direction as a cosine function. A cosine function is ambiguous, since except at maxima and minima it could refer to two angles. Therefore, a frequency change in a single neuron would not completely determine the actual movement the eyes make, nor would averaging values from many such units with the same on-direction supply this information. What would be necessary to determine the angle of movement would be that either another parameter such as latency be used to indicate the exact direction, or that there be other units present whose on-direction is shifted.

It is of interest that the highest resolution for each directional unit would not be in the vicinity of its peak values of frequency, but would be shifted by 90° from the peak values. This is shown in Fig. 11. Schematically two PRF units are plotted, one with a peak frequency at 180°, another at 110°. One can see that the unit with

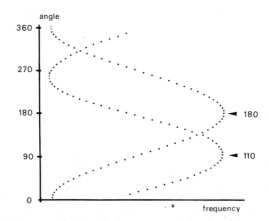

FIG. 11. Schematic representation of two PRF units with peak frequencies at 180° (horizontal left) and 110° (upward and to the left). It can be seen that the unit with the peak frequency at 110° has the highest resolution for eye movements in the horizontal plane. For further explanation see text.

the peak frequency in the horizontal plane (180°) could not transmit precise information about eye movements in the horizontal plane, since small reductions in frequency would lead to rather large changes in the direction of eye movement. On the other hand, the unit with a peak frequency at 110° would have much better resolution in the horizontal plane, i.e. its frequency changes could determine different horizontal directions with much more accuracy. If the information from two such units were combined, it would unequivocally and precisely determine the direction of eye movements.

Comparing these data to the results of stimulation studies it is striking that when the PRF is activated, the induced eye movements were always in the horizontal plane, and after PRF lesions only horizontal eye movements were affected. In the unit studies, however, there were a large percentage of neurons with vertical or oblique on-directions. Our hypothesis of how the information regarding direction of eye movements might be coded offers an explanation for why such neurons would be necessary for precisely generating eye movements in the horizontal plane.

It is also possible to speculate on the location of the pulse integrator which is believed responsible for causing sustained frequencies in motoneurons during periods of fixation. As shown, there are almost no PRF units whose firing can be closely related to the position of the eyes during periods of fixation. In spite of this during electrical stimulation of the PRF, the eyes first move in the horizontal plane and then hold the new positions for extended periods of time (Cohen and Komatsuzaki, 1972). Similarly, after PRF lesions, one of the most striking defects is an absence of eye position in the ipsilateral hemifield. The unit data suggest that it is primarily movement parameters which are coded in the PRF. Therefore the high sustained frequencies which are required by motoneurons to hold the eyes in position must be produced in the vicinity of motoneurons. In theoretical terms, the neural integrator seems to be located in or around the motor nuclei. The apparent deficit in fixation therefore after PRF lesions would be primarily a movement deficit. That is, the eyes cannot hold positions in the ipsilateral hemifield because they cannot move there and do not transfer the information to the integrators located proximally in the vicinity of the oculomotor and abducens nuclei.

It was shown previously that the position change of the eyes caused by the activity of motoneurons can be described as follows:

$$P2 - P1 = A.\cos \alpha. \tag{3}$$

That is, the position change produced by the motoneurons can be reduced to two parameters, the amplitude of the overall eye movement and the cosine of the angle between the direction of this eye movement and the on-direction of the motoneuron under consideration. These two parameters are present in the PRF, coded in separate units. The formal description suggest that these two parameters are multiplied. The result of this multiplication is the equivalent of the frequency changes in motoneurons.

It was shown by Küpfmüller and Jenigk (1961) that if there are two inputs converging onto one neuron, within certain limits the output frequency of the neuron will be equivalent to a multiplication of the two input frequencies. Therefore, multiplication is one of the basic functions that neurons can perform. It would be premature to speculate about the actual nature of information processing in the PRF and motor nuclei. However, the formal description of units which we gave in the preceding chapters use parameters which actually could be used to perform all the required operations.

There are many units in the PRF which exhibit some relation to eye movements but whose behavior is rather complex. In the present study only quick movements and periods of fixation were investigated, although the PRF most probably plays a more complex role in generating slow phases of nystagmus or in producing visually guided pursuit movements. Keeping all these complex functions in mind one should not expect to reduce all parameters found in PRF units only to direction or amplitude of quick movements. It is remarkable that many units seem to code just one parameter, i.e. amplitude independent of direction, or direction independent of the size of movement. Therefore it is conceivable that still another parameter is coded separately: the exact timing of beginning of eye movements. There are many units, e.g. pause units, whose latency to onset of eye movements are kept very precisely while in other units, e.g. those coding direction of movement, latencies might vary over a wider range. However, as this one parameter would be constant for all movements, we have no experimental proof that it is coded separately from the others.

VESTIBULAR NUCLEI

It is known for over a century (Flourens, 1842) that the vestibular system exerts strong control over the eyes and Duensing and Schaefer (1957, 1958, 1960) were the first to relate activity of single units in the vestibular nuclei to eye movements. Extensive investigation in recent years has shown that excitation of each of the vestibular receptors can produce contraction or relaxation of eye muscles at short latencies (for reviews see Brodal and Pompeiano, 1972, and Cohen, 1974). This activity travels over disynaptic reflex arcs extending through the MLF or brachium conjunctivum. Polysynaptic pathways are probably also utilized in transmitting vestibular information. Activity qualitatively corresponding to the slow phases of vestibular nystagmus is present in the vestibular nuclei and in MLF axons (Maeda et al., 1971; Berthoz et al., 1973).

In view of the specific and potent drive of the vestibular system on the eyes, an attractive hypothesis is that the vestibular system is a site of integration or production for all types of eye movements (Spiegel and Price, 1939) including saccades and quick phases of vestibular or optokinetic nystagmus. In apparent support of this, units in rostral parts of the vestibular nuclei have a close relation to all quick eye movements with latencies from frequency change to onset of eye movement in the range of 5 to 20 ms (Duensing and Schaefer, 1958). The main objection to accepting this theory is that saccades are not produced by vestibular nuclei stimulation (Tokumasu et al., 1969) and that lesions in different parts of the vestibular system have little or no effect on spontaneous eye movements and quick phases of nystagmus (Uemura and Cohen, 1974).

Recently it has been shown that head and eye movements in the horizontal plane are produced by separate neural mechanisms which are coordinated by the vestibular system (Bizzi et al., 1971; Dichgans et al., 1973a). An alternative speculative hypothesis which could account for part of the unit activity in the vestibular nuclei associated with quick eye movements is that it is in some way related to production of head movements (Miles, 1974). Anatomical, stimulation and lesion studies are in accordance with this since there are also major outputs from the vestibular nuclei to the neck musculature (reviewed in Wilson, 1972), and head movements and changes in head posture can be striking after vestibular nuclei stimulation or lesions (Uemura and Cohen, 1974). Other central vestibular neurons, which probably are second-order afferents from horizontal canals can also be influenced strongly during OKN, but this effect seems to depend on sensing motion and is not primarily related to production of nystagmus (Dichgans et al., 1973b; Henn et al., 1974).

Several other brainstem structures, including the median longitudinal fasciculus (MLF), the superior colliculi, and thalamus are known to participate in producing eye movements. However, as in the case of the MLF there is a relative paucity of information about unit activity during spontaneous eye movements, or in the case of the superior colliculi and thalamus the causal relationship of the unit activity is unclear (Wurtz and Goldberg, 1972; Schlag et al., 1973; Büttner and Fuchs, 1973) and they will not be considered further here.

COMMENT

Parameters of quick eye movements are widely represented in unit activity in the brainstem and close statistical relationship can often be established between frequency changes and amplitude and direction of quick eye movements. Except in the immediate vicinity of the motoneurons, activity of few units can be related to eye positions in any precise way. Moreover, stimulation of the frontal eye fields, the superior colliculus, and the pontine reticular formation cause the eyes to move in a certain direction over a certain distance independent of the starting position. We propose that these central structures primarily code eye movement, and that this movement information is transformed into information of eye position only at the level of the motoneurons. Even analysis of frequency changes in motoneurons have shown that these frequency changes are more closely related to movement than to absolute position of the eyes.

Most eye movements are done to move the fovea to view something of interest. A simple signal for that would be a vector determining the distance and angle between the fovea and the spot on the retina where it is actually seen. It seems that using such a signal no major information processing has to be done as the motoneurons could utilize just this vector to move the eyes in its desired position. Parameters for this vector, i.e. amplitude, direction, and timing, seem to be represented by different neurons. This corresponds well with clinical evidence: amplitude and direction of eye movements can be affected separately. Even if both of these parameters are affected, it is rare that the onset of quick eye movements is different in both eyes.

As the eyes rotate only over a limited angle, the brain would, of course, have to know the approximate position of the eyes. Several units which are coarsely related to eye position could serve such a function. Our argument is that this information alone, however, would not be exact enough to move the eyes as precisely as we empirically can do.

A theory of eye movements which is in close agreement with the experimental findings was originally put forward by Hering (1868). His notion was that the neural signal to move the eyes would not use the absolute position of the eyes in the orbit, but rather it would be a vector which moves the eyes relative to a prior position. Most eye movements are within 15° of the primary position. In this area any distortions of eye movements because of changing pulling directions, especially of the oblique muscles, play only an insignificant role. In the normal individual a head movement is done at the same time as the eye movement for larger gaze shifts. Hering also showed that false localizations occur when the eyes are in extreme positions. He took this as proof that the brain has no exact information of absolute eye position, such as would be required if the eyes were to move within absolute coordinates of the orbits. This theory of Hering, and its deductions and implications, were overshadowed by the theory of Helmholtz (1856–66) who postulated that the nervous signal to move the eyes uses orbital coordinates. Following Helmholtz, Donder and Listing elaborated rules as to how the eyes move and reach positions in the orbits. However, actual measurements show consistent deviations from these rules.

Taken together it seems that experimental evidence favors Hering's conception. At a level prior to the motoneurons, amplitude and duration of eye movements are found to be coded in neurons. More specifically, these parameters seem to be coded in separate sets of neuron. This information is then transformed in the high maintained frequencies of motoneurons only at the level of the motor nuclei.

REFERENCES

ADAMUEK, E. (1870) Ueber die Innervation der Augenbewegungen. *Centralbl. med. Wiss.* **5,** 65.

BAKER, R. G., MANO, N. and SHIMAZU, H. (1969) Intracellular recording of antidromic responses from abducens motoneurons in the cat. *Brain Res.* **15,** 573.

BAKER, R. G. and PRECHT, W. (1972) Electrophysiological properties of trochlear motoneurons as revealed by IVth nerve stimulation. *Exptl. Brain Res.* **14,** 127.

BENDER, M. B. and SHANZER, S. (1964) Oculomotor pathways defined by electric stimulation and lesions in the brainstem of monkey. In: *The Oculomotor System*, p. 81. New York: Harper & Row (Hoeber).

BERTHOZ, A., BAKER, R. and PRECHT, W. (1973) Labyrinthine control of inferior oblique motoneurons. *Exptl. Brain Res.* **18,** 225.

BIZZI, E., KALIL, R. E. and TAGLIASCO, V. (1971) Eye–head coordination in monkeys: evidence for centrally patterned organization. *Science,* **173,** 452.

BOND, H. W. and HO, P. (1970) Solid miniature silver–silver chloride electrodes for chronic implantation. *Electroenceph. Clin. Neurophysiol.* **28,** 206.

BRODAL, A. and POMPEIANO, O. (Eds.) (1972) Basic aspects of central vestibular mechanisms. *Prog. Brain Res.,* vol. 37. Amsterdam: Elsevier.

BUETTNER, U. and FUCHS, A. F. (1973) Influence of saccadic eye movements on unit activity in simian lateral geniculate and pregeniculate nuclei. *J. Neurophysiol.* **36,** 127.

CHENG, K. and BREININ, G. M. (1966) A comparison of the fine structure of extraocular and interosseus muscles in the monkey. *Invest. Ophthal.* **5,** 535.

COHEN, B. and FELDMAN, M. (1968) Relationship of electrical activity in pontine reticular formation and lateral geniculate body to rapid eye movements. *J. Neurophysiol.* **31,** 806.

COHEN, B., KOMATSUZAKI, A. and BENDER, M. B. (1968) Electro-oculographic syndrome in monkeys after pontine reticular formation lesions. *Arch. Neurol. (Chic.)* **18,** 78.

COHEN, B. and HENN, V. (1972a) The origin of quick phases of nystagmus in the horizontal plane. In: *Cerebral Control of Eye Movements and Motion Perception. Bibl. Ophthal.* vol. **82,** 36. Basel: Karger.

COHEN, B. and HENN, V. (1972b) Unit activity in the pontine reticular formation associated with eye movements. *Brain Res.* **46,** 403.

COHEN, B. and KOMATSUZAKI, A. (1972) Eye movements induced by stimulation of the pontine reticular formation: evidence for integration in oculomotor pathways. *Exptl. Neurol.* **36,** 101.

COHEN, B. (1974) The vestibulo-ocular reflex arc. In: *Handbook of Sensory Physiology,* KORNHUBER, H. H. (Ed.), vol. 6. Springer, Berlin–Heidelberg–New York.

DICHGANS, J., BIZZI, E., MORASSO, P. and TAGLIASCO, V. (1973a) Mechanisms underlying recovery of eye–head coordination following bilateral labyrinthectomy in monkeys. *Exptl. Brain Res.* **18,** 548.

DICHGANS, J., SCHMIDT, C. L. and GRAF, W. (1973b) Visual input improves the speedometer functions of the vestibular nuclei in the goldfish. *Exptl. Brain Res.* **18,** 319.

DUENSING, F. and SCHAEFER, K. P. (1957) Die Neuronenaktivität in der Formatio reticularis des Rhombencephalons beim vestibulären Nystagmus. *Arch. Psychiat. Nervenkr.* **196,** 265.

DUENSING, F. and SCHAEFER, K. P. (1958) Die Aktivität einzelner Neurone im Bereich der Vestibulariskerne bei Horizontalbeschleunigungen unter besonderer Berücksichtigung des vestibulären Nystagmus. *Arch. Psychiat. Nervenkr.* **198**, 225.

DUENSING, F. and SCHAEFER, K. P. (1960) Die Aktivität einzelner Neurone der Formatio reticularis des nicht gefesselten Kaninchens bei Kopfwendungen und vestibulären Reizen. *Arch. Psychiat. Nervenkr.* **201**, 97.

FERRIER, D. (1876) *The Functions of the Brain.* New York: Putnam & Sons.

FLOURENS, P. (1842) *Recherches expérimentales sur les propriétés et les fonctions du système nerveux dans les animaux vertébrés.* Bailliére, 2nd ed., Paris.

FREEMAN, W. (1922) Paralysis of associated lateral movements of the eyes. A symptom of intrapontile lesion. *Arch. Neurol. Psychiat. (Chic.)* **7**, 454.

FRITSCH, G. and HITZIG, E. (1870) Ueber die elektrische Erregbarkeit des Grosshirns. *Arch. Anat. Physiol. Wiss. Med.,* p. 300.

FUCHS, A. F. and ROBINSON, D. A. (1966) A method for measuring horizontal and vertical eye movement chronically in the monkey. *J. Appl. Physiol.* **21**, 1068.

FUCHS, A. F. and LUSCHEI, E. S. (1970) Firing patterns of abducens neurons of alert monkeys in relationship to horizontal eye movement. *J. Neurophysiol.* **33**, 382.

FUCHS, A. F. and LUSCHEI, E. S. (1971) The activity of single trochlear nerve fibers during eye movements in the alert monkey. *Exptl. Brain Res.* **13**, 78.

GASSER, H. S. and GRUNDFEST, H. (1939) Axon diameters in relation to the spike dimensions and the conduction velocity in mammalian A fibers. *Am. J. Physiol.* **127**, 393.

GOEBEL, H. H., KOMATSUZAKI, A., BENDER, M. B. and COHEN, B. (1971) Lesions of the pontine tegmentum and conjugate gaze paralysis. *Arch. Neurol. (Chic.)* **24**, 431.

GOLDBERG, S. C., HULL, C. D. and BUCHWALD, N. A. (1974) Afferent projections in the abducens nerve: an intracellular study. *Brain Res.* **68**, 205.

HELMHOLTZ, H. V. (1856–1866) *Handbuch der physiologischen Optik.* Voss, Leipzig.

HENN, V. and COHEN, B. (1972) Eye muscle motor neurons with different functional characteristics. *Brain Res.* **45**, 561.

HENN, V. and COHEN, B. (1973) Quantitative analysis of activity in eye muscle motoneurons during saccadic eye movements and positions of fixation. *J. Neurophysiol.* **36**, 115.

HENN, V., YOUNG, L. R. and FINLEY, C. (1974) Vestibular nucleus units in alert monkeys are also influenced by moving visual fields. *Brain Res.* **71**, 144.

HERING, E. (1868) *Die Lehre vom binokularen Sehen.* Leipzig.

HIGHSTEIN, S. M., COHEN, B. and MATSUNAMI, K. (1974) Monosynaptic projections from the pontine reticular formation to the IIIrd nucleus in the cat. *Brain Res.* **75**, 340.

HORCHOLLE-BOSSAVIT, G. and TYČ-DUMONT, S. (1969) Phénomènes synaptiques du nystagmus. *Exptl. Brain Res.* **8**, 201.

JUNG, R. and KORNHUBER, H. H. (1964) Results of electronystagmography in man: the value of optokinetic, vestibular, and spontaneous nystagmus for neurologic diagnosis and research. *The Oculomotor System,* BENDER, M. B. (Ed.) p. 428. New York, Harper & Row.

KELLER, E. L. (1974) Participation of medial pontine reticular formation in eye movement generation in monkey. *J. Neurophysiol.* **37**, 316.

KELLER, E. L. and ROBINSON, D. A. (1972) Abducens unit behavior in the monkey during vergence movements. *Vision Res.* **12**, 369.

KUEPFMUELLER, K. and JENIGK, F. (1961) Ueber die Nachrichtenverarbeitung in der Nervenzelle. *Kybernetik,* **1**, 1.

LORENTE DE NÓ, R. (1933) Vestibulo-ocular reflex arc. *Arch. Neurol. Psychiat. (Chic.)* **30**, 245.

LUSCHEI, E. S. and FUCHS, A. F. (1972) Activity of brain stem neurons during eye movements of alert monkeys. *J. Neurophysiol.* **35**, 445.

MAEDA, M., SHIMAZU, H. and SHINODA, Y. (1971) Inhibitory postsynaptic potentials in the abducens motoneurons associated with the quick relaxation phase of vestibular nystagmus. *Brain Res.* **26**, 420.

MAEDA, M., SHIMAZU, H. and SHINODA, Y. (1972) Nature of synaptic events in cat abducens motoneurons at slow and quick phase of vestibular nystagmus. *J. Neurophysiol.* **35**, 279.

MAYR, R., STOCKINGER, L. and ZENKER, W. (1966) Elektronenmikroskopische Untersuchungen an unterschiedlich innervierten Muskelfasern der äusseren Augenmuskulatur des Rhesusaffen. *Z. Zellforsch. mikrosk. Anat.* **75**, 434.

MILES, F. A. (1974) Single unit firing patterns in the vestibular nuclei related to voluntary eye movements and passive body rotation in conscious monkeys. *Brain Res.* **71**, 215.

PRECHT, W., RICHTER, A. and GRIPPO, J. (1969) Responses of neurones in cat's abducens nuclei to horizontal angular acceleration. *Pflügers Arch.* **309**, 285.

ROBINSON, D. A. (1970) Oculomotor unit behavior in the monkey. *J. Neurophysiol.* **33**, 393.

SASAKI, K. (1963) Electrophysiological studies on oculomotor neurons of the cat. *Jap. J. Physiol.* **13**, 287.

SCHAEFER, E. A. (1888) Experiments on the electrical excitation of the visual area of the cerebral cortex in the monkey. *Brain*, **11**, 1.

SCHAEFER, .K. P. (1965) Die Erregungsmuster einzelner Neurone des Abducens-Kernes beim Kaninchen. *Pflügers Arch. ges. Physiol.* **284**, 31.

SCHEIBEL, M. E. and SCHEIBEL, A. B. (1958) Structural substrates for integrative patterns in the brain stem reticular core. In: *Reticular Formation of the Brain*, p. 31. Boston: Little, Brown & Co.

SCHILLER, P. H. (1970) The discharge characteristics of single units in the oculomotor and abducens nuclei of the unanesthetized monkey. *Exptl. Brain Res.* **10**, 347.

SCHLAG, J., LEHTINEN, I. and SCHLAG-REY, M. (1973) Neuronal activity correlated with eye movements in "nonspecific" thalamic nuclei. *Brain Res.* **62**, 268.

SCHUBERT, G. and BORNSCHEIN, H. (1962) Einzelfaseraktivität im *N. oculomotorius* bei vestibulärer Reizung. *Pflügers Arch.* **275**, 107.

SPARKS, D. L. and TRAVIS, R. P. JR. (1971) Firing patterns of reticular formation neurons during horizontal eye movements. *Brain Res.* **33**, 477.

SPIEGEL, E. A. and PRICE, J. B. (1939) Origin of the quick component of labyrinthine nystagmus. *Arch. Otolaryng. (Chic.)* **20**, 576.

SZENTÁGOTHAI, J. (1964) Pathways and synaptic articulation patterns connecting vestibular receptors and oculomotor nuclei. In: *The Oculomotor System* p. 205. New York: Harper & Row (Hoeber).

TENG, P., SHANZER, S. and BENDER, M. B. (1958) Effects of brainstem lesions on optokinetic nystagmus in monkeys. *Neurology (Minneap.)* **8**, 22.

TOKUMASU, K., GOTO, K. and COHEN, B. (1969) Eye movements from vestibular nuclei stimulation in monkeys. *Ann. Otol. (St. Louis)* **78**, 1105.

TSUCHIDA, U. (1906) Ueber die Ursprungskerne der Augenbewegungsnerven und über die mit diesen in Beziehung stehenden Bahnen im Mittel- und Zwischenhirn. *Arb. Hirnanat. Inst. Zürich*, **2**, 1.

UEMURA, T. and COHEN, B. (1974) Effects of vestibular nuclei lesions on vestibulo-ocular reflexes and posture in monkeys. *Acta Oto-laryng. (Stockh.)*, Suppl. **315**, 1.

WARWICK, R. (1953) Representation of the extra-ocular muscles in the oculomotor nuclei of the monkey. *J. Comp. Neurol.* **98**, 449.

WILSON, V. J. (1972) Physiological pathways through the vestibular nuclei. In: *International Review of Neurobiology*, p. 27. New York: Academic Press.

WURTZ, R. H. and GOLDBERG, M. E. (1972) Activity of superior colliculus in behaving monkey. IV. Effects of lesions on eye movements. *J. Neurophysiol.* **35**, 587.

YAMANAKA, Y. and BACH-Y-RITA, P. (1968) Conduction velocities in the abducens nerve correlated with vestibular nystagmus in cats. *Exptl. Neurol.* **20**, 143.

CLINICAL CLUES FOR THE ORGANIZATION OF HORIZONTAL QUICK EYE MOVEMENTS AND SUBSEQUENT PERIODS OF FIXATION†

GUNTRAM KOMMERELL

SUMMARY

1. Neurogenic eye muscle palsies offer the opportunity to study the firing behavior of human single motor units by means of EMG. Most of the units encountered belong to the "phasic-tonic" group. Only one "tonic" unit was found, but this unit may have been deprived of its burst ability by a prenuclear lesion.
2. In patients with one paralysed eye muscle, the action of the opposing eye muscle alone can be studied. Data in such patients indicate that the main task of an agonistic eye muscle in its "off" field is to accelerate the globe during saccades. In its "on" field the agonist is important for both holding eccentric eye positions as well as acceleration during saccades.
3. Clinical observations of internuclear ophthalmoplegia of adduction as well as abduction and of different kinds of gaze palsies suggest that, on the level between the "center for lateral gaze" and the ocular motor nuclei, eye position is computed independently of rapid eye movements.

THIS paper will be dealing with tonic and saccadic behavior of eye muscles in the horizontal plane. The following three clinical entities will be discussed:

1. peripheral eye muscle palsy,
2. internuclear ophthalmoplegia, and
3. gaze palsy.

The methods for the studies in this paper will be EMG and ENG.

1. PERIPHERAL EYE MUSCLE PALSY

1.1. EMG of Single Motor Units in Paretic Eye Muscles

Fresh neurogenic eye muscle palsies offer the opportunity to study the firing behavior of human single motor units by means of EMG. Most of the neighboring units which would normally interfere and obscure the pattern are missing due to the nerve lesion.

In Fig. 1 two *phasic-tonic* units are shown. Their firing corresponds exactly to the pattern which was found in monkey ocular motor nuclei (Fuchs and Luschei, 1970; Robinson, 1970; Schiller, 1970). A brief burst of activity during on-saccades and a pause during off-saccades is seen. Purely tonic units seem to be very rare. We picked up only one *tonic* unit in a patient with an abducens palsy (Fig. 2). The threshold of this unit was found as the normal fellow eye just passed the primary position.

†This investigation was supported by the Deutsche Forschungsgemeinschaft, SFB 70, B 4.

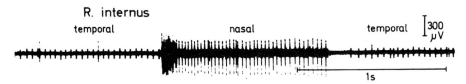

FIG. 1. EMG of two phasic-tonic motor units at a 10° on- and off-saccade. Right oculomotor palsy.

The record demonstrates, at a three-degree on-saccade, a simple step of frequency. Only the first spike interval is a little shorter than the following ones. The lack of bursts was not due to saturation, as the unit was capable of firing at a much higher frequency when the eye was further abducted. Regrettably, in this case we cannot be sure whether we dealt with a normal unit corresponding to the tonic neurons found in monkeys by Henn and Cohen (1972) or with a pathological unit deprived of its burst ability by a prenuclear lesion. A marked slowness of abduction saccades and additional brainstem signs pointed to the latter possibility. Further studies in peripher eye muscle palsies may clarify whether or not purely tonic units exist in a normal human eye muscle.

1.2. Saccadic Eye Movements and Tonic Eye Positions in cases of a Paralysed Antagonist

Several authors described slow "floating" saccades in the working direction of a paralysed muscle (François and Derouck, 1955; Metz et al., 1970; Scott, 1971; Metz and Rice, 1973). In the opposite direction, when the "good" muscle is pulling without the restraining viscosity normally present in the antagonist, O'Meara et al. (1969) and Scott (1971) noted high velocities and even "overshoots" of saccades. We have further studied the time course of these latter saccades (Theopold and Kommerell, 1974). A complete palsy of one of the horizontal eye muscles allows the action of its opposing eye muscle to be studied alone. No reciprocal innervation changes will occur in the antagonist under this condition.

Three patients with a total palsy of one horizontal eye muscle—in two cases a lateral, in one case a medial rectus—were chosen for this study. The eye with the paralysed muscle, for short the "bad" eye, was occluded, and the "good" eye had to perform 10° or 20° horizontal saccades which were initiated from various positions in the horizontal plane (Fig. 3).

The response of the "bad" eye can be divided into two components: a phasic jerk and a tonic change of position. The jerk is readily seen regardless of the position of the eyes at saccade onset and resembles quite closely the saccade of the "good" eye. The jerk is only a little short of the normal amplitude and increases very little

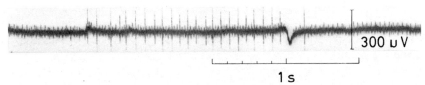

FIG. 2. EMG of a tonic motor unit at a 3° on- and off-saccade. The eye movements show up as short term deviations of the base line. Left lateral rectus, in a case with abducens palsy.

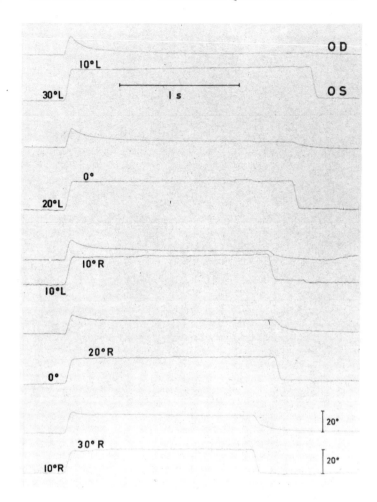

FIG. 3. Right 3rd nerve plegia; 20° horizontal saccades initiated from various positions in the horizontal plane. OS fixating, OD occluded. DC record.

the further the eye gets into the "on" field of the pulling muscle. The tonic part is hardly visible in the "off" field and increases tremendously as the eye proceeds into the "on" field (Fig. 4 a, b, and c).

These results fit nicely to Collin's (1974) measurements of *in situ* tendon forces in freely moving eyes and allow to draw some inferences as to the division of labor in the agonist and antagonist. The main task of the agonist in its "off" field is to accelerate the globe during saccades. The ensuing new position is held predominantly by relaxation of the antagonist. In its "on" field, the agonist is important for both, holding eccentric eye positions as well as acceleration during saccades.

One drawback of using eyes with a paralysed antagonist for such studies is that the agonist works at lengths which are shorter than normal because of smaller restraining forces. Mainly in its "off" field, the muscle has to overcome some slack before

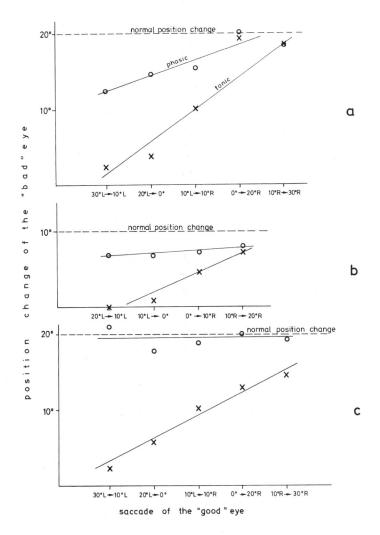

FIG. 4. Phasic and tonic responses of the occluded "bad" eye to refixation saccades of the "good" eye. The saccades were initiated from various positions in the horizontal plane. (a and b) Plegia of left lateral rectus; (c) plegia of right medial rectus as part of a 3rd nerve plegia; (c) is from the same patient as Fig. 3.

it actually pulls the globe. Therefore, the saccade of the "bad" eye begins about 5 ms later and more abruptly than the saccade of the "good" eye, and the "bad" eye reaches only subnormal saccadic velocities (Fig. 5).

2. INTERNUCLEAR OPHTHALMOPLEGIA (IO)
OF ADDUCTION AND ABDUCTION

Adduction deficiency in lateral gaze with adduction preserved in convergence was termed "internuclear" ophthalmoplegia (Paton, 1921; Smith and Cogan, 1959) because the critical lesion is situated topographically between the sixth and third nerve nuclei.

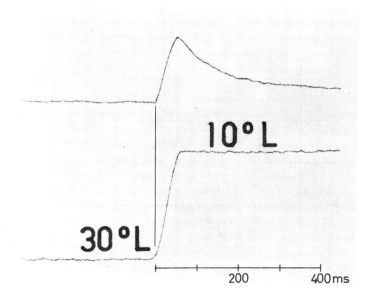

FIG. 5. Magnification of the first saccade in Fig. 3. Because of initial slack of the pulling muscle, the saccade of the "bad" eye begins 5 ms later and more abruptly than the saccade of the "good" eye. (DC record.)

From a physiological viewpoint, this lesion interrupts pathways between the "center for lateral gaze" and the medial rectus cells in the third nerve nucleus. From physiological and pathological evidence it is very likely that the center for lateral gaze is located in the paramedian pontine reticular formation (Hoyt and Daroff, 1971; Balthasar, 1973) and that IO of adduction is caused by lesion of the medial longitudinal fasciculus (Carpenter and Strominger, 1965; Cogan, 1970).

Several authors drew attention to the fact that IO is characterized by slowness of refixation saccades and rapid phases of optokinetic and vestibular nystagmus in the adducting eye (Jung, 1939; Mackensen, 1955; Smith and David, 1964; Fötzsch, 1971; Kommerell, 1971). Adduction saccades may be slow even though the eyes show not the slightest deficit in version ("subclinical" IO, Cogan, 1970). An example of such an IO is demonstrated in Fig. 6. Adduction saccades in the right eye are markedly slowed as compared to the normal speed of abduction saccades in the left eye. There was no latent palsy demonstrable by Maddox cylinder testing, not even in full lateral gaze.

We have seen one exceptional case in which *abduction* saccades were slow with no defect in tonic versions (Kommerell, in press). This patient's eye movements are shown in Fig. 7 (demonstration of motion pictures to the symposium).

I assume by analogy that the lesion in this case interrupted pathways from the center for lateral gaze to the abducens nucleus, and I suggest that the clinical picture should be called "IO of abduction" or "posterior" IO, according to Lutz's (1923) classification.

As an alternative hypothesis a nuclear or infranuclear lesion of predominantly "phasic" motor units should be discussed. Scott and Collins (1973) demonstrated such units

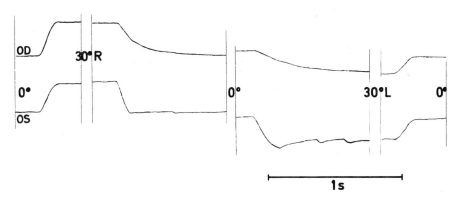

FIG. 6. Right IO of adduction. Slow adduction saccades in the right eye (OD). Dissociated nystagmus in the left eye (OS) after refixation from 0° to 30°L. (DC records.)

in the human eye muscle in layers near the globe. But even these units resumed tonic firing in extreme lateral gaze. This is consistent with microelectrode recordings from ocular motor nuclei in the alert monkey obtained by Fuchs (1970), Robinson (1970) and Schiller (1970). These authors were unable to find neurons with exclusively saccadic discharge. Henn and Cohen (1972), however, demonstrated that "phasic" neurons exist, but this type of motor unit seems to be rare. Therefore, the marked slowness of saccades without the slightest impairment of versions in the two cases described above can hardly be explained on the basis of a nuclear or infranuclear lesion. Moreover, the dissociated post-saccadic nystagmus found in both cases strongly points to a lesion in the brainstem.

Slowness of saccades also occurs in peripheral eye muscle palsies, but then is always accompanied by marked deficiency in tonic version (Scott, 1971). In our two examples of IO, however, saccades were markedly slowed with no latent palsy demonstrable by Maddox cylinder testing, not even in extreme lateral gaze.

Clinical observations in IO of adduction and abduction demonstrate that, on a prenuclear level, phasic activity of eye muscle can be disturbed independently of tonic muscle

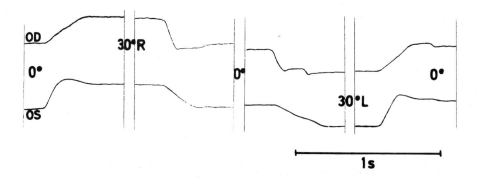

FIG. 7. Bilateral IO of abduction. Electronystagmographic record of 30° horizontal saccades. The abducting eye is always slow. A dissociated nystagmus of the adducting eye is seen after refixation from 0° to 30° L. The correction of overshoots in the left eye after saccades to the right eye may be regarded as "glissadic" (Weber and Daroff, 1972) or rather as the slow phase of a gaze evoked nystagmus beat. (DC records.)

function. The fact that the slower eye reaches the goal as accurately as the quick eye suggests that the final eye *position* may be processed independently of rapid eye *movements*, on the level between the "center for lateral gaze" and the ocular motor nuclei. This suggestion corresponds exactly to Robinson's (1971, 1974) hypothesis of two parallel pathways between a supranuclear "pulse generator" and the ocular motor nuclei. In the two kinds of IO described above one would assume that the "direct pathway" was damaged and the "indirect, integrating pathway" remained intact.

3. HORIZONTAL GAZE PALSY

Isolated Impairment of Phasic and Tonic Activity

From physiological and clinico-pathological evidence, it is quite clear that a lesion of the paramedian pontine reticular formation (PPRF) produces a homolateral horizontal gaze palsy. In a complete "pontine" gaze plegia, the eyes cannot be brought across the midline by voluntary effort or by optical or vestibular stimulation. A partial gaze paresis may appear as a "gaze-paretic" nystagmus (Jung and Kornhuber, 1964).

Little attention has been paid to the fact that a partial gaze paresis may be diagnosed on the basis of slowed saccades. A patient with this kind of gaze paresis has been seen by Jung (1972). Cohen and Henn (1972) noted slow saccades in monkeys after lesion of the PPRF. I would like to add one further observation: A 39-year-old man complained of blurred vision for about half a second when he wanted to look to the left. On the first examination, his refixation saccades and rapid phases of optokinetic

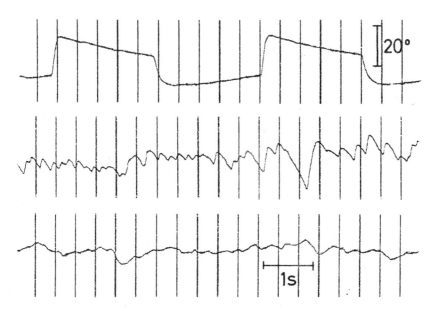

FIG. 8. Slowness of leftward saccades as a sign of gaze paresis. *Upper track.* Refixation from 10° left to 10° right and vice versa. *Middle track.* Optokinetic nystagmus to the right, normal. *Lower track.* Optokinetic nystagmus to the left, greatly reduced. Time constant of recording system 2.0 sec (old record).

and vestibular (caloric and rotational) nystagmus were slow to the left (Fig. 8). At this stage of the patient's disease there was not the slightest limitation of leftward gaze and no gaze-paretic nystagmus. Two weeks later, the patient developed a complete gaze plegia to the left. His leftward saccades in the right field of gaze were extremely slow. Neither optokinetic nor vestibular nystagmus could be elicited to the left. There was a marked spontaneous nystagmus to the right. During the following week, the patient's eye movements gradually improved. He again became capable of gazing to the extreme left, but his saccades to the left remained slow. Six weeks after the onset of his first symptoms, the patient had completely recovered. A discrete short-term lesion of the left PPRF was assumed, but the underlying cause remained uncertain, in spite of extensive general examination.

Although this is a single case, it quite conclusively demonstrates that slowness of saccades can be a sign of partial gaze paresis. It furthermore shows that the "hold mechanism" for all eye positions can be intact while the "saccade mechanism" is damaged. We have no EMG in the case described above, but we assume from the time course of the saccades that many motor units were deprived of their burst ability. As in IO, a lesion of Robinson's (1971, 1974) "direct pathway" may be responsible for the slowness of saccades in the kind of gaze paresis described above. A logical question follows: Can the gaze-paretic nystagmus be regarded as an inverse condition in which the hold mechanism is lost and the saccade mechanism preserved? If this is so, the slow phases of gaze-paretic nystagmus should be a passive sinking back to the primary position, and the velocity of the slow phase should not be constant like in optokinetic and vestibular nystagmus but rather be an exponential curve.

An example of a gaze paretic nystagmus is given in Fig. 9. The patient had had a complete horizontal gaze plegia after removal of an astrocytoma from the cerebellum and the fourth ventricle. His eye movements recovered in so far, as the left eye developed a gaze-paretic nystagmus to the left. Left gaze of the right eye and right gaze of both eyes remained plegic. Frequency and amplitude of the gaze paretic nystagmus varied, apparently due to the amount of attention which the patient paid to eccentric fixation objects. The higher the leftward gaze effort was, the higher the

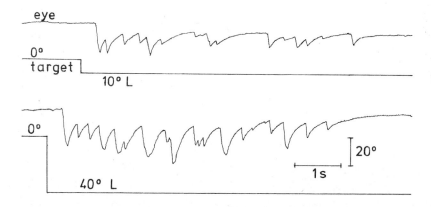

FIG. 9. Gaze-paretic nystagmus. Note the exponential curve of the slow phase. (DC record.)

frequency and the smaller the amplitude became. The speed of the rapid phases of the patient's nystagmus reached normal saccadic velocities, up to 600°/s in large jerks. The slow phases decelerated the closer the eye approached the primary position, with a time course which was approximately exponential. The left eye never returned to the primary position in a saccadic fashion. Slow movements to the left could not be elicited, by either optical or vestibular stimulation.

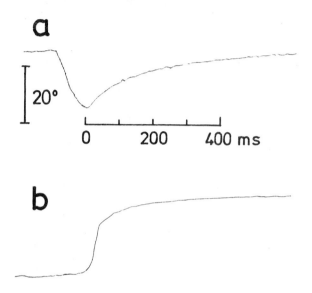

FIG. 10. (a) Rapid and slow phase of gaze paretic nystagmus, taken at high paper speed, from the same patient as Fig. 9. (b) Floating eye movement of a normal subject whose left eye was pulled 20° temporally and then suddenly released.

The shape of the gaze paretic nystagmus can best be explained if one assumes that the patient's eye muscles were tonically innervated according to the primary position, and that this level of innervation could be elevated only intermittently by saccadic bursts which were too short to maintain a lateral eye position. This assumption was further substantiated by comparing the slow nystagmusphase with an experimental condition which had been used by Robinson (1964) and which was evaluated again in our laboratory. A normal subject was asked to look straight ahead at a fixation point. His left eye was occluded and pulled 20° temporally by means of a suture which was placed at the temporal limbus. Then the suture was suddenly released so that the eye floated back to the primary position. The late part of this floating movement compares nicely with the late part of our patient's slow nystagmus phase (Fig. 10).

The first part does not match. The slow nystagmus phase begins more slowly because it takes some time for the muscle fibers to relax after the rapid phase burst, even though the electrical activity may have returned abruptly to the primary position rate.

Our patient with gaze-paretic nystagmus demonstrates that the "center for lateral gaze" may have lost its ability to maintain lateral gaze positions, but nevertheless can be capable of generating normal saccades. According to Robinson's (1971, 1974) hypothesis, one would assume that, in gaze paretic nystagmus, the "neural integrator" is damaged while the "direct pathway" is preserved. From ablation experiments in monkeys (Westheimer and Blair, 1973) it seems likely that the cerebellum constitutes part of this integrator. It is too early to draw such a conclusion from clinical evidence, but it should be noted in this context that our patient with gaze paretic nystagmus had a cerebellar lesion in addition to damage of his pontine tegmentum.

REFERENCES

BALTHASAR, K. (1973) Zur Lokalisation der horizontalen Blicklähmung und der internukleären Ophthalmoplegie. *Arch. Psychiat. Nervenkr.* **217**, 223–246.

CARPENTER, M. B. and STROMINGER, N. L. (1965) The medial longitudinal fasciculus and disturbances of conjugate horizontal eye movements in the monkey. *J. Comp. Neurol.* **125**, 41–66.

COGAN, D. G. (1970) Internuclear ophthalmoplegia, typical and atypical. *Arch. Ophthal.* **84**, 583–589.

COHEN, B. and HENN, V. (1972) The origin of quick phases of nystagmus in the horizontal plane. In: *Cerebral Control of Eye Movements and Motion Perception*, DICHGANS, J. and BIZZI, E. (Eds.). *Bibl. Ophthal.* **82**, 36–55. Basel, Paris, London, New York, Sydney, Karger.

COLLINS, C. C. (1974) The human oculomotor control system. In: *Basic Mechanisms of Ocular Motility and their Clinical Implications*, LENNERSTRAND, G., BACH-Y-RITA, P., COLLINS, C. C. and SCOTT, A. (Eds.). New York, London, Academic Press, this symposium.

FÖTZSCH, R. (1971) Die internukleäre Ophthalmoplegie. *Ophthalmologica*, **162**, 331–342.

FRANÇOIS, J. and DEROUCK, A. (1955) Etude électro-oculographique des paralysies oculaires. *Acta Ophthal.* **33**, 523–550.

FUCHS, A. F. and LUSCHEI, E. S. (1970) Firing patterns of abducens neurons of alert monkey in relationship to horizontal eye movements. *J. Neurophysiol.* **33**, 382–392.

HENN, V. and COHEN, B. (1972) Eye muscle motor neurons with different functional characteristics. *Brain Res.* **45**, 561–568.

HOYT, W. F. and DAROFF, R. B. (1971) Supranuclear disorders of ocular control systems in man: Clinical, anatomical, and physiological correlations. In: *The Control of Eye Movements*, BACH-Y-RITA, P., COLLINS, C. C. and HYDE, J. E. (Eds.). New York, London, Academic Press.

JUNG, R. (1939) Eine elektrische Methode zur mehrfachen Registrierung von Augenbewegungen und Nystagmen. *Klin. Wochenschr.* **18**, 21–24.

JUNG, R. and KORNHUBER, H. H. (1964) Results of electronystagmography in man: the value of optokinetic, vestibular, and spontaneous nystagmus for neurologic diagnosis and research. In: *The Oculomotor System*, BENDER, M. B. (Ed.). New York, Evanston and London, Harper & Row.

JUNG, R. (1972) Conclusions. How do we see with moving eyes? In: *Cerebral Control of Eye Movements and Motion Perception*, DICHGANS, J. and BIZZI, E. (Eds.). *Bibl. Ophthal.* **82**, Basel, München, Paris, London, New York, Sydney, Karger.

KOMMERELL, G. (1971) Die internukleäre Ophthalmoplegie. Nystagmographische Analyse. *Klin. Monatsbl. Augenheilk.* **158**, 349–358.

KOMMERELL, G. Internuclear ophthalmoplegia of abduction. Isolated impairment of phasic ocular motor activity in supranuclear lesions. *Arch. Ophthal.* (in press).

LUTZ, A. (1923) Über die Bahnen der Blickwendung und deren Dissoziierung. *Klin. Monatsbl. Augenheilk.* **70**, 213–235.

MACKENSEN, G. (1955) Zur klinischen Anwendung der Elektronystagmographie (Analyse einer ungewöhnlichen Motilitätsstörung mit Hilfe der elektrischen Registrierung). *Klin. Monatsbl. Augenheilk.* **126**, 685–693.

METZ, H. S., SCOTT, A. B., O'MEARA, D. M. and STEWART, H. L. (1970) Ocular saccades in lateral rectus palsy. *Arch. Ophthal.* **84**, 453–460.

METZ, H. S. and RICE, L. S. (1973) Human eye movements following horizontal rectus muscle disinsertion, *Arch. Ophthal.* **90**, 265–267.

O'MEARA, D. M., METZ, H. S., STEWART, H. S. and SCOTT, A. B. (1969) Eye movement patterns in strabismus. *Invest. Ophthal.* **8**, 651–652.

PATON, L. (1921) Ocular palsies. *Brit. J. Ophthal.* **5**, 250.

ROBINSON, D. A. (1964) The mechanics of human saccadic eye movements. *J. Physiol.* **174**, 245–264.

ROBINSON, D. A. (1970) Ocular motor unit behavior in the monkey. *J. Neurophysiol.* **33**, 393–404.

ROBINSON, D. A. (1974) Physiology and control aspects of supranuclear oculomotor systems. In: *Basic Mechanisms of Ocular Motility and Their Clinical Implications*, LENNERSTRAND, G., BACH-Y-RITA, P., COLLINS, C. C. and SCOTT, A. (Eds.). New York, London, Academic Press, this symposium.

SCHILLER, P. H. (1970) The discharge characteristics of single units in the oculomotor and abducens nuclei of the unanesthetized monkey. *Exptl Brain Res.* **10,** 347–362.

SCOTT, A. B. (1971) Extraocular muscle forces in strabismus. In: *The Control of Eye Movements*, BACH-Y-RITA, P., COLLINS, C. C. and HYDE, J. E. (Eds.). New York, London, Academic Press.

SCOTT, A. B. and COLLINS, C. C. (1973) Division of labor in human extraocular muscle. *Arch. Ophthal.* **90,** 319–322.

SMITH, J. L. and COGAN, D. G. (1959) Internuclear ophthalmoplegia—a review of fifty-eight cases. *Arch. Ophthal.* **61,** 687–694.

SMITH, J. L. and DAVID, N. J. (1964) Internuclear ophthalmoplegia—two new clinical signs. *Neurology,* **14,** 307–309.

THEOPOLD, H. and KOMMERELL, G. (1974) Phasische und tonische Funktion der Augenmuskeln. Untersuchungen an Patienten mit Oculomotorius- oder Abducens-Paralyse. *Albrecht v. Graefes Arch. Ophthal.* **192,** 247–254.

WEBER, R. B. and DAROFF, R. B. (1972) Corrective movements following refixation saccades: type and control system analysis. *Vision Res.* **12,** 467–475.

WESTHEIMER, G. and BLAIR, S. M. (1973) Oculomotor defects in cerebellectomized monkeys. *Invest. Ophthal.* **12,** 618–621.

Discussion Remarks Concerning the Higher Functional Organization of the Saccadic Branch of the Oculomotor System and the Response of the Combined Eye–Head Movement to a Step Input by Gerhard Vossius

Viewing the oculomotor control system as a two-branch signal handling and analysing system (Vossius, 1961, Fig. 1), the saccidically operating branch can be treated as a sampled data system, as was shown by Young and Stark (1963). Conducting experiments with artificially introduced external feedback the saccadic loop should operate under stable conditions within the external feedback limits $-1 \leqslant 0 \leqslant +1$. When we tested the stability limits experimentally it was found that the system remained stable for much larger *negative* external feedback gains than predicted by the model. The most obvious conclusion was that the

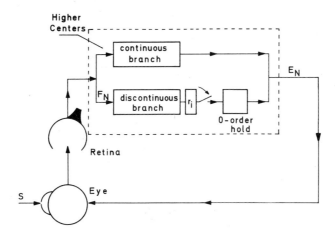

Fig. 1.

subjects conducting the experiments had become used to these sort of experiments and were capable of adjusting their *internal* feedback gain unconsciously to the changing experimental situation. Therefore a subject completely inexperienced in this kind of experiment was asked to follow a steplike target movement. Already in the very first experiment the external feedback gain was set to -3. Figure 2a shows the result. The eye-movement pattern becomes at once unstable till it is limited by the nonlinearities of the recording device, stays unstable for a short while and then starts suddenly to adjust to the new situation. Only three step inputs later the subject is already used of the situation (Fig. 2b). This procedure needs an adaptive mechanism, which enables the subject to adjust his internal gain r_i. Each adaptive procedure has fulfilled two requirements: (1) a goal to adapt on, and (2) an adaptive strategy.

The goal is easily established, it is to center the fovea centralis on the target. The adaptive procedure is revealed by looking at its mathematics. The system equation giving the eye position relative to the head after the Nth saccade is:

$$E_N = E_{N-1} + F_{N-1} \cdot r_i \tag{1}$$

and the remaining error is

$$F_N = S - E_N \cdot (1 - r_e). \tag{2}$$

At the time $N - 1$ the error was:

$$F_{N-1} = S - E_{N-1} \cdot (1 - r_e) \tag{3}$$

from (2) $-$ (3) follows:

$$F_N - F_{N-1} = (-E_N + E_{N-1}) \cdot (1 - r_e) \tag{4}$$

(1) in (4) substituted is

$$F_N = F_{N-1} \cdot \{1 - r_i \cdot (1 - r_e)\} \tag{5}$$

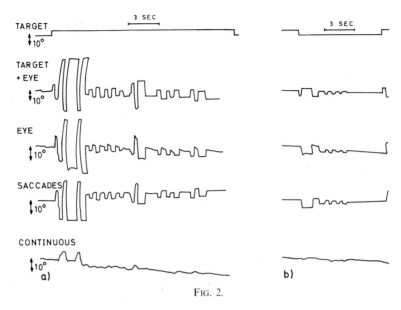

FIG. 2.

from equation (5) follows for the value of the internal gain r_i with the error F being zero ($F = 0$):

$$(1 - r_i) \cdot (1 - r_e) = 0 \tag{6}$$

and

$$r_{i_{opt}} = \frac{1}{1 - r_e}. \tag{7}$$

This rather simple mathematical operation cannot be conducted by the brain, because it has no knowledge about the external gain factor r_e. Reviewing our experiments we found that the internal gain r_i was sometimes adjusted with the second saccadic. This leads to the mode of optimization applied here. Equation (4) transformed is

$$\frac{1}{1 - r_e} = -\frac{\Delta E_N}{\Delta F_N}(= r_{i_{opt}}). \tag{8}$$

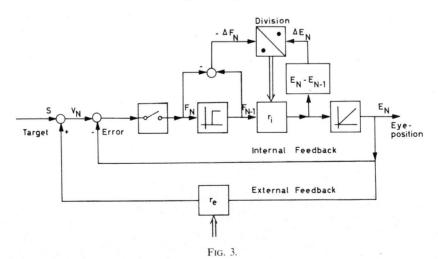

FIG. 3.

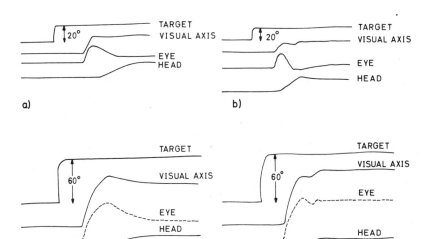

FIG. 4.

From this it follows that the brain has to store the last two values of the eye position and the error, subtract them and divide the differences to find $r_{i_{opt}}$; all these operations may easily be conducted. The scheme of the adaptive system is given in Fig. 3. (Part of this work was conducted together with L. Goodman and G. Bowman, part together with J. Werner.)

While the preceding part gives an example of an adaptive procedure in motor control the following tries to obtain insight into the integration of two systems of voluntary movement.

Following steplike target motions of sufficient size and the head not being fixed, the tracking movement will be conducted by the eyes and the head together. Normally the eyes start first, jump to the target position to center the fovea on it. Then the head follows more slowly due to its bigger mass. During this head movement the eye has to make a backward movement at the same speed as the head moves forward in order to keep the visual axis on the target (Fig. 4a).

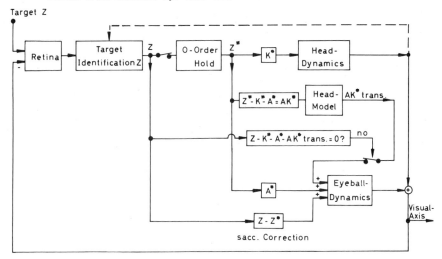

FIG. 5.

Apparently the functional concept of doing this is quite simple. The eyes might be turned back by the stimulation of the various appropriate receptor systems located in the head or by feeding the motor signal turning the head with a negative sign to the oculomotor system.

Looking more closely at our records we found that the gain factor during the phase of the backward movement of the eyes was often not properly adjusted to the head movement. The speed of the eye movement might be too fast so that the visual axis would miss the target. In that case the backward movement of the eye was shut off suddenly to correct this (Fig. 4b).

At other times the initial saccade of the eyes was overshooting the target position by far. In this case the eyes did not make a fast jump back but conducted its backward movement with the same pattern as the head its forward movement but with a higher gain (Fig. 4c). (If the initial eye saccade was too small, a second correcting one followed, Fig. 4d.)

These correcting eye-movement patterns proved that they could not be elicited by stimulation of the receptor system or by forwarding the motor signal turning the head. To create such eye-movement patterns a much more sophisticated control mechanism must be involved. In addition it was noticed that in experiments with unpredictable steplike target motions the backward movement of the eyes was often initiated already before the head started to move. This excludes, together with the examples given above, the generation of the backward eye-movement pattern by simple receptive or motor-control signals. The functional concept covering all the experimental observations asks for a structure where the motor signal turning the head is passed in parallel through a model of the head dynamics and matched there with the size of the initial saccade and possible error signals in order to generate the appropriate eye movement. Figure 5 gives the complete control scheme for the steplike eye–head movement.

These results suggest that the central nervous system apparently prefers a more sophisticated control scheme instead of a simple feedback or even feedforward control. The advantage using higher level control is doubtless the flexibility in adjusting the control process to changing conditions within or outside the nervous system, for instance the death of a few nerve cells. Looking from the outside at the oculomotor system the internal grain r_i of the saccadic branch needs to be set at the value "1" only. But looking at the situation from the brains side, how does it know how big "1" really is? There is no reference to it but experience. All this is avoided by building an adaptive system, with the adaptive procedure being a function of the process itself. The same is true for the combined eye–head movement.

Further on arise big problems from the coordination of the movement of the whole body. All these problems might be solved much better with a centralized highly developed functional concept, which allows the C.N.S. to obtain a continuously updated picture of the dynamics of the ongoing movement, with the possibility to interfere whenever necessary. With this concept it is possible to shift the priority of the control to that subsystem, which has to bear the main part in the oncoming (tracking-) task. Such shifts of the priority have been observed by us when we recorded combined eye–head–hand movement.

(Part of this work was conducted together with D. Fleming.)

REFERENCES

RASHBASS, C. (1961) The relationship between saccadic and smooth tracking eye movements. *J. Physiol.* **159**, 326.

VOSSIUS, G. (1961) Die Regelbewegungen des Auges. In: *Aufnahme und Verarbeitung von Nachrichten durch Organismen*, p. 149. Hirzel, Stuttgart.

VOSSIUS, G. (1965) Der kybernetische Aspekt der Willkürbewegung. In: *Process on Biocybernetics*, p. 111. Elsevier, Amsterdam–London–New York.

VOSSIUS, G. (1965) Higher coordinative functions of the vestibular and oculomotor systems. In: *Vestibular and Oculomotor Problems*, p. 183. University Press, Tokyo.

VOSSIUS, G. (1970) Die Kybernetik der Augenfolgebewegung. In: *Der Mensch als Regler*, OPPELT, W. and VOSSIUS, G. (Eds.), pp. 139–157. VEB Verlag Technik, Berlin.

VOSSIUS, G. (1972) The functional organisation of object directed human intended-movement and the forming of a mathematical model. In: *Displays and Controls*. Swets and Zeitlinger, Amsterdam.

VOSSIUS, G., GOODMANN, L. and BOWMAN, G. (1966) Die Funktion der kontinuierlichen und der sakkadischen Komponente der Augenbewegung. *Pflügers Archiv Physiol.* **89**, R. 65.

VOSSIUS, G. and WERNER, J. (1970) Experimental and generalized mathematical analysis of the human motor control system. *Proc Sixth Annual Conference on Manual Control. Air Force Institute of Technology, Dayton, Ohio, USA*, pp. 269–276.

WERNER, J. (1970) Modellentwicklung für Identifikations- und Vorhersage-eigenschaften der Kontrolle der menschlichen Folgebewegung. Dissertation TH Darmstadt.

WERNER, J. and VOSSIUS, G. (1972) Die Identifizierung der effektiven Rückkoppelung der sakkadischen Augenbewegung durch das ZNS. *Kybernetic*, **10**, 98–102.

YOUNG, L. R. and STARTK, L. (1963) Ein Abtastmodell der Augenfolgebewegung. *Regelungstechnik*, **11**, 148.

SUPRANUCLEAR OCULAR MOTOR CONTROL. SOME CLINICAL CONSIDERATIONS—1974†

WILLIAM F. HOYT and LARS FRISÉN

INTRODUCTION

Many seemingly plausible clinical concepts regarding supranuclear ocular motor control have been challenged during the past 5 years. The hypothesis of the frontal lobes as generators of preprogrammed saccadic eye movements appears untenable. There is now little doubt that the saccadic pulse generator resides in the pontine paramedian reticular formation (PPRF). Also, parallel processing of more than one saccadic program must be assumed, i.e. to explain why saccades can de interrupted in mid-flight.

Important gaps in our understanding of capability and function in cortical and subcortical pursuit systems have been pointed out. The optokinetic system may not be as "kinetic" as we thought. Instead, it appears that its major function is to prevent image slip relative to the fovea during intersaccadic intervals. Our concepts of the roles of the cerebellum also require revision, particularly in view of important findings regarding flexibility of gain control in the vestibulo-ocular reflex arc.

In this chapter we discuss some aspects of contemporary ocular motor research that promise a clearer understanding of supranuclear eye-movement disturbances encountered in the neurologic patient.

HOW DOES THE CEREBELLUM INFLUENCE EYE MOVEMENT?

Elegant evidence for the ways in which the cerebellum utilizes vestibular and retinal information for coordinating head and eye movements is provided elsewhere in this volume. The role of the cerebellar flocculus in modulating these movements is vital to man as he freely moves in his environment. This requires regulation of gain in the vestibulo-ocular reflex (Ito et al., 1973; 1974a, b). When velocity of compensatory eye movements does not match velocity of head movement we experience illusory shifts of fixed objects in our environment: we get difficulties with orientation in space. If disharmony between vestibular and visual systems persists the flocculus gradually resets the gain. The continuous operation and the plasticity of the vestibulocerebellar gain regulator is fact, but how does it apply to clinical disorders of conjugate eye movements? For every output error in a subsystem controlling smooth movements,

†Supported in part by USPHS Training Grant EY-00083-01 (W.F.H.).

the flocculus adjusts the gain, acting as a "test and repairship", in Robinson's words, for the vestibulo-ocular control system. Gain is plastic when challenged by sensory-motor incompatibility, but the cerebellum changes gain slowly, and effects of this change can be long lasting. Floccular adjustment of gain in the vestibulo-ocular reflex arc provides the first explanation for "habituation" to unnatural (pathologic) levels of vestibular input. Acute unilateral or bilateral depression of vestibular input causes immediate visuospatial disorientation (Bender and Feldman, 1967). Recovery of normal, or near normal, gain in the vestibulo-ocular reflex arc occurs as the flocculus "does its job" on the brainstem ocular motor integrator. If function now returns in a hypoactive labyrinth, vertigo recurs. The second phase adjustment of the integrator (by the cerebellum) can take much longer than the first. Vestibulo-ocular gain is abnormal and the patient's nystagmus and illusory "slip" of his environment after rapid head movement continue. Persistent oscillopsia means that the cerebellum cannot eliminate discordance of retinal and vestibular velocity information.

Lateral medullary infarcts disconnect important afferent pathways carrying cervical and olivocerebellar information concerned with cervico–vestibulo–ocular coordination of neck, head, and eye movement. These lesions account for a host of visuomotor disorders, objective and subjective. Diplopia of continuously changing character, often with torsion and oscillopsia of one image, occurs frequently in the acute phase of the illness. This "supranuclear" diplopia may indicate involvement of afferent pathways (? from the inferior olive) that relay retinal velocity information to Purkinje cells in the ipsilateral flocculus. These pathways along with primary vestibular afferents carry the information that the cerebellum needs for modulation of ocular motor output and perception of environment. Unilaterally discordant retino-vestibular input to cerebellum accounts for discordant tonic and phasic output from the ocular motor system. Fixation instability, consisting of low amplitude sporadic saccades and drifts, suggests imbalance in tonic output in the pursuit-fixation system. Transiently blurred vision after rapid head movement is a frequent complaint. This symptom may represent brief periods of discordant retino-vestibular input with resulting disintegration of perception, as occurs during optokinetic or vestibular coriolis stimulation. This blurred vision is not caused by intermittent vascular insufficiency in the vertebral-basilar system. Pronounced tendency for the eyes to drift to the side of the lesion, to bias all saccades toward the side of the lesion, is the ocular motor equivalent of postural "lateropulsion" in Wallenberg's syndrome (Bjerver and Silfverskiöld, 1968; Kommerell and Hoyt, 1973). Sometimes, as the infarct develops, the patient perceives a 90° tilt, or even 180° inversion, of his visual environment (Hagström et al., 1969). This symptom also indicates discordant retino-vestibular input. The complex dysfunctions caused by partial, unilateral vestibulo-cerebellar deafferentation in Wallenberg's syndrome exemplify perfectly the consequences of open-loop cerebellar-ocular motor activity.

In a series of articles, Halpern (1964) described a symptom complex that he termed "sensorimotor induction" or "unilateral disequilibrium". His patients complained of vertigo and postural disequilibrium when closing one eye, symptoms that could be relieved by fixating with the other eye. Halpern's syndrome was bypassed as a curiosity at that time but is now explainable as unilateral disharmony of retinal and vestibular information converging on floccular Purkinje cells. The flocculus has difficulty adjusting retino-vestibular conflict caused by signal distortion related to a single vertical semicircular canal and the patient's bizarre monocular vertigo continues.

A smaller-scale problem of gain control frequently faces the patient with a recently changed spectacle prescription. Nausea, headache, and spatial mislocalization are common complaints during the first few days with the new glasses. These problems are most pronounced during movements. Interestingly enough, once gain has been properly adjusted, our patients find no difficulty in rapidly changing between various means of optical correction (spectacles, contact lenses, or no correction at all) in spite of their different optical imagery.

Dichgans and co-workers (1973) investigated mechanisms underlying recovery of compensatory eye movements during active and passive head turning, following bilateral labyrinthectomy. They showed in monkeys that compensatory eye movements approach 90% of normal within 7 weeks, but only if the animal is permitted to move its head actively. Three mechanisms seem to account for recovery. The gain in the cervico-ocular reflex increases. Compensatory eye movement occurs according to a new "central" program, and there is recalibration of saccadic and head motor systems so that a smaller saccade is evoked by a given retinal error signal. Their findings provide insight into the nature of a patient's slow but remarkable adaptation to loss of both labyrinths. The cerebellum gradually increases the gain in the afferent loop from the neck and adjusts saccadic amplitudes.

If the vestibulocerebellum is excised in a cat, it is no longer possible to habituate the animal to vestibular stimuli (Robinson). The animal no longer possesses the neural apparatus with which it modulates the gain in its vestibulo-ocular system. Normally floccular Purkinje cells are strongly activated by the visual system (Maekawa and Simpson, 1972). These cells inhibit the vestibular nuclei. It is by this mechanism that caloric vestibular nystagmus is damped when the patient is allowed to fixate on an object during the examination. Cohen and Takemori (1973) showed that visual suppression of caloric nystagmus, positional alcohol nystagmus, OKAN, and spontaneous nystagmus was reduced after unilateral floccular lesions and ceased completely after bilateral flocculectomy. These observations imply that destruction of the flocculus by chronic neurologic disease in man might be recognized by absence of vestibular habituation or presence of a jerk-type nystagmus that does not abate.

There are two distinctive forms of nystagmus associated with anomalies of the inferior cerebellar vermis or its medullary connections, and both forms are virtually permanent once they appear. One form is downbeating nystagmus often associated with occult Arnold–Chiari malformation; the other form is PAN (periodic alternating nystagmus). In both instances malfunction of the vestibulo-cerebellum may be the reason that the nystagmus does not go away. Nystagmus with acute pontine lesions, but an intact cerebellum, usually disappears in several days or weeks.

In a recent clinical study of downbeat nystagmus Zee et al. (1974) provided new details regarding the control system defects. Two patients with an occult Arnold–Chiari malformation had defective control of eye movements, that could be described in terms of defective transmission of downward retinal velocity information to the brainstem ocular motor integrator. Downbeating nystagmus is presumably a result of defective cerebellar handling of vertical retinal velocity information. It represents a "pursuit nystagmus" that cannot be "repaired" by the patient's defective cerebellum. Often it is pendular, lacking a fast phase.

In chronic studies of cerebellectomized cats Robinson noted their inability to maintain eccentric gaze. As the cat repeatedly refixated to the side, its eyes slipped back toward center giving the appearance of nystagmus. Clinically this nystagmus has been termed cerebellar, gaze-paretic, and hypotonic. Robinson's suggestion that this disorder is the sign of a "leaky integrator" has merit. Hypotonicity of body musculature, including eye muscles, is a recognized effect of cerebellar disease. This "hypotonicity" indicates a reduced "time constant" of the position holding brainstem integrator. If an integrator leaks, it cannot maintain the same position signal, or the output required to hold the eyes to the side. The curvilinear slow phases of Robinson's "integrator nystagmus", as recorded in cats, has now been documented in man by Kommerell, in this volume. This "integrator nystagmus" can occur in the absence of other cerebellar signs in patients with fourth ventricle tumors or cysts. Perhaps such tumors affect cerebellar efferents to vestibular nuclei coursing under the ependyma. Robinson found that saccades are also slowed in cerebellectomized cats; both phases of evoked nystagmus being equally affected and curvilinear. This observation recalls to mind a form of familial cerebellar degeneration with marked slowing of saccadic velocities (Wadia and Swami, 1971).

Does the cerebellum act to "repair" other supranuclear gaze disorders? If the flocculus monitors and adjusts the gain of vestibulo-ocular and cervico-ocular reflexes by means of its inhibitory control of cells in the brainstem tegmentum (PPRF and vestibular nuclei), it is reasonable to anticipate that the cerebellum plays a similar role in maintenance and correction of other sensory-motor activity. We may anticipate further that most acute (non-cerebellar) saccadic and pursuit eye-movement disorders are modified or repaired by parts of the cerebellum concerned with these functions.

The implications of this are broad. Most of the ocular motor disorders of conjugate gaze are subacute or chronic before we see them. Always the cerebellar "repairshop" has been at work. For example, surgical injury in the rostral floor of the fourth ventricle may cause total ophthalmoplegia during the first hour, pontine gaze palsy with contralateral ocular deviation for 24 hr, partial gaze palsy and abduction nystagmus for the next month, and slight gaze paresis for 9 months. How can we account for repair in the central nervous system that takes this long? Recently it has been recognized that "plasticity" in varying degrees is a general principle of repair in the central nervous system (Bach-y-Rita, 1972). Axonal sprouting is a dynamic process directly related to maintenance or repair of function. This process underlies delayed recovery of ocular motor coordination after trauma or stroke. In the immature brain axonal sprouting can literally "rewire" or replace parts of a neural system (Illis, 1973; Schneider, 1973).

Gradual resolution of spastic conjugate gaze after damage to a hemisphere with return of normal, symmetrical saccadic output is probably another example of cerebellar "repair" following asymmetrical deafferentation of brainstem neurons. Latto and Cowey (1971 a, b) noted that once a monkey recovers from conjugate ocular deviation caused by unilateral ablation of prefrontal cortex, second-stage ablation of prefrontal cortex on the opposite side produces a larger almost permanent conjugate ocular deviation in the opposite direction. They assumed that each prefrontal area exerted "tonic influence" on the brainstem oculomotor system through projections to the mesencephalic reticular formation. Cerebellar modulation of this imbalance in the gaze integrator seems probable. Following the second lesion cerebellar capacity to restore balance in gaze tone is strikingly reduced. This suggests that the first "repair" might have involved axonal sprouting with filling of vacated synaptic terminals by axons from the cerebellum or brainstem.

Any chronic supranuclear disorder of eye movements can be regarded as the net result of (i) the lesion in the neural subsystems controlling eye movements, and (ii) the adaptive processes by which the brain adjusts disordered ocular motor output. Slowly progressive functional damage is adjusted "as it goes", leaving the patient with little or no overt ocular motor problems. If a lesion gradually destroys the greater part of a cerebellar hemisphere, surgical excision of that hemisphere can cause skew deviation, jerk nystagmus, and vertigo that persist unmodified for months or years. The brainstem chronically modified by asymmetrical cerebellar control cannot withstand or adapt to an acute change in input. Improved understanding of these phenomena may in the future suggest alternative surgical procedures that are less apt to create brainstem turmoil.

PREFRONTAL CORTEX—PROGRAMMER OR RECORD-KEEPER?

This year is the first centenary of Ferrier's discovery of the frontal "eye fields" (area 8), long accepted as the centers for voluntary eye movement. Some still contend that these areas initiate saccades. While it is true that unilateral frontal "eye field" lesions in monkeys cause neglect of contralateral visual stimuli and transient deviation of eyes and head, this does not validate Ferrier's conclusion. Neurophysiologists have been unable to find a single cell in area 8 (of monkeys) that discharges before a saccade (Bizzi, 1968; Bizzi and Schiller, 1970; Mohler et al., 1973). Mohler and associates (1973) found that 47% of cells in this area responded only to visual stimuli. Twenty-two per cent responded to saccades into the contralateral hemifield; a majority of these also responded to saccades into the ipsilateral hemifield. A few cells responded after "voluntary" saccades in the dark. Latto and Cowey (1971 a, b) confirmed that unilateral frontal "eye field" lesions produced transient shifts of fixation toward the ipsilateral side and downward. The striking finding in their monkeys was contralateral homonymous "visual neglect". After partial recovery, removal of the remaining frontal "eye field" produced "visual neglect" in the other hemifield that was more severe and more prolonged.

At present no authority seems ready to commit himself regarding the role of frontal area 8 in eye movement. Most agree that it plays a subsidiary role in visuomotor activity. It may exercise tonic control of ocular motor output during fixation. It may receive information about eye movement. Astruc (1971) restudied the corticofugal connections of area 8. Using the Nauta–Gygax technique, he found that the superior colliculus and pretectum were the major recipients of area 8 projections, whereas the periaqueductal gray and lateral mesencephalic tegmentum received scattered projections. Abundant fiber degeneration was observed in the pontine nuclei but none was found near the ocular motor nuclei. Projections also terminated in the basal ganglia, particularly in the intralaminar nuclei of the thalamus. Certainly these connections would permit extensive participation in visuomotor activity.

Kurtzberg and Vaughan (1973) studied the frontal " eye fields" in man using computer-averaging techniques to extract from on-going EEG activity the shape and topography of cortical responses related to movement of eyes across a patterned field. The frontal cortex has a place in the neural substrate for visuomotor function according to these investigators. The temporal relationship to saccadic eye movement is evidenced by an antecedent EMP (eye movement potential) that begins 200 ms beforehand. EMPs have topographic maxima over area 19 and area 8 of the cerebral cortex. The investigators stressed that the antecedent EMP has its end as a sharp spike 20–40 ms preceding the saccade. Eye-movement supranuclear subsystems thus share the same regions of the brain subserving visual experience.

Recordings of random and visually-evoked saccade-linked cortical potentials and simultaneous depths recordings during stereotactic neurosurgical procedures in the thalamus or rostral midbrain may help to define temporal relations of events accompanying the initiation of eye movements (Groll-Knapp *et al.*, 1974).

OCCIPITAŁ OCULAR MOTOR MECHANISMS

Our concepts about the roles of occipital (and frontal) cortex in initiation of eye movements rest insecurely on data from stimulation and ablation experiments. Inference of cerebral function from such data is limited. Large unilateral ablations of occipital cortex produce only short-lasting effects on conjugate eye movements (Pasik and Pasik, 1964). Stimulation of occipital cortex yields data that cannot be reconciled between previous reports. Modern macro- and microelectrode recording techniques provide important insight into cortical neuronal activity related to eye movement without revealing much about the integrated mechanisms that are involved, or their strategy.

Computer techniques using time reversal and averaged EEG data (Becker *et al.*, 1968; Barlow and Cigánek, 1969; Kurtzberg and Vaughan, 1973) have revealed a premotor slow positive ramplike wave beginning about 200 ms prior to a saccade and located bilaterally over the peristriate and prefrontal regions. This finding of bilateral presaccadic positively, taken together with the brief recovery period for eye movements after unilateral cortical lesions, indicates bilateral hemispheric participation in ocular motor events, each hemisphere having the capacity to generate signals for contralateral and ipsilateral eye movements. Although no single unit has been found in the cerebral cortex with identifiable pre-motor activity (Straschill and Schick, 1974) the parieto-occipital association areas seem to be the best "candidates" for the cortical generator of eye movements.

We are approaching a time when single unit studies in the brain will fail to meet demands of control system analysts. Investigation of spatial and temporal patterns of visuomotor activity in the brain will be required before we fully can appreciate the extent of cerebral activity during pursuit and saccadic eye movements.

The occipital ocular motor subsystem for smooth pursuit has been characterized as a continuous, visual feedback control system with a reaction time of 125 ms. Smooth eye movements can be executed under voluntary control only under unusual circumstances. Heywood (1972) recorded eye movements in a subject who could make such movements with eyes open in the dark, and could change the velocity at will. Heywood concluded that the smooth movement system does not require moving stimuli or any information about movement. In some subjects, and possibly in some neurologic diseases, smooth output is available as a substitute voluntary motor system. Recent demonstration of foveal velocity detectors in the monkey visual cortex responsive to target movement of 0.01°/sec indicates how sensitive the temporal response of the system must be (see Robinson this volume).

Anatomical details of the pursuit system are incompletely defined. Although it is convenient for clinical purposes to consider it as an ipsilaterally projecting system, there is no sound anatomical or physiological evidence to justify this formulation. Considering the demand for precision in the system during tracking of targets with changing velocity, and during fixation (pursuit at zero velocity), it seems more probable that both occipital lobes participate to produce smooth pursuit in all directions. The clinical dictum that occipital lobe lesions impair ipsilateral smooth pursuit is unreliable.

Extensive lesions of visual cortex rarely impair pursuit function. In patients with central macular-splitting homonymous hemianopic defects fixation is remarkably stable. When smooth pursuit is impaired the lesion involves deep white matter and trans-callosal connections of the occipital lobe.

Trans-callosal Influences

The Pasiks (1964, 1973) showed that neither optic tract section nor midline section of the chiasm had any effect on optokinetic responses in monkeys. Additional section of the corpus callosum and hippocampal commissure resulted in a markedly defective optokinetic response to stimuli moving toward the "deprived" hemisphere. Amplitude of saccadic phases was often reduced and velocity of slow phases was damped. The findings indicated that hemianopia alone does not disturb optokinetic responses. Some degree of slowing of quick phases of OKN has been observed recently in hemianopic patients by Koerner (see this author's chapter). Lesions of an optic tract do not exclude all visual sensory information from occipital and parietal portions of the "blind" hemisphere. Section of corpus callosum and other forebrain commissures excludes the inter-hemispheric transfer of such visual information.

In optic tract-sectioned and chiasm-sectioned "split brain" monkeys, vertical optokinetic responses are of low frequency and are oblique. They veer toward the "deprived" hemisphere in tract-sectioned animals. The same is true for chiasm-sectioned animals when tested monocularly. Binocular vertical stimulation of chiasm-sectioned "split-brain" monkeys evokes symmetrical vertical responses (Pasik et al., 1971). If both sides of the brain receive visual input from either afferent visual pathways or from interhemispheric pathways, optokinetic responses will be normal. If input is withheld from one hemisphere, the brain still can generate an optokinetic response but it will be a subnormal one in one horizontal direction.

In animals with a predominantly crossed visual input to each hemisphere, there is corresponding asymmetry of monocular horizontal responses to optokinetic stimulation following unilateral ablation of striate cortex. A low-frequency response occurs in the naso-temporal direction (Wood et al., 1973). Unilateral absence of striate cortex in the monkey or man does not cause such naso-temporal slowing of optokinetic responses. Hemispherectomy in man produces definite optokinetic asymmetry, but even this does not abolish the response (Troost et al., 1972 a, b).

If a function such as movement discrimination requires both sides of the brain, then the commissures connecting the hemispheres must participate in movement perception and its ocular motor response. Motion perception, like pattern perception, cannot be transferred between hemispheres in a "split-brain" animal. Hamilton and Lund (1970) used this principle to prove that foveal judgments of motion utilize cerebral, not mid-brain, mechanisms. They compared monocular training times in chiasm-sectioned monkeys (differentiating opposite pairs of moving stimuli) with training times in chiasm-sectioned, "split-brain" monkeys. Learning time for accurate up–down and right–left discriminations was compared in the first and second eyes of animals in each group. The chiasm-sectioned group showed a striking saving of training time for the second eye indicating the occurrence of interhemispheric transfer. The "split-brain" group showed no saving for the second eye. The fact that learning was not transferred via pretectal commissures in the "split-brain" group is evidence that accurate judgment of motion is a cerebral function.

Cortico-thalamic Disorders

Involvement of white matter deep in the cerebral hemispheres, basal ganglia, or both can produce severe ocular motor disorders when the disease is bilateral. Such disorders tell us little about cerebral mechanisms controlling saccadic or smooth pursuit eye movements. An attempt to define these diseases in terms of control-system disorders would be premature.

The patients manifest complex dysfunction of memory, attention, and mentation—factors that profoundly alter ocular motor performance. Despite ignorance of normal hemispheric physiology of visuomotor activity, it is entertaining to speculate on how these ocular motor disturbances can be defined in more modern terms.

Jerky "cogwheel" decomposition of normally smooth pursuit movements are commonplace in neurologic patients, but little has been accomplished toward identification of types of pursuit irregularities and their clinical significance. Even the term "cogwheel" is inappropriate since cogwheels are designed to transmit movement smoothly. Ratchet movement is a better description. Some of the parameters that can be tested include reaction time, pursuit velocity gain, amplitude-frequency relationship of eye and target movements, and ratio of saccadic and smooth motor output. Tsutsui and Fukai (1973) used DC electro-oculography and sinusoidal target movement to study pursuit disorders in a group of Japanese patients with chronic mercury poisoning (Minamata disease). This disease affects cerebral gray matter, basal ganglia, cerebellar cortex, and even neurons in the brainstem. They analysed differences in monocular and binocular pursuit attempts, parallelism of conjugate movements, version asymmetries, and smoothness of eye movements. They described eight basic patterns of "cogwheel" movements in this one disease: (1) compensatory saccades (cogwheel, staircase, and single step); (2) varying parallelism; (3) phase reversal; (4) asymmetrical versions; (5) fatigue phenomenon; (6) regular jump; (7) nystagmoid movements; and (8) pursuit palsy.

Yamazaki (1970), studying various neurological disorders, demonstrated damped pursuit velocity, fixation instability with amplified microsaccades, saccadic couplets, and "staircase" saccadic pursuit evolving from a pattern of random pursuit jerks at lower target velocities.

In patients with bilateral basal ganglia movement disorders voluntary saccades are so slow that it can be argued that the slow saccade is instead a voluntary smooth pursuit movement. These patients frequently employ head thrusts to attain fixation laterally.

In rare cases of Huntington's Chorea there is global saccadic palsy and the smooth pursuit system acts alone. What produces the suspension of saccades is not known. Could exclusion of position information from the hemispheric circuit that generates saccadic commands account for this palsy?

Bilateral "pursuit" palsy appears to be present in some patients with presenile dementia. The saccadic system seems to compensate for the smooth pursuit deficiency. Fixation is unstable, being interrupted by frequent, grossly visible saccadic jerks to-and-fro. During sinusoidal tracking at low frequency there is evidence of very low velocity smooth pursuit. As target velocity increases to approximately 3°/sec pursuit becomes a staircase sequence of equal size, equal frequency small saccades. Pursuit palsy from hemispheric disease is a disorder in which pursuit gain is greatly reduced, but is not zero. Could it be that failure of cortical integration of velocity information constitutes "pursuit" palsy?

Reduced pursuit velocity gain may occur unilaterally in the absence of homonymous hemianopia in patients with acute parietal or parieto-thalamic lesions. Cogwheel pursuit toward the damaged hemisphere is an incidental finding compared to the contralateral hemiplegia and parietal signs, however.

Cerebellar Modulation of Smooth Pursuit Output?

How the cerebellum participates in the smooth pursuit control system is not clear, but evidence is growing that it does. Some investigators argue that the cerebellum is unnecessary for proper functioning of the pursuit system while proposing that the deep nuclei of the cerebellum control the hold (fixation) function of the ocular motor system (Kornhuber, 1971). Other investigators argue convincingly that fixation is essentially ocular pursuit at zero target velocity. This implies that a "hold" system is a part of the smooth pursuit system (Zee et al., 1974).

It is not firmly established how velocity information reaches the cerebellum from the occipital lobes in monkeys, but several physiological and anatomical studies in the cat provide good anatomical information on how this might occur. Brodal (1972) found that the visual cortex of cats (areas 17, 18, and 19) projects onto several sharply delimited, mainly transverse bands in the rostral half of the pontine nuclei. All parts of area 17 project onto pontine nuclei but the representation of the macula is sparse compared to the remaining areas of the visual fields. The total projection from area 17 covers the same pontine region as does the projection from areas 18 and 19. This visual projection on pontine nuclei has a definite retinotopic organization: rostral projections represent lower visual fields and caudal projections upper fields. All projections from visual cortex reach ipsilateral terminals in the pons. Glickstein et al. (1972) recorded from pontine cells that responded to visual stimuli and found that area 18 sends dense projections to the rostral nuclei. They found that these visual cells of the pons (in cats) respond best to targets moving in a preferred direction over a large receptive field, usually including the center of gaze. They concluded that these cells in pontine visual areas relay information about the direction and velocity of moving objects to the cerebellum. As mentioned earlier in this chapter, Maekawa and Simpson (1972) showed that climbing fibers to Purkinje cells of the flocculus are activated by moving visual stimuli, and Buchtel et al. (1973) demonstrated units in the cerebellum that were directionally sensitive and whose discharge rate was proportional to target velocity. This information about the flocculus implicates a relay of visually coded information from cells in the ponto-medullary area and near the inferior olivary nucleus. The latter receives tectal and pretectal projections (Walberg, 1956).

Clinically all diffuse cerebellar diseases affect ocular pursuit making the eye movements jerky and ataxic. Other cerebellar diseases cause rapid salvos of to-and-fro eye
movements (flutter) during steady fixation and attempts to pursue a moving target.
Furthermore, there is little doubt that retinal velocity information and vestibular velocity
information is equalibrated in the cerebellar flocculus, or that the posterior vermis
plays a role in maintaining velocity gain in the smooth pursuit control system (Zee
et al., 1974).

SUPERIOR COLLICULUS—STILL A RIDDLE

Details of retinotopic organization of visual projections on the superficial gray and
optic layer of the superior colliculi are known. Retinotopic organization of premotor
saccadic activity evoked from the stratum intermedium of the superior colliculus has
recently been described by Wurtz and Goldberg (1971) and Schiller (1972). Also the
major projection between frontal area 8 and the deep layer of the colliculus is established
(Astruc, 1971). It is further known that macular projections from cortex are relayed
through the superior colliculus to the pons (Wilson and Toyne, 1970) Despite rapid
growth of this type of data, the role of the superior colliculus in control of saccadic
or pursuit movements of the eyes remains as elusive as ever.

One area of neurophysiologic research with possible clinical implications concerns
secondary effects of visual cortical deprivation on visuomotor development in cell
columns of the superior colliculus. Monocular squint amblyopia is associated with
major changes in receptive field organization in the striate cortex (areas 17, 18, and
19). Monocular or bilateral astigmatic refractive errors produce meridional amblyopia
and consequent striate changes in early life. Cortical units may respond only to lines
with a specific orientation (Mitchell et al., 1973). Cells of the superior colliculus reflect
directly developmental deficiencies of the visual cortex. Collicular cells with motor
properties are next in line. They too must be affected. In clinical terms, this means
that amblyopia is not merely a cortical problem, but instead has collicular repercussions
and beyond (Sterling and Wickelgren, 1970). This physiologic principle exemplifies the
futility of trying to classify congenital nystagmus strictly into sensory or motor types.
Congenital defects of an occipital lobe, or visual pathways, must produce profound
deprivation of visuomotor input at the collicular level, and must have implications
for development of eye movement control and for associated control of head movements
(Wickelgren-Gordon, 1972).

Schneider (1973) destroyed the superficial layers of superior colliculus unilaterally
at birth in the hamster and found that axons from the eye contralateral to the lesion
not only reached the area of early damage, but also formed an abnormal decussation,
crossing the tectal midline to terminate in the medial zone of the undamaged colliculus.
Axons from the two eyes competed for terminal space in this intact colliculus, for
they terminated in a non-overlapping manner, and if the axons from the eye contralateral
to the remaining superior colliculus were eliminated at birth, the anomalously recrossing
axons increased in quantity and spread across the entire superior colliculus on the
"wrong" side of the midbrain. Hamsters with such an anomaly showed wrong-direction
turning in response to visual stimuli in a large part of the visual field.

Logically, the type of process described above must account for congenital (supranuclear) anomalous innervation syndromes involving eye movements, and perhaps some

cases of congenital nystagmus. In a young woman, reported by Daroff *et al.* (1973) a vertical line suppressed horizontal pendular ocular oscillations. Her congenital nystagmus was associated with a large hyperopic refractive error and meridional cortical amblyopia. It is interesting to consider how her superior colliculus might have participated in and contributed to her nystagmus.

PRETECTAL VISUOMOTOR INTEGRATION

Ocular signs of pretectal lesions need no review here. This is one area of the brain that provides unequivocal clinical guideposts for localization of disease.

Several developments from laboratory science and stereotaxic surgery have physiologic and clinical implications. It is no surprise that cells of the rostral midbrain are critically sensitive to certain stimuli unique to this level of visuomotor integration. Straschill and Hoffmann (1969) studied, in cats, effects of visual stimuli on cells in the pretectum. Selectivity for relatively low stimulus background contrasts was recorded from some units. Evidence of retinotopic organization was confirmed. Some neurons responded reliably to visual and tactile, or visual and acoustic stimuli (multisensory convergence). Cells of the nucleus of the posterior commissure were directionally sensitive to *vertical* target movement, while others were coded for target movement *toward* the midline. Also, cells responding only to visual stimuli *moving forward or backward* in the midsagittal plane are found here but not in other portions of the brain. Directional selectivity in a frontal plane may represent elements of the pursuit control system. Selectivity of units for approaching or receding targets may be related to motor activity in the vergence system. Such cells may also provide alarm signals to the animal. Lee and Hill (1972) demonstrated (in rabbits) marked effects of refractive blur on responsiveness of midbrain cells. Such cells in bifoveate animals could provide the error signals for the vergence-accommodation control systems.

Nashold (1970), in the course of stimulation with implanted midbrain electrodes for study and treatment of a patient with intractable pain, reported on phosphenes seen each time electrical stimulation was carried out between two adjacent electrodes located just beneath the superior colliculus (evoked at 120 Hz to 300 Hz with 1 ms square wave pulse). The patient reported seeing patterns of a flashing light which seemed to vary slightly in intensity. He saw two kinds of "white" or "cold" lights arranged in straight or wavy lines. These lights were located in the visual field slightly off center and contralateral to the side of stimulation. The lights were superimposed upon the visual scene without distorting it. When he saw the phosphene, his eyes tended to look toward it. This seemed to be voluntary but by increasing voltage, forced involuntary contralateral horizontal gaze occurred and the patient saw the phosphene more laterally. We have witnessed similar events during midbrain stimulation with stereotactically implanted electrodes. In one instance our patient announced, as the stimulating current was turned on, that his left eye was going to turn upward. Immediately thereafter it did. The electrode was placed about 5 mm from the mid-sagittal plane and the stimulating point was at the level, and just ventral to, the superior colliculus (on the left). This response occurred several times. The patient denied illusory environmental movement and diplopia. He was acutely aware of the relative position of his left eye in his orbit during and just before active movement.

Sano and colleagues (1972) treated a patient with post-traumatic bitemporal hemianopia and see-saw nystagmus by placing a stereotactic lesion near the nucleus of Cajal. Electrical stimulation of the nucleus amplified the pendular see-saw eye movements. Neck movement (lateral flexion of head to the side ipsilateral to the electrode) was also recorded with each stimulation. Stimulation below the level of the nucleus caused only neck movements. Using radiofrequency current, a 3–4 mm lesion was produced in the region of the nucleus of Cajal and the see-saw component of the nystagmus immediately stopped. Slight rotary nystagmus (clockwise) persisted after the operation, but the disjunctive vertical eye movements did not recur. As proof that the see-saw nystagmus was present before operation and gone after operation, Sano and co-workers provided EMG recordings from the inferior rectus and the inferior oblique muscles. They made no claim to understanding of the mechanism of the patient's nystagmus or the explanation for the favorable surgical result.

REFERENCES

ASTRUC, J. (1971) Corticofugal connections of area 8 (frontal eye field) in *Macaca mulatta*. *Brain Res.* **33,** 241.

BACH-Y-RITA, P. (1972) *Brain Mechanisms In Sensory Substitution*. Academic Press, New York and London.

BARLOW, J. S. and CIGÁNEK, L. (1969) Lambda responses in relation to visual evoked responses in man. *Electroencephalogr. Clin. Neurophysiol.* **26,** 182.

BECKER, W., HOEHNE, O., IWASE, K., KORNHUBER, H. H. and TÄUMER, R. (1968) Bereitschaftspotential und evozierte Potentiale der menschlichen Grozhirnrinde bei willkürlichen Blickeinstellbewegung. *Pfluegers Arch.* **300,** 105.

BENDER, M. B. and FELDMAN, M. (1967) Visual illusions during head movement in lesions of the brain stem, *Arch. Neurol.* **17,** 354.

BIZZI, E. (1968) Discharge of frontal eye field neurons during saccadic and following eye movements in unanesthetized monkeys. *Exptl Brain Res.* **6,** 69.

BIZZI, E. and SCHILLER, P. H. (1970) Single unit activity in the frontal eye fields of unanesthetized monkeys during head and eye movement. *Exptl Brain Res.* **10,** 151.

BJERVER, K. and SILFVERSKIÖLD, B. P. (1968) Lateropulsion and imbalance in Wallenberg's syndrome. *Acta Neurol. Scand.* **44,** 91.

BRODAL, P. (1972) The corticopontine projection from the visual cortex in the cat. I. The total projection and the projection from area 17. *Brain Res.* **39,** 297.

BUCHTEL, H. A., RUBIA, F. J. and STRATA, P. (1973) Cerebellar unitary responses to moving visual stimuli. *Brain Res.* **50,** 463.

COHEN, B. and TAKEMORI, S. (1973) Visual inhibition of nystagmus by the flocculus. *Trans. Am. Neurol. Ass.* **98,** 52.

DAROFF, R. B., HOYT, W. F., BETTMAN JR, J. W. and LESSELL, S. (1973) Suppression and facilitation of congenital nystagmus by vertical lines. *Neurology,* **23,** 530.

DICHGANS, J., BIZZI, E., MORASSO, P. and TAGLIASCO, V. (1973) Mechanisms underlying recovery of eye-head coordination following bilateral labyrinthectomy. *Exptl Brain Res.* **18,** 548.

FERRIER, D. (1874) The localization of function in the brain. *Proc. R. Soc. Lond. (Biol.)* **22,** 299.

GLICKSTEIN, M., STEIN, J. and KING, R. A. (1972) Visual input to the pontine nuclei. *Science,* **178,** 1110.

GROLL-KNAPP, E., GANGLBERGER, J. A. and HAIDER, M. (1974) Voluntary movement related slow potentials in cortex and thalamus. Paper read at *Int. Symp. on Cerebral Evoked Potentials in Man,* Brussels.

HAGSTRÖM, L., HÖRNSTEN, G. and SILFVERSKIÖLD, B. P. (1969) Oculostatic and visual phenomena occurring in association with Wallenberg's syndrome. *Acta Neurol. Scand.* **45,** 568.

HALPERN, L. (1964) Different optic influences of the homolateral and contralateral eye on various functions in unilateral disequilibrium. *Psychiatr. Neurol. (Basel)* **147,** 345.

HAMILTON, C. R. and LUND, J. S. (1970) Visual discrimination of movement, midbrain or forebrain? *Science,* **170,** 1428.

HEYWOOD, S. (1972) Voluntary control of smooth eye movements and their velocity. *Nature,* **238,** 408.

ILLIS, L. S. (1973) Regeneration in the central nervous system. *Lancet,* **1,** 1035.

ITO, M., NISIMARU, N. and YAMAMOTO, M. (1973) Specific neural connections for the cerebellar control of vestibulo-ocular reflexes. *Brain Res.* **60,** 238.

ITO, M., SHIIDA, T., YAGI, N. and YAMAMOTO, M. (1974a) Visual influence on rabbit's horizontal vestibulo-ocular reflex that presumably is effected via the cerebellar flocculus. *Brain Res.* **65**, 170.

ITO, M., SHIIDA, T., YAGI, N. and YAMAMOTO, M. (1974b) Modification of rabbit's horizontal vestibulo-ocular reflex during sustained head rotation combined with visual stimulation. *Brain Res.* (in press).

KOMMERELL, G. and HOYT, W. F. (1973) Lateropulsion of saccadic eye movements. Electro-oculographic studies in a patient with Wallenberg's syndrome. *Arch. Neurol.* **28**, 313.

KORNHUBER, H. H. (1971) Motor functions of cerebellum and basal ganglia. The cerebellocortical saccadic (ballistic) clock, the cerebellonuclear hold regulator, and the basal ganglia ramp (voluntary speed smooth movement generator). *Kybernetik,* **8**, 157.

KURTZBERG, D. and VAUGHAN Jr., H. G. (1973) Electrocortical potentials associated with eye movement. In: *The Oculomotor System and Brain Functions,* ZIKMUND, V. (Ed.), p. 137. Butterworths, London.

LATTO, R. and COWEY, A. (1971a) Visual field defects after frontal eye-field lesions in monkeys. *Brain Res.* **30**, 1.

LATTO, R. and COWEY, A. (1971b) Fixation changes after frontal eye-field lesions in monkeys. *Brain Res.* **30**, 25.

LEE, J. M. and HILL, R. M. (1972) Responses of midbrain cells to blur. *Pfluegers Arch.* **336**, 213.

MAEKAWA, K. and SIMPSON, J. I. (1972) Climbing fiber activation of Purkinje cells in the flocculus by impulses transferred through the visual pathway. *Brain Res.* **39**, 245.

MOHLER, C. W., GOLDBERG, M. E. and WURTZ, R. H. (1973) Visual receptive fields of frontal eye field neurons. *Brain Res.* **61**, 385.

MITCHELL, D. E., FREEMAN, R. D., MILLODOT, M. and HAEGERSTRÖM, G. (1973) Meridional amblyopia: evidence for modification of the human visual system by early experience. *Vision Res.* **13**, 535.

NASHOLD Jr., B. S. (1970) Phosphenes resulting from stimulation of the midbrain in man. *Arch. Ophthalmol.* **84**, 433.

PASIK, P. and PASIK, T. (1964) Oculomotor functions in monkeys with lesions of the cerebrum and superior colliculi. In: *The Oculomotor System,* BENDER, M. B. (Ed.), p. 40. Harper & Row, New York.

PASIK, P., PASIK, T., VALCIUKAS, J. A. and BENDER, M. B. (1971) Vertical optokinetic nystagmus in split-brain monkey. *Exptl Neurol.* **30**, 162.

PASIK, T. and PASIK, P. (1973) Transmission of "elementary" visual information through brain commissures as revealed by studies on optokinetic nystagmus in monkeys. In: *The Oculomotor System and Brain Functions,* ZIKMUND, V. (Ed.), p. 268. Butterworths, London.

ROBINSON, D. A., this volume.

SANO, K., SEKINO, H., TSUKAMOTO, Y., YOSHIMASU, N. and ISHIJIMA, B. (1972) Stimulation and destruction of the region of the interstitial nucleus in cases of torticollis and see-saw nystagmus. *Confin. Neurol.* **34**, 331.

SCHILLER, P. H. (1972) The role of the monkey superior colliculus in eye movement and vision. *Invest. Ophthalmol.* **11**, 451.

SCHNEIDER, G. E. (1973) Early lesions of superior colliculus: factors affecting the formation of abnormal retinal projections. *Brain Behav. Evol.* **8**, 73.

STERLING, P. and WICKELGREN, B. G. (1970) Function of the projection from the visual cortex to the superior colliculus. *Brain Behav. Evol.* **3**, 210.

STRASCHILL, M. and HOFFMANN, K. P. (1969) Response characteristics of movement-detecting neurons in pretectal region of the cat. *Exptl Neurol.* **25**, 165.

STRASCHILL, M. and SCHICK, F. (1974) Neuronal activity during eye movements in a visual association area of cat cerebral cortex. *Exptl Brain Res.* **19**, 467.

TROOST, B. T., WEBER, R. B. and DAROFF, R. B. (1972a) Hemispheric control of eye movements. I. Quantitative analysis of refixation saccades in a hemispherectomy patient. *Arch. Neurol.* **27**, 441.

TROOST, B. T., DAROFF, R. B., WEBER, R. B. and DELL'OSSO, L. F. (1972b) Hemispheric control of eye movement. II. Quantitative analysis of smooth pursuit in a hemispherectomy patient, *Arch. Neurol.* **27**, 449.

TSUTSUI, J. and FUKAI, S. (1973) Classification of abnormal patterns in slow pursuit movements by electrooculography. *Folia Ophthalmol. Jap.* **24**, 608.

WADIA, N. H. and SWAMI, R. K. (1971) A new form of heredo-familial spinocerebellar degeneration with slow eye movements, *Brain,* **94**, 359.

WALBERG, F. (1956) Descending connections to the inferior olive. *J. Comp. Anat.* **104**, 77.

WICKELGREN-GORDON, B. (1972) Some effects of visual deprivation on the cat superior colliculus. *Invest. Ophthalmol.* **11**, 460.

WILSON, M. E. and TOYNE, M. J. (1970) Retino-topic and cortico-tectal projections in *Macaca mulatta.* *Brain Res.* **24**, 395.

WOOD, C. C., SPEAR, P. D. and BRAUN, J. J. (1973) Direction-specific deficits in horizontal optokinetic nystagmus following removal of visual cortex in the cat. *Brain Res.* **60**, 235.

WURTS, R. H. and GOLDBERG, M. E. (1971) Superior colliculus responses related to eye movements in awake monkeys. *Science,* **171,** 82.

YAMASAKI, A. (1970) Electrophysiological study on saccades during fixation and small smooth pursuit movement in neurological disorders. *Arch Soc. Ophthalmol. Jap.* **74,** 882.

ZEE, D. S., FRIENDLICH, A. R. and ROBINSON, D. A. (1974) The mechanism of downbeat nystagmus. *Arch. Neurol.* **30,** 227.

Discussion remarks of M. D. Sanders

I would like to discuss the production of "slow velocity" saccadic eye movements. These may be produced by lesions of the central nervous system, the ocular motor nerves or the ocular muscles. In the central nervous system, slow eye movements may be seen in cortical, subthalamic, cerebellar, and pontine disease. Preservation of oculocephalic and vestibular reflexes usually indicates integrity of the brainstem and serves to localize lesions to the cerebral cortex or subthalamic region.

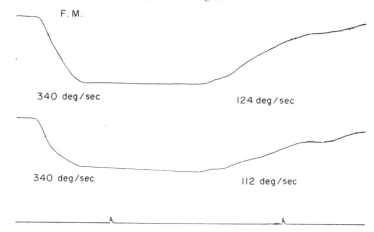

F. M.

340 deg/sec   124 deg/sec

340 deg/sec   112 deg/sec

FIG. 1. Electro-oculographic tracing to show impaired gaze to the right (upward deflection of trace), with the upper tracing representing the right eye, and the lower the left eye.

FIG. 2. Transverse section of the pons to show a metastatic lesion on the right side involving the paramedian pontine reticular formation.

Loss of peak velocity of saccadic eye movements to both voluntary, optokinetic, and vestibular testing suggests a lesion of the paramedian reticular formation (PPRF) and is usually termed a pontine gaze palsy. There are very few reports demonstrating focal lesions in the paramedian pontine reticular formation in man to correspond with the excellent work in monkeys by Bender. I would like to demonstrate a patient with impaired saccadic velocity to the right to voluntary, optokinetic and vestibular testing (Fig. 1) and in whom autopsy examination showed a metastatic deposit in the right PPRF (Fig. 2). It is interesting to speculate, however, on whether all pontine gaze palsies are due to intrinsic brain stem disease or whether inhibitory effects from the cortex or thalamic region can also produce impaired velocity of saccadic movements.

This meeting has not considered the organization of vertical ocular movements and there is strong clinical evidence that suggests integration and generation of these movements occurs at a different site from horizontal movements.

A supranuclear dissociation between vertical and horizontal disturbances is well exemplified by certain neurolipidoses. Thus some mainly affect the horizontal system (e.g. Gaucher's Disease) whereas others involve mainly the vertical system (e.g. Juvenile Niemann-Pick Disease). Pathological studies have not revealed any explanation for these findings.

OCULOMOTOR EFFECTS ON VISION[1]

Robert M. Steinman

FOVEATION

Over the past day and a half, we have heard many intriguing facts and speculations about the machinery used to rotate the eye and disorders that disrupt its normal function. My task is to describe how this machinery contributes to normal vision. This is not an easy task. It can be simplified by making two assumptions. The first is that much of this machinery compensates for movements of the body—not simply the large movements that we use to get about, but also small movements produced by such things as the heart beat and breathing. It also helps to assume that the stabilizing machinery works exceedingly well. It must in order to cope with a disease of the retina that I will call "hereditary localized hyperplasia".

The etiology of this disease is known. It derives from the widespread incidence of a fovea of which only a small portion has the neural substrate required for the kind of vision that has become important for modern human life. (Polyak called this region the foveal floor.) The foveal floor occupies only one one-hundredth of one percent of the area of the retina which forces high-quality human vision to rest on a speck of tissue floating in a sea of relatively crude light sensitive substance.

Many characteristics of human oculomotor performance make sense only as attempts to cope with this genetic defect. There would be no need to move the eyes if the retina were homogeneous and if the foveal floor covered its entire surface. If it did, machinery for head rotation and stabilization of the eye would be all we need to see everything very well. We would be even better off with lateral rather than frontal eyes. These would allow us to dispense with most head movements as well. Note, however, that I am not emphasizing the desirability of such arrangements in order to criticize Charles Darwin, or Jehovah, or whomever else you hold responsible for deficiencies in the way that we are constructed. Rather, I find it helpful to keep this affliction in mind while considering the effects of eye movements on vision. Many of our eye movements are made because of such shortcomings.[2]

Perhaps the simplest way to see how the oculomotor system copes with this disease is to look at the performance of the cat. This animal has a specialized central region but it is less hyperplastic than man's. Figure 1A shows one of three cats studied by Winterson in Professor Robinson's apparatus. The cat is alert and ready for two-dimensional recordings of the way in which she looks about in an ordinary visual scene. The scene the cat could see and the typical visual search pattern of the cat are also shown.

[1] Raised figures refer to Notes at end of paper, pp. 411–413.

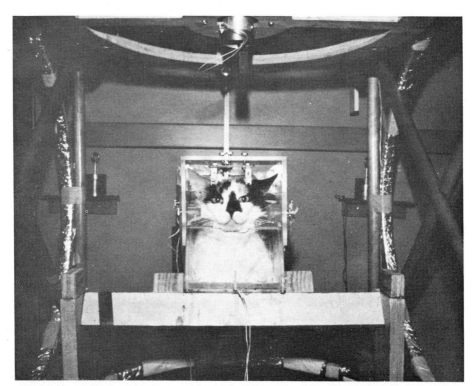

Fig. 1(A).

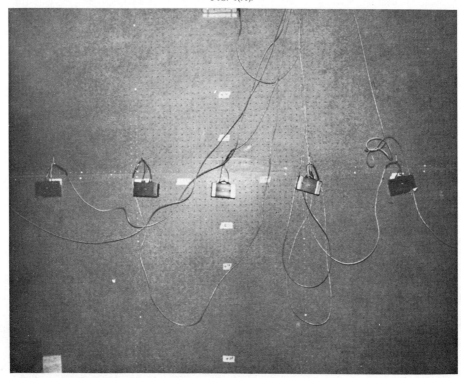

Fig. 1(B).

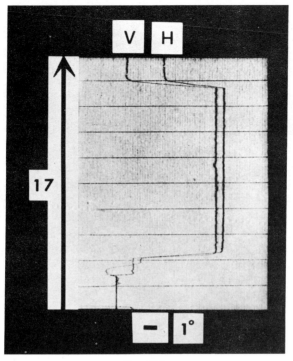

FIG. 1(C).

FIG. 1. (A) A cat positioned for recording eye movement by means of the magnetic field search coil technique. The search coil (not visible) is held to the sclera of the right eye and its leads are carried under the skin to a connector screwed to the skull just above the eye. The head is held in place with respect to the field coils surrounding the animal by means of a metal band screwed to the skull while the cat is supported and confined in a fitted plastic box. (B) Assorted objects located two meters in front of the cat's eye that could be inspected. (C) The typical two-dimensional search pattern of an alert cat. The record begins at the bottom. Repetitive horizontal lines show 1 sec periods of time and the bar shows 1° of arc on both the horizontal (H) and vertical (V) meridians.

Cats make one or two saccades to shift their lines of sight to a region of their choice and then inspect that region for several seconds while using slow control to keep the eye in place. The average fixation pause of the three cats studied lasted 6 sec and very long pauses were occasionally observed. Figure 2A shows a cat using slow control during a 17-sec visual inspection of a single region in visual space and Fig. 2B shows that the cat's slow control is an active process. When visual stimulation is removed (the room lights are turned off), the eye rapidly drifts away from the preferred fixation direction. A saccade may be made to restore eye position when this happens but eye position cannot be maintained when there is no visible target to activate slow control. The fine grain nature of slow control is shown in Fig. 2C where drift direction can be seen to change 4 to 6 times each second. Such irregular drift oscillations keep the eye in place very well (standard deviations of the cat's line of sight do not exceed 2 to 4 min of arc during slow control).[3]

Now, let us consider how the naïve rhesus monkey looks at a visual target. The rhesus has a much higher degree of hyperplasia than the cat. It approaches that of man. Figure 3A shows a fixation record of one of the four monkeys studied in detail

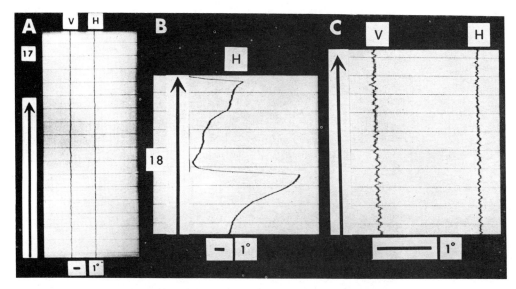

FIG. 2. (A) A two-dimensional record of a cat using slow control during a 17-sec inspection of a single object: (B) Horizontal (H) eye movements of a cat trying to maintain its line of sight in total darkness. (C) High-gain two-dimensional recording of a 10-sec period of slow control. All records begin at the bottom; repetitive horizontal lines show 1 sec periods of time and the black bars show 1° of arc on the horizontal (H) and vertical (V) meridians.

by Skavenski. Note that this monkey makes saccades frequently. Sometimes as often as three each second. Also, note that these saccades tend to be smaller than the cats'—about 2.5° on the average. Figure 4A shows the typical human fixation pattern recorded under much the same conditions. The subject's head was not bolted, but it was stabilized by a bite-board. Again we see fairly frequent saccades but they are one-thirtieth the size of those seen in the rhesus monkey—they average only 5 or 6 min of arc.

It is difficult to know what the drifts are doing in man and the rhesus because both jump around so much. Does a high degree of foveal specialization cause the slow control subsystem to be lost? This is not the case as can be seen in Fig. 4B where a human subject is shown using slow control in the record on the right. The difference is simply a matter of changing the instructions. Man has not lost the capacity (shown by the cat and the rabbit) to hold his eye in place with drifts. Skavenski has also shown this to be true of rhesus monkeys. First he spent several months training them to fixate like humans (make micro- rather than large saccades). This is shown in Fig. 3B. Skavenski then changed the discrimination problem, which encouraged the monkey to suppress saccades, and found that slow control kept the eye in place. A good example of this is shown in Fig. 3C.[4]

What is the significance of these comparative results? They suggest that retinal hyperplasia provokes a frenzy of saccadic activity. This is probably the most striking symptom of the disease. The best way to see these symptoms is to hold the head rigidly and require the patient to be very careful while he inspects a small portion of the visual array. The disease is most advanced in man where something more than genetic limitations are probably operating because there is no reason to believe that man requires smaller saccades than those seen in the fixation pattern of the untrained rhesus. This

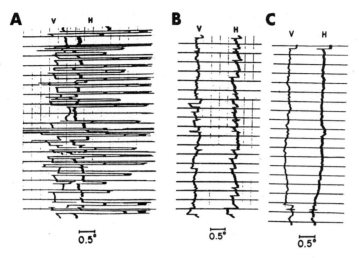

FIG. 3. (A) A representative two-dimensional record of rhesus fixation before special training. (B) A representative two-dimensional record of rhesus fixation after several months of special training. (C) A record of rhesus slow control. All records begin at the bottom; repetitive horizontal lines show 1 sec periods of time and the bars beneath the records show 0.5° of arc on both horizontal (H) and vertical (V) meridians.

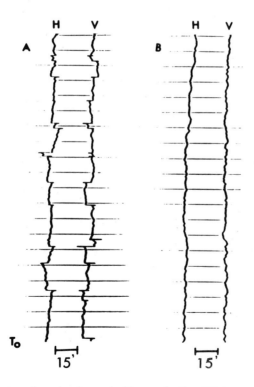

FIG. 4. (A) A representative two-dimensional record of human fixation. (B) A representative two-dimensional record of human slow control. Both records begin at the bottom (T_0); repetitive horizontal lines show 1 sec periods of time and the bars show 15 min of arc on both horizontal (H) and vertical (V) meridians.

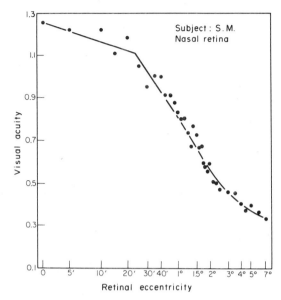

FIG. 5. Visual acuity as a function of retinal eccentricity. The abscissa is on a logarithmic scale. (The curve is drawn by inspection.) Taken from Millodot (1966).

is shown in Fig. 5 where one of Millodot's graphs of visual acuity as a function of retinal eccentricity is reproduced. Acuity dropped only about 25% as the test target moved from the preferred fixation position out to the edge of the foveal floor—about 40 min of arc away from the center. The 5 min of arc saccades made by human beings during maintained fixation seem much too small to be required for visual acuity. Particularly, since the fixation target is typically a point of light in darkness. Such targets appear much the same anywhere on the foveal floor.[5]

EYE MOVEMENTS USED TO ENHANCE OR TO MAINTAIN VISIBILITY

I will postpone speculation about this pathology and will now briefly review research that relates specific features of the human fixation pattern to visual processes. This research asks how miniature eye movements (micro-saccades, drifts, and physiological nystagmus) contribute to vision once a target is brought to the central fovea.

About 50 years ago Weymouth proposed that physiological nystagmus provided the basis of visual acuity. This proposal was developed quantitatively by Marshall and Talbot and Jones and Higgins in the 1940s. By the early 1950s Riggs and Ditchburn and their co-workers had shown that physiological nystagmus was too small to make a dynamic theory workable—tremor does not sweep the light distribution back and forth across any reasonable number of cones. Shortly after, we found out that small high-frequency displacements of the retinal image (by high frequency I mean frequencies above 8 Hz) actually have adverse affects on visual acuity. This was shown by moving targets that were stabilized on the retina by a variety of optical devices. Frequencies around 2 or 3 Hz prevent the disappearance of a stabilized image. This result suggests that drifts of the kind observed during slow control are used to maintain high-quality

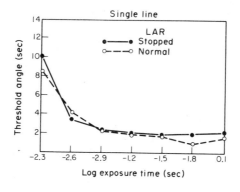

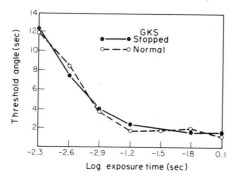

FIG. 6. Threshold curves for detection of single black lines as a function of exposure time under normal and stopped image conditions of viewing. Taken from Riggs (1965) who reproduced it from Keesey (1960).

vision. They are not, however, essential to vision as it is normally used. This can be seen in Fig. 6 where Keesey's data from a study on the effect of exposure duration on the minimum angle resolved is reproduced. Acuity was the same under both normal and stabilized viewing—even after exposure duration was long enough for acuity to be as good as it can be. Acuity is known to deteriorate when a stabilized image begins to fade but fading takes a second or longer—much longer than we normally use to process visual input. For example, we make three or four saccades each second when we read. Keesey's result suggests that we would see very well during reading pauses even if the eye did not move at all.[6]

EFFECTS OF MOVING THE EYE ON VISUAL THRESHOLDS

Not all eye movements maintain visibility. Drifts do. But saccades are different. Although required to place an attended target at the foveal center, they have adverse effects on visibility. These adverse effects, however, seem to be beneficial to the organism because they reduce blurring that would be caused by saccades when they jump the visual array across the retinal surface.

This observation was made long ago. The first report of what is currently called "saccadic suppression" was made by Erdman and Dodge in 1898 who noted that words that were recognized in the periphery during reading pauses could not be seen

during saccades that shifted the line of sight to another position in the text. Initially,
Dodge thought that there was an anesthesia during saccades but by 1900 had rejected
this notion because he noticed that with careful attention it is possible to see stimuli
during a saccade. They are not invisible—only faint. Dodge suggested that the more
intense stimulation seen following the saccade made the faint stimulation visible during
the saccade barely perceptible. In this, Dodge seems to be anticipating a backward
masking (or metacontrast) explanation—a phenomenon that would be reported 12
years later. Holt rejected this central explanation and proposed that impulses from
the extraocular muscles blocked the visual afferent message during the saccade. Wood-
worth questioned both explanations because the visual world looks the same during
a saccade as it does when the visual field is moved rapidly and the eye remains
stationary.

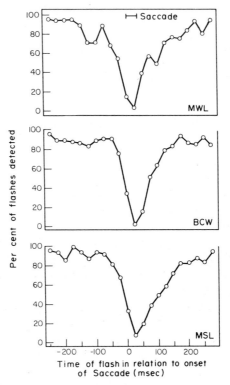

FIG. 7. Percentage of flashes detected by each of three subjects as a function of the temporal relation
of the flash to the onset of a saccade. The average duration of the saccade is shown at the top of the
figure. Taken from Volkmann et al. (1968).

Interest in this problem was rekindled by Ditchburn in the mid-1950s. Since then
several mechanisms have been described and supported experimentally. The phenomenon is interesting because it cannot arise simply from the blurring of images during
saccades—suppression can be shown with flashes too brief to allow blurring. It is
also interesting because the threshold elevation precedes and follows the actual saccade.
A typical result under photopic light conditions is shown in Fig. 7 where it can
be seen that the hit-rate falls for a test flash delivered from 30 ms before to 50

ms after the saccade begins. Such results have been interpreted by Volkmann and others as evidence for central inhibition which begins when the saccade is programmed.

However, similar results are obtained when the eye remains stationary and the visual field is displaced rapidly. This result has led MacKay and a number of others to propose that backward masking is sufficient to explain the threshold elevation. Still other mechanisms have been proposed and supported. For example, Richards suggests that saccades set up shearing forces in the retina that introduce noise signals into the visual system. These signals are large relative to the ordinary visual afferent message and therefore travel rapidly toward the cortex arriving in time to reduce the detectibility of visual afferent signals sent before the saccade. Similarly, new shearing forces at the end of the saccade reduce detection during and sometimes after the eye movement is over.

We have then smear, shear, masking, and central inhibition as possible explanatory mechanisms. Most recently, Riggs and co-workers have shown that masking cannot be the whole story. They found that electrical phosphenes were suppressed by saccades made in a totally dark environment. There are at least two problems remaining. How many of these proposed mechanisms actually contribute to the threshold elevation and what is their relative contribution? Note, that although there is one report of a threshold elevation as large as 1.5 log units, it did not control for the retinal position of the test target. The usual result is only 0.3 to 0.4 of a log unit. At this point I see no basis for favoring one explanation over the others and propose as an impartial non-expert that, in the interest of fairness to a large number of distinguished investigators, we ascribe slightly less than 0.1 of a log unit to each mechanism.[7]

Later I will consider the importance of this phenomenon for position constancy but let me point out here that saccadic suppression, despite its small size, may be significant in considering the contribution of eye movements to vision. Note that it is a suppression and not an enhancement. We have seen that small slow drifts are required to maintain vision. Here we see that saccades have an opposite effect. They raise thresholds before, during, and after their occurrence. Occasionally, it is proposed that saccades produce significant visual information. Information that is used for seeing. The phenomenon I have just described suggests that quite the reverse may be true. This becomes important in looking for the significant visual message in the nervous system. It would seem safest to look only at neural events that precede and follow saccades by about 50 ms if you want to find the electrophysiological correlates of vision in a freely moving eye. Or, if working with an immobilized eye, the most natural input would be a small irregular drift-like movement of the stimulus rather than a sudden jump that simulates a saccade.[8]

EFFECTS OF EYE MOVEMENTS ON
PERCEPTION

Next I will turn to how eye movements influence the way we perceive. We need to know a good deal more about the visual world than can be gleaned from a single foveal view. This view presents only a tiny fraction of the visual array with clarity. We must know the shapes of things, whether they are stationary or moving, and where they are in respect to ourselves. Movements of the eye play an important role in piecing together this kind of information.

First, let us consider the role of eye movements in the perception of shape and size—an area in which eye movement theories have appeared on and off for more than 100 years. The most radical of these eye movement (or motor) theories hold that the eye-movement pattern is determined by the shape of the visual stimulus and that perception of shape is constructed from the sensations that accompany the eye movements used to inspect the stimulus. This kind of theory was proposed by Wundt (the man often considered to be the founder of modern scientific psychology).

Traditionally, such theories are supported by showing that eye movements are larger on the perceptually longer side of the Müller–Lyer illusion. Attacked by showing that the Müller–Lyer illusion is vivid when presented tachistoscopically, and revived by showing that the illusion becomes smaller when scanned repeatedly. This entire cycle had been completed by 1912 when interest in motor theories abated as Gestalt Psychology became ascendant in perception. Motor theories were revived by Hebb in 1949, who suggested that the perception of shape by adults was based, in part, on implicit as well as actual eye movements. This is a clever business. It eliminates the problem raised by the fact that an adult can see forms without actually making eye movements. Hebb also avoids the problem of awareness of the eye movement pattern by explaining perception on the basis of neurophysiological processes rather than sensations. He calls these processes "cell assemblies" and "phase sequences". Terms that refer to neural traces of corner analyzers and their connecting circuits. Both are built up slowly in childhood by using eye movements to look around. Such traces eventually allow the child to discriminate forms without actually moving his eye. By 1960 interest in this theory had waned because psychologists, speculating about neurological processes, turned to Hubel and Wiesel who had begun to describe the actual analyzers present in the visual cortex. Hebb's theory was weakened considerably by the fact that infant animals had the same hardware as their parents.

In the mid-1960s Festinger revived interest by proposing a motor theory that does not make the empiristic assumptions so prominent in Hebb's theory. Festinger's theory, like Hebb's, is not an overt motor theory. It links perception to programming rather than executing eye movements but it avoids Hebb's empiricism. It does not assume that these programs could not be hard-wired with their templates given by the genetic code. The theory seems timely because it borrows terminology from von Holst and talks of "efferent readiness" and "efferent copies" when it refers to physiological processes. So far support comes primarily from the study of visual illusions where some suggestive results have been obtained. The Müller–Lyer illusion is reproduced in Fig. 8. The reader can scan the illusion for several minutes and judge for himself how much the illusion is reduced by prolonged inspection.[9]

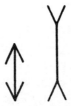

FIG. 8. The Müller Lyer Illusion. The vertical line segments are the same length.

Next I would like to consider how we know where things are in space relative to ourselves. (By ourselves I mean the mid-saggital plane of the upper torso or the straight-ahead of the body image if you prefer psychological to anatomical terms.) To know where things are we must know the orientation of the head with respect to the body, the orientation of the eye with respect to the head, and where the object of interest falls on the retina. We have all this information but there is some question as to its source. The visual afferent message gives us the distance and direction of a visual object with respect to the center of the fovea. But how do we know the orientation of the fovea with respect to the head? (The third problem, how we know where the head is with respect to the body, I will leave to Professors Bizzi and Abrahams.)

Two schemes have been proposed. The most influential has been Helmholtz's who said that we know the direction the eye is pointing because we know the effort of the will we used to orient the eye. We not only know what we told the eye to do, we can remember what we told it to do for a considerable period of time. The alternative scheme, proposed by Sherrington, assumes that the large number of mechanoreceptors found in extraocular muscle tell the human how his eye is oriented in the orbit. This is sometimes called an "inflow" theory.

Helmholtz supported his view (sometimes called "outflow") by pointing out that passive displacements of the eye cause shifts of the positions of objects in space. He also pointed out that impeded attempts to move the eye lead to a loss of position constancy—objects appear to shift in the direction of the attempted but blocked eye movement. These elegant demonstrations have been interpreted as showing that the eye is devoid of a position sense—only knowing where it is because of the monitored and stored efferent command.

There have been developments in the past few years which show that the story is not this simple. Skavenski, who did this work, was probably the first to note the danger of making inferences about the oculomotor system from experiments that were concerned with the perception of direction rather than with the control of eye position itself.

He performed an experiment in which subjects used inflow to control the position of the eye in the absence of any other information. The way this was done and the results of the experiment are shown in Figs. 9 and 10. Note that both subjects began to correct eye position as the load was being applied. This means that very small proprioceptive signals can be used to maintain the position of the eye in the orbit.

Skavenski also used a forced-choice psychophysical procedure to show that the application and direction of the load could be sensed. This result conflicts with a report of Brindley and Merton who were not able to sense the position of their eyes. These authors probably had difficulty for two reasons. They used an insensitive psychophysical method and a distracting technique for displacing the eye. Grasping the eye with forceps could mask the relatively subtle but easily sensed feelings that are produced by passive displacements.

Next Skavenski and Haddad investigated the relative contribution of outflow and inflow to the perception of direction and quantified Helmholtz's observation that changing the efferent command to maintain eye position against a load causes shifts in the perceived location of the fixated target. They also put the outflow signal in conflict

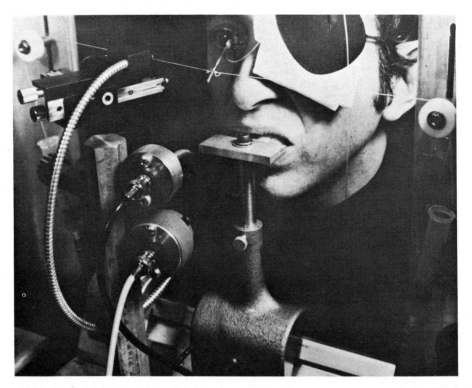

FIG. 9. Subject RS in position in the apparatus used to record horizontal eye movements while loading his right eye. RS is biting on an acrylic-bite board which holds his head rigidly in place. Horizontal rotations of his right eye were recorded by means of an infrared light transmitting and a collecting fiber optic mounted on the microscope stage just to his right. Loads were applied by adding water to the plastic chambers shown below the pulleys on the left and right. Loads were transmitted to the eye by means of the dacron threads that pass over the pulleys and connect to the 3-cm stalk attached to the scleral contact-lens. The contact-lens was held firmly to the eye by suction applied through the thin polyethylene tubing that can be seen as it passes up over the bridge of the nose and, again, as it passes in front of the left eye patch on its way to the suction apparatus (not shown). The suction tubing was arranged so that it did not, at any time during these experiments, touch the nose or face at any place except where it was taped to the forehead near the hairline. This contact with the skin could not have provided eye position information because the lateral displacement of the end of tubing at this junction with the contact-lens was too small and the tubing too flexible to produce any tactile cues on the forehead. With this apparatus loads of various magnitudes could be applied to the right eye gradually and completely silently. Taken from Skavenski (1972).

with the inflow signal and found that a conflicting inflow signal did not influence the perceived direction of the fixated target. Taken together, these results show that some non-visual afferent can be used to control eye position. It can be sensed but does not change where things appear to be in space when its message conflicts with the efferent command.

Recently there has also been work by the Matins and co-workers who measured what happens to position constancy during saccadic eye movements. They found that the map of retinal position with respect to perceived direction shifts in rather complicated ways. The shift begins about 130 ms before the saccade and continues after the eye movement is completed. During this period subjects have difficulty reporting the spatial location of a test target. Eventually objects appear to be appropriately

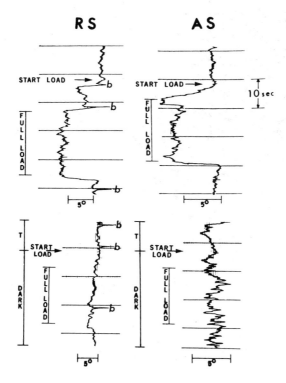

FIG. 10. Representative records of RS's and AS's horizontal eye-position control when loads were applied to their right eyes. In the upper records Ss fixated the visible target with their left eyes. Right eyes were occluded. Application of the load began at the time indicated by the arrow head and the verical bar on the left indicates the period of time the *full load* was applied. The final seconds of each record show eye position returning to baseline as the load was removed. The two lower records show RS's and AS's ability to correct eye position when loads, equal to those applied in the upper records, were applied during the dark period. For these records S's right eyes were uncovered and their left eyes were closed and covered. Records begin with 10 sec of fixation of the visible target (T). The target was switched-off at the time indicated by the arrow and the remainder of the record shows eye position control in the dark (*DARK*). Application of the load began just after the time indicated by the arrow and the vertical bar shows the period the *full load* was applied. The load was removed during the final seconds of each record. Pulse-like changes in the trace, labeled *b*, are blinks. Horizontal bars beneath each record show 5° arc rotations on the horizontal meridian. Taken from Skavenski (1972).

placed but this takes about 400 ms. Note, however, that saccadic suppression occurs during the same period. This has lead Ethel Matin to suggest that saccadic suppression, despite its modest size, has functional significance. It attenuates perception of the poorly localized visual world while a saccade is programmed and made. But this disturbance of visual localization only applies to the perception of direction, not to the control of eye position. Hallett and Lightstone have shown recently that the oculomotor system is not confused during saccades. It processes information about a change in the position of a fixation target that is displaced during a saccade with a high degree of accuracy. Here, once again, we see that our oculomotor system can use information that differs from what we perceive. There seems to be no simple correspondence between what the little engineer in the brainstem sees and the perceptions of the little man in the cortex who tells us what is really out there in the visual world.[10]

WHAT *IS* THE ROLE OF EYE MOVEMENTS IN VISION?

This completes my review of highlights from the laboratory where the effect of eye movements on visual and perceptual processes has been studied extensively during the past 25 years. The impression one gets from most of the visual research is that eye movements are fundamental. They establish and maintain visibility. Their role in perception is less clear but interest continues and it seems only a matter of time before we know how we perceive as well as how we see.

There is, however, something disturbing about how we interpret much of this painstaking research. We tend to talk as though we believe that the eye moves because image motion is required to drive many of the visual neurons. Neurons that respond to changing rather than constant stimulation. This seems to suggest that eye movements evolved to drive these neural elements. I think that quite the reverse is true. It seems more likely that the oculomotor system evolved to stabilize retinal images because the retinal image is displaced by everything we do. Our ordinary activities place an enormous burden on the oculomotor system. Just how large this burden is had not been studied which encouraged Winterson, Robinson, Skavenski, and I to begin to look at what the eye actually does in natural circumstances—circumstances in which the head is not held rigidly in place. How this was done is shown in Fig. 11 which

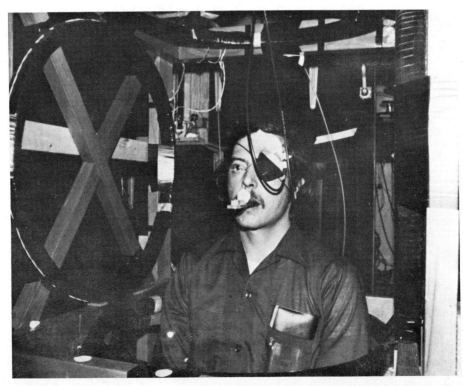

Fig. 11. Skavenski in position for simultaneous two-dimensional recording of rotations of his head and right eye by means of the magnetic field search coil technique. The eye search coil is embedded in a tight-fitting scleral contact lens held to the eye by suction. The head search coil is mounted to a dental bite plate. The field coils can be seen surrounding the subject who is looking at a target at optical infinity.

shows Skavenski rigged-up to use Robinson's search coil technique to make simultaneous recordings of the rotations of his head and eye while he attempts to sit as still as possible and maintain his line of sight on a fixation target. Figure 12 shows a record of both eye and head rotations. There was a great deal of head rotation and the eye was very busy trying to compensate for these rotations.

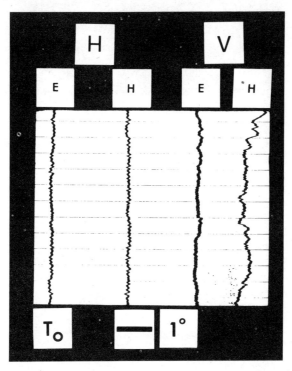

FIG. 12. A representative simultaneous eye (E) and head (H) recording of rotations on the horizontal (H) and vertical (V) meridians made while the subject sat as still as possible. The record begins at the bottom (T_0); the repetitive horizontal lines show 1 sec periods and the bar shows 1° of arc for both eye and head traces.

We have not analysed these records and are not yet prepared to say whether all eye movements other than voluntary saccades are made in response to rotations and translations of the head signalled either by its orientation, acceleration, or by displacements of the retinal image. But, what with rotations caused by breathing (which have a peak to peak amplitude of about half of a degree), the pulse (which requires about 10 min of arc compensation every second or so), and oscillations in the servo working to hold the head steady (which have a frequency of about 3 to 5 Hz and an amplitude of about 10 min of arc), the eye is kept quite busy trying to maintain the target image in the center of the fovea.

Can a subject do better than this under the most ideal conditions—when the chin is supported by the hands and the breath is held? Both of these acts are in the normal behavioral repertoire. They might be used to steady the head while trying to pay close attention to some detail in the visual world. Figure 13 shows eye and head traces when Skavenski supported his head, held his breath, and tried to keep his eye on a visual target. There was still a great deal of activity. Such activity is not confined to Skavenski's head. His rotations are not early symptoms of Parkinsonism. We all have this problem. The head rotations of five other subjects have been recorded. They all moved as much no matter how hard they tried to keep still.[11]

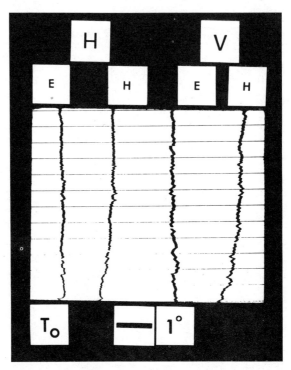

FIG. 13. A representative simultaneous eye (E) and head (H) recording of rotations on the horizontal (H) and vertical (V) meridians made while the subject sat as still as possible while supporting his head on his hands and held his breath. The record begins at the bottom (T_0); the repetitive horizontal lines show 1 sec periods of time and the bar shows 1° of arc for both eye and head traces.

These data suggest that there may have been too much emphasis on the importance of eye movements for guaranteeing retinal image motion in recent years. The retinal image is in no danger of standing still if the head is not attached to a rigid metal plate. It seems likely to me that the oculomotor system evolved to compensate for such disturbances in orientation of the eye—disturbances that are inescapable outside of the laboratory. The problem for man and other foveate animals is colossal. We must not only compensate for bodily movements we must also adjust the orientation of the fovea so that we can see attended objects. We also must be able to track smoothly so that attended moving objects can be kept relatively stationary within this tiny specialized region. A great deal of machinery must develop to allow these tricks. We also need more than the ability to stabilize and swing the eyeball. We need considerable cognitive capacity to construct a perceptually meaningful world from the sequence of small snapshots that we typically acquire in a haphazard order. We also need selective attention to acquire what we need to know when we need to know it. We also need short- and long-term memory to put this material together

Fig. 14. A chameleon.

and to hold on to it long enough to know where we are relative to where we have been. In short we need a human brain.

It is tempting to propose that man's high degree of perceptual and cognitive development arose in his evolutionary effort to compensate for problems inherent in foveal specialization—or "hereditary localized hyperplasia" as I called this burden earlier. I find this an attractive way to think about the development and role of the oculomotor system in visual processing. It makes this system seem terribly important. I suspect, however, that not everyone will share my enthusiasm for this approach particularly since it is probably not without shortcomings. This can be seen in Fig. 14 which shows a chameleon—an animal with a high degree of foveal specialization. Its pit is deeper and more densely packed than man's. I know almost nothing about reptilian brains and even less about reptilian behavior. Is this lizard really as wise as she looks?[12]

ACKNOWLEDGEMENTS

I thank my colleagues G. Haddad, E. Kowler, P. McGrath, B. Murphy, and B. Winterson for valuable suggestions and experimental results that were used in the preparation of this paper. Also, D. A. Robinson and A. A. Skavenski who collaborated on various aspects of the research described in this paper and provided the facilities as well as ideas, experimental results, and technical skills required for various aspects of this work. The technical assistance of I. Nicholson and J. Mathews is also gratefully acknowledged.

This report and the research on human fixation was supported by Grant No. EY325 from the National Eye Institute to the author. Research on the oculomotor performance of the normal cat was supported by Grant No. EY598 from the National Eye Institute to D. A. Robinson and the research on the oculomotor performance of the rhesus and human head and eye rotations by Grant No. EY1049 from the National Eye Institute to A. A. Skavenski. I thank Profs. D. M. MacKay and L. A. Riggs for their comments on this manuscript.

NOTES

1. This article is an abridged version (fewer figures) of the paper read in Stockholm. The assigned topic was very broad. It covered several areas of visual and perceptual research. Any one of these areas could easily fill a chapter in this volume. Each has been reviewed in recent years and is discussed in current textbooks on visual and perceptual processes. For this reason I decided to publish my lecture as it was given and add notes to provide the unspecialized reader with additional information and some of the sources that influenced my thinking. See Ditchburn (1973) and Festinger (1971) for alternatives to my approach to this topic. See Walls (1962) for a similar approach to mine written before slow control had been demonstrated in man.

2. The primate retina (and man's in particular) shows a great deal of foveal specialization. The classical source for its structure is Polyak (1941). I chose this characteristic to organize the lecture—inventing an imaginary disease to make the presentation consistent with the title of this symposium. This specialization is not only anatomical. A good deal of differential function has also been demonstrated psychophysically—a fact that makes this "disease" plausible. My emphasis on specialization is old-fashioned, however, because it has become popular recently to use transfer functions to describe the visual system—a methodology that is easier to use if the functional properties of the human retina are treated as though they were relatively uniform across large regions. (See Cornsweet, 1970, for an introduction to the use of the transfer function to study the spatial resolving power of the retina.) I have chosen to be old-fashioned because the human scan pattern is easier to understand when the retina is viewed as exceedingly heterogeneous. I am not at all convinced, however, that normal humans actually have the kind of tunnel vision my

"disease" implies. Phenomenologically the visual world seems to have excellent form and color vision through-out. The extent to which this compelling subjective impression is constructed by memory through serial processing of foveal snapshots is by no means worked out. See Monty and Senders (1974) for a recent discussion of this problem at a specialists' meeting on the role of eye movements on psychological processes. It is my impression that at this time it is as reasonable to believe that eye movements are used to confirm already organized percepts as to believe that eye movements are used to piece together the visual world from a series of foveal snapshots.

3. Winterson (1974) described the normal visual exploration of the cat in greater detail recently and a complete report of this material is in press (Winterson and Robinson). Some of her results do not agree with the other published studies of the cat's fine-grain oculomotor performance (Hebbard and Marg, 1960; Pritchard and Heron, 1960). Winterson found that the cat, unlike ourselves but like untrained monkeys, never makes microsaccades (flicks smaller than 10 min of arc). Occasional microsaccades had been reported by Hebbard and Marg (1960). Winterson never observed any in several thousand seconds of recording and concluded that the prior report of microsaccades was a misinterpretation of the cat's eye movement pattern. Hebbard and Marg only recorded on the horizontal meridian. Winterson's two-dimensional recordings showed that "microsaccades", observed occasionally on one meridian, were actually components of rotation associated with large saccades on the other meridian. Pritchard and Heron (1960) reported that their cats' intersaccadic drifts were rapid and uncompensated. It is not clear why these authors failed to notice slow control—the most striking feature of feline oculomotor performance. It might have been because their cats were drowsy following the administration of anesthesia. A drowsy cat, like a drowsy man, drifts all over.

The fine-grain characteristics of slow control in the cat are very much like those of the rabbit who has been extensively studied by Collewijn and co-workers (1969, 1970, 1972). The rabbit has no fovea, does not show fixation saccades, and uses slow control exclusively to maintain eye position. Slow control in the rabbit, like the cat and man (Skavenski and Steinman, 1970), is lost when visual stimulation is not available.

4. Recently, Skavenski (1974b) reported these characteristics and described the training procedures for establishing them. A description of earlier phases of his work can be found in Steinman, et al. (1973). This article also contains description of the discovery of slow control in the human and a summary of several lines of evidence supporting the notion that the miniature saccades, typically seen in the fixation pattern of adult humans, represent an overlearned motor skill unique to man and probably without any useful visual function.

5. I chose to use Millodot's (1966) data for the VA/eccentricity function in the fovea because these measurements were made very carefully under conditions where the exact placement of the test target could be known. Millodot (1972) finds that, in general, the isoacuity area is relatively large in the central fovea (ranging from 24 to 50 min arc depending on the type of target). Other authors consider this function to be steeper. For example, LeGrand (1967, p. 136) draws his curve summarizing data gathered from a number of experimenters such that acuity seems to fall off very rapidly as tests are made small distances from the fixation point. Many of the data points, however, seem consistent with Millodot's measurements. I would prefer to believe that acuity is relatively uniform on the foveal floor because it makes it easier to understand the fixation stability/eccentricity function. See Timberlake et al. (1972) for a discussion and data that bears on this problem.

6. There is a very large literature on the role of eye movements in visual processes studied by means of the stabilized image technique. See Alpern (1972) for a recent discussion of the current status of such research and Weymouth et al. (1923) for descriptions of the "dynamic" theory of visual acuity that inspired much of the subsequent stabilized image research. Also, see Ditchburn (1973), Riggs (1965), and Yarbus (1967) for summaries of research done in the laboratories most active in studying this problem during the 1950s and 1960s (much of this material was reviewed by Heckenmueller, 1965). See Gerrits and Vendrik (1970, 1972, 1974) for current work by very ingenious investigators and Arend (1973) for a theoretical paper that imputes a very large role to monitored eye movements in the processing of contours, brightness, and color.

The stabilized image technique has also been used to study visual perception. Here I am referring to the work of Pritchard et al. (1960) and Pritchard (1961) who reported meaningful perceptual fragmentation of stabilized complex stimuli. These results received widespread attention probably because they bridged the gap between vision and visual perception with material that could be readily described in introductory psychology texts. Many of us suspected at the time of the initial reports that these perceptual fragments might not represent visual organizing processes revealed by stabilization because direct phenomenal report was used in these studies. Such reports are easily biased. The frequent reappearances of the stimuli also suggested that the stabilization was poor as well. Over the ensuing years a number of authors have expressed such concerns (e.g. Cornsweet, 1970, p. 408), and recently Shuck and Leahy (1966) and Shuck (1973) have shown that similar phenomenal reports are obtained without stabilized images when subjects describe ambi-guous figures verbally. As matters now stand it seems parsimonious to assume that constraints of language determine the way ambiguous figures will be described and that most, if not all, of the perceptual effects reported by Pritchard are based on cognitive rather than visual processes.

7. I am greatly indebted to Ethel Matin (1974b) for allowing me to read a preprint of her review on saccadic suppression. This excellent article analyzes methodological problems and evaluates theoretical issues in this area of research. It also provides a very complete bibliography of the large number of publications this problem has generated over the past 75 years.

8. See Fischer and Krüger (this volume) for an example of an electrophysiological study where I believe this caution is warranted. The electrophysiological responses produced by saccade-like movements of a stimulus outside of the receptive field do not seem likely to provide significant visual information to the cat. The barrage of activity associated with these step displacements might, however, be the neurological basis of or produce the need for a saccadic suppression mechanism.

9. See Murphy et al. (1974) for a brief discussion of motor theories of form processing. These authors found that simple forms, confined to the foveal floor, do not constrain the oculomotor pattern. The problem is still open for extra-foveal forms—whose shape can not be seen without using saccades to scan the display. I believe that the oculomotor system provided with photopically effective stimulation is largely free from stimulus constraints. See Steinman (1974) for a summary of evidence supporting this view. Most of the reported effects of eye movements on form perception or visual illusions are very small and subject to alternative interpretations. See Bolles (1969), Boyce and West (1967, 1968), Delabarre (1897), Festinger et al. (1968), Festinger (1971), Hebb (1949), Judd (1905), McLaughlin et al. (1969), Lewis (1908), Lötze (1852), Mollon (1968), and Wundt (1910) for some representative material on the role of eye movements in the perception of form and illusions of visual extent.

Some comment about the relationship of Hubel and Wiesel's (1962) observations and Hebb's (1949) motor theory of form perception is necessary. For Hebb all percepts more complicated than "primitive unity" (a segregation of figure from ground that has no shape) are built-up empirically by the infant as it scans the visual field. The first constructions are line, slope, and corner detectors. These are subsequently connected by the eye-scan pattern. The infant's eye tends to look from corner to corner. These repeated visual stimulations establish "phase sequences" the physiological correlate of the perceived form. Hubel and Wiesel's (1962) demonstration of orientation specific cortical units is, as they point out, suggestive of the elements that might, working together, form corner analyzers—a notion similar to the kind of cortical organization Hebb suggested. However, these units, according to Hebb, should not be present without prior coordinated visual and oculomotor experience. This seems not to be the case according to Hubel and Wiesel (1963). The most distinctive feature of their results with newly sighted kittens is the demonstration of pre-wired functional arrangements similar to their parents'. The most distinctive feature of Hebb's theory, on the other hand, is its emphasis on empiricism. Eye movements are used to construct percepts which do not exist without prior "learning". I find it hard to reconcile Hebb's theory with Hubel and Wiesel's conclusion. The problem for the newly sighted kitten seems to be visuomotor (they do not track targets or avoid obstacles) rather than visual if the Hubel and Wiesel cells are responsible for the perception of form—an assumption that is open to question (Blum, in preparation). Even the Hubel and Wiesel conclusion with the kitten is open to question (Blakemore and Cooper, 1970; Spinelli et al., 1972) and it may be some time before we know enough about how form is abstracted in the visual system to be able to find out how or if the oculomotor system contributes (see Blum, 1973, for a recent discussion of alternative models for form perception).

10. See Skavenski and Steinman (1970), Skavenski (1971, 1972, 1974a), and Skavenski et al. (1972) for recent work on oculomotor inflow and references to prior work. See Matin (1972) for a description of the work of his group on eye movements and perceived direction and Ethel Matin (1974a) for a discussion of the importance of saccadic suppression for the maintenance of position constancy during saccades. See Hallett and Lightstone (in preparation) and Jurgens and Becker (this Symposium) for evidence that the saccadic system processes information during the period that perception of direction is disturbed. Also, see MacKay (1970, 1973) for evidence that shifts in apparent spatial location can be induced by passive as well as active displacements of the retinal image and recent discussion of the role of the eye movements in the perception of spatial location.

11. See Steinman (1974) for a quantitative treatment of the rotational components of the head movements of five subjects. See Troelestra (1972) for measurements of the effects of normal physiological activities on motions of the eyeball.

12. A number of problems that relate eye movements to visual or perceptual processes were not included because of time (space) limitations. See Royce et al. (1966) and Levy (1972) for an evaluation of the methodology and bibliography on autokinesis—an illusion that has been studied for more than a century and Crone and Verduyn Lunel (1969) and Matin and McKinnon (1964) for particularly interesting modern experimental papers that relate this phenomenon to the eye movement pattern. I also omitted consideration of the role of eye movements in the perception of motion (see, for example, Gibson, 1968; Kinchla and Allan, 1969; Orban et al. 1973 for representative papers) and also their role in determining the perceived orientation of the visual field (see, for example, Howard and Templeton, 1964; Petrov and Zenkin, 1973).

REFERENCES

ALPERN, M. (1972) Eye movements. In: *Handbook of Sensory Physiology*, vol. VII/4, JAMESON, D. and HURVICH, L. (Eds.). Springer-Verlag, New York.

AREND, L. E. (1973) Spatial differential and integral operations in human vision: implications of stabilized retinal image fading. *Psychol. Rev.* **80**, 374.

BLAKEMORE, C. and COOPER, G. F. (1970) Development of the brain depends on the visual environment. *Nature*, **228**, 477.

BLUM, H. (1973) Biological shape and visual science (Part 1). *J. Theor. Biol.* **38**, 205.

BLUM, H. (1975) Biological shape and visual science (Part 2). *J. Theor. Biol.* (in preparation).

BOLLES, R. (1969) The role of eye movements in the Müller–Lyer illusion. *Percept. & Psychophys.* **6**, 175.

BOYCE, P. R. and WEST, D. C. (1967) A perceptual effect on the control of fixation. *Optica Acta*, **14**, 119.

BOYCE, P. R. and WEST, D. C. (1968) Reply to "Fixation and Perception". *Optica Acta*, **15**, 299.

COLLEWIJN, H. (1969) Optokinetic eye movements in the rabbit: input-output relations. *Vision Res.* **9**, 117.

COLLEWIJN, H. (1970) The normal range of horizontal eye movements in the rabbit. *Exptl Neurol.* **28**, 132.

COLLEWIJN, H. and VANDERMARK, F. (1972) Ocular stability in variable feedback conditions in the rabbit. *Brain Res.* **36**, 47.

CORNSWEET, T. N. (1970) *Visual Perception.* Academic Press, New York.

CRONE, R. A. and VERDUYN LUNEL, H. F. E. (1969) Autokinesis and the perception of movement: the physiology of eccentric fixation. *Vision Res.* **9**, 89.

DELABARRE, E. B. (1897) A method of recording eye movements. *Am. J. Psychol.* **9**, 572.

DITCHBURN, R. W. (1973) *Eye Movements and Visual Perception.* Oxford Univ. Press, New York.

FESTINGER, L. (1971) in *The Control of Eye Movements*, BACH-Y-RITA, P. and COLLINS, C. C. (Eds.). Academic Press, London.

FESTINGER, L., WHITE, C. W. and ALLYN, M. R. (1968) Eye movements and decrement in the Müller–Lyer illusion. *Percept. Psychophys.* **3**, 376.

GERRITS, H. J. M. and VENDRIK, A. J. H. (1970) Artificial movements of a stabilized image. *Vision Res.* **10**, 1443.

GERRITS, H. J. M. and VENDRIK, A. J. H. (1972) Eye movements necessary for continuous perception during stabilization of retinal images. *Bibl. Ophthal.* **82**, 339.

GERRITS, H. J. M. and VENDRIK, A. J. H. (1974) The influence of stimulus movements on perception in parafoveal stabilized version. *Vision Res.* **14**, 175.

GIBSON, J. G. (1968) What gives rise to the perception of motion? *Psychol. Rev.* **75**, 335.

HALLET, P. E. and LIGHTSTONE, A. D. (1975) Saccadic eye movements due to stimuli triggered during prior saccades. (in prep.)

HEBB, D. O. (1949) *The Organization of Behavior.* John Wiley & Sons, Inc., New York.

HEBBARD, F. W. and MARG, E. (1960) Physiological nystagmus in the cat. *J. Opt. Soc. Am.* **50**, 151.

HECKENMUELLER, E. G. (1965) Stabilization of the retinal image: A review of method, effects, and theory. *Psychol. Bull.* **63**, 157.

HOWARD, I. P. and TEMPLETON, W. B. (1964) Visually induced eye torsion and tilt adaptation. *Vision Res.* **4**, 433.

HUBEL, D. H. and WIESEL, T. N. (1962) Receptive fields, binocular interaction and functional architecture in the cat's visual cortex. *J. Physiol.* **160**, 106.

HUBEL, D. H. and WIESEL, T. N. (1963) Receptive fields of cells in striate cortex of very young, visually inexperienced kittens. *J. Neurophysiol.* **26**, 994.

JONES, L. and HIGGINS, G. (1948) Photographic granularity and graininess. IV. Visual acuity thresholds; dynamic versus static assumptions *J. Opt. Soc. Am.* **38**, 398.

JUDD, C. H. (1905) Movement and consciousness. *Psychol. Monogr.* no. 34.

KEESEY, U. T. (1960) Effects of involuntary eye movements on visual acuity. *J. Opt. Soc. Am.* **50**, 769.

KINCHLA, R. A. and ALLAN, L. G. (1969) A theory of visual movement perception. *Psychol. Rev.* **76**, 537.

LEGRAND, Y. (1967) *Form and Space Vision.* Bloomington, Indiana Univ. Press.

LEVY, J. (1972) Autokinetic illusion: a systematic review of theories, measures, and independent variables. *Psychol. Bull.* **78**, 457.

LEWIS, D. O. (1908) The effect of practice on the perception of the Müller-Lyer illusion. *Brit. J. Psychol.* **2**, 294.

LÖTZE, R. H. (1852) *Medicinische Psychologie.* Reprinted by E. J. Bonet, Amsterdam, 1966.

MACKAY, D. M. (1970) Mislocation of test flashes during saccadic image displacement. *Nature*, **227**, 731.

MACKAY, D. M. (1973) in *Handbook of Sensory Physiology* JUNG, R. (Ed.), vol. **VII/3A**. Springer, Heidelberg and New York.

MCLAUGHLIN, S. C., DESISTO, M. J. and KELLY, M. J., JR. (1969) Comment on "Eye Movements and decrement in the Müller-Lyer illusion". *Percept. Psychophys.* **5**, 288.

MARSHALL, W. and TALBOT, S. (1942) Recent evidence for neural mechanisms in vision leading to a general theory of sensory acuity. *Biol. Symp.* **7**, 117.

MATIN, E. (1974a) Role of eye movements in maintaining a phenomenally clear and stable world. Presented at the specialists' meeting on eye movements and psychological processes. Princeton, New Jersey (to be published by NRC).

MATIN, E. (1974b) Saccadic suppression: a review and an analysis. *Psychol. Bull.* **81**, 899.

MATIN, L. (1972) in *Handbook of Sensory Physiology*, vol. VII/4, JAMESON, D. and HURVICH, L. (Eds.) Springer-Verlag, Berlin.

MATIN, L. and MACKINNON, G. E. (1964) Autokinetic movement: selective manipulation of directional components by image stabilization. *Science*, **143**, 147.

MILLODOT, M. (1966) Foveal and extra-foveal acuity with and without stabilized retinal images. *Brit. J. Physiol. Optics*, **23**, 75.

MILLODOT, M. (1972) Variation of visual acuity in the central region of the retina. *Brit. J. Physiol. Optics*, **27**, 24.

MOLLON, J. D. (1968) Fixation and perception. *Optica Acta*, **15**, 295.

MONTY, R. A. and SENDERS, J. W. (1974) Organizers of the specialists' meeting on eye movements and psychological processes. Princeton, New Jersey (to be published by NRC).

MURPHY, B. J., HADDAD, G. M. and STEINMAN, R. M. (1974) Simple forms and fluctuations of the line of sight: Implications for motor theories of form processing. *Percept. Psychophys.* **16**, 557.

ORBAN, G., DUYSENS, J. and CALLENS, M. (1973) Movement perception during voluntary saccadic eye movements. *Vision Res.* **13**, 1343.

PETROV, A. P. and ZENKIN, G. H. (1973) Torsional eye movements and constancy of the visual field. *Vision Res.* **12**, 2015.

POLYAK, S. L. (1941) *The Retina.* University of Chicago Press, Chicago.

PRITCHARD, R. M. (1961) Stabilized images on the retina. *Sci. Amer.* **204**, 72.

PRITCHARD, R. M. and HERON, W. (1960) Small eye movements of the cat. *Can. J. Psychol.* **14**, 131.

PRITCHARD, R. M., HERON, W. and HEBB, D. O. (1960) Visual perception approached by the method of stabilized images. *Can. J. Psychol.* **14**, 67.

RIGGS, L. (1965) Visual acuity. In: *Vision and Visual Perception*, GRAHAM, C. (Ed.). John Wiley & Sons, Inc., New York.

ROYCE, J. R., CARRAN, A. B., AFTANAS, M., LEHMAN, R. S. and BLUMENTHAL, A. (1966) The autokinetic phenomenon: a critical review. *Psychol. Bull.* **65**, 243.

SCHUCK, J. R. (1973) Factors affecting reports of fragmenting visual images. *Percept. Psychophys.* **13**, 382.

SCHUCK, J. R. and LEAHY, W. R. (1966) A comparison of verbal and nonverbal reports of fragmenting visual images. *Percept. Psychophys.* **1**, 191.

SKAVENSKI, A. A. (1971) Extraretinal correction and memory for target position. *Vision Res.* **11**, 743.

SKAVENSKI, A. A. (1972) Inflow as a source of extraretinal eye position. *Vision Res.* **12**, 221.

SKAVENSKI, A. A. (1974a). The nature and role of extraretinal eye position information. Presented at the specialists' meeting on eye movements and psychological processes. Princeton, N.J. (to be published by NRC).

SKAVENSKI, A. A. (1974b) Fixation eye movement in rhesus monkey. Paper read at ARVO, May 1974.

SKAVENSKI, A. A., HADDAD, G. M. and STEINMAN, R. M. (1972) The extraretinal signal for the visual perception of direction. *Percept. Psychophys.* **11**, 287.

SKAVENSKI, A. A., and STEINMAN, R. M. (1970) Control of eye position in the dark. *Vision Res.* **10**, 193.

SPINELLI, D. N., HIRSCH, H. V. B., PHELPS, R. W. and METZLER, J. (1972) Visual experience as a determinant of the response characteristics of cortical receptive fields in cats. *Exptl Brain Res.* **15**, 289.

STEINMAN, R. M. (1974) Role of eye movements in maintaining a phenomenally clear and stable world. Presented at the specialists' meeting on eye movements and psychological processes. Princeton, New Jersey (to be published by NRC).

STEINMAN, R. M., HADDAD, G. M., SKAVENSKI, A. A. and WYMAN, D. (1973) Miniature eye movement. *Science*, **181**, 810.

TIMBERLAKE, G. T., WYMAN, D., SKAVENSKI, A. A. and STEINMAN, R. M. (1972) The oculomotor error signal in the fovea. *Vision Res.* **12**, 1059.

TROELESTRA, A. (1972) Intraocular noise: origin and characteristics. *Vision Res.* **12**, 1313.

VOLKMANN, F. C., SCHICK, A. M. L. and RIGGS, L. A. (1968) Time course of visual inhibition during voluntary saccades. *J. Opt. Soc. Am.* **58**, 562.

WALLS, G. L. (1962) The evolutionary history of eye movements. *Vision Res.* **2**, 69.

WEYMOUTH, F., ANDERSEN, E. and AVERILL, H. (1923) Retinal mean local sign: a new view of the relation of the retinal mosaic to visual perception. *Am. J. Physiol.* **63**, 410.

WINTERSON, B. The way cats look. Paper read at ARVO, May 1974.

WUNDT, W. (1910) *Grundzüge der Physiologischen Psychologische*, 5th ed., vol. 2. W. Engelmann, Leipzig.

YARBUS, A. L. (1967) *Eye Movements and Vision.* Plenum Press, New York.

OCULOMOTOR EFFECT ON VISION—CLINICAL ASPECTS

Gunter K. von Noorden

The function of the oculomotor system is to transform the field of vision into the field of fixation, to bring the image of the object of attention onto the fovea and keep it there, and to position the eyes so that at all times they are properly aligned, ensuring and maintaining binocular vision. Thus, although the oculomotor system clearly subserves the function of vision, motor anomalies such as certain forms of strabismus in turn may have a profound effect on visual functions. This effect is limited not only to functional disorders (e.g. reversible disturbances such as suppression, amblyopia, or anomalous retinal correspondence) but also may cause anatomical and neurophysiological changes in the primate visual system (von Noorden, 1973a and b; Baker et al., 1974). However, since the emphasis of this symposium is on eye movements, I shall not dwell on these oculomotor effects on vision but shall attempt to complement the preceding speaker's presentation from a clinical point of view, following the same outline.

1. THE ROLE OF EYE MOVEMENTS IN FIXATION

The aim of a fixation movement is to place the image of a visual object attracting one's attention onto the fovea, which is the retinal area of highest photopic function. The fovea also may be considered the "zero" point or the center of reference of the oculomotor system: a foveal image elicits no gross eye movements, whereas peripheral retinal stimulation elicits a motor response, the size of which depends on the distance of the stimulated area from the fovea. Because of miniature eye movements, fixation is not maintained with a foveal point but rather with a fixation area of apparently equal motor value (Hofmann, 1925).

We shall now consider how abnormal conditions may alter this fixation reflex. In strabismic amblyopia, for instance, the fovea no longer is the area of optimal retinal function, and with eccentric fixators an extrafoveal retinal area becomes the new reference point of the oculomotor system. In an earlier report, we showed that the size of this eccentric fixation area is directly proportional to its distance from the fovea (von Noorden and Mackensen, 1962).

The etiology of eccentric fixation has been the subject of dispute. Current opinions are divided between three theories: that eccentric fixation is maintained by a shift of the principal visual direction from the fovea to the eccentric retinal area (Cüppers,

1956), or that eccentric fixation occurs in the retinal area in which visual function is best under monocular conditions (Oppel and Jorde, 1964). The third possibility is that eccentric fixation is caused by an abnormal fixation reflex as a result of functional inhibition of the macula in early infancy (von Noorden, 1969). Comparison of the fixation reflex in normal eyes with that of eyes with recently acquired maculopathy or with amblyopia and eccentric fixation is of interest.

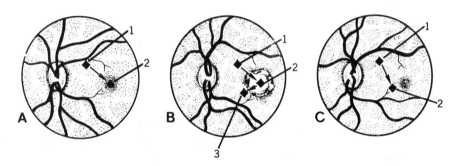

FIG. 1. Fixation reflex in a normal eye (A), with organic maculopathy (B), and with strabismic amblyopia and eccentric fixation (C). For explanation, see text. (From von Noorden, G. K.: The etiology and pathogenesis of fixation anomalies in strabismus. *Trans. Am. Ophthalmol. Soc.*, **67**, 698–751 (1969).)

In normal eyes (Fig. 1A), the image of visual objects in the peripheral visual field will fall on (1); a fixation movement is elicited for the purpose of shifting this image directly to the fovea (2), the zero point of oculomotor orientation. In unilaterally acquired maculopathy (Fig. 1B), the fovea remains the center of oculomotor orientation, even though the function of peripheral retinal elements may be superior. When the sound eye is occluded, a saccadic eye movement will position the image from (1) to the fovea (2) where it may not be seen. Subsequent secondary searching eye movements are then performed, and the image is viewed with more peripheral, parascotomatous retinal elements (3). The patient has a sensation of indirect vision and is aware that he must look to one side of an object in order to see it. In amblyopia with eccentric fixation, this situation is quite different (Fig. 1C). When the image of a visual object falls upon peripheral retina (1), the resulting eye movement will position the image *directly* on the eccentric fixation area (2) without first placing it on the fovea. Thus, zero motor value has now become associated with the eccentric fixation area rather than the fovea.

That such an adaptation may exist was suggested initially by Bielschowsky (1898) and is supported by visuscopic observations: the adjustment of the fixation reflex to nonfoveal retinal elements can be demonstrated easily by projecting a visuscope star somewhere on the periphery of the patient's fundus and observing the excursions of the star on the retina when the patient attempts to fixate it.

This behavior, I believe, is an indication that an abnormal fixation reflex may be fundamentally important in maintaining eccentric fixation in many amblyopic patients. Such an abnormal fixation reflex never develops in adult patients with maculopathy of one eye, but it may be observed occasionally in adults after longstanding macular lesions in both eyes (von Noorden and Mackensen, 1962).

Unlike fixation in normal subjects, eccentric fixation does not necessarily occur in the retinal area of highest visual function. Aulhorn and Lichtenberg (1972) showed in a number of cases that visual acuity was not higher but was as high or even lower in the anomalous fixation area than in the area of the anatomical fovea.

2. EYE MOVEMENTS TO ENHANCE OR MAINTAIN VISIBILITY

Steinman *et al.* (1973) emphasized that the purpose of eye movements is to permit a human being to maintain a stable foveal view of his visual world in the presence of movements of his body or of the objects themselves. It is of interest to speculate on the purpose of eye movements when the function of the fovea is reduced such as in strabismic amblyopia. Inability to fixate a stationary target steadily, lack of precision during saccadic eye movements, and inability to perform smooth pursuit movements at low target velocities are characteristic motor disturbances encountered in amblyopic eyes (Mackensen, 1957 a and b; von Noorden and Burian, 1958; von Noorden and Mackensen, 1962). Even though the severity of these anomalies cannot be correlated directly with the amount of reduction of vision in the amblyopic eye, motor disturbances as a rule are more pronounced with severe amblyopia (Mackensen 1957 a and b; von Noorden and Mackensen, 1962), but improve as visual acuity and fixation improve with therapy (von Noorden and Burian, 1958).

The question arises as to what extent and in what manner abnormal eye movements in amblyopic eyes enhance or maintain vision. Several possibilities exist. First, one may assume that if the foveal function is reduced, scanning saccades are performed to enhance form perception by moving the image across the macula to stimulate larger areas of retinal perceptors. We have shown that such scanning eye movements do occur during fixation of a stationary target and that saccadic eye movements lack their normal precision if foveal function is temporarily reduced in a normal eye after dazzling the fovea with a bright light (von Noorden and Mackensen, 1962). To further support this hypothesis, correlation of the size of the suppression scotoma in amblyopic eyes with the amplitude of saccades during fixation of a stationary target would be of interest.

A second etiologic factor in abnormal eye movements in amblyopic patients is the lack of afferent feedback from the fovea or, in the case of an eccentric fixator, from the peripheral retina. It is reasonable to assume that such feedback is essential for maintaining fixation of a stationary visual object and that its lack interferes with the fixation lock. In support of this concept is the clinical observation that pendular nystagmus, a frequent feature with bilateral congenital cataracts, may disappear as soon as the patient has been fitted with aphakic corrective contact lenses after surgery.

Finally, we must consider the possibility that unsteadiness of fixation in amblyopia, and perhaps certain forms of pendular nystagmus, serves to counteract abnormally accelerated local retinal adaptation. For instance, rapid image fading has been reported when mechanically fixating amblyopic eyes with forceps or a retrobulbar injection (Cibis, 1948) or after prolonged voluntary fixation of a stationary visual target (Lawwill, 1968). However, it is unlikely that this mechanism is more than a minor cause of the unsteadiness of fixation in amblyopic eyes since, as pointed out by the preceding speaker, it is unlikely that eye movements can maintain target visibility in any situation in which the head is not stabilized on a bite board.

The foregoing observations illustrate that foveal dysfunction and anomalies of fixation cause the oculomotor behavior to attain different characteristics, and perhaps even different purposes, than in normal eyes. Whether the motor disturbances observed in amblyopia are merely exaggerations of normal optomotor functions or whether new qualities have been added can be determined only by further study of eyes with functional or organic foveal dysfunction, using more refined recording techniques than electro-oculography.

3. EFFECT OF EYE MOVEMENTS ON VISUAL THRESHOLD

The effect of abnormal eye movements on visual threshold is significant in patients with nystagmus. Such abnormal eye movements clearly cause blurring of vision or illusionary movement of the environment (oscillopsia), as demonstrated by a patient we examined who was able to induce voluntary nystagmus with a frequency of 18 c/s. His normal visual acuity of 20/12 was reduced to 20/400 during the nystagmus phase (Blair *et al.*, 1967). Another common example of the manner in which visual functions may be adversely effected by abnormal motor behavior is in the patient with latent nystagmus. Visual acuity of each eye may be normal if tested under binocular conditions, but will be markedly reduced when one eye is occluded and the nystagmus becomes manifest (Awaya *et al.*, 1972).

We differentiate between sensory defect and motor defect congenital nystagmus according to Cogan (1967). In sensory defect nystagmus, the primary lesion consists of inadequate image formation on the macula caused by disease affecting the optical media of the eye, by congenital anomalies of the posterior pole, or by high refractive errors. A poorly focused or distorted image interrupts the afferent sensory feedback from the fovea, causing a disturbance of oculomotor control of fixation likened by Cogan to ataxia of the limbs. Clearly, in such cases the motor disturbance is secondary to the sensory defect. Cogan pointed out that adequate visual stimulation of the macula is a factor in the stabilization of the eyes, similar to the role of proprioception in co-ordinating the function of the muscles in other parts of the body. In this connection, ten Doeschate (1952) observed that pendular nystagmus occurred after the stimulus for fixation was abolished by stabilization of the foveal image.

The reverse situation prevails with motor defect nystagmus in which no ocular anomalies are present and the primary defect is in the efferent mechanism, possibly involving the center or pathways for conjugate oculomotor control. Unlike sensory nystagmus, with motor defect nystagmus the visual problems are secondary. Visual acuity in such cases may be reduced as low as 20/200 (Lafon, 1914; Gamble, 1934; Anderson, 1953; Forssman, 1964). However, amplitude, frequency, and velocity of nystagmus do not necessarily correlate with the level of visual acuity (Lafon, 1914). More clinical research is needed to determine the extent to which visual acuity is influenced by these various components of the nystagmus. However, since convergence innervation has a dampening effect on the amplitude of nystagmus (Kestenbaum, 1924) and may improve visual acuity at near fixation, the amplitude appears to be of some significance in this regard.

Of special interest for the clinician are the compensatory mechanisms which some patients with congenital motor defect nystagmus employ in order to decrease blurring of vision or oscillopsia. In many patients, a neutral zone (Kestenbaum, 1953) exists in a certain position of gaze in which the nystagmus is less pronounced or even absent. Such patients habitually will assume a compensatory head turn or head tilt in order to achieve optimal visual acuity or to avoid oscillopsia. An operation on all four horizontal rectus muscles may be indicated to shift this neutral zone toward the primary position (Kestenbaum, 1953; Anderson, 1953).

In addition to reduction of nystagmus by conjugate deviation of the eyes in the direction of the neutral zone, other less well-known compensatory mechanisms may prevail, such as the dampening effect of convergence innervation on nystagmus amplitudes mentioned earlier. Franceschetti *et al.* (1952) noted that nystagmus sometimes decreases with the fixating eye in adduction (see also Adelstein and Cüppers, 1966). In other words, for better vision such patients may use their right eye for fixation in left gaze and fixate with the left eye in right gaze, and the direction of the head turn is determined by the dominant eye. With alternate fixators, periodic shifting of the head from side to side has been observed (Robb, 1972).

4. EFFECTS OF EYE MOVEMENTS ON PERCEPTION OF DIRECTION AND MOTION

The effects of eye movements on perception of direction and motion are of clinical relevancy with respect to false orientation, a symptom of recent oculomotor palsy, and in conjunction with illusionary movements of the environment associated with certain forms of nystagmus. With volitional eye movements, visual impressions retain their stable localization in subjective space even though images sweep across the retina. As attention changes direction, the absolute spatial values of the retina change and compensate accordingly for the image displacement, which is of greatest importance for maintaining stability of our visual world in spite of eye movements. With involuntary eye movements such as those produced by shifting the position of the eyes mechanically, by interposition of a prism, or with certain forms of nystagmus this central adjustment does not take place, and apparent movements of the visual environment (oscillopsia) occur as the retinal image changes position. Likewise, if the amplitude of the actual eye movement does not correspond to the intended movement, such as in oculomotor paralysis, absolute localization in visual space is inaccurate and pastpointing occurs (von Graefe, 1854; Helmholtz, 1962; Bielschowsky, 1939).

The question has been raised in the past whether extraretinal factors, especially myosensory feedback from the extraocular muscles, may contribute to perceptual direction (Sherrington, 1918; von Tschermak, 1952; Irvine and Ludwigh, 1936; Oppel, 1967). This discussion recently was given new impetus by the ingenious experiments of Skavenski (1971, 1972) and Skavenski *et al.* (1972), who challenged the exclusive role of the outflow system by showing that the oculomotor system is capable of processing inflow information. These authors have shown that although inflow contributes to the control of eye position, it does not contribute to the perception of direction. Clinical observations agree with this conclusion. Inflow is not employed to correct for an apparent shift of the environment when the eye is displaced passively, when the movement of the eye is restricted because of paralysis, or during involuntary eye movements. Furthermore, we have found that blind individuals may have no information about the position of their eyes at any given moment, may be unaware that they have nystagmus, and are incapable of moving or holding their eyes in certain positions of gaze. Thus, there is currently no clinical evidence to indicate the significance of inflow in either complementing or counteracting the information provided by outflow in the control of eye position or the perception of direction.

Finally, we must consider the question of why certain patients with nystagmus have oscillopsia and others do not. If the general notion that involuntary eye movements are accompanied by illusionary movements of the environment holds true, all patients with nystagmus should be tormented by constant oscillopsia. Clearly, this is not the case, and clinical observations indicate that, with a few exceptions, oscillopsia usually is present with acquired and vestibular nystagmus and absent with congenital nystagmus. Köllner (1923) has stated that whether oscillopsia occurs depends on the frequency rather than on the involuntary nature of nystagmus. With low frequencies, central adjustment of absolute localization takes place and oscillopsia is not present. With high frequencies, such adjustments no longer take place and oscillopsia occurs. From perusal of the pertinent literature cited by Cogan (1967), it becomes evident that our current views of this subject are based largely on conjecture and would benefit from a more systematic investigative approach, including electronystagmographic recording techniques. Whether the presence or absence of oscillopsia is a function of the duration of the nystagmus, of its frequency, or of saccadic suppression and whether it has any localizing value are certainly important clinical questions that warrant further exploration.

REFERENCES

ADELSTEIN, F. and CÜPPERS, C. (1966) Zum Problem der echten und der scheinbaren Abducenslähmung (Das sognannte "Blockierungssyndrom"). *Klin. Monatsbl. Augenheilkd.* **46,** 271.

ANDERSON, J. R. (1953) Causes and treatment of congenital eccentric nystagmus. *Brit. J. Ophthal.* **37,** 267.

AULHORN, E. and LICHTENBERG, C. (1972) Central and peripheral acuity of eyes suffering from strabismic amplyopia. In: *Orthoptics: Proceedings Second International Orthoptic Congress,* MEIN, J., BIERLAAGH, J. J. M. and BRUMMELKAMP-DONS, T. E. A. (Eds.), p. 153. Excerpta Medica, Amsterdam.

AWAYA, S. and VON NOORDEN, G. K. (1972) Visual acuity of amblyopic eyes under monocular and binocular conditions: further observations, *J. Pediat. Ophthal.* **9,** 8.

BAKER, F. H., GRIGG, P. and VON NOORDEN, G. K. (1974) Effects of visual deprivation and strabismus on the response of neurons in the visual cortex of the monkey, including studies on the striate and prestriate cortex in the normal animal. *Brain Res.* **66,** 185.

BIELSCHOWSKY, A. (1898) Über monokuläre Diplopie ohne physikalische Grundlage nebst Bemerkungen über das Sehen Schielender. *Graefes Arch. Ophthal.* **46,** 143.

BIELSCHOWSKY, A. (1939) Die Motilitätsstörungen der Augen, in *Handbuch der gesamten Augenheilkunde,* 2nd ed., vol. 8, GRAEFE, A. and SAEMISCH, T. (Eds.), chap. 11: J. Springer, Berlin.

BLAIR, C. J., GOLDBERG, M. F. and VON NOORDEN, G. K. (1967) Voluntary nystagmus. Electro-oculographic findings in four cases. *Arch. Ophthalmol.* **77,** 359.

CIBIS, P. (1948) Zur Pathologie der Lokaladaptation. I. Mitteilung. *Graefes Arch. Ophthalmol.* **148,** 1.

COGAN, D. G. (1967) Congenital nystagmus. *Can. J. Ophthalmol.* **2,** 4.

CÜPPERS, C. (1956) Moderne Schielbehandlung. *Klin. Monatsbl. Augenheilkd.* **129,** 579.

FORSSMAN, B. (1964) A study of congenital nystagmus. *Acta Otolaryngol.* **57,** 427.

FRANCESCHETTI, A., MONNIER, M. and DIETERLE, P. (1952) Analyse du nystagmus congénital par la méthode electronystagmusgraphique (ENG). *Bull. Schweiz. Akad. med. Wiss.* **8,** 403.

GAMBLE, R. G. (1934) The visual prognosis for children with congenital nystagmus. A statistical study. *Trans. Am. Ophthalmol. Soc.* **32,** 485.

GRAEFE, A. VON (1854) Beiträge zur Physiologie und Pathologie der schiefen Augenmuskeln. *Graefes Arch. Ophthal.* **1,** 1.

HELMHOLTZ, H. VON (1962) In *Treatise of Physiological Optics*, vol. 3, Southall, J. P. C. (translator), chap. 29. Dover Publications, New York.

HOFMANN, F. B. (1925) Die Lehre fom Raumsinn. In: *Handbuch der gesamten Augenheilkunde*, 2nd ed., GRAEFE, A. and SAEMISCH, T. (Eds.), p. 346. J. Springer, Berlin.

IRVINE, S. R. and LUDWIGH, E. J. (1936) Is ocular proprioceptive sense concerned in vision? *Arch. Ophthal.* **15,** 1037.

KESTENBAUM, A. (1953) Nouvelle opération du nystagmus. *Bull. Soc. Ophthal. Fr.* **6,** 599.

KÖLLNER, H. (1923) Scheinbewegungen beim Nystagmus und ihr diagnostischer Wert. *Arch. Augenheilkd.* **93,** 130.

LAFON, C. (1914) La vision des nystagmiques. *Ann. Ocul.* **151,** 4.

LAWWILL, T. (1968) Local adaptation in functional amblyopia. *Am. J. Ophthal.* **65,** 903.

MACKENSEN, G. (1957a) Das Fixationsverhalten amblyopischer Augen (Elektrookulographische Untersuchungen). *Graefes Arch. Ophthal.* **159,** 200.

MACKENSEN, G. (1957b) Blickbewegungen amblyopischer Augen (Elektrookulographische Untersuchungen). *Graefes. Arch. Ophthal.* **159,** 212.

NOORDEN, G. K. VON (1969) The etiology and pathogenesis of fixation anomalies in strabismus. *Trans. Am. Ophthal. Soc.* **67,** 698.

NOORDEN, G. K. VON (1973) Experimental amblyopia in monkeys. Further behavioral observations and clinical correlations. *Invest. Ophthal.* **12,** 721.

NOORDEN, G. K. VON (1973) Histological studies of the visual system in monkeys with experimental amblyopia. *Invest. Ophthal.* **12,** 727.

NOORDEN, G. K. VON and BURIAN, H. M. (1958) An electro-ophthalmographic study of the behavior of the fixation of amblyopic eyes in light- and dark-adapted state: a preliminary report. *Am. J. Ophthal.* **46,** 68.

NOORDEN, G. K. VON and MACKENSEN, G. K. (1962) Phenomenology of eccentric fixation. *Am. J. Ophthal.* **53,** 642.

OPPEL, O. (1967) Über die motorischen und sensiblen Nerven-einrichtungen im menschlichen Augenmuskelapparat und ihre sinnesphysiologische Bedeutung. *Graefes Arch. Ophthal.* **171,** 337.

OPPEL, O. and JORDE, W. (1964) Über Untersuchungen der Sehschärfe in verschiedenen Gesichtsfeldbereichen bei Amblyopien mit exzentrischer Fixation unter besonderer Berücksichtigung des Gesichtsfeldzentrums. *Graefes Arch. Ophthal.* **167,** 145.

ROBB, R. M. (1972) Periodic alternation of null point in congenital nystagmus. Association with alternating gage deviation and esotropia. *Arch. Ophthal.* **87,** 169.

SHERRINGTON, C. S. (1918) Observations on the sensory role of the proprioceptive nerve supply of the extrinsic ocular muscles. *Brain*, **41,** 332.

SKAVENSKI, A. A. (1971) Extraretinal correction and memory for target position. *Vision Res.* **11,** 743.

SKAVENSKI, A. A. (1972) Inflow as a source of extraretinal eye position information. *Vision Res.* **12,** 221.

SKAVENSKI, A. A., HADDAD, G. and STEINMAN, R. M. (1972) The extraretinal signal for the visual perception of direction. *Percept. Psychophys.* **11,** 287.

STEINMAN, R. M., HADDAD, G. M., SKAVENSKI, A. A. and WYMAN, D. (1973) Miniature eye movement. *Science*, **181,** 810.

TEN DOESSCHATE, J. (1952) Amblyopic nystagmus induced in non-amblyopic observers. *Ophthalmologica*, **124,** 361.

TSCHERMAK-SEYSENEGG, A. VON (1952) *An Introduction to Physiological Optics*, Boeder, P. (translator). Charles C. Thomas, Springfield, Ill.

Panel Discussion. Synopsis prepared by David G. Cogan

In the first session the assigned discussants were requested to address their comments to specific essayists.

Dr. Vossius noted the complex computation that is required for the combined eye–head movements in Professor Jones' experiments. It is much more complicated than animal experiments which permit testing of the vestibular response only and probably requires the active participation of the cerebellum. Professor Jones agreed that clinical trials require the incorporation of the entire system but stated it is still possible to select specific parameters for testing single degrees of freedom.

Dr. Abrahams spoke on behalf of participation of the neck receptor mechanism, suggesting that the vestibular responses (as represented by Drs. Precht and Dichgans) had received a disproportionate amount of attention. The neck afferents to the ocular motor system are highly organized. It is well known that the neck muscles have a dense accumulation of spindles, as many as 100 spindles/gram of muscle compared with the hind limb muscles which have 5–20 spindles/gram. Surprisingly, these neck muscle afferents have little or no direct connection with either the vestibular nuclei or the cerebellum except through the trigeminal nucleus and through the cerebral cortex (Area 3A) but are abundantly represented in the superior colliculi where they join with the input from the extraocular muscle proprioceptors and from the retina.

In discussing Dr. Precht's paper, Dr. Bizzi described the work of a graduate student at MIT, Larry Ritchie, who had also investigated the functional role of the cerebellum in the monkey. Specifically he had studied the effect of ablation of Areas V, VI, and VII on eye movements in response to a visual target. The characteristic dysmetria which resulted could be characterized as a function of the position of the eye in the orbit and the magnitude of the retinal error signal, but the position of the eye in the orbit was the overriding parameter. With the retinal error signal held constant severe hypometropia and hypermetropia could be observed if the saccades were made from the center of the orbit to the periphery or the periphery of the orbit to the center, respectively. No problem with smooth pursuit was found in these animals.

To the question from Dr. Precht as to whether sensory input has any correlation in the cerebellar area with eye movements, Dr. Bizzi replied that that was a question which remains to be answered.

Dr. Tyc Dumont, addressing her comments to Dr. Henn's presentation, described the finding of interneurons for the ocular motor system. These interneurons, identified by recording of action potentials and by histologic staining with Procain Yellow are intermixed with motor neurons and raise the question of their functional significance.

In reply, Dr. Henn argued that from extracellular recording in the monkey the existence and function of interneurons cannot be decided, although there is some suggestion that a few of the units recorded in the nuclear area might be interneurons. In reply to a second question whether the cells in the pointine reticular formation are causally related to eye movements, Dr. Henn pointed out that decisive support for this hypothesis comes from lesion and stimulation studies.

Dr. Sanders, referring to Dr. Kommerel's exposition of a pulse generator in the PPRF for saccadic movements, illustrated the case of a patient with metastatic carcinoma to one side of the brainstem (see p. 392, this volume). This has caused an extreme slowing of saccadic movements to the ipsilateral side. This accords with the concept presented by Dr. Kommerel but the question facing the clinician is that many areas other than the PPRF are concerned with saccadic movements. Thus abnormal saccades occur with acute hemispheric disease, basal ganglia disease (Parkinson's disease, Huntington's chorea, Wilson's disease, and some neurolipidoses) as well as with cerebellar disease. Can slow saccades result from lesions elsewhere than in the PPRF?

Dr. Kommerel replied that we can be sure we are dealing with involvement of the brainstem only when we have a lesion of the medial longitudinal fasciculus but it is certainly possible that lesions elsewhere may produce slow saccade.

In the second session comments were invited from the general audience rather than from assigned discussants.

Dr. Vossius opened the discussion with reference to coordinated eye–head movements in man. Unlike the eye movements of other primates, those of man occurring during the combined eye–head movement do not always represent simply the linear addition of a reflex vestibular movement and a voluntary saccade. Dr. Vossius showed examples of coordinated eye–head movements in which the amplitude of either the saccade or the vestibular compensatory movement was inappropriate for the individual stimulus alone (i.e. retinal error or head velocity). Moreover, smooth compensatory movements can be observed prior to the induced head movements and therefore do not necessarily arise from vestibular stimulation. By way of explanation, Dr. Vossius presented a model. He emphasized a central controller that, using internal models of head and eye dynamics, could program the appropriate eye movement according to the task at hand.

Dr. Robinson agreed in substance with Dr. Vossius' comments adding that a similar mechanism may be needed to raise the gain of the vestibulo-ocular reflex from 0.4–0.6 in the dark to 1.0 in the light.

Dr. Melville Jones commented on the possible mechanism for plasticity in the vestibulo-ocular reflex. The stimulus for plasticity may not be the inappropriate slip but rather the compensatory optokinetic movements required to move the eyes in the direction opposite to the vestibular drive. Information about the appropriateness of eye movements (either by monitoring ocular muscle afferents or efferent motor commands) may be compared to vestibular signals.

Dr. Jones asked Dr. Precht if neuronal circuitry exists in the cerebellum that could participate in such a hypothetical model for control of the vestibulo-ocular reflex. Dr. Precht replied that the vestibular neurons project not only to the flocculus and nodulus but indirectly (vestibulo-reticulo-cerebellar) to the vermis in proximity to the projection of the extraocular muscle afferents. In addition, efferent projections from the vermis transmit information related to head rotation to the vestibular nuclei by way of the fastigial nuclei. These connections could also participate in the type of modifications of the vestibulo-ocular reflex suggested by Dr. Jones.

Dr. Steinman asked Dr. Jones about the psychological accompaniments of inversion of the vestibulo-ocular reflex. Did one's total perception of the left and right reverse? Dr. Jones replied that in the early stages of the experiment his own experience was thoroughly traumatic. It was accompanied by severe motion sickness so that he was able to enjoy his meals again only after 7 days. He did not feel that his psychological and perceptual adjustment was simply an inversion of right and left but the establishment of a totally new image appropriate to the new perceptual situation.

Dr. Westheimer questioned the gain of the vestibulo-ocular reflex of only 0.5 in the dark since post-rotary nystagmus had a gain of 1.0. Dr. Jones replied that the gain is a function of frequency. At 1 hertz, when the pursuit system fails, the gain of the vestibulo-ocular reflex becomes one.

Dr. Dichgans asked if one could account for a depression of the vestibulo-ocular reflex during fixation of a target moving with the subject on the basis of Simpson's and Maekawa's study of Purkinje cell responses in the vestibulo-cerebellum to moving targets. Dr. Precht replied that these studies suggest that Purkinje cells enhance rather than inhibit the vestibulo-ocular reflex unless they project to an inhibitory interneurone.

Dr. Abrahams reiterated the complexity of the neck musculature with its multitude of histochemical fiber types and polysegment innervation. The monosynaptic reflex from 1A afferents is much less evident than in other spinal cord segments. Dr. Young recalled the contribution of neck proprioception to ocular stabilization during head movements and its linear addition to the vestibulo-ocular reflex.

Dr. Sanders ended the discussion by showing a moving picture film of a blind patient with "windmill nystagmus". This consisted of a jerk nystagmus in the direction of gaze while the eyes showed a continual and spontaneous clockwise change in direction. The direction of the fast component was in the direction of "gaze" and each clockwise rotation of "gaze" required several minutes. All observers agreed that such bizarre movements were enigmatic and unexplained.

CONCLUDING REMARKS:

BASIC MECHANISMS OF HUMAN OCULAR MOTILITY—RETROSPECT AND PROSPECT

GERALD WESTHEIMER

THE title and program layout of this conference suggest that there may be more than one motivation for studying eye movements. The organizers have clearly spelled out two: searching for basic mechanisms and seeking clinical implication. And in bringing the two together under one roof, so to speak, they have taken an important step in the direction of unification rather than diversification of knowledge, of making the clinician aware of rather than impatient with the findings of the laboratory scientist, of making the researcher consider the richness of clinical material rather than its paucity of documentation and control; in short they have tried to do something about relevance rather than merely preaching about it.

A specialized subject, such as ocular motility, has always had devotees in the century or century and a quarter of its clear identification as a scientific discipline. But just consider what has happened to science and medicine in the 125 years since Helmholtz accepted a call to an Associate Professorship at Königsberg in 1849 and promptly invented the ophthalmoscope! The phenomenal growth in all branches of science now prevents any one of us from even surveying more than a very limited area, but whereas in Helmholtz's days this represented a variety of branches not far from the mainstem of knowledge, we are restricted to just a few twigs far removed from the trunk.

The simile of the tree of knowledge should not be taken too far, because in its implication of successive separation by branching it is just wrong. If this is already evident in this conference, it will probably be much more so in future ones. We have here heard about results obtained using electron microscopes, sophisticated optical and electronic equipment, and computers. We may confidently expect to hear results obtained with subtler histological, histochemical and pharmacological techniques, with yet more highly developed products of the electro-optical technology, experiments carried out on a new generation of biological materials, not only deliberately chosen atavistic ones like limulus or necturus, but also man-made preparations highlighting or exposing precisely predetermined facets of anatomy or physiology. Far from thinking that our endeavors make us climb further and further out on a limb, we may take pride in recognizing that they have the potentiality of deepening and enriching other branches of scholarship even as we are enriched by theirs.

Now that we have reached the end of two days of formal presentations I will not add to an overfull cup by imposing on you yet another set of experimental results, another set of slides, another set of graphs, equations, hypotheses and conclusions. Nor can I even attempt to summarize the state of knowledge at the present juncture: it would be presumptuous for me to try to do this in a brief time where it has been done so authoritatively by the individual speakers themselves.

Advances on a broad front of research problems in oculomotility were reported on in this conference. The configuration they assume depends on the perspective from which they are viewed. A major framework of consideration is implicit in the title of the conference and, as directed to the laboratory scientist, it may take the form of a question phrased somewhat like this: Dr...., you have reported on the contributions in your laboratory; how do you envisage this work to be applied to clinical problems? In a moment of exasperation, the laboratory scientist may be tempted to pose to the clinician the counter-question: What clinical problems remain after a hundred years of academic ophthalmology? What can you *not* heal with your lenses and prisms, occluders and synoptophores, and your surgical skill? I leave it to your imagination to develop a series of questions and counter-questions, gradually increasing in severity, recrimination and shrillness, that is guaranteed to drive scholars back to philosophy, philanthropists back to collecting art, legislators back to appropriating money for defense budgets, patients back to offering prayers, and students further into mysticism. So these questions are not usually raised, because the clinician tries not to drive away patients, students, legislators or philanthropists, and on occasion he even recognizes the help of scholars or the clergy.

But the attempt to avoid offense runs the risk of inducing another kind of response, a yawn. It comes as no secret to anyone that in the current phase of science we are faced with a surfeit of facts. Assuming for the moment that every fact quoted, every graph drawn, every reference cited, stands up to subsequent verification, and that all contradictions are satisfactorily resolved, we are still getting dangerously close to an overload situation. True, our memories are capable of extension by a factor of 2 or 4, and none of us has developed the most efficient system of card indexing. And with the increasing availability of small and large computers, there is lurking in the background a capacity of loading and recalling memory banks of unbelievable dimensions.

But I used the word lurking advisedly, and not because a computer is anyone to be afraid of. It is by nature a gentle and infinitely patient beast. What one sees lurking behind a full set of abstracts, *Index Medicus*, *Excerpta Medica*, is an ocean of facts and results so voluminous, that it can be accommodated only in electromagnetic memories.

What kind of a science or medicine is it that does not fit into a human mind, or even into a reasonably handy library of books and journals? Are we to be reduced to a craft of bookkeepers, transcribing findings (via conferences like these) to tape and disk, and shuffling them back and forth between electromagnetic memories? Or is this kind of question as pathetic an exercise as that of the forgotten prophet who 5000 years ago thundered against the unnatural, counter-natural, new fad of wedge notation on wet clay?

The extension of memory from a written page to a 10-million word computer disk with about equal access time is, of course, merely a quantitative change, but as a school of thinking has it, quantitative change in sufficient measure becomes a qualitative one. Surprisingly, the discussion applies equally to basic sciences and clinical practice in spite of their diverging motivation and purpose. I here speak predominantly from the point of view of a scientist, but a roughly equivalent argument can be made to apply to medicine and I leave it to my clinical friends to articulate it.

The dilemma can be expressed quite readily in concrete terms and, if you will allow me to indulge in a favorite pastime, I would like to cast it in an historical perspective. Within the span of a few years, three of the greatest books on ocular motility were written. They are Helmholtz's *Physiological Optics*, Donder's *Accommodation and Refraction of the Eye*, and Hering's *Die Lehre vom binocularen Sehen*. If we read these books now, we find an incredible amount of space given up to things we now find trivial. Elaborate tables give "exact" coordinates of the attachment of the ocular muscles; precise computations predict to a second of arc the amount of cyclotorsion in various positions of gaze; discussions of the horopter are developed with unbelievable vigor and even vituperation. But also included in these books are items still in everyone's armamentarium a century later. We still use Donder's table of accommodation and defer to Donder's law; the reafference principle, resurrected by v. Holst and Mittelstaedt, was first stated by Helmholtz; and to Hering we owe, among other things, the law of equal innervation.

Let me use the latter as an example. If you pick up *Die Lehre vom binokularen Sehen* there are tables in small print of experimental versus theoretical values for torsion with convergence and elevation and depression of the lines of sight. But if you put the book back on the shelves because this justifiably bores you, you would have missed the following paragraph, which is here quoted verbatim:

1. When we cover one eye, the covered eye follows the movement of the other eye, of which one can easily convince oneself on a second person, if one observes the loosely covered eye from the side. Volition cannot squash the co-movement of the covered eye which is visually quite useless.

2. When one eye is completely blind, it still accompanies the movement of the other. When both eyes are completely blind, they move simultaneously just the same.

3. Strabismics who can be proved to utilize the retinal image of only one eye, nevertheless move both eyes in common.

4. The involuntary eye movements during nystagmus take place in both eyes simultaneously and in an analogous manner.

5. Patients with paresis of certain eye muscles, though bothered by diplopia, are still not able to fixate certain targets with both eyes when they can nevertheless fixate these targets individually with each eye. If they could move each eye independently, they should be able to fixate simultaneously with both eyes all those points which they can fixate with each eye individually.

Now this seems an evident, almost obvious, statement but when placed in the context of its time of writing, it is almost revolutionary. The towering figure of the period was Helmholtz who propagated the idea that coordination of eye movement is a learned skill, a view which Helmholtz derived by drawing certain clear consequences from his *Weltanschauung*—and you can say whatever you like about Helmholtz's *Weltanschauung*, but he translated it into more progress in scientific understanding than almost any of his contemporaries.

Hering's statement about the yoking of the two eyes, founded as it is on a variety of observations on normal and abnormal pairs of eyes, nevertheless implies some contradictions. Note that Hering talks about the co-movement of the covered eye as being *visually useless*. When this was written, Darwin's *Origin of the Species* had just been published and had made an inordinate impression on Hering. A "visually useless" eye movement does not conform with any simple expectations from the theory of evolution and must therefore be a compelling, and possibly decisive, indicator of a deeper order of things, which in turn must, of course, also be compatible with the theory of evolution.

Hering's principle of the two eyes moving as one—"Bewegung des Doppelauges" (movement of the double-eye) he called it—has served us well. It demanded, for example, a particular summation of conjugate and vergence movements during the convergence response to the Panum-Wheatstone Grenzfall. We were proud to be able to demonstrate it with the eye movement recording facilities at our disposal in the 1950s, but in fact Hering himself noted that such a movement could be seen when the eyes are closely watched. Conjugacy of eye movements is so ubiquitous in the human that it must represent a major physiological design feature of the supranuclear oculomotor apparatus in the primate. This means that the input to the motoneuron pools of the twelve extra-ocular muscles are automatically coordinated to take care of the varying mechanical purchase of the individual muscles. Because the two orbits with the peculiar arrangement of the six extra-ocular muscles are, for the purposes of conjugate movements, not identical but mirror symmetrical, this binocular coordination is no mean feat of design and can surely be no accident. And the fact that, as Hering has pointed out, there is usually no modification of response when there is paresis of one muscle, implies that this whole arrangement is hard wired. The existence of a distributing network automatically partitioning signals into components appropriate to the mechanical action of the individual muscles, clearly has the advantage of making the organization of the *input* a great deal easier. Any supranuclear signal to move the eyes, be it vestibular, saccadic, pursuit (*Stier-* or *Schau-*), need only be applied to this distributing network, and conjugacy is attained automatically, unfortunately also under conditions of paresis. Under such a scheme the direct communication between higher centers and an individual motoneuron pool would be disallowed. Now there are certain apparently conflicting anatomical findings. For example, direct fibers from the cerebellum to the oculomotor nuclei have been described. Since in our own work we have never seen any non-comitancy in monkeys due to any sort of cerebellar lesion or ablation, one of the following conclusions is forced on us: (1) these cerebello-oculomotor fibers are functionally irrelevant or not operative, (2) the distributing network is situated in the oculo-motor nucleus or (3) the cerebello-oculomotor fibers are concerned with disjunctive eye movements, such as convergence. The latter is an intriguing possibility because cerebellectomy does interfere with convergence and, in any case, convergence operates somewhat outside the scheme just sketched: after all, convergence can be maintained when there is severe disruption of the conjugate apparatus as in the MLF syndrome.

The existence of direct connection between the vestibular nuclei and the extra-ocular motoneurons is much more firmly grounded than the cerebello-oculomotor connection, and it has excellent physiological confirmation, extending even to the welcome demonstration of an inhibitory connection. But the same arguments about the inappropriateness of direct communication with motoneuron pools apply here also, although they may be phrased a little differently: either the Hering's law distributing network operates via the vestibular nuclei, or the vestibular nuclei have their own conjugacy circuit, or perhaps both statements are true. Lorente de Nó had suggested a long time ago that there may be more than one path between the vestibular nuclei and the ocular motoneurons. And after we have thought for a while along these lines of conjugacy and internuclear circuits, are we not in a better position to evaluate and assign interest in, as well as relevance of, extraordinary animal behavior, such as in a goldfish, who merrily makes saccades in opposite directions in the two eyes, or in the chameleon, who can orient both eyes quite separately? Surely anatomical techniques (and the strategies of their use!) will one day be refined enough to demonstrate to us the anatomical differences between these animals and the more universally conjugate ones.

The lesson to be learned from Hering's law is clear and heartening. Facts, widely diverging facts, be they of clinical origin, be they derived from animal experiments or from psychophysical observation, can be gathered together into explanatory principles, which may be called physiological organization. Hering was, of course, one of the great masters here. There is nothing wrong with facts, even the plethora of facts characterizing science in the second half of the twentieth century. What we have to pray for is the insight that would permit us to weave them into principles of physiological organization, or at any rate, the patience and humbleness to await the emergence of such principles and the clarity and openness of mind to recognize one when it emerges. And once such an overarching explanatory principle has been accepted, *it* becomes central and its detailed factual support moves to the periphery.

Here is another example of an important guiding principle, developed this time by Barany. The credit for postulating the existence of a supranuclear network goes to v. Monakow, who insisted that the eye movements due to cortical stimulation in the dog could not be due to direct pathways between the cortex and the ocular motoneurones, or ganglion cells as they were then called. Instead v. Monakow postulated the existence of *Schaltzellen*, switching cells, which serve to distribute excitation to the motoneurones of the individual muscles. Nystagmus was, of course, well known as a condition, but the realization that eye movements could be saccadic or slow had appeared on the scene only a few years before Barany saw the interesting patient in the Vienna polyclinic. This patient had lost the capacity to execute saccades but he could still make smooth movements; at the same time his vestibular responses lacked the return steps that made a nystagmus out of doll's-head response. The observation permitted Barany to lump the fast return movement of nystagmus together with voluntary saccades and, because the patient's lesion was in the pons, allowed him to conclude that ipsiversive fast response originated in Schaltzellen in the pons. Once the two major components of vestibular nystagmus, the saccade-like return sweep and the slow phase, had been recognized as separate entities, attention could properly focus on the origin and possible defects in either, and arguments about essential rhythmicity could be abandoned. A major clue to the clinical and behavioral analysis of states involving nystagmus is contained here: the number of beats per second is in most instances of only minor significance, attention has usually to be paid to the velocity of the slow phase, or the total movement in a unit of time. Even so, just why there should be and what initiates the fast return in nystagmus still remains a mystery, particularly when there is no need for it, as in vestibular nystagmus in the dark. Thus it is not at all futile to seek a connecting link between saccade generation and smooth eye movements.

One of the most venerable guiding principles in human oculomotor physiology is also the one that must have been the most difficult to discover—Listing's law. Like all the other guiding principles it not only sharpens our understanding of the motor part of the oculomotility, but is also firmly rooted in its afference. The reduction in the degrees of freedom of the eye-position states from three to two must enormously simplify the evaluation of retinal images in the perceptual processes leading to the creation of a single global representation of space. But it also poses strictures on the distribution of excitation to the extra-ocular muscles. Any scheme of the lower central oculomotor operation must take account of the fact that simple summation of movement impulses will not in the end yield an eye position that obeys Listing's law unless the summation process is always specially shaped, passively or actively, or unless a separation is postulated between the movement impulse and the system that holds the eyes in intersaccadic intervals. The fact that Donder's law is not obeyed in converged states of the eyes and during pursuit eye movements will no doubt fit into the picture before long.

The guiding principles we have dealt with so far have some things in common: they express constraints about the operation of the immediate supranuclear motor apparatus, they were developed from external observation of the movement behavior of the human eyes and they have important roots in visual perception. Their timeliness has increased rather than decreased now that their synthesis with the results of the recent round of single unit recording seems imminent. It will be most interesting to see how complete a synthesis can be achieved, in view of neuroanatomical peculiarities of the brainstem that are being faced here. Lest we lost patience, let us remember that good description of neural interaction has so far been reached only where the ensembles studied were either very small or tight, or where their anatomical layout is quite regular. We need take second place to no other field in the realm of neurophysiology that has to deal with intertwined, dispersed and distributed nerve connections and particularly those in which the distinctive aspects of the function are retained only in the alert animal.

Not, of course, that all important guidance principles have already been fully expressed. Some interesting ones are waiting in the wings, and some now on the stage are only shadows that need incarnation. Among the latter are the questions centering around feedback from muscle spindles, uniqueness of impulse coding for a given eye position, subjective knowledge of where the eye is pointing, and so on. The problem here is that the conventional knowledge is simple to understand and very persuasive. It is that the eyes are held by position-coded signals to the eye muscles and that subjective knowledge of eye position comes from the monitoring of the outflow to the eye muscles together with analysis of the retinal image. Because the analysis of the retinal image goes via perceptual channels subject to memory, logical deduction and irrational prejudice, there is ample room for the introduction of obscuring phenomena at that end, although carefully controlled psychophysical experiments, as they are now being done, minimize and often effectively eliminate such factors. The neurophysiologist tends to rely more on the records he obtains with electrodes, but here again clarity of results is not always synonymous with completeness of description. The impression is that the current state of knowledge does not allow firm conclusion about the primate and man until we have satisfactorily answered some questions about the ensemble of neurons involved, the extent of the co-variation in impulse rates in motoneurones, the pathway of the centripetal impulses from the sensory organs and so on. Many of us keep on being disturbed therefore by the jarring dissonance between the presence of muscle spindles, and the unlikelihood of excellent neuromuscular control being totally openloop on the one hand, and the essential lack of subjective information about eye position as well as the permanence of paretic defects on the other.

It would be anyone's guess as to the guiding principles that are waiting in the wings. A likely candidate is the nature of the higher supranuclear organization of the oculomotor apparatus, here distinguished from the network that concerns itself with the distribution of the excitation and inhibition to the individual muscles needed to move and hold the eyes. Superimposed on this latter apparatus there is surely also some regularity of function (or dysfunction in disease) that betrays specific neural channeling. Low amplitude focal stimulation in the brainstem may give saccadic inhibition, or it may produce conjugate movement of the eyes. Depending on the location and the mode of stimulation, the movement may be smooth or saccadic, it may be to a given position or in a given direction, and it may be either across the midline or across the horizontal plane. There is something special about the sagittal plane and the horizontal plane, because on some occasions stimulation will lead the eyes only there, and in some neural defects the excursions of one or both eyes are restricted by them, or, as in total cerebellar ablation in the primate, the eyes will always drift back there. Beyond that, there is the distinct possibility, once outlined by Dr. Blair and me, that the cyclotorsional orientation laid down by Listing's law, the requirement for self-congruence of line segments demanded by the perceptual unity of a long straight line, and the firing pattern of a nest of cells high in the midbrain reveal the outline of a polar coordinate system superimposed on whatever horizontal/vertical neural organization can be unequivocally demonstrated.

More and more mention is made of the cerebellum when it comes to the supranuclear oculomotor apparatus. In spite of its conspicuous presence and massive size in all the animals we are interested in, it may well be that the function it performs differs significantly from one species to the other. An extreme example of this is illustrated by the effect of complete cerebellectomy on the rabbit, where it eliminates saccades and leaves tracking intact, and the macaque, where it essentially does the reverse. This poses an almost unsurmountable dilemma about the applicability of the wealth of rabbit single-cell data to the primate. Perhaps we need to examine with some care the implication and consequences of such ideas as the one that would have the cerebellum smooth the execution of cortical commands by switching, shunting and generally rearranging lower reflexes, or the one that would make the cerebellum learn and then automatically execute routine motor behavior, or the one that would give the cerebellum a homeostatic function by having it readjust the gain of reflex arcs as injuries occur.

Do you detect here, as I do, a faint foreshadow of a new discipline, the ontogeny of oculomotor behavior? Can you already see the generations of monkey babies attempting to grow up normal in spite of stitched and excised muscles, unilaterally and bilaterally fixed eyeballs, half or no cerebellum, one or no labyrinths, colliculi, occipital cortices, frontal eyefields?

We are even more insecure in our knowledge of the function of those higher neural structures that always have been implicated in oculomotor behavior. For example, in spite of the universally acknowledged capacity to evoke eye movements when electrically stimulated, the superior colliculi and the frontal eyefields do not provide indispensible contribution to eye movements. While not normal, the oculomotor behavior of animals with lesions or ablations in these areas is not defective in a simple sense, such as in the absence of one or more classes of eye movements, or of one or more positions or directions or quadrants of eye movements.

We are here dealing with a most interesting and most difficult subject, because we have left the immediate well-charted confines of the sensory visual apparatus and have not yet reached the comparatively well-charted regions of the low supranuclear and internuclear ocular motor paths. The colliculi and frontal eye fields are examples of neural regions that do seem to play a role in, but are not absolutely crucial to the proper execution of eye movements, in the way that the MLF or pontine reticular formation seems to be crucial. To the extent that we at this conference are anatomists, physiologists or clinicians, we are out of our depth here and might as well admit it. At the present juncture we have two alternatives. We can either accept, or at any rate listen to, accounts or theories couched in terms that to *our* ears are intolerably tentative: engrams, centers, configuration, images, memory traces, and the like. Or we can wait for the development of outlines in to us more acceptable terms, or perhaps try our hands at such a task. There is, of course, no guarantee that the basic understanding of the primate oculomotor behavior will in the foreseeable future approach that of the cat's spinal reflex or the aplysian abdominal ganglion. The latter is an extremely primitive preparation, and the former has so far only been studied in isolation from the higher centers. The moment rubro-spinal, ponto-spinal, cerebello-spinal influences are allowed, the story becomes quite opaque. In an overall description of oculomotor behavior in the primate, we are not only allowing but inviting the participation of these pathways, and the mesencephalic, thalamic, striatal and cortical ones as well. Small wonder that we are still far from a unitary description in language where rigorous meaning can be attached to terms. But the paradox keeps on intruding itself that the more results we are accumulating, couched in impeccably definable terms, the more still seem to be needed. In the end, the bulk of them will be gathered together to create unifying principles, or shorthand symbols and, since there is no future at all in a subject that does not have these, and, moreover, only as few and as powerful ones as one can possibly get away with, the emphasis must be on the development of such guiding principles.

As far as the clinician is concerned, there will certainly be occasions when he will be confronted with a patient presenting a syndrome that reveals the operation of as yet only suspected pathways, but it will only be apparent on a knowing and perceptive analysis. Similarly, strategies of the use of present anatomical, electrophysiological recording and stimulating techniques can certainly be refined and extended. New techniques will surely be devised, and work on experimental animals will see more and more application of alert, behaving animals, as well as animals that have had specific surgical or behavioral preparation. Both clinicians and basic scientists will have profited from this conference if they have been made more knowledgeable and perceptive to the possibilities in their own field as well as in that complementary to theirs.

CONCLUDING REMARKS:

SUMMARY OF CLINICAL PRESENTATIONS

Robert B. Daroff

This Symposium was organized to cover the broad expanse of the basic sciences of eye movements and the clinicians were charged with making clinical correlations. In many instances the tasks were difficult or even impossible. Some clinicians were forced to contrived speculation to fulfil their charge and, for this, they are to be admired. Perhaps the next such Symposium should be organized in the reverse manner; let the clinician first present the perplexing phenomenology he ofttimes encounters, and have the scientists discuss possible explanations.

The major problem I face in fulfilling my specific charge is an admitted lack of expertise in some of the clinical areas discussed. As a neurologist with training in clinical neuro-ophthalmology, my particular interest is in oscillatory eye-movement disturbances and acquired motility disorders. I therefore cannot comment authoritatively on much of the material covered by the clinical speakers.

Jampolsky's paper was obviously meant to be controversial and his message has applicability for all of clinical medicine. Unexplained clinical phenomenology constitute fertile territory for the imaginative. An operational explanatory hypothesis may be introduced, often only heuristically. Such constructs can be expanded cleverly to explain other phenomena. In time, despite its speculative origins, the hypothesis may become regarded as established fact. This is obviously counter-productive to scientific advancement unless periodically challenged and such is Jampolsky's taunt to his colleagues in the "Squint Club". Is there compelling evidence to believe in omnipresent convergence–divergence forces, the imbalance of which explains certain clinical signs? If the evidence is not compelling, should we not search for another, perhaps more parsimonious, explanation? I share his doubts about divergence palsy as a distinct entity; it is probably bilateral abducens weakness (Kirkham et al., 1972). There are, I believe, rare cases of true convergence palsies with normal accommodation and pupillary constriction. The clinical support for Jampolsky's ultimate hypothesis has merit but I am not convinced that convergence–retraction nystagmus is a good example of medial rectus dominance. He implies that the medial and lateral recti are receiving equal innervation, but at times there is no convergence accompanying retraction nystagmus; here I think there is equal innervation. When convergence does coexist with retraction,

435

the medial recti may be getting greater innervation than the lateral. How else would the opposite situation be explained, that of divergence–retraction nystagmus, a case of which we have seen?

The field of extraocular muscle morphology has always been difficult for the "outsider". In large measure this has resulted from a lack of communication amongst investigators who have not correlated their findings with the previous literature on the subject. This is particularly essential when different laboratory techniques, animal models, and nomenclatures result in seemingly disparate conclusions. The excellent paper by Alvarado and Van Horn fills an obvious void. They are to be congratulated for their meticulous investigation and particularly for their comparative analysis of other studies.

Unfortunately, to date, we have *no clear correlation between structure and function in extraocular muscles.*

Miller's paper on the aging changes in extraocular muscle further demonstrates the pitfalls inherent in evaluating muscle biopsy material as a diagnostic procedure; an area in which I have had some previous interest (Daroff et al., 1966; Daroff, 1969). Normal aging induces changes that many unwary microscopists would call "pathological". Although Miller does not favor a neurogenic etiology, it must remain unsettled. The whole question of myopathic versus neurogenic atrophy in any muscle, skeletal or extraocular, is an area of raging controversy (Rowland, 1974). A clinical researcher in myology once remarked that the only "pure" muscle disease was that of crush injury. The muscle beneath the truck tire marks suffers from direct damage; all other conditions most likely represent disturbed neural trophic influences upon the muscle. This was an admitted exaggeration but the ophthalmologist is well advised to be circumspect before diagnosing "ocular myopathy" on the basis of an eye-muscle biopsy. To my chagrin, papers with such conclusions are constantly appearing in the clinical literature.

The functional effects of the aging changes provokes speculation. We have not found any decrease in horizontal saccadic velocity in the few elderly patients studied, the oldest being 75. Do the changes explain the progressive limitation of upward gaze seen in the elderly (Chamberlain, 1971)? Miller did not find any difference between the elevators and the depressors. Given equal deterioration, the mechanical disadvantage consequent to the insertion of the superior rectus might explain the gaze limitation. My own pet, but unproven, theory is that relative disuse accounts for the finding. We rarely maintain our eyes in a deviated upward position. This hypothesis could be tested by measuring vertical gaze amplitudes in aged midgets or dwarfs. I would predict little or no restriction as compared to normal-sized folk.

Reinecke's observation of a reduced latency of the eye movement when the prism was removed compared to its introduction is intriguing. His postulation concerning the role of spindle afferents in providing the brain with parallelism information deserves investigation and his prism-phoria model with the differential latencies might prove suitable for testing his hypothesis. I know that he plans to perform such tests on patients with trigeminal nerve lesions whose brainstems would be deprived of such afferent information.

Scott's report that saccades in the "off" direction are driven primarily by antagonist relaxation troubled me initially since we found no difference in peak velocities between the two directions (Boghen et al., 1974). Why should a saccade initiated primarily by antagonist relaxation be as fast as one moved by agonist contraction? He provided the answer later in the manuscript. Eccentric saccades, those in the "on" direction, are inhibited by restrictions consequent to the ever-lengthening antagonist. This serves to equalize centering and eccentric velocity and is an acceptable explanatory concept. The loss of the sudden clamping effect of the stretched antagonist at the end of a large saccade also accounts for the overshoot of the agonist when the antagonist is paralyzed. Kommerell studied the same phenomenon and his conclusions are difficult to reconcile with Scott's. Kommerell found the overshoot to be maximum in the "off" direction of the agonist (with a paretic antagonist) and it gradually decreased as the saccades moved to the "on" direction. The decreased overshoot was explained by the graded emergence of the tonic holding force in the agonist as it moved to the "on" direction. If I interpret Scott correctly, the overshoot would not be expectedly decreased in the "on" direction.

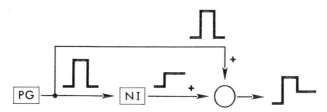

FIG. 1. Simplified schema depicting the formation of the pulse-step increase in firing frequency, at the motoneuronal level, responsible for saccades. The output of the pulse generator (PG) is integrated at the neural integrator (NI) to form a step. The pulse also bypasses the integrator and is summed with the step to form the final pulse-step. The entire operation probably takes place in the pontine paramedium reticular formation at the segmental level of the abducens nuclei. Specific disruptions produce the pulseless and stepless saccades discussed in the text.

Scott presented a man with a sixth nerve palsy and only a slight limitation of abduction but markedly slowed saccadic velocity. The EMG during the abduction did not show the usual sudden pulse of increased activity at the onset of the movement. He favored a nuclear rather than a peripheral abducens palsy, but the absence of a seventh nerve palsy on the side of the abducens weakness mitigates strongly against a nuclear etiology. Hence, I would conclude that a partial nerve lesion selectively blocked the faster conducting axons. Kommerell's strong assertion that eye muscle palsies consequent to nerve lesions *always* show a deficiency in amplitude may be an overstatement. I believe that the amplitude may be full and the problem recognized only by slow saccades and deviation under cover when fusion is eliminated; others seem to share my impression (Kirkham *et al.*, 1972).

I certainly concur that Scott's alcoholic with slow, seemingly pulseless, saccades had a pontine lesion. This patient was similar to Kommerell's who had unilaterally slow saccades but with full excursions and the ability to maintain the eccentric deviation. These slowed saccades can be readily explained if Robinson's (1970) conclusions concerning oculomotor unit behavior are correct. (Contrary opinions are held by Henn and Cohen [1973, and in this volume] and Barmack [1974].) Saccades are created by a pulse-step innervational increase, according to Robinson. The pulse moves the eyes rapidly to the new position and the step holds it there. If the pulse increase in firing frequency does not occur and there is simply a step increase, a slow saccade with full excursion and normal positional maintenance (no nystagmus) would develop. From Fig. 1 it is apparent that a pulseless saccade cannot represent a defect in the pulse generator, the integrity of which is established by its integral, the step response. The problem is best explained by a lesion in the pathway that bypasses the integrator and which, in the normal situation, provides the pulse to sum with the step. It is probable that the pulse generator, the neural integrator, and perhaps even the summing junction are located anatomically in the pontine paramedium reticular formation at the level of the abducens nucleus.

Kommerell presented another interesting patient with normal velocity saccades who could not maintain the eccentric deviation and drifted back toward the center with an exponential time course, only to be corrected with repeated eccentric saccades, constituting gaze-paretic nystagmus (Daroff and Hoyt, 1971). This is best explained by a stepless saccade where repeated pulses interrupt the exponential return drift and produced the nystagmus. Referring back to Fig. 1, the pulse but not the step was reaching the motoneurons.

The pulse and step firing patterns discussed above were common to both muscles of the yolk pair and the dysfunction was therefore supranuclear. Dissociations between pulses and steps can also occur in single eyes in internuclear ophthalmoparesis (INO) due to lesions of the medial longitudinal fasciculus (MLF). Kommerell presented such a case in which the slowed adduction saccade seemed pulseless. We reported a patient with an INO whose slow adduction saccade was best explained by the pulse being too small, necessitating completion of the movement by the step with the possible addition of a uniocular vergence component (Dell'Osso et al., 1974). While on the subject, I am compelled to comment about the oft-mentioned connections which do not traverse the MLF between the pontine paramedium reticular formation or the vestibular nuclei and the medial rectus motoneurons. The functional significance in humans of these pathways are uncertain as the eyes will not move, either voluntarily or reflexly, past the midposition in a versional adduction when there is complete destruction of the ipsilateral MLF. Finally, Kommerell deserves kudos for presenting what probably is the first well-documented case of a Lutz posterior INO, a condition whose existence has been the subject of considerable clinical controversy (Smith and Cogan, 1959; Daroff, 1970; Daroff and Hoyt, 1971).

Henriksson presented a review of basic vestibular aspects of clinical neuro-otology. The literature in this area is replete with atrociously naïve outpourings by alleged neuro-otologists. Many have regarded the vestibular system in a vacuum and seemed to deny, or were ignorant of, the remaining aspects of the ocular motor system. Henriksson has clearly avoided this shielded compartmentalization which has tended to keep vestibular neuro-otology on the same scientific plane as, perhaps, chiropractics. His observation of the dampening effects of eye-closure on caloric or rotational nystagmus confirms the work of others (Spiegel and Aronson, 1933; Mahoney et al., 1957). The latter authors, however, found that the suppression was irregular and unpredictable. Indeed, the average amplitude of caloric induced nystagmus with eyes closed was 19°, whereas it was only 13° with eyes open in darkness; the frequency did not change significantly. There is always the technical problem with AC EOG of eye drift behind closed lids which could suppress the nystagmus and be unrecognized (Cawthorne, 1968; Hood and Dix, 1973). These complicating variables aside, how are we to interpret vestibular nystagmus suppression with eye closure when we know that fixation is inversely proportional to nystagmus intensity (Hart, 1967)? The intensity is also affected by mental activity to which it is proportional; during states of mental relaxation, the nystagmus response decreases. Eye closure might promote a state of revery and, hence, nystagmus inhibition (Collins, 1962; Collins and Guedry, 1962) despite the lack of visual fixation.

TABLE 1. "CEREBELLAR SYSTEM" EYE SIGNS

1. Cogwheel (saccadic) pursuit movements
2. Hypometric saccades
3. Skew deviation
4. Square wave jerks (*Gegenrücke*)
5. Macro square wave jerks (*Kippdeviationen*)
6. Paresis of gaze and conjugate deviation
7. Nystagmus
   (a) Gaze-paretic
   (b) Upbeat
   (c) Positional
   (d) Rapid horizontal bidirectional
8. Ocular dysmetria
9. Ocular flutter
10. Opsoclonus
11. Ocular myoclonus
12. Asthenia of upward gaze

Dichgans discussed two basic problems; that of spinal afferents to the ocular motor system and cerebellar eye signs. Regarding the former, I share his opinion concerning the lack of evidence that disturbed spinal influences produce recognizable eye-movement disturbances. The literature on this subject is unconvincing; cervical cord nystagmus is something we have never recognized. His caution to non-neurologists about the infrequency of isolated cerebellar lesions in clinical material deserves reiteration. Cerebellar tumors usually compress the brainstem and their clinical manifestations represent combined dysfunction. The most common conditions affecting the cerebellum: multiple sclerosis, occlusive vascular disease, and heredo-familial degenerations, all usually involve the brainstem concurrently. Furthermore, it is often impossible to distinguish clinically the extremity ataxia secondary to lesions of the cerebellum from those of cerebellar pathways in the brainstem. This creates a conceptual problem in discussing cerebellar eye signs. These are usually defined as signs which occur in patients with an extremity or truncal ataxia of presumed cerebellar origin. The eye signs listed in Table 1 are under the heading "Cerebellar System" implying that they may result from involvement of cerebellar pathways within the brainstem as well as the cerebellum proper.

The list is long and might seem bewildering to the non-clinician. Needless to say, not all patients with cerebellar disease have all or even any of these disturbances. The clinical pathological correlation with the specific signs are poor, primarily for reasons previously provided. Some of the descriptions of these disorders will differ from those of Dichgans. This is to be expected in that alternate names for the same phenomenology tend to evolve in different centers and, particularly, continents. These are particularly compounded when language translations are involved. I know from experience that Dichgans and I would draw the same general conclusions about the

significance of a given eye-movement disturbance even though we might label it differently. The descriptions provided enjoy common usage amongst neuro-ophthalmologists
in the United States and the United Kingdom. More detailed discussions of these
phenomena appear elsewhere (Daroff, 1970; Daroff and Hoyt, 1971; Daroff and Troost,
in press).

Cogwheel pursuit movements represent small segments of pathologically slow pursuit
interspersed with catch-up saccades and probably results from a decrease in the velocity
gain of the pursuit system (Troost *et al.*, 1972). The sign is definitely not specific
for cerebellar disease. *Hypometric saccades* consist of multistepped fragmented refixations
and might reflect decreased gain in the saccadic system. We (Troost *et al.*, 1974)
agree with Dichgans that these abnormal saccades are not specific for cerebellar dysfunction, as implied by others. *Skew deviation* is a vertical tropia occasionally attributed
to involvement of the middle cerebellar peduncle. *Square wave jerks* are the English
translation of Gegenrücke, a word which we believe was initially used by Jung (1953)
and represents the same eye movement described earlier by Ohm (1935, 1943) as *Zickzackbewegungen*. They are small amplitude (1° to 3°) saccades which move the eyes
away from fixation and then return after a short latency. The eccentric saccade, the
brief maintenance of the deviated position, and the return saccade, constitute the square
wave. These may occur normally behind closed lids but, in our experience, are pathological and reflect cerebellar dysfunction when they interrupt fixation. *Macro square wave
jerks* is a term we utilize to describe large amplitude (20° or more) square waves.
It corresponds to the German word *Kippdeviationen* (Jung and Kornhuber, 1964). *Paresis
of gaze* and *conjugate deviation* of the eyes occur transiently following acute ipsilateral
cerebellar hemispheric lesions.

Cerebellar nystagmus is undoubtedly overemphasized in that most nystagmus represent
vestibular or brainstem dysfunction. However, *gaze paretic* and *up-beat nystagmus* unequivocally occur with cerebellar lesions. The former is ipsilateral to a diseased hemisphere and the latter, when coarse, suggests a lesion in the anterior vermis (Daroff
and Troost, 1973). *Positional nystagmus* of the central type has often been ascribed
to cerebellar disease but this requires critical scrutiny (Salmon, 1969). The most common
nystagmus seen clinically is a *bidirectional horizontal jerk* form with the fast phase
in the direction of gaze and a rate of between 3 to 5 Hz. Evidence is scanty in human
material that this results from cerebellar disease (Daroff, 1970; Daroff and Hoyt,
1971).

Ocular dysmetria is provoked by refixation saccades and manifest as either (1) conjugate under- or overshooting followed by a brief small amplitude oscillation before
the eyes come to rest at the new fixation point, or (2) conjugate overshooting followed
by a single corrective movement back to the target. The latter situation need not
be pathological for small amplitude saccades (Weber and Daroff, 1971) but are abnormal
as the dominant pattern for refixations of amplitudes of 30° or more. *Ocular flutter*
is defined as any brief, intermittent, binocular, horizontal ocular oscillation occurring
spontaneously during straight-ahead fixation. This tends to be a "waste-basket" term
which includes many diverse types of oscillations. Patients with flutter usually have
dysmetria as well. *Opsoclonus* is the most bizarre oscillation and consists of rapid,
involuntary, chaotic, unpredictable, conjugate saccades which are multi-vectorial: horizontal, vertical, diagonal, and circular in direction. "Saccadomania" represents the most
descriptive term.

Ocular myoclonus is a pendular oscillation of the eyes associated with synchronous rhythmical movements of other structures such as the soft palate, tongue, facial muscles, pharynx, larynx, and diaphragm. It is continuous, usually in the vertical plane, with a rate from 1.5 to 5 Hz. Only the coexisting movements of the other midline structures distinguishes ocular myoclonus from pendular nystagmus. This form of myoclonus results from pathological changes in the inferior olivary nucleus of the medulla consequent to primary lesions in either the central tegmental tract or the dentate nucleus. *Asthenia of upward gaze* is an inability to maintain upward gaze, causing the eyes to slowly drift back toward primary position without up-beating nystagmus. It is an infrequent sign attributed to lesions of the superior cerebellar peduncle (Crosby *et al.*, 1970; Carey *et al.*, 1971).

Von Noorden reviewed the clinical aspects of eye movements in the process of fixation in amblyopes and the role of extra-retinal afferents in a most scholarly fashion. I can add nothing of substance to his discussion of oscillopsia nor resolve the unanswered questions he raised. He brought up the subject of congenital nystagmus (CN) which has been a major interest in our laboratory. We share the conclusions of the Freiburg neurological group that a simple distinction between motor and sensory forms of CN is unwarranted (Jung and Kornhuber, 1964). Our impressions, to date, can be summarized as follows:

1. CN is caused by a high gain instability in the slow eye-movement subsystem (Dell'Osso *et al.*, 1972; Dell'Osso, Flynn, and Daroff, 1974; Dell'Osso and Daroff, 1974).

2. A visual system abnormality in a patient with CN does not establish a causal relationship. Both the visual disturbance and the nystagmus may coexist independently and no primary visual defect can be the cause of nystagmus noted at birth. That a pendular form of CN may be more commonly associated with a primary visual defect than jerk nystagmus could reflect genetic association rather than causality (van Vliet *et al.*, 1973; Dell'Osso, Flynn, and Daroff, 1974).

3. Etiological classification cannot be based upon nystagmus waveform in that family members who share the same genetic defect in hereditary CN may have entirely different patterns (Dell'Osso, Flynn, and Daroff, 1974). The ultimate form of the nystagmus depends upon unknown variables in the ocular motor control systems.

4. Fixation attempt (the effort to see) is the main driving force for CN (Dell'Osso, 1973). Poor vision may increase fixation effort, thereby increasing the gain of the slow eye-movement system and hence cause the manifestation, or increased intensity, of CN; but the basic motor instability must be present. Von Noorden's comment that pendular nystagmus may disappear when the congenital cataract patient is fitted with aphakic lenses after surgery is explained by the consequent decreased fixation effort.

5. There are many types of CN waveforms (Ohm, 1943; Jung and Kornhuber, 1964) and classification into two types, pendular or jerk, is an oversimplification. The detailed characteristics of the waveform requires quantitative eye-movement recording with electronic differentiation to uncover small braking saccades which are otherwise unnoticed in the position analogue.

Hoyt and Frisen faithfully attempted to fulfil the plan of this Symposium and considering the rather overwhelming nature of their basic science counterpart's manuscript, they negotiated their charge in a remarkable manner. Their chapter reflects considerable preparation and its extensiveness precludes any satisfactory discussion of the material. I was particularly impressed by their conceptualization of acquired ocular motor defects in relationship to cerebellar repair, and modulation from other intact areas. The ultimate defect thereby represents modification by, or failure of, these adaptive processes. Such an approach to the pathophysiology of eye-movement disorders had not been stressed previously. It further complicates an already difficult conceptual process but, undoubtedly, more nearly approaches the reality. For the record, I am unwilling to join the bandwagon and dispose of the frontal cortex as the orchestrator of saccades in man.

I reserved comment on Jung's introductory gem for last, because for me it has very personal relevance. The clinician-scientist, aware of the contemporary thrusts of the basic science of his specialty and thereby knowing what "questions" are relevant, is indeed in an exceptional position to demonstrate physiological mechanisms through nature's experiments with patient material. The contributions of Jung and his associates have certainly reflected the utilization of that unique opportunity and stands as a model to which we might all strive.

By way of conclusion, I know of no other area in medicine with as strong and vital a linkage between clinician, clinician-scientist, and pure scientist as in our own world of eye movements. Such exciting interactions were clearly evident at this Symposium and have provided a wellspring for future endeavors.

REFERENCES

BARMACK, N. H. (1974) Saccadic discharges evoked by intracellular stimulation of extraocular motoneurons. J. Neurophys. **37**, 395.

BOGHEN, D., TROOST, B. T., DAROFF, R. B., DELL'OSSO, L. F. and BIRKETT, J. R. (1974) Velocity characteristics of normal human saccades. Invest. Ophthal. **13**, 619.

CAREY, J. H., CROSBY, E. C. and SCHNITZLEIN, H. N. (1971) Decorticate versus decerebrate rigidity in subhuman primates and man. Neurology, **21**, 738.

CAWTHORNE, T. (1968) Examination of the vestibular system. Ann. Otol. **77**, 727.

CHAMBERLAIN, W. (1971) Restriction in upward gaze with advancing age. Am. J. Ophthal. **71**, 341.

COLLINS, W. E. (1962) Effects of mental set upon vestibular nystagmus. J. Exptl Psych. **63**, 191.

COLLINS, W. E. and GUEDRY, F. E. (1962) Arousal effects and nystagmus during prolonged constant angular acceleration. Acta oto-laryng. **54**, 349.

CROSBY, E. C., TAREN, J. A. and DAVIS, R. (1970) The anterior lobe and the lingula of the cerebellum in monkeys and man. Topical Probl. Psychiat. Neurol. **10**, 22.

DAROFF, R. B. (1969) Chronic progressive external ophthalmoplegia. A critical review. Arch. Ophthal. **82**, 845.

DAROFF, R. B. (1970) Ocular motor manifestations of brainstem and cerebellar dysfunction. In: Neuro-ophthalmology, vol. V, SMITH, J. L. (Ed.), p. 104. Huffman Publishing Co., Hallandale, Florida.

DAROFF, R. B. and HOYT, W. F. (1971) Supranuclear disorders of ocular control systems in man: clinical, anatomical and physiological correlations, 1969. In: The Control of Eye Movements, BACH-Y-RITA, P., COLLINS, C. C. and HYDE, J. E. (Eds.), p. 175. Academic Press, New York.

DAROFF, R. B., SOLITARE, G., PINCUS, J. H. and GLASER, G. H. (1966) Spongiform encephalopathy with chronic progressive external ophthalmoplegia. Neurology, **16**, 161.

DAROFF, R. B. and TROOST, B. T. (1973) Upbeat nystagmus. J. Am. Med. Ass. **225**, 312.

DAROFF, R. B. and TROOST, B. T. (in press) Nystagmus and other ocular oscillations. In: Clinical Ophthalmology, vol. II, GLASER, J. (Ed.). Harper & Row, Hagerstown, Maryland.

DELL'OSSO, L. F. (1973) Improving visual acuity in congenital nystagmus. In: Neuro-ophthalmology, vol. VII, SMITH, J. L. and GLASER, J. (Eds.), p. 98. C. V. Mosby Company, St. Louis.

DELL'OSSO, L. F. and DAROFF, R. B. (1974) Functional organization of the ocular motor system. Aerospace Med. **45**, 873.

DELL'OSSO, L. F., FLYNN, J. T. and DAROFF, R. B. (1974) Hereditary congenital nystagmus: an intrafamilial study. Arch. Ophthal. **92**, 366.

DELL'OSSO, L. F., GAUTHIER, G., LIBERMAN, G. and STARK, L. (1972) Eye movement recordings as a diagnostic tool in a case of congenital nystagmus. *Am. J. Optom.* **49**, 3.

DELL'OSSO, L. F., ROBINSON, D. A. and DAROFF, R. B. (1974) Optokinetic asymmetry and internuclear ophthalmoplegia. *Arch. Neurol.* **31**, 138.

HART, C. W. (1967) Ocular fixation and the caloric test. *Laryngoscope*, **77**, 2103.

HENN, V. and COHEN, B. (1973) Quantitative analysis of activity in eye muscle motoneurons during saccadic eye movements and positions of fixation, *J. Neurophys.* **36**, 115.

HOOD, J. D. and DIX, M. R. (1973) The significance of optic fixation in tests of vestibular function. *Equilibrium Res.* **3**, 1.

JUNG, R. (1953) Nystagmographie Zur Physiologie und Pathologie des optisch-vestibulären Systems beim Menschen. In: *Handb. d. Inn. Medizin*, vol. V, p. 1325. Springer, Berlin.

JUNG, R. and KORNHUBER, H. H. (1964) Results of electronystagmography in man: the value of optokinetic, vestibular, and spontaneous nystagmus for neurologic diagnosis and research. In: *The Oculomotor System*, BENDER, M. B. (Ed.), p. 428. Harper & Row, New York.

KIRKHAM, T. H., BIRD, A. C. and SANDERS, M. D. (1972) Divergence paralysis and raised intracranial pressure. *Brit. J. Ophthal.* **56**, 776.

MAHONEY, J. L., HARLAN, W. L. and BICKFORD, R. G. (1957) Visual and other factors influencing caloric nystagmus in normal subjects. *Arch. Otol.* **66**, 46.

OHM, J. (1935) Zur Augenzitternkunde. 37. Mit. Über Zickzackbewegungen. *Graefe Arch. Ophthal.* **134**, 27.

OHM, J. (1943) *Die Mikroneurologie des Auges und seiner Bewegung*, Ferdinand Enke, Stuttgart.

ROBINSON, D. A. (1970) Oculomotor unit behavior in the monkey. *J. Neurophys.* **33**, 393.

ROWLAND, L. P. (1974) Are the muscular dystrophies neurogenic? *Ann N. Y. Acad. Sci.* **228**, 244.

SALMON, S. D. (1969) Positional nystagmus. *Arch. Otol.* **90**, 84.

SMITH, J. L. and COGAN, D. G. (1959) Internuclear ophthalmoplegia. *Arch. Ophthal.* **61**, 687.

SPIEGEL, E. A. and ARONSON, L. (1933) Continuous stimulation of the labyrinth with sustained nystagmus. *Arch. Otol.* **17**, 311.

TROOST, B. T., DAROFF, R. B., WEBER, R. B. and DELL'OSSO, L. F. (1972) Hemispheric control of eye movements. II. Quantitative analysis of smooth pursuit in a hemispherectomy patient. *Arch. Neurol.* **27**, 449.

TROOST, B. T., WEBER, R. B. and DAROFF, R. B. (1974) Hypometric saccades. *Am. J. Ophthal.* **78**, 1002.

VAN VLIET, A. G. M., WAARDENBURG, P. J., FORSIUS, H. and ERIKSSON, A. W. (1973) Nystagmographical studies in Aland eye disease. *Acta Ophthal.* **51**, 782.

WEBER, R. B. and DAROFF, R. B. (1971) The metrics of horizontal saccadic eye movements in normal humans. *Vision Research*, **11**, 921.

FREE CONTRIBUTIONS

NEUROPHYSIOLOGY OF OCULOMOTOR SYSTEMS

DIFFERENCES IN THE ACTIVITY OF EYE-POSITION CODED NEURONS IN THE ALERT MONKEY DURING FIXATION AND TRACKING MOVEMENTS†

ROLF ECKMILLER

INTRODUCTION

It is known that the muscle tone of various human muscles can be shifted consciously at constant load conditions (Lindsley, 1935; Basmajian *et al.*, 1965). This paper deals with the question, whether this kind of shift in the neural activity level can be demonstrated electrophysiologically in the primate oculomotor system when the mode of movement changes between fixational and tracking movements.

METHODS

Single and double unit recordings from eye position coded neurons in the regions of the IIIrd and IVth nerve nuclei in the macaque brainstem were correlated with the corresponding EOG-time courses. This was done in those cases where a tracking period was preceded and followed by fixational movements. Because of their stereotaxic localization, which was checked histologically in some cases, and because of their activity patterns the analyzed neurons are very likely to be oculomotor motoneurons. Details of the methods have been described elsewhere (Eckmiller *et al.*, 1974; Eckmiller, 1974). The method which was used for the simultaneous recording was developed by Westheimer and Blair.

RESULTS

Care was taken to ensure that all the results which are reported here are independent of the orthogonal eye positions and the direction of movement (horizontal or vertical). Figure 1 shows a part of a simultaneous recording of two motoneurons with opposite on-directions during a vertical tracking movement. Neuron A was located in the IIIrd nerve root and neuron B at the IVth nerve nucleus. The middle trace gives the time course of the vertical EOG. The instantaneous impulse rate IR(t) is shown for both

†Supported in part by the National Eye Institute, U.S. Public Health Service under Grant EY-00592 to Dr. G. Westheimer and by the Deutsche Forschungsgemeinschaft.

D 155$_2$-0 496

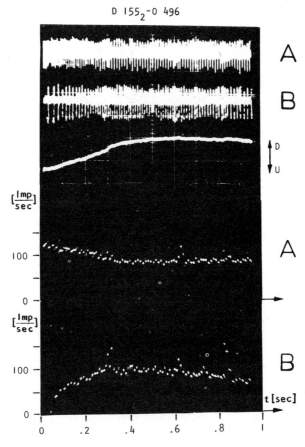

FIG. 1. Simultaneous recording of two oculomotor motoneurons with opposite on-directions (on for A: up, on for B: down) with their instantaneous impulse rate IR(t) and the vertical EOG. Neuron A was recorded in a IIIrd nerve root and neuron B in the vicinity of the IVth nerve nucleus as identified histologically. The short transients in the impulse rate courses are probably due to microsaccades.

neurons in the bottom traces. They indicate the smooth impulse rate changes which are interrupted occasionally by short transients probably due to micro-saccades.

A comparison of the dynamic behaviour of the two motoneurons during tracking with their static characteristic is given in Figs. 2 a and b. The circles are various fixational values which occurred immediately before or after the tracking period of about 1.2 sec. The broken line indicates the static characteristic in the mode of fixational movements. Because of the small number of static values no distinction was made between those values reached in the on-direction and those reached in the off-direction (Eckmiller, 1974). The crosses are dynamic values which were measured consecutively every 20 ms during the tracking period and connected by lines with the arrows indicating the direction of the tracking course.

In the case of both neurons, it was found that while the impulse rates are close to their static values when the tracking is in the muscle's off-direction they reach significantly higher values during tracking in the on-direction. Both examples support

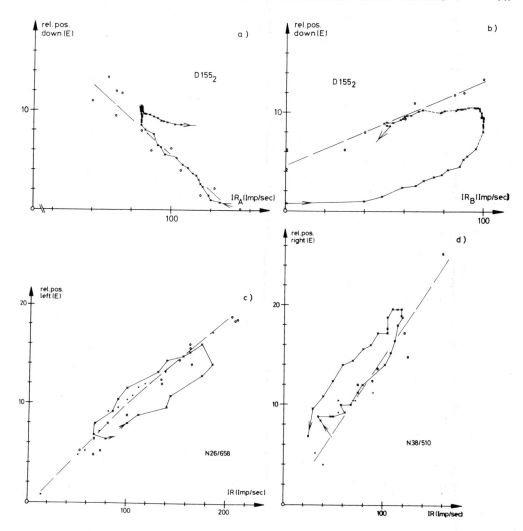

FIG. 2. Correlation of the eye position (given in relative units E) with the impulse rate IR for various oculomotor motoneurons. Circles and dots are static values for various fixational eye positions. The crosses are dynamic values which were measured consecutively in fixed time intervals T during tracking periods. The interrupted lines indicate the static characteristics. The figure demonstrates various activity shifts between fixating and tracking. (a) Neuron A as explained for Fig. 1. $T = 20$ ms. (b) Neuron B as explained for Fig. 1. $T = 20$ ms. (c) This motoneuron was recorded at the IIIrd nerve nucleus. $T = 30$ ms. (d) This motoneuron was recorded in the IIIrd nerve root. $T = 50$ ms.

the hypothesis that tracking movements are generally performed on a higher impulse rate level which in turn leads to a higher muscle tone. However, this is not a general property, since the same analysis of several other motoneurons shows just the opposite result. An example is given in Fig. 2d. The neuron was recorded from a IIIrd nerve root. The dynamic course during tracking which was measured in this case every 50 ms is clearly shifted into the direction of lower impulse rate values relative to the static fixational values which preceded or followed this tracking period. The last example in Fig. 2c was chosen to demonstrate that there are motoneurons acting in the horizontal plane which are shifted in their activity in the direction opposite to that example in Fig. 2d, but similar to those in Figs. 2a and 2b. Note, however, that the tracking course in Fig. 2c does not just touch but crosses the static characteristic although the shift is still significant. The neuron was recorded at the IIIrd nerve nucleus and the dynamic values were measured every 30 ms.

DISCUSSION

The presented results clearly show that the neural activity of oculomotor motoneurons is increased or decreased during tracking movements relative to the static characteristic for fixational movements. To interpret this finding one has to bear in mind that the single unit activity was correlated with the eye movement, which in turn was caused not by a single motor unit of an extraocular muscle but by synchronous action of all these muscles acting together. The activity shifts illustrate one aspect of reciprocal innervation: the interplay between agonist and antagonist is always such that the eyeball will move if the agonist increases its force, the antagonist decreases its force or both forces are varied together.

In any case the results show that static values of various fixational eye positions *cannot* be qualitatively described by the same linear first-order differential equation as the dynamic values from tracking movements (Robinson, 1970). If that equation held in both modes of eye movements, then the tracking course would have to describe some type of ellipse *around* the static characteristic rather *than on either side* of this characteristic. The elliptical shape itself means dynamic hysteresis in the final common pathway which can be explained by the dynamic properties of the orbit plant (Robinson, 1964).

At present the underlying neural mechanisms for the described activity shifts are unknown. In some cases it was checked that the direction of the shift remains constant for a given motoneuron when the mode of eye movements changed several times between fixating and tracking. However, the amount of shift appeared to be different for tracking periods which were separated in time by only about 2 min. It therefore seems to be advisable to restrict the time period for a quantitative analysis of the final common pathway as much as possible (about 1 min) and not to mix measurements from various tracking periods (Robinson, 1970). It remains to be shown whether the state of alertness or attention has some influence on the amount of the shifts.

CONCLUSION

The finding that the described activity shifts occur for various motoneurons in either one or the other of both possible directions, supports the hypothesis that there are at least two oculomotor sub-systems, one more influential in the mode of fixation and the other one in the mode of tracking movements.

ACKNOWLEDGEMENT

The author wishes to thank Dr. G. Westheimer and Dr. S. Blair for allowing him to use their experimental equipment and for their helpful advice and discussion.

REFERENCES

BASMAJIAN, J. V., BAEZA, M. and FABRIGAR, C. (1965) Conscious control and training of individual spinal motor neurons in normal human subjects. *J. New Drugs* **5**, 78.

ECKMILLER, R. (1974) Hysteresis in the static characteristics of eye position coded neurons in the alert monkey. *Pflügers Arch.* **350**, 249.

ECKMILLER, R., BLAIR, S. M. and WESTHEIMER, G. (1974) Oculomotor neuronal correlations shown by simultaneous unit recordings. *Exptl. Brain Res.* **21**, 241.

LINDSLEY, D. B. (1935) Electrical activity of human motor units during voluntary contraction. *Am. J. Physiol.* **114**, 90.

ROBINSON, D. A. (1964) The mechanics of human saccadic eye movement. *J. Physiol.* **174**, 245.

ROBINSON, D. A. (1970) Oculomotor unit behaviour in the monkey. *J. Neurophysiol.* **33**, 393.

THE ROLE OF THE EXTRAOCULAR MOTONEURON MEMBRANE IN THE REGULATION OF "SACCADIC DISCHARGE"

N. H. BARMACK

SACCADIC eye movements are preceded by a stereotyped discharge from the participating extraocular motoneurons. A saccade in the "on" direction is presaged by a transient increase in discharge frequency of motoneurons innervating the agonist muscle. The duration and frequency of this burst are proportional to saccadic amplitude. The burst is followed by a net increase in steady-state discharge which is proportional to commanded eye position (Fig. 1A). Conversely, motoneurons which innervate the antagonist muscle are transiently silenced prior to a saccade before resuming a lower net rate of steady-state discharge. The patterns of motoneuronal discharge produce a "pulse-step" increment in force in extraocular muscles, overcoming viscosity of these muscles and thereby producing a rapid (saccadic) change in eye position (Collins, 1971; Fuchs and Luschei, 1970; Henn and Cohen, 1973; Robinson, 1964; Schiller, 1970).

It would be of interest to know how the saccadic burst in extraocular motoneurons is generated. This knowledge would be of importance in determining which parameters of eye movement are programmed centrally and which parameters are the consequence of more peripheral mechanisms. Saccadic bursts may be the consequence of separate sets of premotoneuronal elements synapsing on the motoneuron. One set of premotoneuronal elements would be associated with the maintenance of eye position and a second set would provide information concerned with saccades (Fig. 1B). Alternatively the premotoneuronal command may indicate commanded eye position, and through either a rate sensitive "synaptic current-to-voltage conversion" (Fig. $1B_{2a}$) or a rate sensitive "voltage-to-frequency conversion" (Fig. $1B_{2b}$), the input may be transformed to an output which is appropriate for both saccades and fixation.

In the present report an attempt was made to decipher the premotoneuronal command signal by recording intracellularly the activity of antidromically identified extraocular motoneurons in response to various waveforms of intracellular current stimulation. The recordings have been obtained from motoneurons of the IVth and VIth nuclei in cats anesthetized with pentobarbital sodium and paralyzed with gallamine trethiodide.

When extraocular motoneurons are stimulated intracellularly with depolarizing exponential steps of current, discharges are evoked which are similar in frequency and duration to the motoneuron discharges which accompany saccadic eye movements. A small exponential step of depolarizing current evokes a transient discharge exclusively, with a 10–15-ms duration and with a peak frequency of 200–250 imp/s (Fig. 2A).

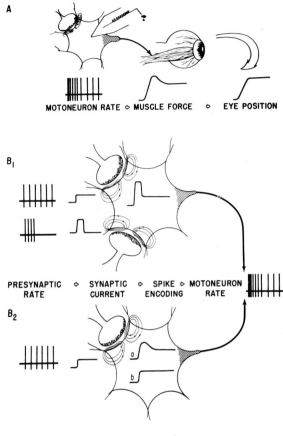

FIG. 1

Larger steps evoke higher frequency, longer duration transient discharges followed by a maintained steady state discharges (Fig. 2A$_2$). These motoneurons are also sensitive to the rate of change of intracellular current in the hyperpolarizing direction (Fig. 2A$_{1,2}$). The effect of manipulating the rate of change of intracellular current stimulation independently of amplitude can be determined by holding the amplitude of the depolarizing current step constant while varying the time constant of the exponential rise. By varying the time constant of the exponential rise of the depolarizing current step it is possible to influence the shape of the initial transient discharge (Fig. 3).

The frequency and duration of the transient discharges evoked by steps of intracellular current are similar to those recorded extra-cellularly from extraocular motoneurons of chronic monkeys. These data would suggest that the premotoneuronal command signal might indicate commanded eye position. If this central position command signal were changed abruptly, as in the case where a visual target is given a step displacement on the retina, then a saccadic burst would be generated by virtue of the rate sensitivity of the extraocular motoneuron membrane (Barmack, 1974). This represents an important mechanism by which saccades may be generated, but it also represents a formidable problem for the central neural structures concerned with eye movements. The signal

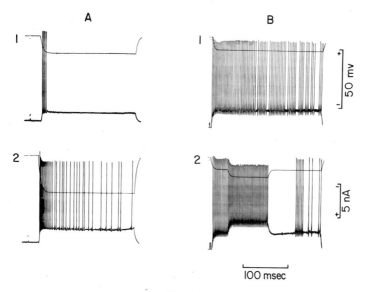

FIG. 2

to the motoneuronal pool must be sufficiently "noise free" so as not to cause saccades when they are not appropriate. The difficulty in making smooth pursuit eye movements in the absence of visual, vestibular or proprioceptive inputs might be a reflection of the difficulty in generating centrally a continuously varying, low-frequency position command to the motoneuronal pool. It would be expected that pharmacological agents

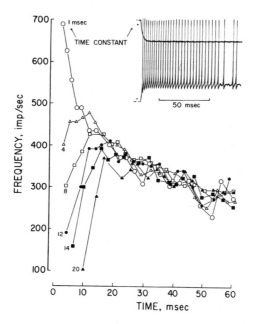

FIG. 3

which impair with central nervous system function, such as barbiturates, would cause an increase in the frequency of saccadic eye movements (Rashbass, 1961) by passing higher frequencies of synaptic currents directly to the motoneuron pool.

REFERENCES

BARMACK, N. H. (1974) Saccadic discharges evoked by intracellular stimulation of extraocular motoneurons. *J. Neurophysiology*, **37**, 395–412.

COLLINS, C. C. (1971) Orbital mechanics. *The Control of Eye Movements*, BACH-Y-RITA, P., COLLINS, C. C. and HYDE, J. E. (Eds.), pp. 283–325. New York, Academic Press.

FUCHS, A. F. and LUSCHEI, E. S. (1970) Firing patterns of abducens neurons of alert monkeys in relationship to horizontal eye movement. *J. Neurophysiol.* **33**, 382–392.

HENN, V. and COHEN, B. (1973) Quantitative analysis of activity in eye muscle motoneurons during saccadic eye movements and positions of fixation. *J. Neurophysiol.* **36**, 115–126.

RASHBASS, C. (1961) The relationship between saccadic and smooth tracking eye movements. *J. Physiol.* **159**, 326–338.

ROBINSON, D. A. (1964) The Mechanics of human saccadic eye movement. *J. Physiol.* **174**, 245–264.

SCHILLER, P. H. (1970) The discharge characteristics of single units in the oculomotor and abducens nuclei of the unanesthetized monkey. *Exptl Brain Res.* **10**, 347–362.

THE EFFECT OF HEAD POSITION ON OCULOMOTOR DISCHARGE PATTERNS IN RABBITS†

Kurt-Peter Schaefer, Dietrich Lothar Meyer, Ulrich Büttner and Ditmar Schott

INTRODUCTION

The interactions of neck proprioceptive, e.g. joint afferents and oculomotor mechanisms, have already been well documented. When the head is in a fixed position and the trunk is moved, the eyes reach and maintain a constant deviation in the spatial plane of trunk movement (De Kleijn, 1921; Magnus, 1924; and others). The so-called tonic neck-reflexes of the eyes are not very distinct, and play an important role only when the head is in very excentric positions. The basic mechanisms can also be demonstrated in man (Barany, 1918; Grahe, 1922; Bos and Philipszoon, 1963).

Recent investigations have also demonstrated interactions of vestibular afferents and neck-proprioception during head movements (Bizzi et al., 1971; Dichgans et al., 1973), but interactions of neck-proprioceptive and visual afferents have not yet been studied intensively. In animals and man close connections between the visual and the neck-proprioceptive systems are necessary, since slow eye movements are mainly controlled visually. Therefore it appears more useful to study how the visual, rather than the vestibular, input interacts with neck-proprioceptive afferents to control eye position.

One of the possible approaches to this problem is to study the eye–head coordination during optokinetic nystagmus. Rabbits are useful animals to work on, since spontaneous eye movements are rare (Schaefer, 1965). We have recorded from thirty rabbits (a) the eye-nystagmus during optokinetic stimulation (EOG) in different head-positions (GRASS platinum needle electrodes) and (b) the extracellular activity pattern of forty rectus medialis nucleus cells (tungsten or glass-insulated platinum electrodes). Optokinetic stimulation was applied by turning the animal at constant velocities ranging from 5°/sec to 50°/sec (most frequently 10°/sec) on an electronically controlled turntable. For on- and off-line processing of the data a PDP-8/E computer was used.

RESULTS

EOG recordings demonstrated a variation in the number of nystagmus beats per 360° of stimulation, as a function of head-position. For example, if the animal was turned at a constant velocity in one direction, and the head deviation was towards

†Supported by the "Deutsche Forschungsgemeinschaft", SFB 33.

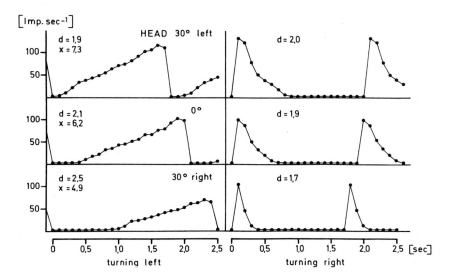

FIG. 1. Frequency plot of the activity of one neuron of the left internal rectus nucleus during ten nystagmus beats in each head-position. The length of intervals between beats, the maximum discharge frequency, and the slope of the curves changes as a function of the head position. d = time interval between the beats. x = frequency increase of neuron discharges per 0.1 sec. The animal has been turned on a turntable at a constant velocity of 10°/sec.

the same direction, then the number of nystagmus beats was increased up to 80%, while the amplitude of each beat was reduced.

These phenomena observed by recording oculograms have then been studied on the neuronal level. Optokinetic stimulation in different head-positions resulted in distinct changes of the activity patterns of oculomotor neurons. For example, neurons in the left internal rectus nucleus displayed a more "tonic" discharge pattern when the head deviation was towards the left (see upper part of Fig. 1). These changes were seen during fast and slow nystagmus phases, as well as in the resting position of the eye. If constant velocity turning was towards the left, the frequency of discharges during the slow nystagmus phase increased, the further the head was deviated from the mid-position. The same unit was excited during the fast phase when the animal was turned towards the right. With the head in a position 30° towards the left turning right caused a "tonic" after-discharge.

Opposite effects were observed if the head was deviated towards the right (see lower part of Fig. 1). Under these conditions neurons of the left internal rectus nucleus displayed a more "phasic" discharge pattern and the frequency of discharges was decreased during the fast and slow phases of nystagmus. If the head was in a position 30° to the right, turning towards the left caused an activation of the unit which was lower in frequency than the slow phase activation observed with the head in the normal position. During turning in the opposite direction only a short burst of spikes was observed at the onset of the fast phase.

In another series of experiments the oculomotor discharge rates were measured during 1° stepwise turning of the animal. A one degree turn caused an increase or decrease of activity, which varied depending on the head position. The slopes of the frequency curves so obtained were found to increase more or less linearly, if the head-deviation was within the physiological range from 30° left to 30° right.

All the phenomena described above have also been studied under the influence of Curare (i.v. injection of 0.5 mg/kg methylcurarine). Although eye movements did not occur any more, the basic effects of head positions on the discharge pattern of oculomotor neurons were unaffected. This can be interpreted as showing that these effects were not caused by proprioceptive afferences from the eye muscles. Under curare the only sensory input most likely to account for the results appears to be the one that originates from the joint receptors of the neck.

CONCLUDING REMARKS

The presented results demonstrate that the head position exerts a distinct influence on optokinetic nystagmus. In another series of experiments in free-moving rabbits similar phenomena of eye–head coordination have been observed under "dynamic" conditions of optokinetic head nystagmus. The results of these latter experiments (unpublished) are well predicted by data from the more static experiments described above. An important part of the control of naturally occurring eye movements might therefore be attributed to the interaction of neck-proprioceptive and visual mechanisms. Further evidence for an integration of visual inputs with proprioceptive afferents from the neck has been obtained by stimulation of the optic tectum in rabbits. In these experiments the threshold for eliciting an orienting response by tectal stimulation was dependent on the starting position of the head.

SUMMARY

Forty oculomotor neurons have been recorded in rabbits during optokinetic nystagmus with the head in different positions. Under these conditions neurons in the internal rectus nucleus displayed either more "tonic" or more "phasic" response to optokinetic stimulation. This behaviour was not influenced by the application of curare. These findings are interpreted as demonstrating an interaction of neck-joint afferents with the oculomotor system.

REFERENCES

BARANY, R. (1918) Über einige Augen- und Halsmuskelreflexe bei Neugeborenen. *Acta Otolaryngol.* **1**, 97.
BIZZI, E., KALIL, R. E. and TAGLIASCO, V. (1971) Eye-head coordination in monkeys: evidence for centrally patterned organization. *Science,* **173**, 452.
BOS, J. H. and PHILIPSZOON, H. J. (1963) Some forms of nystagmus provoked by stimuli other than accelerations. *Practiva oto-rhino-lar.* **25**, 108.
DE KLEIJN, A. (1921) Tonische Labyrinth- und Halsreflexe auf die Augen. *Pflügers Arch.* **186**, 82.
DICHGANS, J., BIZZI, E., MORASSO, P. and TAGLIASCO, V. (1973) Mechanisms underlying recovery of eye head coordination following bilateral labyrinthectomy in monkeys. *Brain Res.,* p. 548.
GRAHE, K. (1922) Über Halsreflexe und Vestibularreaktion beim Menschen. *Z. HNO-Heilk.* **3**, 550.
MAGNUS, R. (1924) Köperstellung. Springer-Verlag Berlin.
SCHAEFFER, K.-P. (1965) Die Erregungsmuster einzelner Neurone des Abducens-Kernes beim Kaninchen. *Pflügers Arch.* **284**, 31.

ELECTROTONIC INTERACTION BETWEEN MOTONEURONS OF THE ABDUCENS NUCLEUS OF THE CAT

P. Gogan, J. P. Gueritaud, G. Horcholle-Bossavit and S. Tyc-Dumont

Electrotonic coupling between teleost oculomotor neurons has been described by Kriebel *et al.* (1969) and this mechanism has been shown to synchronize firing (Korn and Bennett, 1972) in the oculomotor system of fish. By analogy, it could be predicted that synchronization is performed in the same way in mammals. This work presents results that support strongly our hypothesis of the presence of *electrotonic coupling between oculomotor neurons* in the cat (Gogan *et al.*, 1974 a, b).

The experiments were performed in adult "Encéphale isolé" cats without anesthesia. The intramuscular portion of the abducens nerve was dissected, cut, and placed over one pair of silver chloride electrodes in the orbit. The pair of electrodes could be used either to stimulate the abducens nerve antidromically, or to record its oculomotor discharges. The recording microelectrodes (KCl 3 M with an average DC resistance of 5 MΩ) were introduced to the abducens nucleus according to stereotaxic coordinates at an angle of 30°. All these experiments were done with *an intact brain* and a closed head. The ablation of the cerebellum was carefully avoided in order to prevent damage of the nervous structures located beneath the IVth ventricle. Indeed, nerve cells of the bulb might show signs of anoxia after cerebellectomy (unpublished data).

Direct evidence that cells are electrotonically coupled requires the simultaneous impalement of two cells and the demonstration that current applied on either side spreads between cells as if they were connected by a low resistance path (Bennett, 1966). This has not yet been achieved in the abducens motoneurons of the cat. Therefore, indirect criteria were utilized to test the possible presence of electrotonic coupling between abducens motoneurons. One manoeuvre consists of blocking the initiation of action potentials in the impaled motoneuron when its excitability is tested by its antidromic excitation. An action potential induced by a direct *intracellular stimulation* (3 nA) will collide with the antidromic action potential providing that the time interval between the foot of the directly evoked potential and the antidromic stimulus is correctly chosen. Any electrical event recorded during the collision period must be interpreted as being dispatched to the motoneuron through a channel other than via its own axon.

Intracellular recordings were obtained from 128 *abducens* motoneurons showing a resting membrane potential of -60 mV or more. The amplitude of the antidromic action potential following electrical stimulation of the abducens nerve varied from 60 to 90 mV. Each motoneuron was submitted to a sequence of tests. The threshold (T) for

461

the antidromic invasion, the latencies of the antidromic invasion for a stimulus delivered at T and above T, and the absolute refractoriness were determined. The effect of antidromic stimulation of the abducens nerve was then observed following direct excitation of the impaled motoneuron. Figure 1 illustrates the situation encountered in one motoneuron which was typical of 21 of the 128 impaled motoneurons. In A, the strength of the stimulation was set at T for the impaled motoneuron and the latency of this antidromic response was 750 μs. In B, the recorded antidromic action potential following stimulation delivered at $4T$ had a latency of 600 μs. The use of paired stimuli indicated a refractoriness of 850 μs. When a depolarizing current was

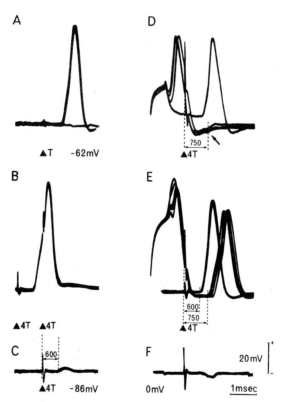

FIG. 1. Demonstration of electrotonic coupling between abducens motoneurons. Intracellular recordings from one abducens motoneuron (resting potential -62 mV) following stimulation of the abducens nerve. A: Antidromic invasion of the motoneuron following threshold (T) (50% failure) stimulation of the abducens nerve. B: Double antidromic stimulation of the abducens nerve delivered at $4T$ and at a time interval (850 μs) corresponding to absolute refractoriness; the second stimulus fails to trigger an IS–SD spike. C: The cell is artificially hyperpolarized to -86 mV. The antidromic invasion of the soma and initial segment is blocked and only the M spike is observed with the same latency (600 μs) as the antidromic response in B. D: The antidromic stimuli ($4T$) are delivered during the period of axon blockade following direct activation of the impaled cell and generate small depolarizations at a latency of 750 μs (arrow). When the direct activation of the cell fails to generate a spike, a normal antidromic response appears with a 600-μs latency. In E, the direct activation of the impaled motoneuron is followed by antidromic stimuli ($4T$) delivered during the period of blockade. Action potentials are still triggered *but with a latency of 750 μs*. Without direct activation of the cell, the normal antidromic response appears *with a latency of 600 μs* (single tracing). In that case, antidromic stimuli always generate full action potentials at the same latency of 750 μs as the small depolarization (arrow) shown in D. F.: Antidromic extracellular field potential recorded after destroying the impaled cell. Calibration: 20 mV. Time: 1 ms.

passed through the microelectrode (D), direct action potentials were generated that blocked the antidromic invasion of the cell. In D, the antidromic stimuli (4T) were delivered 600 μs after the foot of the direct potentials, thus during the collision period. However, the blockade did not suppress a small depolarization (arrow) that occurred at 750 μs. The one sweep shown without direct excitation illustrated the latency of the true antidromic response of the impaled motoneuron (600 μs). In E, the direct excitation of the cell generated action potentials that block the antidromic invasion but did not block the generation of action potentials at 750 μs latency. Neither the small depolarization (D) nor the spikes (E) that occurred at 750 μs can be confused with the excitation (C) of the axon of the motoneuron (M spike) since the two pheno-mena have different latencies. As it is shown in C, an hyperpolarization (-86 mV) of the cell blocked the SD and IS spike and left only the M spike. The M spike showed a latency of 600 μs similar to the latency of the antidromic response. The small depolarization illustrated in D would most often initiate action potential like in E, the latency of which varied from 750 μs to 1.0 ms.

The criterion chosen in these experiments to identify an electrotonic coupling was the presence of a membrane depolarization following the antidromic invasion during the collision period. The difference in latencies of the true antidromic invasion and the depolarization (or action potentials) ranged from 100 to 500 μs with a mean at 200 μs. This time is too fast to admit a chemical synapse. In all the observed cases, the small depolarization was most of the time large enough to initiate action potentials. These findings suggest strongly the presence of a functionally efficient electro-tonic coupling between abducens motoneurons in the cat.

REFERENCES

BENNETT, M. V. L. (1966) Physiology of electrotonic junctions. *Ann. N.Y. Acad. Sci.* **137**, 509–539.

GOGAN, P., GUERITAUD, J. P., HORCHOLLE-BOSSAVIT, G. and TYC-DUMONT, S. (1974a) Couplages électrotoniques entre les motoneurones du noyau abducens chez le chat. *J. Physiol. (Paris)* **69**, 154A.

GOGAN, P., GUERITAUD, J. P., HORCHOLLE-BOSSAVIT, G. and TYC-DUMONT, S. (1974b) Electrotonic coupling between motoneurons in the abducens nucleus of the cat. *Exptl Brain Res.* **21**, 139–154.

KORN, H. and BENNETT, M. V. L. (1972) Electrotonic coupling between teleost oculomotor neurons; restriction to somatic regions and relation to function of somatic and dendritic sites of impulse initiation. *Brain Res.* **38**, 433–439.

KRIEBEL, M. E., BENNETT, M. V. L., WAXMAN, S. G. and PAPPAS, G. D. (1969) Oculomotor neurons in fish: electrotonic coupling and multiple sites of impulse initiation. *Science,* **166**, 520–524.

PRIMARY MESENCEPHALIC PROJECTIONS OF THE *RECTUS LATERALIS* MUSCLE AFFERENTS IN CAT: PHYSIOLOGICAL AND ANATOMICAL EVIDENCE

R. M. Alvarado-Mallart, C. Buisseret-Delmas, J. F. Guéritaud and
G. Horcholle-Bossavit

INTRODUCTION

Although typical muscle spindles have neveʀ been found in cat eye muscles, responses from stretch receptors have been observed in the oculomotor muscle nerves (see Bach-y-Rita, 1971). On the other hand, we know at present by some anatomical experiments in progress that a variety of complex sensory endings do exist in these muscles (Alvarado-Mallart, Batini and Raymond, in preparation).

The localization of the first-order neurons of these receptors is still a matter of controversy (see Osakawa, 1961). Using electrophysiological methods Fillenz (1955) found that these neurons are located in the trigeminal mesencephalic nucleus (MesV). Using electrophysiological (Buisseret *et al.*, 1971) and anatomical methods we have been able to demonstrate that the afferents projections from the *Rectus Lateralis* muscle (RL) of the cat are indeed localized in MesV.

PHYSIOLOGICAL EXPERIMENTS

The physiological experiments have been performed in adult "encephale isolé" animals without anesthesia and in darkness. Neuronal responses of the MesV were recorded with steel microelectrodes when the RL was stretched. The recording points were located histologically after iron deposition around the tip of the microelectrode by the Prussian blue method. Muscle afferents were activated mechanically by medial rotation of the eye in the horizontal plane which results in stretching the RL and by stretching the RL isolated from the surrounding tissues except for the proximal tendon, after the ennucleation of the eye.

Among the units recorded in MesV, only forty-one, exhibiting responses following manipulation of the eye muscle, will be considered here. All of them were activated either by horizontal deviation of the eye or by muscle stretch. To be identified as units specifically responding to eye muscle stretches these neurons have been submitted to additional tests in order to ascertain that they fulfilled the following requirements:

1. not to respond either to jaw movements or to pressure applied to the eye ball, teeth or other adjacent tissues;

465

2. be activated with a short latency by stretching the eye muscle (Fig. 1);
3. be activated by light touch applied to a small area of the eye muscle with a glass rod on the isolated muscle only.

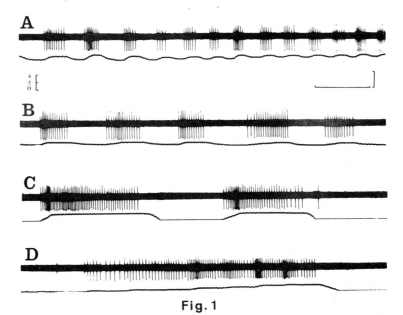

Fig. 1

FIG. 1. Responses of one unit in the MesV to stretches of the RL. Upper traces: unit recordings. Lower traces: stretch signal, with an upward deflection corresponding to changes of length calibrated in mm (top left). A and B: Responses of the unit to brief, periodic changes of length in the RL. C: Prolonged stretches showing the dynamic and static phases of the responses. D: Response to a "step-by-step" stretch: frequency increases at each change of length. Calibration: 500 μv. Time: 500 ms.

Only ten of the units examined could be identified as specifically responding to RL stretch. In spite of the small number of the cells meeting the criteria the fact that such cells were found in MesV demonstrated that the soma of the primary stretch receptors from the RL is located in this nucleus.

ANATOMICAL EXPERIMENTS

We have tried to confirm these results using the peroxydase method for tracing nervous pathways (Kristensson *et al.*, 1971).

Five to ten microliters of horseradish peroxydase (HRP) in Ringer solution have been injected to newborn, young and adults cats in the RL or in other extraocular muscles of one eye, under pentobarbital anesthesia. Twenty-four to forty-eight hours after the injection, the animals were sacrificed by perfusion *in vivo*. The brainstem and the homolateral Gasserian ganglion were cut in 40-μm thick serial sections. These sections were treated by the histochemical method to reveal the peroxydase activity (Graham and Karnowsky, 1966) and counterstained with cresyl violet.

The enzyme was clearly identified in the motoneurons of the ipsilateral VI nucleus when the injection was made in the RL, of the contralateral IV nucleus or of the ipsilateral III nucleus when the superior oblicus or other extraocular muscle were

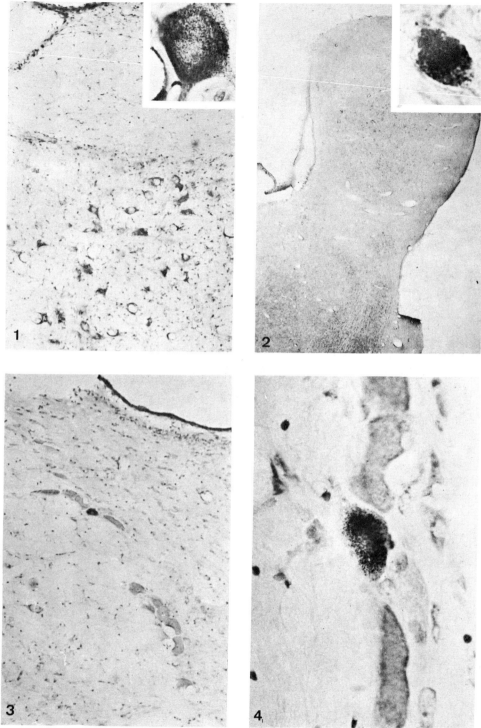

Fig. 2

Fig. 2. Labelled cells in the brainstem after injection of the HRP in an extraocular muscle of the cat. 1 and 2: Injection in the RL. 3 and 4: Injection in the superior oblicus. 1. The VI nucleus showing the peroxydase histochemical reaction, detail of the soma of one motoneuron, showing the peroxydase granulas in the inset. 2. Frontal section of the mesencephalon at the level where most of the labelled cells of the MesV were found. In the inset we can observe one of the cells found there. 3. Horizontal section of the mesencephalon, one cell of MesV is labelled by the HRP. 4. Detail of the same labelled cell as in 3 showing the peroxydase granules.

Fig. 1 ×100 (inset ×400); Fig. 2 ×10 (inset ×400); Fig. 3 ×70; Fig. 4 ×500.

467

injected respectively, showing that the peroxydase has been taken up at the motor nerve endings and transported to their cell bodies. In view of a possible diffusion of the HRP to other extraocular muscles during the injection of the RL, the motor nuclei of the cranial III and IV were always controlled. It appears that the motoneurons of the III and IV nerves were often partially labelled. However, in two cases, the tracer could be observed only in the motoneurons of the VI nucleus.

The HRP is identified in the perikeria and in the dendritic processes of the motoneurons as brown-yellow granules.

We observed that few cells bodies located in the ipsilateral MesV showed also the histochemical reaction (Fig. 2). The number of these labelled cells was always small, a minimum of one and a maximum of seventeen, but we believe that not all the cells of MesV related to the eye muscles could be traced together by this method. The paucity of the labelled cells, on the other hand, is in accord with our electrophysiological results. Their location was also similar to that of the neurons identified by our electrophysiological experiments.

We observed that some neurons of the Semilunar ganglion present also the HRP histochemical reaction. Some of them could be related to periorbital nerve endings since it is not possible to exclude an eventual diffusion of the enzyme to these tissues. However, we assume that some of them could be the first-order neurons of different eye muscle receptors. Szentagothai (1948) demonstrated for the masticatory muscles of the cat that the sensory endings of the tendon organs have their cell bodies in the ganglion, while the sensory endings of the muscle spindles have their cell bodies in MesV. In view of our present results and of others in progress (Alvarado-Mallart, Batini and Raymond, in preparation) it is possible that an analog situation exist for the extraocular muscles.

CONCLUSION

Our results establish that the trigeminal mesencephalic nucleus is the location of, at least, part of the first-order neurons of the stretch receptors of the RL and of the others extraocular muscles of the cat.

In addition, these experiments show also that the sensory nerve endings in muscles are able to take up the HRP and transport it to their cell bodies.

REFERENCES

ALVARADO-MALLART, R. M., BATINI, C. and RAYMOND, M. Terminaisons sensorielles dans les muscles extraoculaires chez le chat (in preparation).
BACH-Y-RITA, P. (1971) Neurophysiology of eye movements. In: *The Control of Eye Movements*, BACH-Y-RITA, P. and COLLINS (Eds.), pp. 7–46. Academic Press, New York and London.
BUISSERET, P., GUÉRITAUD, J. P., HORCHOLLE-BOSSAVIT, G. and TYC-DUMONT, S. (1971) Projections mésencéphaliques des afférences proprioceptives de la musculature extrinsèque des yeux. *J. Physiol. Paris* **65**, 369A.
FILLENZ, M. (1955) Responses in the brain stem of the cat to stretch of extrinsic ocular muscles. *J. Physiol. London*, **128**, 182–189.
GRAHAM, R. C. JR. and KARNOWSKY, M. J. (1966) The early stages of absorption of injected Horseradish peroxydase in the proximal tubules of mouse kidney. Ultrastructural cytochemistry by a new technique. *J. Histochem. Cytochem.* **14**, 291–302.
KRISTENSSON, K., OLSSON, Y. and SJÖSTRAND, J. (1971) Axonal uptake and retrograde transport of exogenous proteins in the hypoglossal nerve. *Brain Res.* **32**, 399–406.
OSOKAWA, H. (1961) Proprioceptive innervation of striated muscles in the territory of cranial nerves. *Texas Rep. Biol. Med.* **19**, 405–464.
SZENTAGOTHÀI, J. (1948) Anatomical consideration of monosynaptic reflex arcs. *J. Neurophysiol.* **11**, 445–454.

CENTRAL CONTROL OF EYE AND HEAD MOVEMENTS IN MONKEYS

EMILIO BIZZI

IN the last few years, at the Massachusetts Institute of Technology, my colleagues, Drs. Dichgans, Kalil, Morasso, Tagliasco and I have investigated the spatial and temporal characteristics of the motor programs underlying the orderly sequence of eye and head movements in monkeys.

We have shown that the appearance of a target in the visual field is usually followed by an orderly sequence of eye and head movements. First, a fast eye movement (generally called a saccade) carries the most sensitive part of the retina, the fovea, to the image of the target. Second, after a latency of 20–40 ms, a head movement follows in the same direction. Since the eyes have moved first, and with a higher velocity than the head, their lines of sight reach and fixate the target while the head is still moving. Then, for the duration of the head movement, the eyes maintain their target fixation by performing a rotational movement which by being counter to that of the head, allows the fovea of the eye to remain constantly on the target it has just acquired. Understandably this movement has been called compensatory eye movement (Bizzi et al., 1971).

To achieve this orderly sequence of movements, i.e. to direct the eyes and the head toward the target and ultimately fixate it with the fovea, the subject must make a number of computations. To begin with, he must compute the angular distance between the initial lines of sight and the position of the target which is to be acquired. Although we do not have a clear understanding of the manner in which this angular distance is computed by cortical and subcortical visual areas, we do know that this "signal" is translated into both the oculomotor and head motor systems at approximately the same time. In fact, the electrical activity recorded from eye and neck muscle fibers shows that motor commands are delivered in near synchrony to these muscles. From this follows that both the oculomotor and head motor control systems must be making use of the same angular distance information at approximately the same time. As a result, amplitudes of eye and head movements are produced which are well correlated with the angular distance of the target (Bizzi et al., 1971).

We have shown that this finding is valid in the case where a head movement begins from the straight-ahead position and the eyes are centered in the head at the time the target is presented. Usually, however, the eyes will not be centered in the head when a target appears. Then the head-movement control system must have access to eye-position information and combine it with the angular distance signal to achieve a coordinated eye–head movement. Information about the eye position in the orbit

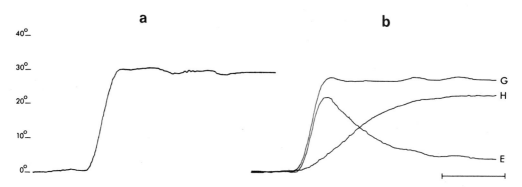

FIG. 1. Comparison of eye saccades and gaze. (a) Eye saccade to a suddenly appearing target with head fixed. (b) Coordinated eye saccade (E) and head movement (H) to the same target with head free. The gaze movement (G) represents the sum of E and H. Note the remarkable similarity of eye saccade in (a) and gaze trajectory in (b) as well as reduced saccade amplitude in (b). Time calibration 100 ms. (From Morasso *et al.*, *Exptl Brain Res.* **16**, 492 (1973).)

can be supplied by "sensors" sensitive to stretch placed in the eye muscles or by monitoring, internally, the oculomotor positional commands.

The activation of eye and neck muscles does not only lead to movements of the eyes and head, but also to the activation of a number of sensory receptors. These sensory receptors modify the ongoing eye and head motor programs. In Fig. 1, a difference in amplitude between saccades made during head movement and those made when no head turning is shown; the former are markedly smaller than the latter. Clearly, this decrease in amplitude during head turning is needed to prevent an over-shoot of the target by the combined eye–head movement. Our experimental evidence indicates that the vestibular afferents alone are responsible for this observed pheno-menon (Morasso *et al.*, 1973; Atkin, 1964). In fact, by surgically interrupting the pathway linking the vestibular receptors to the brainstem, the saccade amplitude during head turning was identical to saccade amplitude with no head movement, which resulted in a remarkable overshoot of the gaze (eye movement plus head movement) (Dichgans *et al.*, 1973).

The modification of saccade characteristics is one aspect of the interaction between central programming and reflex activities. Although this interaction plays a decisive part in the process of target acquisition by a combined eye and head movement, the role of feedback from peripheral sensory organs (vestibular and neck afferents) extends beyond saccadic modulation to control and generate the compensatory eye movement.

Compensatory eye movements have been studied by several investigators and, although it is generally agreed that these eye movements are influenced critically by visual, vestibular, and proprioceptive reflexes, the suggestion has been made that they are initiated centrally (Fleming *et al.*, 1969). In our recent work, we have demonstrated that they result from the reflex action of the vestibular system (Dichgans *et al.*, 1973). As a consequence of the head movement, vestibular receptors are stimulated and their activity induces a compensatory eye movement which allows the fovea to remain fixed in relation to a point in visual space while the head is rotating. This fixation permits a second visual sampling and consequently the repetition of the same sequence.

In summary, if we take the repetitive sequence of eye saccade—head movement—compensatory eye movement as one definition of eye–head coordination, then it is clear that a central nervous system motor program *only initiates* in an impulsive manner movements of the head and eyes. Since there is no central programming of saccadic adjustment and of the compensatory eye movement, it follows that the *behavioral coordination* of head and eyes is the joint result of a central initiation accompanied by the crucial intervention of vestibular activities. This conclusion somewhat simplifies our views of the neural mechanisms underlying motor coordination in so far as, contrary to common assumptions, we find no need to postulate a special, central population of "executive neurons" with exclusive responsibility for *coordinating* the eyes and head.

REFERENCES

BIZZI, E., KALIL, R. E. and TAGLIASCO, V. (1971) Eye–head coordination in monkeys: evidence for centrally patterned organization. *Science*, **173**, 452–454.

MORASSO, P., BIZZI, E. and DICHGANS, J. (1973) Adjustment of saccade characteristics during head movements. *Exptl Brain Res.* **16**, 492–500.

ATKIN, A. (1964) Effect of head movement on gaze movement velocity. *The Physiologist*, **7**, 82.

DICHGANS, J., BIZZI, E., MORASSO, P. and TAGLIASCO, V. (1973) Mechanisms underlying recovery of eye-head coordination following bilateral labyrinthectomy in monkeys. *Exptl Brain Res.* **18**, 548–562.

FLEMING, D. G., VOSSIUS, G. W., BOWMAN, G. and JOHNSON, E. L. (1969) Adaptive properties of the eye-tracking system as revealed by moving-head and open-loop studies. *Ann. New York Acad. Sci.* **156**, 825–850.

BASIC PHYSIOLOGY OF THE
HEAD–EYE MOVEMENT SYSTEM†

V. C. ABRAHAMS, F. RICHMOND and P. K. ROSE

To A substantial degree the head-movement system is synergistic to and integrated with the oculomotor system. While the oculomotor system has been thoroughly examined, the head movement system has been relatively neglected. We have examined the physiology of some of the component parts of the head movement system in the cat. This includes typing the muscles most directly concerned with head movement, examining the morphology and distribution of the receptors of these muscles, and examining the ascending projections from these muscle receptors and their relationship to descending systems to the motoneurons of the neck.

Five pairs of dorsal neck muscles insert on the lamboidal crest in the cat and serve to elevate and turn the head. Using the histochemical technique for ATPase (Padykula and Herman, 1955), we found that the ratio of dark (fast) to light (slow) staining fibres varied within the five muscles (Abrahams and Rancier, 1973). Table 1 illustrates this data. More extensive histochemical testing has shown that as in other cat muscles, fast fibres of neck muscle can be further divided into two types, implying that three functional types of neck motoneurons exist (Burke *et al.*, 1971; Burke *et al.*, 1973).

TABLE 1. WEIGHTS OF NECK MUSCLES IN THE CAT AND THE RATIO OF DARK TO LIGHT ATPASE STAINING IN INDIVIDUAL FIBRES OF THE MUSCLES

	Muscle weights, g				Dark/Light		
	Mean	n	S.E.M.	% total mass	Mean	n	S.E.M.
Occipitoscapularis	0.672	6	0.12	6	0.69	8	0.06
Splenius	3.66	6	0.60	34	2.64	8	0.19
Biventer cervicis	2.74	6	0.40	25	0.717	10	0.05
Complexus	2.90	6	0.42	27	1.26	7	0.026
Rectus Captis major	0.913	6	0.14	8	2.68	7	0.19

Neck muscles have long been known to be extraordinarily rich in their spindle density. Data obtained from human material by Voss (1958), and by Cooper and Daniel (1963), showed that neck muscles have the highest density of muscle spindles in the body. We have examined neck-muscle spindles in serial sections cut from the five dorsal neck muscles of the cat previously referred to. Except in occipitoscapularis, spindle density is very high, ranging from 46 to 106/g. Occipitoscapularis has a density

† Work supported by the Medical Research Council of Canada.

comparable to hind leg muscles in the cat of 13–18/g (Table 2). Spindle types found include single and tandem spindles, multiple arrays, and dyads with both spindles and Golgi organs in apposition.

TABLE 2. SPINDLES OF DORSAL NECK MUSCLES. EACH PAIR
OF FIGURES WAS TAKEN FROM AN INDIVIDUAL MUSCLE

Muscle	Absolute number of spindles	Density (spindles/g)
Rectus capitis	33	53.6
major	44	58.8
	38	61.0
	57	83.8
Splenius	148	46.6
	189	63.1
	172	66.4
Complexus	190	71.5
	254	106.8
Biventer cervicis	68	74.8
	180	74.4
	173	95.9
Occipitoscapularis	6	13.2
	11	18.7
	15	16.2

The spinal and medullary course of Gp I and II afferents from neck muscles has been examined in chloralose anaesthetized cat. Fibres were found to enter the dorsolateral part of the dorsal column system as predicted by the known anatomy (Imai and Kusama, 1969; Kerr, 1972). Group I and II primary afferents were sparsely distributed in the ventral portion of the cuneate nucleus, and also in a narrow strip between the spinal tract and the spinal nucleus of the trigeminal nerve. They were most abundant in the area of subnucleus gelatinosa of the spinal nucleus of the trigeminal nerve where they synapse within 2 or 3 mm of the obex.

While the ascending course of neck muscle afferent system beyond the spinal nucleus of the trigeminal nerve is not entirely clear, one major central projection is to the superior colliculus (Abrahams and Rose, 1975).

Like the visual projection to the superior colliculus, the neck muscle afferent projection is distributed to all layers of the superior colliculus and most units excited by neck muscle afferents may also be excited by a brief flash of light. These units are also excited by extraocular muscle afferent projections. The muscle afferent projections from the neck and extraocular system do not constitute the sole proprioceptive projections to the superior colliculus and a less dense projection exists from both the fore and hind leg.

Both the tectospinal tract and the tectoreticular tract are disynaptically connected to neck motoneurons (Anderson et al., 1971). Antidromic excitation has been used to identify cells of origin of the tectospinal tract within the superior colliculus and the sensory input to these cells have been examined. Table 3 shows that the majority of tectospinal cells receive input from neck and extraocular muscle afferents and from the retina, as do cells of origin of the tectoreticular system.

The head-movement system therefore includes a loop with afferents from neck muscle, extraocular muscle and the retina converging on the superior colliculus where they excite cells disynaptically connected to motoneurons of the neck.

TABLE 3. CONVERGENCE ON CELLS OF ORIGIN OF TECTOSPINAL TRACT

Trimodal	Extraocular	27
	Neck	
	Visual	
Bimodal	Extraocular and visual	3
	Neck and visual	2
Unimodal	Extraocular	2
	Visual	5
Unresponsive to orthodromic stimuli		18
	Total number of units	57

This collicular system can alter neck motoneuron excitability as a result of the eye movement and position. The eyes of chloralose anaesthetized cats have been passively moved using a shaker controlled by a function generator. Such movements activate units in the superior colliculus which regularly fire in a brief burst when the eye reaches a certain displacement. Providing a certain minimal velocity is exceeded, the discharge occurs regularly at a fixed eye displacement. A histogram (Fig. 1) relates unit firing to the minimum deflection from the centre of gaze and shows that the system tends to signal large eye excursions. The previous experiments would suggest

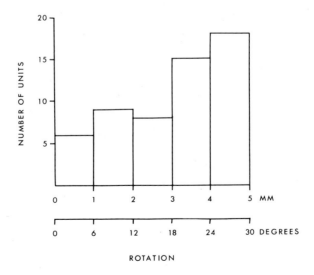

MINIMUM ROTATION REQUIRED
TO EXCITE UNITS IN SC

FIG. 1. Histogram showing eye displacement required to excite individual units of the superior colliculus. Velocity of displacement 100 mm/s.

that some of the cells responding to eye movement are cells of origin of the tectospinal and tectoreticulospinal tracts. The superior colliculus of the cat thus has the potential for the impulse traffic to neck motoneurons to be initiated when the eye reaches a new position. Since it is well known that the preferred visual stimulus is an object moving away from the fovea, it would seem that the superior colliculus can initiate head movements when eye movement is no longer able to secure foveation. The role of the neck muscle afferents may be in the control of such movements once initiated.

REFERENCES

ABRAHAMS, V. C. and RANCIER, F. (1973) ATPase distribution in dorsal neck muscles of the cat. *Can. J. Physiol. Pharmacol.* **51,** 549–552.

ABRAHAMS, V. C. and ROSE, P. K. (1975) Projections of extraocular, neck muscle and retinal afferents to the superior colliculus in the cat: their connections to the cells of origin of the tectospinal tract. *J. Neurophysiol.* **38,** 10–18.

ANDERSON, M. E., YOSHIDA, M. and WILSON, V. J. (1971) Influence of superior colliculus on cat neck motoneurons. *J. Neurophysiol.* **34,** 898–907.

BURKE, R. E., LEVINE, D. N., TSAIRIS, P. and ZAJAC, F. E. III (1973) Physiological types and histochemical profiles in motor units of the cat gastrocnemius. *J. Physiol.* **234,** 723–748.

COOPER, S. and DANIEL, P. M. (1963) Muscle spindles in man; their morphology in the lumbricals and the deep muscles of the neck. *Brain,* **86,** 563–594.

IMAI, Y. and KUSAMA, T. (1969) Distribution of the dorsal root fibres in the cat. An experimental study with the Nauta method. *Brain Res.* **13,** 338–359.

KERR, F. W. L. (1972) Central relationships of trigeminal and cervical primary afferents in the spinal cord and medulla. *Brain Res.* **43,** 561–572.

VOSS, H. (1958) Zahl und Anordnung der Muskelspindeln in den unteren Zungenbeinmuskeln dem M. sternocleidomastoideus und den Mauch- und tiefen Nackmuskeln. *Anat. Anz.* **105,** 265–275.

VESTIBULO-OCULAR AND OPTOKINETIC REACTIONS IN THE RABBIT: CHANGES DURING 24 HOURS OF NORMAL AND ABNORMAL INTERACTION

H. Collewijn and H. J. Kleinschmidt

SUMMARY

Rabbits were subjected to visual and/or vestibular stimulation with sinusoidal motion (0.17 Hz, amplitude 1°). The two inputs were given apart, in normal (synergic) combination or with inversion of vision (conflict). In four subgroups, each of these possibilities was used as a continuous (24 hr) conditioning stimulus, while responses to the other three stimulus types were briefly tested every 30 min. Habituation (response decline) effects were not seen. Vestibulo-ocular responses were not decreased or inverted. Yet, in the three abnormal conditions, considerable functional adaptation of the systems was observed, resulting in a satisfactory retinal image stabilization in the particular situation. Improvement of optokinetic response was one factor in this process, but the results indicate that the integrative processing of visual and vestibular control of eye position itself is modified by prior experience.

INTRODUCTION

Recently, several accounts have been published on attempts to modify canal-ocular reflexes to rotation by prolonged left–right inversion of the optical input. Gonshor and Melvill Jones (1973) and Melvill Jones (this Symposium) reported that continuous vision reversal by "Dove" prisms in freely behaving man led first to a progressive decline of canal-ocular reflexes to zero in 4–7 days and the emergence of reversed responses thereafter. Even mirror-inverted vision during passive sinusoidal motion for a period of 1 hr significantly reduced vestibulo-ocular gain. Ito *et al.* (1974a) reported a decrease and in one case a reversal of canal-ocular reflexes in rabbits after 12 hr of conflicting optical and vestibular stimulation. Robinson (this Symposium) has obtained a similar decrease of canal-ocular gain in cats. Young and Henn (1974) found short-term effects of optical motion information on subsequent canal-ocular reactions in man.

We performed a series of related experiments on rabbits, the results of which are somewhat different from those of Ito *et al.* (1974a).

METHODS

Young adult Dutch belted rabbits were briefly anaesthetized with halothane and provided with a tracheal cannula, a scleral induction coil for measuring the eye movements

(Robinson, 1963) and a dental biteboard, cemented to the upper teeth with acrylic. After this they were tied down firmly in a hammock and mounted on the platform of the stimulating apparatus, with the biteboard rigidly fixed. Stimulation and recording were started 6 hr after termination of anaesthesia, when the rabbits were fully recovered. Body temperature was maintained at $38 \pm 0.5°C$.

The stimulator consisted of a platform, surrounded by an optokinetic drum with a pattern of alternating white and black stripes, each 10° wide. Platform and drum could be independently driven in a sinusoidal motion around a vertical axis, by different motors and levers. In view of the known input–output relations of canal-ocular and optokinetic systems of the rabbit (Baarsma and Collewijn, 1974) a sinusoidal movement with frequency 0.17 Hz and amplitude 1° was chosen as the basic stimulus.

The different motors and the illumination were controlled by an automatic switching system. Four stimulus conditions were available:

1. Platform moving (0.17 Hz, 1°), lights off: vestibular stimulation only.
2. Platform moving (0.17 Hz, 1°), lights on: vestibular and optokinetic stimulation in the normal, synergic combination.
3. Optokinetic drum moving (0.17 Hz, 1°), lights on: optokinetic stimulation only.
4. Platform moving (0.17 Hz, 1°) and drum moving in phase but with double amplitude (2°), lights on. In this situation, the platform rotates 1° in one direction and simultaneously the striped drum rotates 1° in the same direction relative to the platform. This procedure effectively inverts the normal optical motion signal. Our main intention was to test the influence of this conflict situation on canal-ocular reflexes.

In the experiments, one of these four stimulus types ("conditioning stimulus") was applied continuously for 24 hr, while the reactions to the other three stimuli ("test stimuli") were recorded each during 1 min every half hour.

Vestibular, optokinetic, synergic and conflicting stimulation were each used as conditioning stimulus in four subgroups of five rabbits each.

RESULTS

In all conditions approximately sinusoidal eye movements were elicited. Fast eye movements were very rare due to the small amplitude of the movements. Gain (amplitude of eye movement/amplitude of stimulus) and phase relations were determined every 30 min. Changes of gain and phase during 24 hr are illustrated for the four stimulus types in Figs. 1–4 with synergic, conflicting, vestibular and optokinetic stimulation as the conditioning stimuli, respectively. Each graph represents the average results of five rabbits.

The initial values for gain and phase were, as should be expected, rather similar for all types of experiments. Gain of canal-ocular reactions (G_v) was about 0.3, of optokinetic reactions (G_o) about 0.5–0.6, and of synergic reactions (G_h) about 0.6–0.7. Canal-ocular reactions showed a small phase-lead (20–30°), the other reactions a small lag (about 10°). In the conflict situation, with our particular stimulus parameters, reactions were dominated by the visual input. The eyes moved about in phase with the drum, but with a gain (G_c) below that of optokinetic stimulation alone. Thus, the interaction (positive or negative) of canal-ocular with optokinetic reactions was present as expected (Baarsma and Collewijn, 1974).

In the course of 24 hr, systematic changes of gain, contingent on the conditioning stimulus, were observed. In interpreting these changes, it is helpful to realize that in our situation the only functional demand upon the systems was to stabilize the retinal image, by minimizing the mismatch between the movements of eye and striped drum.

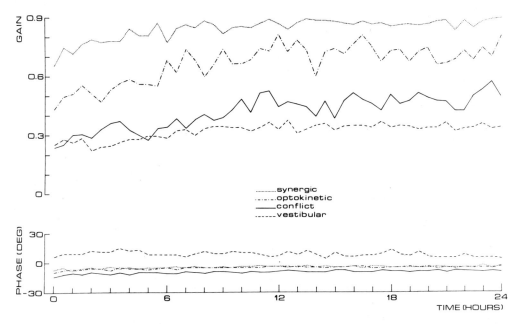

FIG. 1. Gain and phase relations for synergic, optokinetic, conflict and vestibular stimulation with synergic input as the conditioning stimulus. Measurements were made every 30 min. Average results of five rabbits.

Figure 1 illustrates the changes during continuous synergic stimulation, the most "normal" of our experimental conditions. G_h increased from 0.7 to 0.9 within 10 hr, thus satisfactory stabilization was achieved by the combined systems. G_o was markedly lower, but also improved (from about 0.5 to 0.7). G_v remained nearly constant at 0.3, without any tendency to habituation. In the conflict situation, eye movements were in the appropriate direction for visual stabilization but the gain (G_c) was remarkably low (0.3–0.4). The changes during 24 hr were small, but favourable for retinal image stability. Phase relations did not change at all.

Figure 2 shows the changes during continuous conflicting stimulation, the most unnatural of our experimental conditions. The most significant difference with the synergic situation was the rapid increase of G_c from 0.3 to 0.6 within 4 hr, followed by a more gradual increase to nearly 0.8 after 24 hr. Exactly the same value was reached by G_o and G_h. In this way, quite efficient retinal stabilization was achieved, although no systematic change of canal-ocular gain or phase relations was observed at any time, such in contrast to the results by others mentioned in the introduction.

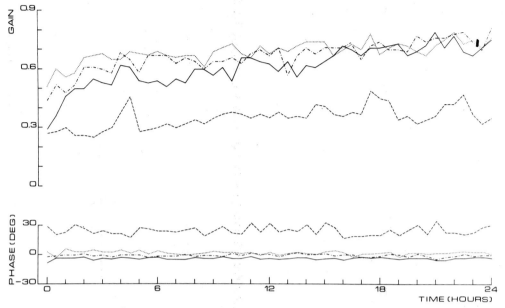

FIG. 2. As Fig. 1, with conflicting input as the conditioning stimulus.

Figure 3 illustrates the changes during continuous vestibular stimulation alone. In this situation, the animal was always in the dark except during the test stimuli once every 30 min. Normal interaction between visual and vestibular inputs was thus practically absent. Nevertheless, reactions changed in such a way that the visual input dominated entirely whenever it was present. G_h, G_o and especially G_c improved and

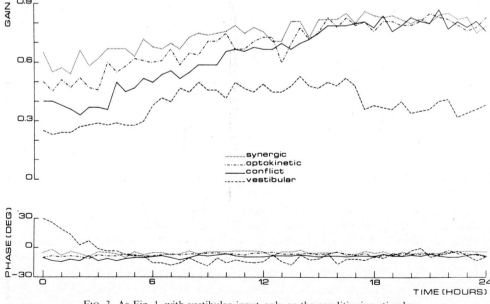

FIG. 3. As Fig. 1, with vestibular input only as the conditioning stimulus.

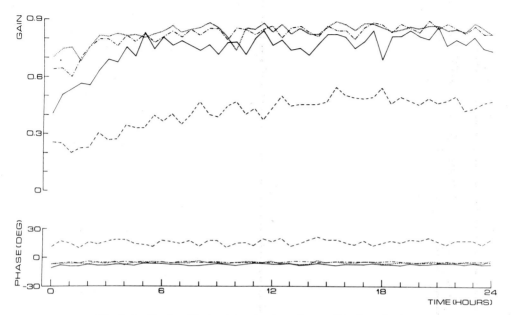

Fig. 4. As Fig. 1, with visual input only as the conditioning stimulus.

after 18 hr converged to identical values of about 0.85. Again, effective retinal image stabilization was thus achieved at the moments when it was relevant. Canal-ocular reactions showed a remarkable, possibly circadian pattern. A consistent increase of G_v was seen during the nightly period of 12 hr when the animal used to be in darkness in the animal rooms, prior to the experiment. Possibly, this indicates a switching of G_v to a higher value during the night, when visibility is low and visual cues for stabilization may be deficient. The absence of this change of G_v in the other situations could be due to the continuous illumination. The phase lead (30°) of canal-ocular reactions gradually changed into a lag of 10°. This was the only systematic change in phase observed in the present experiments.

Figure 4 shows changes during continuous optokinetic stimulation. In this condition too, very effective responses to optical input were developed. G_h and G_o improved to about 0.9 in 10 hr, and G_c was only slightly lower. Also G_v markedly improved (from 0.3 to 0.5), nevertheless in the end G_h was not higher than G_o.

DISCUSSION

The present results reveal a considerable ability of the rabbit's oculomotor reflexes for functional adaptation to unusual requirements. In all conditions, the stabilization of the retinal image was optimized. The time course of changes suggests that a steady level of adaptation was reached within 24 hr and often sooner, although a further improvement after longer periods of stimulation cannot be excluded.

A prominent difference between our findings and those of Melvill Jones (this Symposium), Robinson (this Symposium) and Ito *et al.* (1974a) is the absence of any systematic alteration of the basic canal-ocular reflex by inverted vision, although such an inversal might have been useful in the conflict situation. On the other hand, we found a marked improvement of the effect of visual input in all conditions. Ito *et al.* (1974 a, b) used a sinusoidal movement of 0.10–0.15 Hz with an amplitude of 10°, and a single light slit instead of a striped drum. The authors state that the latter stimulus was ineffective in eliciting optokinetic reactions, which agrees with our experience (Collewijn, 1969). Yet, the visual motion signal which is undoubtedly elicited by such a stimulus might affect the vestibular gain. Therefore, the results of Ito *et al.* (1974a) and our own are not necessarily in conflict, but might reflect different options of the system to adapt to the need of the circumstances.

An important question is, whether the changes in G_c and G_h can be entirely explained by a change in G_o, or whether plasticity at a higher level is involved. If plasticity were restricted to a simple adjustment of the gain of the fundamental components (G_o and G_v), then similar values for G_o and G_v should always lead to similar values for G_h and G_c. A simple inspection of Fig. 1 and 2 convincingly demonstrates that this cannot be true. During the last 6 hrs of the experiments, G_o was about 0.7 and G_v about 0.3 both for continuous synergic (Fig. 1) and continuous conflicting input (Fig. 2). However, G_c was about 0.5 in the continuous synergic and about 0.8 in the continuous conflict situation, while G_h was about 0.9 and 0.75 respectively.

A more systematic theoretical treatment was also attempted. Assuming linear interaction, neglecting the small phase errors and bearing in mind that the canal-ocular system is a feed-forward and the optokinetic a feed-back system, we postulated the following relations. In the synergic situation, a movement of 1° will elicit a compensatory eye movement of G_v° through the canal-ocular reflex arc. The remaining optical stimulus is $(1 - G_v)$°, of which $G_o(1 - G_v)$° will be compensated optokinetically. Thus:

$$G_h = G_v + G_o(1 - G_v). \tag{1}$$

In a similar way, one can derive:

$$G_c = G_o(1 + G_v) - G_v \tag{2}$$

in which positive values of G_c indicate a reaction in phase with the optical-, and negative values a response in phase with the vestibular stimulus.

Using (1) and (2), theoretical average curves for G_h and G_c were calculated for the four situations. The fit of the theoretical with the actual data was only moderate, and particularly failed to reproduce the low values for G_c in the continuous synergic situation. Baarsma and Collewijn (1974) attempted a similar calculation for G_h in short-term experiments and were also unsuccesful to obtain a satisfactory result.

These findings demonstrate that oculomotor output is not a constant function of canal-ocular and optokinetic reactions apart. The processing of simultaneous vestibular and visual inputs into an integrated output appears to be non-linear and contingent on prior experience and other (e.g. circadian) factors. Obviously, a feedback signal is required for optimizing the way in which both systems interact in a particular situation.

Recently, the vestibulo-cerebellum has been implicated in the integration of visual with vestibular information. Melvill Jones (this Symposium), Precht (*ibid.*) and Robinson (*ibid.*) proposed that the vestibulo-cerebellar loop might adjust gain and phase of vestibulo-ocular reflexes at the basis of visual motion information.

Ito *et al.* (1974 a, b) also provided evidence for a role of the flocculus in the integration of visual and vestibular reflexes, both on a short- and long-term basis. The possibility that the cerebellum is involved in the somewhat more complex parameter settings indicated by our results deserves careful investigation.

ACKNOWLEDGEMENT

We wish to thank Ineke Zuidam for her excellent assistance in the analysis of the recordings.

REFERENCES

BAARSMA, E. A. and COLLEWIJN, H. (1974) Vestibulo-ocular and optokinetic reactions to rotation and their interaction in the rabbit. *J. Physiol.* (*London*) **238**, 603–625.
COLLEWIJN, H. (1969) Optokinetic eye movements in the rabbit: input-output relations. *Vis. Res.* **9**, 117–132.
GONSHOR, A. and MELVILL JONES, G. (1973) Changes of human vestibulo-ocular response induced by vision-reversal during head rotation. *J. Physiol.* **234**, 102P–103P.
ITO, M., SHIIDA, T., YAGI, N. and YAMAMOTO, M. (1974a) The cerebellar modification of rabbit's horizontal vestibulo-ocular reflex induced by sinusoidal head rotation combined with visual stimulation. *Proc. Japan Acad.* **50**, 85–89.
ITO, M., SHIIDA, T., YAGI, N. and YAMAMOTO, M. (1974b) Visual influence on rabbit horizontal vestibulo-ocular reflex presumably effected via the cerebellar flocculus. *Brain Res.* **65**, 170–174.
MELVILL JONES, G. This Symposium.
PRECHT, W. This Symposium.
ROBINSON, D. A. (1963) A method of measuring eye movements using a scleral search coil in a magnetic field. *IEEE Trans. Bio-Med. Electron.* **10**, 137–145.
ROBINSON, D. A. This Symposium.
YOUNG, L. R. and HENN, V. S. (1974). Selective habituation of vestibular nystagmus by visual stimulation. *Acta oto-lar.* **77**, 159–166.

RESPONSES OF RETINAL AND GENICULATE NEURONS TO CONTRAST SHIFTS AND THEIR RELATION TO EYE MOVEMENTS

Burkhart Fischer and Jürgen Krüger

The classical receptive fields of retinal and geniculate on- and off-centre cells cover a region of several minutes of arc in the central retina up to several degrees in the peripheral retina. McIlwain (1964) was the first to observe that black objects moved by hand far away from the receptive field elicit small facilitatory effects upon on- as well as off-centre retinal ganglion cells. This effect is called periphery-effect. It mainly consists of a lowering of threshold of flashing spot in the receptive field centre.

Shifts of the retinal image similar to those elicited by eye movements were used in the present studies of extracellularly recorded behaviour of retinal and geniculate units.

RETINA

In cats with immobile eyes (flaxedil, N_2O) rapid displacements of patterns (mostly grids of different spatial frequencies and contrast) elicited exitatory responses after about 50 ms simultaneously in all on-centre and off-centre neurons, when the receptive fields and a surrounding area up to 90 degree in diameter (blank area) were excluded from any change of light (Krüger and Fischer, 1973). When the receptive fields were not excluded from stimulation, similar responses were observed given that sufficiently high spatial frequency grids were used. Therefore it seems quite misleading to call these responses periphery-effect. We rather propose the name "shift-effect", since shifts of the retinal contrast seem to be the most obvious condition to obtain it.

The retinal shift-effect is always excitatory. It could be elicited with shift amplitudes down to 6–10 min of arc corresponding to micro-saccades, which are well below the limits of receptive field centre sizes. Grid contrast could be as low as 5–10%. Above threshold the strength of the retinal shift-effect was nearly invariant under changes of shift-amplitude and grid contrast. However, steady illumination of the receptive field increased the shift-effect in on-centre neurons, and darkening of receptive fields increased it in off-centre cells. Increasing the diameter of the blank area results in an increase of latency by about 30 ms corresponding to a lateral conduction velocity of about 0.35 m/s. Very impressive prolongation of latency (up to 200 ms measured from the beginning of the movement) are obtained by shifts of decreasing velocity between 600° and 5°/sec. The relationship is linear. Thus the responses are triggered whenever the grid has moved over a constant retinal distance of about 0.75°. Down to velocities of 15°/sec the response amplitude shows no significant changes and has still a risetime of less than 50 ms. For slower movements the peak decreases steadily to zero. Quantitative evaluation of the latency data suggests, that under certain conditions the shift-effect precedes centre and surround responses elicited by the same contrast movement. In fact, we observed, that at contrast velocities between 50° and 200°/sec the shift-effect occurred earlier than responses elicited at the time, when the contrast crossed the receptive field, provided that the starting position was a few degrees away from the receptive field. In order to get all receptive field responses earlier or during the shift-effect discharges contrast velocities above 1000°/sec are necessary, which presumably exceed natural eye-movement velocities in cat.

Rapid displacements of a single contrast border at different distances from the receptive fields elicited shift-effects of different strength in on- and off-centre cells depending on whether the receptive field is at the bright side or at the dark side.

LATERAL GENICULATE NUCLEUS

In subsequent experiments 1.5 mg/kg of amphetamine were supplied to keep the animals awake. Stationary bright or dark spots surrounded by dark or bright areas were projected on to the receptive field centre and surround, respectively, in order to favour the shift-effect in afferent fibres from retinal on-centre cells or off-centre cells. In on-centre cells, whose receptive field centre was stationary illuminated, while the surround was in darkness ("adequate" illumination), each shift of the peripheral grid elicited a burst of spikes with a latency of about 50 ms. If, on the other hand, the centre was in darkness and the surround was steadily illuminated ("inadequate" illumination), each shift resulted in a suppression of firing occasionally followed by a rebound burst. The reverse was obtained in off-centre cells.

Under the condition where on-centre cells are excited off-centre cells are inhibited and vice versa. Improper adjustment or incorrect size of the stationary bright or dark spots greatly reduced the shift-effect, probably by the inhibitory surround mechanism. Shift-effects like these were observed in 43 out of 62 geniculate cells, studied completely. The main result is, that under appropriate conditions a large proportion, 106 out of 112 geniculate cells, have an excitatory or inhibitory shift-effect depending on the stationary light distribution in the receptive field centre and surround.

The transmission of the retinal shift-effect through the lateral geniculate may also be under control of some other brain structures, which themselves are involved in eye movements. Therefore, in a subsequent series of experiments the mesencephalic reticular formation was electrically stimulated by applying short volleys of high-frequency impulses which elicit conjugate eye movements. The electrode was fixed and the animal was paralysed. Simultaneous stimulation of the reticular formation and the retina showed a facilitation of the visually evoked responses. This facilitation was, however, not specific for the shift-effect, but also for exitatory centre responses. Unfortunately, these experiments did not prove that eye movements are necessary for the facilitation.

The functional significance is still unclear. The shift-effect occurs with retinal image displacements normally produced by eye movements. It has a rather long latency as compared to centre type responses. However, the shift-effect will be triggered by the *onset* of the movement, and in many cases, the corresponding discharge will occur during the movement. Whenever the receptive field itself encounters a contrast on its path through the visual scene, an additional centre-type response will occur after the shift-effect except when a contrast is immediately at the starting-point of the path. Thus, the shift-effect may signal the beginning of an eye movement. On the other hand, on- and off-center neurons, which remain in a homogeneous field during the eye movement have shift-effects of different magnitude according to the luminance. The difference of the on- and off-centre neurons' shift-effect may help to signal the constant brightness of these areas. Fading of the fixated objects may be prevented by sustained units in the area centralis, but the restoration of the total information on brightness and darkness uses the shift-effect elicited by intermittent saccades of a few degrees. The invariance of the shift-effect under variation of shift-amplitude and direction makes it quite unlikely that it is involved in the reafference principle of von Holst and Mittelstaedt (1950).

REFERENCES

FISCHER, B. and KRÜGER, J. (1974) The shift-effect in the cat's lateral geniculate neurons. *Exptl Brain Res.* **21**, 225–227.

HOLST, E. VON and MITTELSTAEDT, H. (1950) Das Reafferenzprinzip (Wechselwirkungen zwischen Zentralnervensystem und Peripherie). *Naturwissenschaften*, **37**, 464–476.

KRÜGER, J. and FISCHER, B. (1973) Strong periphery effect in retinal ganglion cells. Excitatory responses in ON- and OFF-center neurones to single grid displacements. *Exptl Brain Res.* **18**, 316–381.

MCILWAIN, J. T. (1964) Receptive fields of optic tract axons and lateral geniculate cells: peripheral extent and barbiturate sensitivity. *J. Neurophysiol.* **27**, 1154–1173.

EFFECT OF FLICKER ON OCULOMOTOR PERFORMANCE†

Genevieve M. Haddad and Barbara J. Winterson

This work began as an investigation of the effect of flicker on saccades. Prior work on this problem is confined to a paper by West and Boyce (1967) who reported that slowly flickering lights have an entrainment effect on the saccadic pattern. We found that flicker did not elicit saccades when subjects were told not to make them. However, flicker did have a surprising and powerful effect on slow control (drift correction).

METHOD

Three subjects participated in these experiments—two through the whole series (the authors, one a highly experienced contact lens subject and the other participating in her first eye movement experiment), and a third experienced subject who confirmed the basic results. The subject, head supported on a biteboard, looked with the right eye at a 17° circular field in Maxwellian view. The source was a green LED (λ_{max} 540 nm $\pm$ 2) whose average luminance was 22 mL. The subject was instructed to suppress saccades and use slow control to maintain the line of sight for 5 sec on a 16' diam black disk located at the center of the 17° field. When the subject began each trial, the field, which had been steadily illuminated, began to flicker at one of several frequencies (0.5, 1, 2, 5, or 10 Hz). In most experiments a square-wave of 100% modulation was used. Eye movements were recorded by means of an electronic contact lens optical lever whose position sensitivity was about 10″ (Haddad and Steinman, 1973).

RESULTS

Saccade rate dropped as flicker frequency increased, but the highest rate (at 0.5 Hz) was only 0.3 saccade/sec. When the target flickered at 2 Hz, where the greatest entrainment was found by West and Boyce, saccade rate was only 0.2 saccade/sec—one-tenth of the saccade rate observed during normal fixation of a steadily illuminated field. The failure to find an entrainment effect of flicker on saccades was not confined to 5-sec trials. All three subjects were able to suppress saccades (saccade rates <0.2/sec) throughout 75-sec trials in the presence of a field flickering at 2 Hz. They were also able to execute a variety of specified temporal patterns of saccades in the presence of steady or slowly flickering fields. These results suggest that entrainment effects of flicker arise from voluntary cognitive decisions on the part of the subject rather than

†This research was supported by Grant No. 00325 from the National Eye Institute to R. M. Steinman.

from influences of the stimulus on the oculomotor machinery. The slow control subsystem, however, is not ordinarily under voluntary control and flickering lights affect its activity profoundly. They cause the eye to drift from the target position and oscillate as it drifts. These effects are illustrated for each of the subjects in Fig. 1.

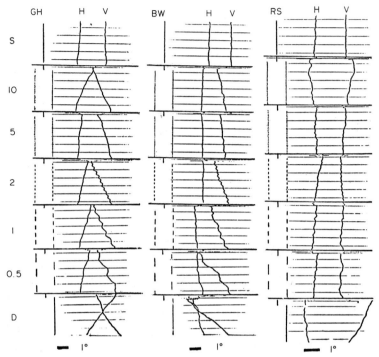

FIG. 1. The effect of a 100% modulation square-wave flicker on the slow control of three subjects (GH, BW, RS). Each of the seven records shown for each subject begins towards the bottom of the figure. The repetitive horizontal lines are a 1 sec time marker and the scale bar beneath each set of records indicates the size of 1° rotations on both the horizontal (H) and vertical (V) meridians. The bottom records show slow control in the dark (D), indicated by the stimulus trace on the left side of each record that is towards the right. Subject GH drifted rapidly up and to the right (the vertical and horizontal traces crossed after 3 sec). Subject BW drifted up and to the left (the eye traces also crossed after 3 sec). RS drifted slowly to the left and rapidly down. The top records show effective slow control when the field was steadily (S) illuminated and the intermediate records show what happened when the field flickered at one of five frequencies (0.5, 1, 2, 5, and 10 Hz). The stimulus marker to the left of the eye traces means that the light was completely off when the marker was to the right and fully on when the marker was to the left.

The top records show slow control in the presence of a steadily lighted field where small irregular drifts tend to keep the eye in place very well (S.D. < 3′). The bottom record shows that slow control is lost in the dark and the eye rapidly drifts from its starting position. The intermediate records show oscillations of the eye synchronized with the flicker and also a progressive drift away from the target position. The peak to peak amplitudes of these oscillations are appreciable and inversely related to flicker frequency (ranging from 6′ at 5 Hz to 20′ at 0.5 Hz). The oscillations of the eye follow the flicker with a mean latency of 130 ms (S.D. = 40) for the frequencies where latency could be measured directly from our oscillographic records (0.5, 1, and 2 Hz).† At

† Computer analysis of magnetic tape records is in progress.

10 Hz oscillations are not visible in the eye traces but the progressive uncompensated drift remains.† Two of the subjects (*GH* and *BW*) show these effects on the vertical meridian. *RS* showed the effects on both meridians. These effects are easily obtained as is illustrated in Fig. 2.

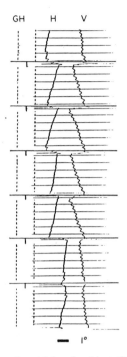

FIG. 2. Seven representative 5 sec consecutive trials of subject GH using slow control to maintain her line of sight at the center of a field that flickered at 2 Hz (100% modulation square-wave). The drift oscillations caused by the flickering light are prominent on the vertical (*V*) meridian and uncompensated drifts are seen on both meridians. Saccades (always confined to the horizontal meridian) were infrequent (0.2 saccades/sec). They were not entrained by the stimulus. The time base, eye-position scale, and stimulus marker are explained in Fig. 1.

These results are not limited to lights moderately high in the photopic range. The basic experiment was repeated 2 log units down (at 0.2 mL) where the peak to peak amplitude of the slow oscillations was found to be the same but the uncompensated drift was considerably reduced. These effects also do not require large flickering fields and do not arise exclusively from either the fovea or the periphery. The experiment was repeated with a foveal disk (4° diam) and also with a peripheral annulus (ID = 7°, OD = 17°). In both cases the oscillations and uncompensated drift remained. The oscillations were about twice as large with the peripheral annulus as with the foveal disk but in both regions their frequency depended completely on the frequency of the flickering field. These effects are also not limited to square-wave stimulation. Both sine and triangle flicker caused the eye to oscillate.

† Several trials were run at 20 and 50 Hz. The oculomotor response at 20 Hz is similar to that at 10 Hz, but at 50 Hz, where the stimulus is just below CFF, slow control returns and there is a suggestion that the stability of the eye is better than it is with a steady light.

Are these effects surprising? At first we thought not. Such results might be expected if the eye drifts in the dark and stabilizes when the light comes on. Oscillations, as well as a progressive drift, would be a natural by-product of alternating uncompensated drifts made in the dark with periods of slow control activated when the field reappears. Both effects could be caused by the periodic removal of the signal for slow control. But the next experiment showed that this was not correct.

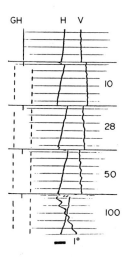

FIG. 3. The effect of modulation depth on oscillations and uncompensated drifts while viewing a 1 Hz square wave flickering field. The percentage of modulation is shown on the right of each record, and the top record shows slow control with a steadily lighted field of the same average luminance. The time base, eye-position scale, and stimulus marker are explained in Fig. 1.

Subjects were provided with a clearly visible non-flickering light that was used throughout the trial to maintain the line of sight at the center of the flickering field. The progressive drift was reduced but the oscillations remained. However, we found that decreasing modulation depth reduced the oscillations. This is illustrated for one subject in Fig. 3 where oscillations are evident at 50%, suggested at 28%, but gone when the modulation was reduced to 10%.

To insure that these effects were oculomotor a number of control experiments were performed. We checked that there was no stimulus artifact by reflecting the stimulus from a mirror attached to the biteboard holder and found no leakage of the stimulus light into the infrared recording system. We taped the lids so that they could not touch the contact lens, repeated the experiment, and found that the oscillations and progressive drift were unaffected. We paralyzed the iris and the lens with a cycloplegic drug and obtained the same result.

SUMMARY

Flickering lights do not force saccades. The entrainment effect found by West and Boyce (1967) was probably due to the fact that subjects, instructed to "fixate", voluntarily correct fixation errors that are produced by uncompensated drifts in the dark and noticed when the target reappears. Our subjects were instructed to suppress saccades and ignore fixation errors. They were able to do so. Suppression of saccades revealed that flickering lights have a driving effect on slow control. They cause the eye to drift away from target position and oscillate as it drifts.

The underlying mechanism and functional significance of these effects are not known. They might be caused by cross-talk between neural elements in the lower brain where afferent signals, which provide input for accommodation of the lens and iris or for blinking, leak into neural centers used for slow oculomotor control.

ACKNOWLEDGMENTS

We thank R. M. Steinman for allowing us the use of his laboratory, for serving as the third subject in our basic experiments, and for valuable suggestions and observations. We also appreciate the technical assistance of K. Larson, E. Kowler, I. Nicholson and L. Watkins.

REFERENCES

HADDAD, G. M. and STEINMAN, R. M. (1973) The smallest voluntary saccade: Implications for fixation. *Vision Res.* **13,** 1075–1086.
WEST, D. C. and BOYCE, P. R. (1967) The effect of flicker on eye movements. *Vision Res.* **8,** 171–191.

SYSTEMS ANALYSIS
OF OCULOMOTOR FUNCTIONS

DYNAMIC PROPERTIES OF CAT EXTRAOCULAR MUSCLE†

T. Vilis and J. S. Outerbridge

From histology and electrophysiology (see Lennerstrand, this volume), the inferior oblique muscle of the cat is known to contain many fiber types. Two classes are twitch fibers singly innervated by large diameter nerve fibers and amphibian-like fibers, multi-innervated by what is generally considered as small diameter nerve fibers. These will be described as phasic and tonic fibers, respectively. The purpose of our experiment was to determine whether these fibers have uniform mechanical properties.

Acute experiments were performed in adult cats anesthetized with pentobarbital, using a preparation first developed by Bach-y-Rita and Ito (1960) and described by Lennerstrand (this volume).

Two forms of muscle activation were used. In one the muscle nerve was electrically stimulated through bipolar platinum electrodes. In the other, the muscle was activated with an intravenous injection of succinylcholine chloride (or SCH) which has been shown to selectively activate the multi-innervated tonic fibers.

In the first experiment static length tension curves were obtained. The muscle was activated with 200 ms periods of tetanic stimulation while stretched at extremely low velocities (0.2 mm/s). After subtraction of passive tension, the active tension curves were found to be dependent on both the rate of tetanic stimulation and the stimulus strength. The particular position of maximum active tension was found to shift to shorter muscle length with increases in stimulus rate and to longer muscle length with increases in stimulus strength.

On the basis of a three-component model of muscle described by Pringle (1960), it is proposed that the shift of the peak to shorter muscle length which occurs with increases in the stimulus rate is the result of a proportional increase in the stiffness of the series component relative to the force generated by the contractile component. Such an increase in stiffness has been shown to occur in the lateral rectus of the cat by Carter Collins (1971). This predicts correctly that the maximum tension of single twitches occur at longer lengths than those for tetanic stimulation.

With increases in stimulus strength, on the other hand, the shift of the peak is toward longer lengths. Such an effect would occur if the newly recruited fibers were not uniform, but instead had progressively more compliant series elastic elements. Since these fibers are recruited at the higher voltages, they likely correspond to the multi-innervated tonic component. Evidence for this is found in the fact that maximum

†Experimental work was conducted in the Otolaryngology Research Laboratory, Royal Victoria Hospital, and was supported by Medical Research Council Grant No. MA—4483.

497

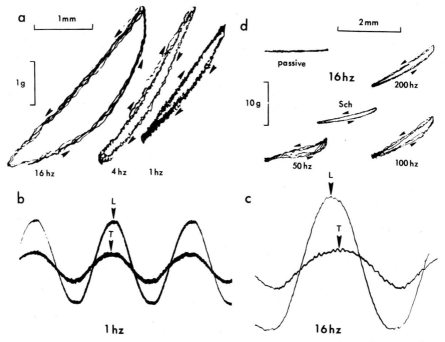

FIG. 1. Tension changes resulting from sinusoidal length changes in the inferior oblique muscle activated by an intravenous injection of Sch (200 μg/kg) (a, b, c) and electrical activation of nerve stump (d). (a) Length tension curves at 1, 4, and 16 Hz. (b) Length and tension of 1 Hz with respect to time. (c) Same as (b) at 16 Hz. (d) Length tension curves (16 Hz) for passive, Sch activated and electrically activated (stimulus rate 50, 100, and 200 Hz).

active tension for the Sch activated muscle occurs at longer lengths than that of the electrically activated muscle.

Now to study the difference in the dynamic responses of the two fiber types small (±1 mm) sinusoidal length changes of various frequencies were applied to both the Sch and electrically activated muscle. Figure 1 shows the force length relationship of the Sch activated muscle for length changes of 1, 4 and 16 Hz. The 1- and 4-Hz plots show clockwise hysteresis loops indicating a dissipation of energy by some form of friction. In the low-frequency range the area of these loops seemed to be velocity independent. At 16 Hz the length tension curve shows a loop in the counter-clockwise direction, indicating that the muscle is acting as an energy source. Counter-clockwise loops were also found in the electrically activated muscle for various rates of stimulation. In time clockwise loops correspond to force leading length and counter-clockwise loops to force lagging length. The lagging effect has not been previously demonstrated in mammalian muscles. Jewell and Ruegg (1966) have shown similar results in insect fibrillar muscle and have suggested that this behavior is due to an intrinsic property of the contractile protein system.

In order to study more fully this phase lag and lead in the two fiber types the total muscle stiffness was considered as the vector sum of three mechanical stiffness vectors. Using a digital computer this vector was calculated by dividing the primary fourier component of the force change by that of the length change. The mechanical stiffness vector of the active tonic fibers was estimated by subtracting from the Sch activated muscle the passive mechanical stiffness; that of the active phasic component by subtracting from the electrically activated muscle (200 Hz stimulus rate and supra-maximal stimulus strength) the mechanical stiffness of the Sch activated muscle. The mechanical stiffness vectors were plotted as a function of the frequency of length change. Three things were noted: (1) In low frequencies (1 to 8 Hz) of length change the phase lead is greater in the active phasic component. This is consistent with these fibers having the less compliant series elastic component as noted in the static results. (2) At high frequencies (8 to 32 Hz) phase lag is greater in the active tonic component. (3) Phasic component can generate force for higher rates of length change before a drop in mechanical stiffness occurs.

The above two experiments indicate the presence of fibers with non-uniform mechanical properties. Previous studies by Barmack *et al.* (1971) and Close and Luff (1974) indicate that in the isometric twitch response a slight decrease in the time to peak contraction occurs with increase in stimulus strength. In comparison to similar work in other muscles (Eccles *et al.*, 1958), such a response is indicative of a muscle consisting of fairly uniform fiber types. Such a conclusion would conflict with our previous results. However, this paradox could be reconciled if the high threshold fibers were only poorly activated by a single twitch. Indeed in amphibian multi-innervated fibers little or no twitch tension is present due to the non-propagation of action potentials. However, large tensions are generated by tetanic stimulation (Kuffler and Vaughan Williams, 1953; Orkand, 1963).

In order to study this possibility, the muscle was subjected to step changes in stimulation rate from a given low rate to a given high rate. The difference between the

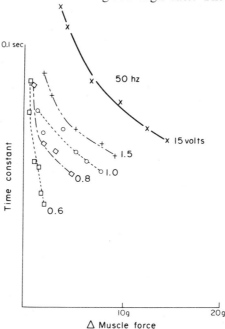

FIG. 2. Time constant of tension rise as a function of tension change. Changes in tension produced by step changes in stimulus rate about a carrier of 50 Hz (maximum and minimum modulation depth 20% and 137% respectively). Stimulus strength 0.6, 0.8, 1.0, 1.5 and 15.0 volts.

low and high rates was defined as the modulation depth. The dynamics of tension rise were quantified by fitting it with a first-order time constant. Increases in the modulation depth resulted in increases in the magnitude of force change up to saturation. Figure 2 shows that as the magnitude of tension change increases, the time constant of tension rise becomes smaller. More importantly, for equal magnitudes of tension rise the response at higher stimulus strength was slower, indicating that slow muscle fibers are recruited. Since these do not seem to contribute to the twitch tension, they likely correspond to amphibian-like tonic fibers with multi-innervation that do not propagate action potentials.

However, as shown by Lennerstrand (1972; also this volume), both action potential propagating and non-propagating multi-innervated fibers exist in the inferior oblique muscle of the cat. Since the former should exhibit a twitch tension the above evidence would suggest that these fibers have either rapid twitch responses or they are innervated by large diameter nerve fibers.

In conclusion, the fibers of the inferior oblique muscle of the cat do not have uniform mechanical properties. How the various differences contribute to eye movements requires further study.

REFERENCES

BACH-Y-RITA, P. and ITO, F. (1966) *In vivo* studies on fast and slow muscle fibers in cat extraocular muscles. *J. Gen. Physiol.* **49**, 1177.

BARMACK, N. H., BELL, C. C. and RENCE, B. G. (1971) Tension and rate of tension development during isometric responses of extraocular muscle. *J. Neurophysiol.* **34**, 6, 1072.

CLOSE, R. I. and LUFF, A. R. (1974) Dynamic properties of inferior rectus muscle of the rat. *J. Physiol.* **236**, 259.

COLLINS, C. C. (1971) Orbital mechanics. In: *The Control of Eye Movements.* BACH-Y-RITA, P. and COLLINS, C. C. (Eds.), p. 283. Academic Press.

ECCLES, J. C., ECCLES, R. M. and LUNDBERG, A. (1958) The action potentials of the alpha motoneurones supplying fast and slow muscles. *J. Physiol.* **142**, 275.

JEWELL, B. R. and RÜEGG, J. C. (1966) Oscillatory contraction of insect fibrillar muscle after glycerol extraction. *Proc. Roy. Soc.* B, **164**, 428.

KUFFLER, S. W. and VAUGHAN WILLIAMS, E. M. (1953) Properties of the slow skeletal muscle fibers of the frog. *J. Physiol.* **121**, 318.

LENNERSTRAND, G. (1972) Fast and slow units in extrinsic eye muscles of cat. *Acta Physiol. Scand.* **86**, 286.

ORKAND, R. K. (1963) A further study of electrical responses in slow and twitch muscle fibers of the frog. *J. Physiol.* **167**, 181.

PRINGLE, J. W. S. (1960) Models of muscle. In: *Symp. of Soc. for Exp. Biol.*, BEAMEMT, J. W. L. (Ed.), vol. 14, p. 41. Academic Press, New York.

CLINICAL ANALYSIS OF VESTIBULARLY INDUCED EYE MOVEMENTS BASED ON A MATHEMATICAL MODEL OF THE VESTIBULO-OCULAR REFLEX†

E. MIRA, R. SCHMID and M. STEFANELLI

To IDENTIFY the status of the vestibulo-ocular reflex (VOR) from nystagmic responses is an age-old endeavor in clinical vestibular analysis. However, the traditional consideration of only the morphological elements of the electronystagmograms (ENG's), such as the number, the frequency and the amplitude of the nystagmic beats, has led to a situation of impasse. Actually, many uncertainties are created by the fact that all these elements depend on the modality of stimulation and cannot be easily related to the functionality of well-defined parts of the VOR. Thus, the way we are now following consists in the use of an anatomo-functional model of the VOR and in the identification of the model parameters from the nystagmus induced by rotatory stimulations of the lateral semicircular canals.

The basic structure of the model is that of two mechanisms working in parallel on the oculomotor nuclei (OMN) (Schmid, 1974). The first mechanism represents the primary vestibulo-ocular arc, and it describes the dynamics of the following subsystems: the lateral semicircular canals, the mechano-neural transduction system, and the neural leaky integrator taking place in the pontine reticular formation. In a simplified form, this mechanism can be defined by the following transfer function:

$$\frac{R(s)}{\Omega(s)} = \frac{K T_3 T_6 s^2}{(1 + sT_2)(1 + sT_3)(1 + sT_6)} \tag{1}$$

where $R(s)$ is the Laplace transform of the time function representing the neural command to the OMN generated by the primary vestibulo-ocular arc; $\Omega(s)$ is the Laplace transform of the time function representing the skull angular velocity; K is the sensitivity factor of the primary vestibulo-ocular arc; T_2 is the long time constant of the lateral semicircular canals; T_3 is the time constant of the adaptation process at the level of the first-order neurons; T_6 is the time constant of the leaky integrator.

†Research partially supported by C.N.R., Programma Speciale TBM, Centro di Teoria dei Sistemi, and Centro Interazione Operatore-Calcolatore.

The second mechanism represents the discrete time system which generates the pulse-step signals to the OMN producing the saccades of the nystagmus fast phase. This mechanism has been localized in the paramedian zone of the pontine reticular formation, and it is probably controlled by the cerebellum. It has been assumed in the model that the input to the saccadic mechanism is an indirect estimation of eye position (efferent copy) obtained from the neural commands to the OMN. The behavior of this mechanism can be characterized by the following parameters: its threshold (δ), its refractory period (T), and its latency (τ).

The dynamics of the final common pathway from the OMN to the eyeballs can be described by a first-order transfer function with a time constant of only 150 ms (Robinson and Keller, 1972).

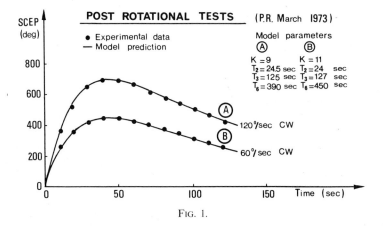

FIG. 1.

In order to identify the model parameters for the examined subjects, the model is implemented on a digital computer. It receives an input reproducing the pattern of stimulation used during the vestibular test, and its response is compared with the recorded ENG data. However, the automatic adjustment of the model parameters through best-fitting procedures cannot be done by a direct comparison of the recorded and predicted nystagmus. The structure of the model suggests the possibility of identifying the parameters of the primary arc and those of the saccadic mechanism separately.

The parameters of the transfer function (1) can be identified from the slow cumulative eye position (SCEP) obtained by removing the fast components of the nystagmus and fitting together the slow components in the way proposed by Meiry (1965). Actually, the dynamics of the extraocular muscles and eyeballs can be neglected during the slow phase of nystagmus, and, therefore, the SCEP can be assumed as to represent the smooth neural command to the OMN produced by the primary vestibulo-ocular arc. Figure 1 shows the diagrams of the SCEP constructed from the nystagmus recorded on the same normal subject during two post-rotational tests of 60 and 120°/sec performed in the same day. By using the best-fitting procedure proposed by Marquardt (1963), the gain and the time constants of the transfer function (1) have been identified from the experimental data shown in Fig. 1 by dots. It is worth noting that no appreciable difference exists between the values of T_2 and T_3 computed from the two sets of data. As far as the sensitivity factor K and the time constant T_6 are concerned, there is a small increase from test A to test B. The variation in the values of K and T_6 may be remarkable during repeated tests, and it can be explained either by a modification of the patient state of alertness or by a process of habituation. It is generally accepted that in both cases the activity of the pontine leaky integrator is modified, and therefore variations in the computed values of K and T_6 are to be expected. In pathological subjects with peripheral disorders, such as Ménière's disease, significant variations of T_2 and T_3 have been observed.

The identification of the parameters δ, T, and τ of the saccadic mechanism is carried out by using simple relationships that the model suggests to exist in a first approximation among the amplitude A_i, the duration D_i, and the mean velocity V_i of the nystagmus slow components (Schmid, 1974). These relations are

$$A_i = \delta + \left(\frac{T}{2} - \tau\right)|V_i| \quad ; \quad D_i = \frac{\delta}{|V_i|} + \left(\frac{T}{2} - \tau\right) \tag{2}$$

for $\quad |V_i| \le \dfrac{\delta}{(T/2) + \tau}$

and

$$A_i = T|V_i| \quad ; \qquad\qquad D_i = T \tag{3}$$

for $\quad |V_i| > \dfrac{\delta}{(T/2) + \tau}.$

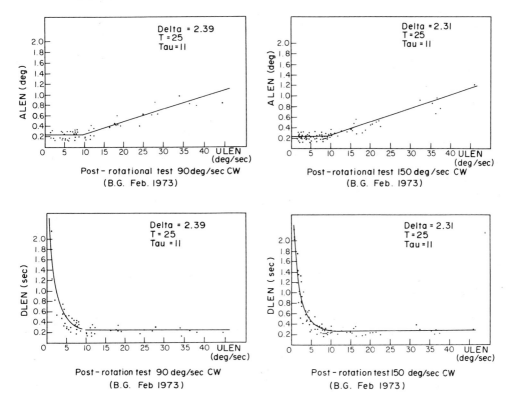

FIG. 2.

The results given in Fig. 2 confirm the validity of eqns. (2) and (3). The nystagmic response of a normal subject was recorded during two post-rotational tests of 90 and 120°/sec, respectively, and it was processed by a minicomputer. For each test, the results are presented on a display as two separate diagrams giving A_i and D_i versus V_i. The experimental data shown by dots are distributed according to eqns. (2) and (3); which are then used to estimate δ, T, and τ through a simple best-fitting procedure. It is worth noting that the same values are determined for δ, T, and τ from the two sets of data. The values assumed by δ, T, and τ in normal subjects tend to cluster in a well-defined region of the parameter space ($2° < \delta < 3°$, 0.25 sec $< T < 0.35$ sec, and 0.10 sec $< \tau < 0.15$ sec). While the number of pathological subjects with central disorders so far examined is not large enough to allow a statistical inference, nevertheless the values of these parameters in the examined cases fall out of this domain in a way that seems to permit a differential diagnosis.

REFERENCES

MARQUARDT, D. W. (1963) An algorithm for least squares estimation of non-linear parameters. *SIAM J.* **11,** 431.

MEIRY, J. L. (1965) The vestibular system and human dynamic space orientation. Sc.D. Thesis, M.I.T., Cambridge, Mass.

ROBINSON, D. A. and KELLER, E. L. (1972) The behaviour of eye movement motoneurons in the alert monkey. *Bibl. Ophthal.* **82,** 7.

SCHMID, R. (1974) Modelling of the vestibulo-ocular reflex and its use in clinical vestibular analysis. Techn. Rep. no. 74–1, CSTS-LCA, Polytechnic of Milan.

TRANSFER FUNCTION ANALYSIS OF THE VESTIBULO-OCULAR REFLEX IN THE CONSCIOUS CAT

P. H. LANDERS and A. TAYLOR

THE vestibulo-ocular reflex (VOR) has been studied in man by the quantitative techniques of linear systems analysis (Meiry, 1966; Benson, 1970) but the same approach in animals has been hampered by the susceptibility of the reflex to anaesthesia. Though some interesting results have been obtained in decerebrate cats (Carpenter, 1972) it is generally found that this preparation shows too much variability for most purposes. Another approach, increasingly popular recently, has been the use of monkeys restrained by a head clamp. As an alternative, we have found it possible to train cats to accept short periods of restraint during whole body rotation (Taylor and Mansourian, 1971) and now report a linear transfer function for the VOR in the frequency range of 0.002 Hz to 5 Hz.

METHODS

The procedure involves selecting docile cats of about 2 kg and training them to take food while having their body slipped up to the forelimbs into a vertical cylinder. They are subsequently operated for the implantation on the skull of a metal stud protruding through the skin at the vertex. They are also implanted with chlorided silver electrodes for EOG recording. Calibration was performed by flash photography of the eyes with synchronizing marks on the pen recording of the eye movements. On resuming training, the animal was accustomed to having its head stabilized by means of a rod attached to the skull stud. The cylinder was installed in a dark, silent room and could be programmed remotely to rotate as a velocity servo about its vertical axis.

RESULTS

Linearity of response was first tested by applying steps of angular velocity in the range 6.5° to 42.5°/sec in random order. The resulting eye velocity measured from the first straight slow phase was a linear function of turntable velocity up to 25°/sec, beyond which the response gain fell progressively.

Sinusoids of angular velocity at amplitudes of 23.5°/sec and 17.6°/sec were presented in random frequency order. The animals did not resent the situation and were tested repeatedly during periods extending to 6 months. The most instructive presentation of the results is the phase plot (Fig. 1). Its general form is one of almost constant small (mean 7.5°) phase advance of eye velocity ($\dot{\theta}_e$) on head velocity ($\dot{\theta}_e$) from 5 Hz down to 0.15 Hz. At lower frequencies the phase advances progressively, passing through 90° at 0.01 Hz and reaching about 135° at 0.002 Hz. The irregularity at around 0.01 Hz is not a general finding.

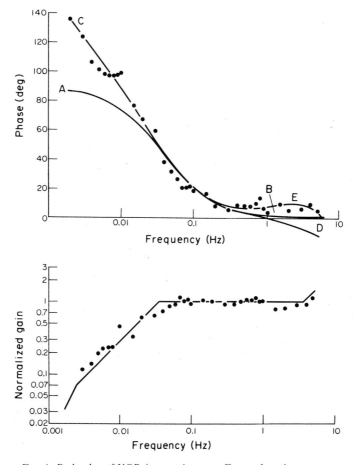

FIG. 1. Bode plot of VOR in conscious cat. For explanation see text.

The line *C–E* represents the transfer function eventually fitted. It was derived as follows: the transition from high- to low-frequency behaviour requires a term in the transfer function of the form $S/(T_1s + 1)$ and this yields the line *A–B*. Clearly, there is another similar term needed at lower frequencies to account for the continuing phase advance and this is represented as $S/(T_2s + 1)$. Taking these two terms, the values of T_1 and T_2 have been computer optimized and the result plotted as line *C–B*. For this, $T_1 = 4.45$ sec and $T_2 = 61$ sec.

Evidently this formulation accounts well for the response below 0.15 Hz but does not give the observed small phase advance at higher frequencies. Moreover, it is clear that the reflex arc must contain a transport delay element (e^{-T_4s}), which will give increasing phase lag at higher frequencies. The line D shows the effect of the addition of such delay of 6 ms. Some phase advance element must be proposed to compensate for this and to give the observed small lead. A term in the numerator of the form $(T_3s + 1)$ was therefore added with the delay and the values of T_3 and T_4 adjusted to give the best fit. The final curve $C–E$ resulted with $T_3 = 43$ ms and $T_4 = 28$ ms, and is a good empirical description of the phase data.

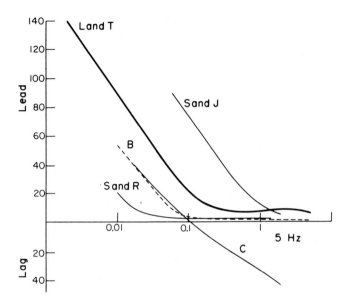

FIG. 2. Comparison of phase data on the VOR from various authors. S. & J.: anaesthetized cat (Sugie and Jones, 1971). L. & T.: present data. C: decerebrate cat (Carpenter, 1972). B: conscious man (Benson, 1970). S. & R.: conscious monkey (Skavenski and Robinson, 1973).

In the gain plot of Fig. 1 the line represents the asymptotes of the proposed transfer function and it is evident that the fit is generally satisfactory. The gain plot gives no useful information about T_2, T_3 or T_4 but supports the value of T_1. The best fit was obtained with gain normalized to 20.1°/sec with stimulus amplitude of 23.5°/sec, which represents a gain in the intermediate frequency band of 0.85. Sinusoidal testing at another amplitude (17.6°/sec) yielded closely similar results and the values of time constants quoted above fitted equally well.

These results are related to other relevant findings in Fig. 2. Neither the lightly anaesthetized cats of Sugie and Jones (1971) nor the decerebrate preparation of Carpenter's (1972) experiments gave very comparable phase plots. The closest match with the conscious cat is the data from human observations by Benson (1970). Here the lower corner frequency might be expected by dimensional considerations (Jones and Spells, 1963). More surprisingly, the monkeys examined by Skavenski and Robinson (1973), though of weight close to that of the cats, showed the onset of phase advance displaced to much lower frequencies. It would be desirable to attempt to confirm this finding with testing in complete darkness and silence.

REFERENCES

Benson, A. J. (1970) Interactions between semi-circular canals and gravireceptors. *Recent Advances in Aerospace Medicine*, Douglas, E. B. (Ed.), pp. 249–261. Dordrecht: Reidel.

Carpenter, R. H. S. (1972) Cerebellectomy and the transfer function of the vestibulo-ocular reflex in the decerebrate cat. *Proc. Roy. Soc.* B, **181**, 353–374.

Jones, G. M. and Spells, K. E. (1963) A theoretical and comparative study of the functional dependence of the semi-circular canal upon its physical dimensions. *Proc. Roy. Soc.* B, **157**, 103–149.

Meiry, J. L. (1966) The vestibular system and human dynamic space orientation. NASA Contract Report CR-628. Washington DC: NASA.

Skavenski, A. A. and Robinson, D. A. (1973) Role of abducens neurones in vestibulo-ocular reflex. *J. Neurophysiol.* **36**, 724–738.

Sugie, N. and Jones, G. M. (1971) Model of eye movements induced by head rotation. *IEEE Trans. Systems, Man, Cybernetics* SNC1, pp. 251–260.

Taylor, A. and Mansourian, P. G. (1971) Eye movements due to optokinetic, vestibular and neck rotation stimuli in the conscious cat. *Proc. Int. Union Physiol. Sci.* **IX,** 1667.

EYE MOVEMENTS DURING AFTER-IMAGE TRACKING UNDER SINUSOIDAL AND RANDOM VESTIBULAR STIMULATION†

Syozo Yasui and Laurence R. Young

ABSTRACT

Vestibular nystagmus was measured during rotation about a vertical axis in the dark (eyes open) and while subjects attempted to fixate a foveal after-image. The after-image inhibited saccades and increased the slow-phase velocity of the vestibulo-ocular reflex. This gain increase supports the hypothesis of smooth eye movements based on perceived target velocity, rather than retinal slip. Comparison of vestibular nystagmus frequency response for sinusoidal and for pseudo-random stimuli yielded the same effect of after-image tracking. Furthermore, unlike the visual tracking case, vestibular nystagmus does not show any sign of prediction based on stimulus periodicity.

INTRODUCTION

Smooth pursuit eye movements can be elicited in the absence of a moving image on the retina, and bring into serious question the entire notion that the purpose of the smooth-movement system is stabilization of the retinal image (Steinbach and Held, 1968; Young, 1971). We suggest that smooth eye movements serve the role of driving the eyes conjugately at a speed related to the *perceived target velocity*. As indicated in Fig. 1, the assumption of a corollary discharge path, together with a connection from perceived velocity to eye velocity, is an alternative to the retinal feedback path for oculomotor control (Yasui and Young, 1974; Yasui, 1973). One way of demonstrating the existence of this path is by use of a standard stimulus to initiate smooth eye movements. In this case, we use standard vestibular stimuli. By generating a visual target which is stationary on the retina, using a foveally centered after-image, we were able to observe the change in slow phase eye movements when a perceived target (the after-image) was actively tracked by the subject (Kommerell and Täumer, 1972; Heywood and Churcher, 1971, 1972; Grüsser and Grüsser-Cornehls, 1972). Observation of an increase in the speed of slow phase eye movements when the subject perceived the target motion (during after-image tracking) supports the notion of the activation of a positive (regenerative) feedback loop from eye movement, to perceived target velocity, to change in eye velocity.

METHODS

The smooth portion of the horizontal vestibulo-ocular reflex was analyzed in terms of the frequency response relating slow-phase eye velocity to angular velocity of a

†Research supported by NASA Grant NGR 22-009-025.

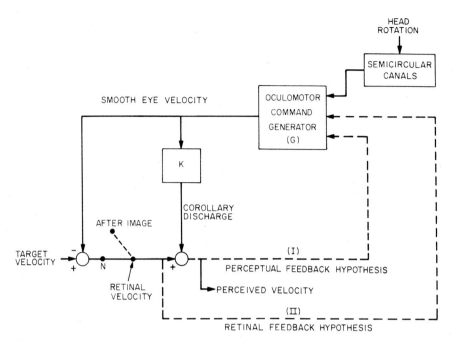

Fig. 1. Schematic representation of the control of smooth eye movements. Perceived velocity of the target is assumed to generate a smooth eye movement, via loop (I). The effect of the eye movement in changing retinal velocity is partially cancelled by the corollary discharge of gain K.

rotating chair under four different cases: (1) sinusoidal rotation about a vertical axis in total darkness; (2) sinusoidal rotation during after-image tracking; (3) pseudo-random head rotation in total darkness; (4) pseudo-random head rotation during after-image tracking. The frequency of oscillation for the sinusoidal test was varied randomly in the range from 0.025 to 0.7 Hz. Peak angular velocity was also varied, but never exceeded 40 deg/sec. For the pseudo-random tests, the input was the sum of ten nonharmonically related sinusoids from 0.01 to 0.7 Hz. Peak velocity for any one component was below 15°/sec. Alertness was maintained through a mental arithmetic task. After several oscillation periods in the dark, a monocular foveal after-image was produced by a fixated flash bulb. Subjects attempted to fixate the target and indicate its direction of motion using a three-position switch. Eye movements were recorded using a photo-electric limbus tracking method. The frequency response of slow-phase eye velocity relative to the chair velocity (vestibulo-ocular reflex transfer function) was calculated from the sinusoidal eye movement trace by hand for the sinusoidal cases, and from the MITNYS eye velocity program (Tole and Young, 1971; Allum et al., 1974) and the fast Fourier spectral analysis for the pseudo-random chair motion.

RESULTS

1. Sinusoidal Stimulation

The vestibulo-ocular reflex recorded prior to the initiation of the after-image agreed with published results for sinusoidal stimulation (Benson, 1969). After the flash was made and the after-image appeared, the fast-phase movement almost disappeared and eye movements tended to become smooth. The apparent motion of the visual after-image relative to the subject was in phase with the smooth eye movements, as expected. The cumulative eye position (sum of slow phases) and slow-phase velocity under after-image tracking were always greater than those of tracking in the dark prior to the flash.

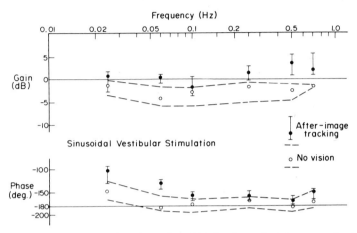

FIG. 2. Frequency response comparison (based on sinusoidal head rotation) between after-image tracking eye movement and vestibular nystagmus slow phase in complete darkness without after-image. Median data points and ± one standard deviation are shown (four subjects).

The frequency response comparing the vestibulo-ocular reflex gain and phase under conventional vestibular stimulation (eyes open in the dark, indicated by "no vision") and the after-image tracking for the same vestibular stimulation are shown in Fig. 2. The frequency response clearly shows the significant effect of the after-image tracking in increasing the gain and advancing the phase of the vestibulo-ocular reflex ($p < 0.05$), as predicted by the hypothesis of a regenerative feedback loop involving perceived velocity. For example, at 0.7 Hz, the slow-phase velocity under after-image tracking was approximately twice as large as that for motion in the dark under the same vestibular stimulus. The phase advance of up to about 40° with after-image tracking held for all frequencies, and was most prominent at the lowest frequencies tested.

2. Pseudo-random Stimulation

Figure 3 is a frequency response for the pseudo-random input vestibulo-ocular reflex under the conditions of rotation in the dark and without the presence of an after-image. There appears to be no substantial difference between the frequency response of the vestibulo-ocular reflex in the dark for sinusoidal and for pseudo-random inputs. Unlike normal visual-oculomotor tracking (Stark *et al.*, 1962), prediction due to target periodicity is apparently not involved in the non-visual oculomotor response, at least in the relatively low-frequency range tested. Eye-movement amplitude ratios became somewhat greater during after-image tracking over the frequency range investigated, although the difference is not as conspicuous as in the previous sinusoidal comparison, nor

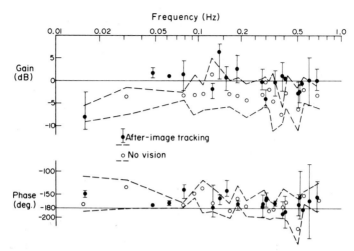

FIG. 3. Frequency response data for two types of smooth eye movement under pseudorandom vestibular stimulation: smooth eye movement during visual tracking of vestibularly induced after-image apparent motion versus normal vestibular nystagmus slow phase in the dark.

is it quite as consistent throughout the frequency range. Nevertheless, the fact that the presence of an after-image and the generation of a perceived angular velocity of this after-image increased the angular velocity of eye movements for random as well as sinusoidal tracking indicates that the important factor is perceived visual motion and not its predictability.

DISCUSSION

The observation that the presence of an after-image during vestibular stimulation increases the velocity of slow-phase eye movements is in support of the theory that such slow-phase movements are generated, at least in part, by the perceived velocity of the target. Since the target is immobilized on the retina, this perceived velocity is clearly not generated by retinal slip, but rather by a mechanism related to the eye movement, such as corollary discharge. As an example, movement of the head to the left generates a slow-phase eye movement to the right, based upon the vestibular stimulation. This right eye movement produces an apparent motion of a foveal after-image to the right relative to the subject. This perceived target motion presumably then generates an increased eye velocity to the right through the positive feedback loop (I) in Fig. 1. The fact that the system is not unstable indicates that the loop gain of this positive feedback loop must be less than unity, which is consistent with the theory that the cancellation associated with the outflow mechanism is less than complete, and is in fact probably only of the order of 60% or 70%. Note that the gain of the vestibulo-ocular reflex during after-image tracking exceeds unity (0 db) in the midfrequency range for both sinusoidal and pseudo-random tracking, although the gain of the human vestibulo-ocular reflex in the dark is only approximately 0.6 in the mid-frequency range.

REFERENCES

ALLUM, J., TOLE, J. and WEISS, A. D. (1974) MITNYS: a digital program for on-line analysis of nystagmus. *IEEE Trans. BME*- (in press).

BENSON, A. (1969) Interaction between semicircular canals. *Recent Advances in Aerospace Medicine*, D. E. BUSBY (Ed.). Reidel Publishing Co., Dordrecht, Holland.

GRÜSSER, O. J. and GRÜSSER-CORNEHLS, U. (1972) Interaction of vestibular and visual inputs in the visual system. *Progress in Brain Research*, **37**, BRODAL, A. and POMPEIANO, O. (Eds.). Elsevier Publishing Co., Amsterdam.

HEYWOOD, S. and CHURCHER, J. H. (1971) Eye movements and the afterimage. I: Tracking the afterimage. *Vision Res.* **11**, 1163–1168.

HEYWOOD, S. and CHURCHER, J. H. (1972) Eye movements and the afterimage. II. The effects of foveal and nonfoveal afterimages on saccadic behaviour. *Vision Res.* **12**, 1033–1043.

KOMMERELL, G. and TÄUMER, R. (1972) Investigations of the eye tracking system through stabilized retinal images. *Bibl. Ophthal.* **82**, 280–287.

STARK, L., VOSSIUS, G. and YOUNG, L. R. (1962) Predictive control of eye tracking movements. *IRE Transactions, Human Factors in Electronics*, **HFE-3**, 52–56.

STEINBACH, M. J. and HELD, R. (1968) Eye tracking of observer-generated target movements. *Science*, **161**, 187–188.

TOLE, J. and YOUNG, L. R. (1971) MITNYS: a hybrid program for on-line analysis of nystagmus. *Aerospace Medicine*, **42**, 508–511.

YASUI, S. (1973) Nystagmus generation, oculomotor tracking, and visual motion perception. Ph.D. Thesis, Department of Aeronautics and Astronautics, M.I.T.

YASUI, S. and YOUNG, L. R. (1974) Perceived visual motion as effective stimulus to pursuit eye movements, submitted to *Science*.

YOUNG, L. R. (1971) Pursuit eye tracking movements. *Control of Eye Movements*, BACH-Y-RITA, P. and COLLINS, C. (Eds.). Academic Press, New York.

THREE REACTION MECHANISMS OF
THE SACCADIC SYSTEM
IN RESPONSE TO A DOUBLE JUMP

R. Täumer

ACCORDING to the model of Young (1963), the saccadic system includes a sample period of about 200 ms. In preliminary experiments (Täumer, 1972) we observed much shorter inter-saccadic intervals. In this paper, we will study the conditions of this occurrence.

METHODS

The target jumps 5° horizontally. This first jump to one side is followed by a second jump of 5° in the same direction (staircase pattern *SP*) or of 10° in the opposite direction (pulse pattern *PP*). The two jumps are separated by the jump-interval *V*. The pattern can begin to the right or left. These four patterns were presented at random. A new pattern appears after each 3 sec. The important parameter *V* was varied in the different experiments between 50 and 500 ms. At each experimental session, five values of *V* were chosen randomly. The eye movements were recorded electro-oculographically. Ten students acted as our subjects. During the analysis, the three following times were measured by a PDP-12 computer: (1) reaction time 1 (*RT1*) from the first target-jump to the first saccade; (2) the inter-saccadic interval (*SI*) from the beginning of the first saccade to the beginning of the second; and (3) reaction time 2 (*RT2*) from the second jump to the second saccade. These times were plotted afterwards as histograms or joint-histograms.

RESULTS

The most frequent response of one person to the *SP* with $V = 100$ ms is drawn in Fig. 1 ($RT1 = 162 \pm 20$; $SI = 106 \pm 52$; $RT2 = 163 \pm 53$). The *RT1* is very short in these experiments. The reason is the short resting period during the repetition of the patterns. There exists a close dependence of the reaction time on the interstimulus interval (Täumer, 1970). The *SI*-histogram has a small peak at 170 ms. Additionally, a large peak occurs at 70 ms. Within the limits of 0 and 120 ms, *SI* takes the average value 69 ± 18 ms. Because *SI* includes the duration of the first saccade, the average resting period between the two saccades lasts only 35 ms. Sometimes, this period is 5 ms or so short, that it is hard to recognize in the record. The *RT2* shows about the same form of the histogram. Within an upper limit of 170, it takes the average of 129 ± 22. So the value of $RT2$ is about 30 ms shorter than $RT1$. This occurs with the other values of V too.

The distribution of SI shows a close dependence on V ($V = 150$ $SI = 128 \pm 41$; $V = 200$ $SI = 146 \pm 26$; $V = 250$ $SI = 196 \pm 31$).

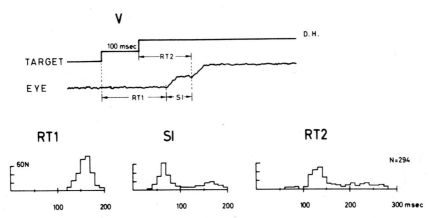

FIG. 1. (a) Most frequent response to a staircase pattern with a jump-interval $V = 100$ ms. (b) Accumulation histograms of the three times of the responses measured by a computer.

The joint-histograms (Fig. 2) give a more detailed view of the mechanisms. On the abscissa, the latency of the first saccade to the *second jump* is given. The ordinate shows the SI value. All responses of one subject to an SP with different V are collected. Responses with only one large saccade, which occur more frequently with shorter V, are not drawn (Wheeles, 1966). Points to the right side mean the first saccade is executed after the second target-jump. Negative signs result from responses with the first saccade before the second jump. This occurs on patterns with long V, longer than $RT1$.

The diagrams of Fig. 2 are taken from two persons. If the theory of a sample period is correct, we would expect a horizontal line with SI of about 200 ms. The person of Fig. 2b shows this tendency. The dotted horizontal line has a SI of 160

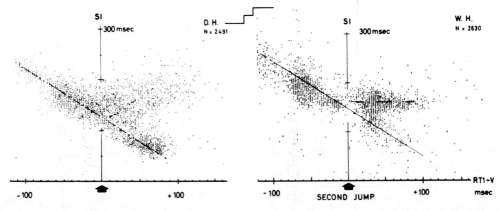

FIG. 2. Joint-histogram $SI/RT1$. (a) Subject with the reaction mechanism 1 and 3 (dotted line). (b) Subject with the reaction mechanism 1 and 2 (dotted line).

ms. In addition, the responses group also around a descending line which has the slope of -1. Points upon this line have the same sum of $RT1$ and SI, which equals $RT2$. These responses show the tendency to compensate longer $RT1$ by shorter SI and hold the $RT2$ constant. The person of Fig. 2a, the same as of Fig. 1, shows the descending line too. Here also, the saccadic system often makes a quick execution of the second saccade with a short SI. A second, ascending line occurs, with the slope of $+1$. On these responses, the SI increases with the longer latency of the first saccade. With most of these responses, the amplitude of the first saccade has an incorrect amplitude. Larger first and smaller second saccades lie upward and more to the right.

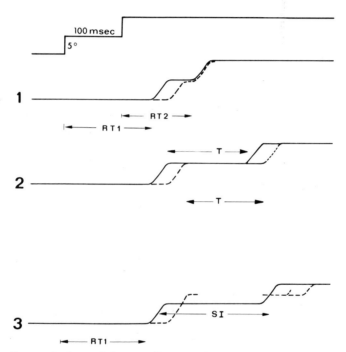

FIG. 3. Three reaction mechanisms of the saccadic system in response to a staircase pattern with small jump-interval. (1) Conditioned parallel-planning. (2) Conditioned successive-planning. (3) Unconditioned successive-planning.

The three mechanisms of the saccadic system in response to a double jump (SP) are drawn schematically in Fig. 3. The first mechanism is a *conditioned parallel-planning* of the two saccades. The conditioning makes the $RT2$ about 30 ms shorter than the $RT1$. The planning of the two saccades has to be parallel, because the resting interval between the two saccades can be shorter than 40 ms. This time appears too short for all the necessary processes, going on from the information intake until the execution of the second saccade. Both these channels work independently. So it is possible that, with a long $RT1$, a short $RT2$ is combined. In this case, the difference, SI, is very short. All of our ten subjects show this first mechanism, but not exclusively.

The second mechanism is the *conditioned successive-planning*. The information intake begins at the end of the first saccade. After a time of about 120 ms, the next saccade is carried out. The effect is a constant interval between the two saccades. This interval is adequate to the constant sample period of Young. Seven out of ten persons react according to this mechanism.

The third mechanism is the *unconditioned successive-planning*. This mechanism works on persons who additionally show the first mechanism. Mostly the first saccade is incorrect in amplitude. Then, the system needs about the same time for the execution of the second saccade (*SI*) as for the first (*RT*1). Longer *SI* appears with longer *RT*1. And furthermore, the smallest second saccades are connected with the longest *SI*. According to Becker (1972), these second saccades have the property of a correction saccades.

These three mechanisms we could only separate for responses to the *SP*. With the *PP*, it seems that the first mechanism is the only one. The saccadic system reacts differently whether the target jumps inside the same part of the visual field or not.

REFERENCES

BECKER, W. (1972) The control of eye movements in the saccadic system. In: *Cerebral Control of Eye Movements and Motion Perception*, DICHGANS, J. and BIZZI, E. (Eds.), pp. 233–243. S. Karger, Basel.

TÄUMER, R., MIE, K. and KOMMERELL, G. (1972) Three kinds of reaction mechanisms of the human saccadic system. *Biocybernetics*, **IV**, pp. 236–242. VEB Fischer, Jena.

TÄUMER, R., SCHLIER, CH., SCHMIDT, C. and SCHUPP, W. (1970) Die Abhängigkeit der Reaktionszeit von der zeitlichen Folge optischer Reize. *Kybernetik*, **7**, 183–191.

WHEELES, L. L. COHEN, G. H. and BOYTON, R. M. (1966) Eye-movement responses to step and pulse-step stimuli. *J. Opt. Soc. Am.* **56/7**, 956–960.

YOUNG, L. R. and STARK, L. (1963) Variable Feedback experiments testing a sample data model for eye tracking movements. *IEEE Trans. Human Factors in Electronics*, **4**, 38–51.

SACCADIC REACTIONS TO DOUBLE-STEP STIMULI: EVIDENCE FOR MODEL FEEDBACK AND CONTINUOUS INFORMATION UPTAKE†

W. Becker and R. Jürgens

INTRODUCTION

The reaction of the saccadic system when presented with a sequence of two rapidly succeeding target steps has been frequently investigated since Westheimer's (1954) experiments with pulse-shaped displacement patterns. However, many of these investigations are based on a very straightforward data analysis which tends to obscure some very important properties of the saccadic system. In particular, the reactions have invariably been considered as a function of the temporal separation of the two target steps, whereas in the present work it appears that their characteristics depend mainly on the time lapse between the second step of the sequence and the start of the response. By analysing the data accordingly, we have been able to show that the saccadic system can continuously change the amplitude of a saccade under preparation until 80 ms prior to its execution. Moreover, evidence has been found which suggests that the system is capable of preparing at least two saccadic reactions simultaneously. This is done by an internal prediction of the effect the execution of a saccade will have on the target's retinal image. Some of our conclusions are supported by the data of Täumer, which have been presented at this symposium.

METHODS

Subjects were presented with a horizontal array of five target points (GaAs-diodes) located at the primary position and 15° and 30° to the left and right. They were required to track a random sequence of plain and double steps, where the double steps comprised all possible combinations of two steps within the given five-point array. Four basic step combinations result from this procedure (Fig. 1). (1) Stair case (SC)—the target steps twice in the same direction; (2) symmetrical pulse (SP)—the target steps and returns to the starting position; (3) pulse over (PO)—the second step goes in the opposite direction and is larger than the first one so that it overshoots the original position; (4) pulse under (PU)—the second step goes in the opposite direction and undershoots the original position. The amplitude of the double-step components was between 15° and 60° with a time separation between them that varied

†This research was supported by the Deutsche Forschungsgemeinschaft (SFB 70).

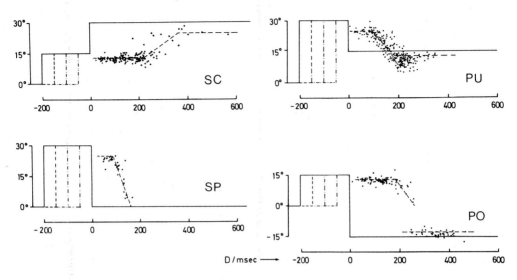

FIG. 1. Transition functions. A typical transition function is shown for each of the four basic step combinations: SC—stair case; PU—pulse under; SP—symmetrical pulse; PO—pulse over. The amplitude of the
first saccadic reaction to the step combination is the ordinate and the delay (D) from the second step
is the abscissa of each graph. Leftmost points of each graph represent responses that were elicited by
step separations of 200 ms, while the points to the right are from patterns with separations of 150, 100
and 50 ms, respectively. The target movement is indicated in each graph by the solid line for a step separation
of 200 ms, and the first steps for separations of 150, 100 and 50 ms are shown by dotted lines. Three
line segments have been fitted to the data of each graph. The left horizontal segment represents the saccadic
amplitude the first step would elicit if it were presented alone. The right horizontal segment shows the
average amplitude that would be obtained if the target reached its final position by a plain step. The oblique
segment was fitted by hand and represents the transition of the saccadic amplitude between the initial and
the final target position.

in 50 ms increments from 50 to 200 ms. The subject was instructed to refixate the
target as rapidly and as accurately as possible each time it changed position. His
eye movements were measured by electrooculogram and analysed by a small computer
for saccadic reactions. The following parameters of the first and second saccade, if
present, were measured: (1) R1—reaction time of the first saccade in response to the
first target step; (2) D—delay between the second target step and the onset of the
first saccade (with the step separations used, D is always positive, i.e. the reaction
starts after the second target step); (3) $\varphi 1$, $\varphi 2$—amplitude of the first and second
saccade; (4) L—latency of the second saccade from the end of the first and (5) I—interval
between the beginning of the first and second saccades.

RESULTS AND DISCUSSION

The characteristics of saccadic responses to double-step stimuli depend almost entirely
upon the time delay between the occurrence of the second step and the onset of
the response. For a given step combination this time lapse determines the amplitude
of the first response saccade as well as the interval between the first and second
saccades.

For each of the four basic step combinations there is a characteristic curve that
establishes the amplitude of the first response saccade as a function of D (Fig. 1).

Generally, the more time available between the second step and the onset of the response, the closer the response is to the final target position and, vice versa, the less time available, the closer it is to the initial target position. We call the relations shown in Fig. 1 "transition functions" because they represent the time course of the programming changes whereby the saccadic amplitude is altered from a value corresponding to the initial target angle to one corresponding to the final angle. The transition functions can be approximated by three line segments as explained in the caption of Fig. 1. The left breakpoint indicates when the second step *starts* to influence the size of the saccade in preparation, whereas the right point shows the time needed to *completely* adapt the response to the final target position. (Slightly different interpretation applies to the transition function of PO-stimuli, see below.) The breakpoint positions exhibit consistent differences that depend on the particular stimulus pattern. In the case of PU-stimuli, the second step may influence (i.e. shorten) a saccade under preparation up to 80–90 ms before its onset (Fig. 1, PU), whereas the second step of a SC-stimulus must precede the response by about 200 ms if it is to influence (i.e. increase) its size (Fig. 1, SC). The left breakpoint of SP-transition functions occurs at about the same time as for PU-responses. Any model explaining the amplitude of a saccade on the basis of a weighted average of the target position (e.g. Young *et al.*, 1968) will not account for the fact that it takes less time to shorten a saccade than to lengthen it. A non-linear process must be involved. A simple explanation would be that a saccade can be stopped in flight by new information, whereas its prolongation would be possible only if the information arrived prior to the start of the saccade. However, saccades that are shortened by the second step are slower from their inception and the transition function of PU- and SP-responses is not a mirror image of the saccade that was originally intended, as it should be if this explanation was right. Hence the amplitude modification must occur at a level prior to the saccadic pulse generator, conceivably during the transition from spatial coding into temporal and intensity coding. The results prove in any case that the system can update its position information continuously up to at least 80 ms prior to a saccade.

The PO-pattern is unique among the four basic combinations because the decision whether to follow or to ignore the first step of the target requires a decision between two directions of movement and not merely an amplitude modification. Accordingly, the transition function is discontinuous (Fig. 1, PO). It consists of two branches. The upper branch shows the size of responses directed towards the initial target position; it approaches zero amplitude as D increases indicating that the second target step may shorten the saccade that was prepared as a response to the first step. However, this takes much more time than in the case of PU- or SP-responses (170 ms *vs.* 85 ms). The lower branch of the transition function represents saccades that aim immediately at the final target position. It is parallel to the abscissa which means that, if the first step is ignored, the amplitude of the response saccade will always be fully adapted to the final target position. The delay values corresponding to the lower branch of the transition function are due to responses that have extremely long reaction times, if referred to the first target step. However, if these responses are considered a reaction to the second step, the reaction time is fairly normal. This supports the view that the direction of a saccade is irrevocably set earlier than the amplitude and that if the second step suppresses the first direction decision, it takes another reaction time to elicit a response that goes in the new direction.

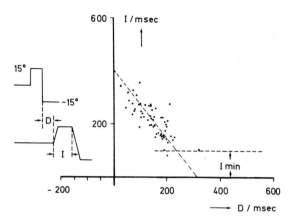

FIG. 2. Interval (I) between the two saccades of a double-step response as a function of the delay (D) between the second target step and the onset of the response. The experimental paradigm is shown in the left inset. A straight line has been fitted to the data by eye, the slope of which is slightly steeper than unity. The broken horizontal line indicates the minimum value for the interval that was found in the present paradigm.

Another important relationship exists between the delay and the interval separating the first and second saccades of the response. For all patterns except PU, it is a general rule that the longer the delay between the second step and the onset of the first response saccade, the shorter the interval between the two saccades of the response will be. In most cases there is an almost linear relationship between I and D with slope-1 or somewhat steeper (Fig. 2). This behavior corresponds to the type 1 mode of reaction to double steps of small size described by Täumer et al. (1972, and this Symposium). It implies that the response to the second step is prepared independently and parallel to the response to the first step. Obviously, the interval cannot decrease indefinitely; if responses occur with a large delay from the second step, I approaches a minimum value which is characteristic for each stimulus pattern and subject. The shortest values are with PO-stimuli and range from 80 to 150 ms in different subjects. The average duration of a 30° saccade may reach this order of magnitude, and therefore, in many cases no time is left between the end of the first saccade and the beginning of the second one (Fig. 3). Frequently the disappearance of any latency between first and second saccade coincides with a diminution of the initial amplitude of PO- and SP-responses. The impression therefore arises that the second saccade "cuts" the first one in midflight, but this is improbable since the initial velocity of these responses is already reduced. One might question whether the second saccade is a precisely programmed movement if the latency becomes shorter than the time required to measure the actual target distance at the end of the first saccade. Interestingly enough, no correlation is detectable between L and the accuracy of the second saccade. The position error that remains after the second movement is quite normal (as compared to plain steps), even though the amplitude of the second movement may be required to vary as a consequence of the first. (Compare the two reactions to 60° pulses in Fig. 3.) This suggests that, when it prepares the second movement, the system already knows where the first saccade is going to bring the eye. We propose that a copy of the command issued to generate the first saccade shifts the internal representation of the

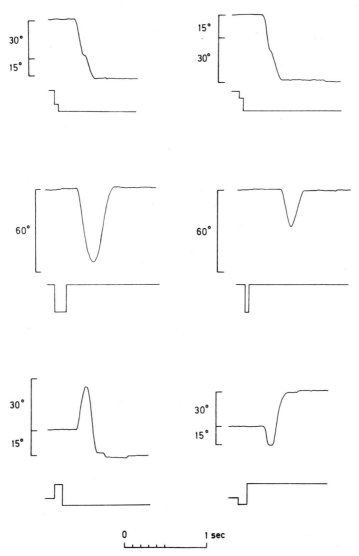

FIG. 3. Examples of extremely short latencies between first and second saccade. Upper trace of pair shows eye movement, lower trace target displacement (different amplitude scale). Note that the second saccade brings the eyes onto target with normal accuracy although no time was available at the end of the first movement to measure the actual target distance. The response for the 60° pulse at the middle right is a good example of the second saccade seemingly cutting the first saccade in midflight.

target's position on the retina by an amount that anticipates the effect the command will have after its execution. In terms of control engineering this is equivalent to model feedback as it is used to improve systems with a large dead time. The models proposed by Johnson and Fleming (1963) and Robinson (this Symposium) are topologically similar to this idea.

524 W. BECKER AND R. JÜRGENS

REFERENCES

JOHNSON, L. I. JR. and FLEMING, D. G. (1963) A model of model feedback control for saccadic eye movement. 16th Ann. Conf. Engng. Med. Biol.

TÄUMER, R., MIE, K. and KOMMERELL, G. (1972) Three kinds of reaction mechanisms of the human saccadic system, In: Biokybernetik DRISCHL, H. (Ed.), vol. 4, p. 236.

WESTHEIMER, G. (1954) Eye movement responses to a horizontally moving visual stimulus. Arch. Ophthal. 52, 932.

YOUNG, L. R., FORSTER, J. D. and VANHOUTTE, N. (1968) A revised stochastic sampled data model for eye tracking movements. 4th Ann. NASA-University Conference on Manual Control, Univ. of Michigan, Ann Arbor, Mich.

IS THERE A LINEAR ADDITION OF SACCADES AND PURSUIT MOVEMENTS?†

R. JÜRGENS and W. BECKER

INTRODUCTION

It is often assumed that the saccadic system and the smooth pursuit system elaborate their responses independently according to their specific stimuli and add linearly their signals in a "common final pathway" (e.g. Robinson, 1972). This hypothesis of "linear addition" implies that nystagmus and the response to a target motion of constant velocity upon which sudden jumps are superimposed are both the sum of a continuous smooth movement and saccadic movements. It should be possible to test this assumption by investigating the relationship between the velocity and duration of saccades during pursuit movements. When pursuit movements are present, the saccadic duration is the only invariable indicator of the "intrinsic" saccadic amplitude due to the saccadic pathway. Thus, if there is a linear addition, saccades going in the same direction as the pursuit movement should have higher velocity and amplitude than saccades of the same duration that go opposite to the pursuit movement.

We are aware of only one attempt to verify the hypothesis of linear addition by investigating the velocity characteristics of saccades in the presence of pursuit movements (Dichgans et al., 1973). However, these authors did not consider the intrinsic amplitude of the saccadic pathway. Rather they compared the relationship between the apparent amplitude (as defined in Fig. 1) and the peak velocity in the presence of pursuit movements to the normal saccadic amplitude–velocity relationship. If a linear addition exists, the apparent amplitude and the velocity are both increased or decreased by the pursuit signal; therefore, their ratio is not different from the corresponding ratio of normal saccades, while the above authors assumed that there would be a difference.

In the present study it was found that direction and velocity of smooth pursuit movements are taken into account while programming the amplitude of the saccade; however, a linear addition could not be verified.

METHODS

In forty experiments, the subjects with fixated heads tracked periodical ramp stimuli of alternating direction, which were presented on a TV screen. Jumps of ± 5, ± 10, ± 15 and ± 20 degrees were superimposed on the ramp movement in a random order.

†This research was supported by the Deutsche Forschungsgemeinschaft (SFB 70).

525

Saccades started at randomized positions which were balanced for velocity differences that might arise from different starting positions and movement directions. To avoid predictive effects on pursuit velocity, no target jumps ended near the edge of the screen. Eye position was recorded by means of bi-temporal EOG and was analysed using a laboratory computer. In ten other experiments optokinetic nystagmus was recorded and analysed by a similar computer program.

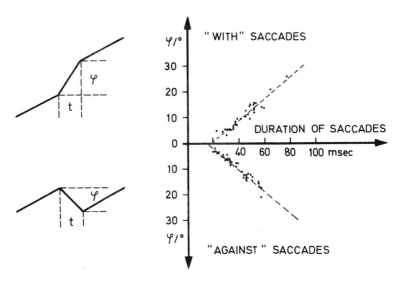

FIG. 1. Amplitude of "with" and "against" saccades as a function of their duration. The left figures show the definition of "with" and "against" saccades. Their amplitudes (φ) and durations (t) were measured as indicated. (This corresponds to measuring "apparent" amplitudes, because they may contain amplitude contamination from the pursuit system, if some form of linear addition exists.) The right half shows the slope of amplitude on duration for "with" and "against" saccades as given by the broken regression lines. The slopes are identical, while linear addition would predict a 45°/sec difference.

RESULTS AND DISCUSSION

For saccades responding to a given stimulus amplitude, those going in the same direction as the ramp movement ("with" saccades) are larger than the stimulus jump and those going in the opposite direction of the ramp stimulus ("against" saccades) are smaller than the stimulus jump.

This amplitude difference is, of course, *compatible* with linear addition, but it does not *prove* it. As outlined above, in the case of linear addition the saccadic amplitude is increased or decreased by the pursuit signal, while the duration of the saccade remains unaffected; the duration is the only invariable indicator of what amplitude the saccadic system intended to execute. Thus, in order to verify the existence of linear addition it must be shown that "with" and "against" saccades that have the *same* duration have *different* amplitudes.

Figure 1 shows the amplitude of "with" saccades and "against" saccades as a function of the duration. For a given duration, "with" amplitudes and "against" amplitudes are almost equal, i.e. with and against saccades have the same amplitude-on-duration

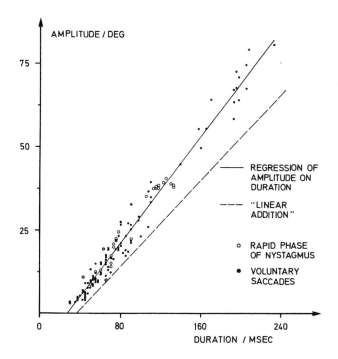

FIG. 2. Amplitude–duration relationship for voluntary saccades in the absence of pursuit movements and for the rapid phases of optokinetic nystagmus. Slow-phase velocity was 80°/sec. Both voluntary saccades and rapid phases scatter around the same regression line. The broken line has a slope that is 80°/sec less than that of the regression line. It shows the relationship predicted for the rapid phase by the linear addition hypothesis.

slope. For ideal linear addition we would expect the slope difference to be equal to twice the pursuit velocity. The actual average of differences is almost zero. Therefore, it seems unlikely that the smooth and the saccadic signals add up linearly. This is confirmed by our analysis of optokinetic nystagmus. The rapid phase of the optokinetic nystagmus was considered like an "against" saccade and was compared to voluntary saccades between stationary points. Subjects reach slow phase velocities of up to 80°/sec. Therefore, if there is a linear addition, one would expect rapid phases to have 8° less amplitude than normal saccades of 100 ms duration. This is not the case as Fig. 2 shows. Both amplitude–duration functions scatter around the same regression line. From this it may be concluded that the amplitude difference between with and against saccades elicited by jumps of the same size is not due to an amplitude contribution from the pursuit system. Instead we propose that this results from a "saccadic strategy".

The strategy suspends the pursuit movement during a saccade and programs the saccadic amplitude so as to take over the contribution of the suspended pursuit movement. A simple model of this strategy has a switch between the output of the smooth pursuit system and the common final pathway which is opened during saccades; the input into the saccadic branch is the perceived target displacement to which a term of the form (perceived target velocity)-(saccadic duration) is added.

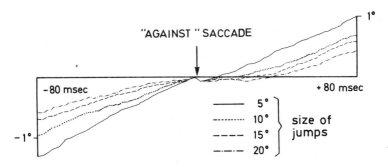

FIG. 3. Pursuit movement preceding and following against saccades. The target moved at constant velocity and saccades were elicited by target jumps of 5, 10, 15 and 20°. For each target jump amplitude, 100 movements were averaged over 80 ms preceding and following the subject's response saccade. The saccades themselves were cut out prior to averaging. Note that the pursuit velocity before and after the saccade becomes increasingly slower as the jump size (and hence the saccade size) rises.

If a strategy like this exists, one might expect that the pursuit system does not resume instantaneously its full velocity after a saccade. Then one should observe a transient decrease of pursuit velocity right after the saccade. Therefore we measure the pursuit velocity in the 80-ms interval preceding and following "with" and "against" saccades. Figure 3 shows average pursuit movements preceding and following against saccades. The saccade itself is cut out of this plot. There is a marked decrease of pursuit velocity both *before* and *after* the saccade which depends on the saccadic amplitude. The pursuit velocity reduction prior to the saccade makes it particularly clear that the reduction of "against" saccades is due to a strategy that changes the saccadic amplitudes and the pursuit velocity. The velocity decrease prior to the "against" saccade reminds us of the well-known results from step-ramp stimuli. In these situations a predictive strategy suppresses the "against" saccade that would go to the opposite direction of smooth movement (Rashbass, 1961). The velocity of smooth pursuit movements is also reduced after "with" saccades. The reduction increases with the angle of the stimulus step and reaches a maximum of 30%. Before "with" saccades there is no reduction of velocity. We consider these results compatible with the idea that the pursuit movement is suppressed during saccades.

CONCLUSIONS

A linear addition of saccades and pursuit movements in the sense that the smooth pursuit signal would continue during a saccade and would simply be added to the saccadic signal could not be shown. Rather we found a strategy which consists of suppressing the pursuit signal and the take over of its amplitude contribution by changing the saccadic amplitude accordingly.

REFERENCES

DICHGANS, J., NAUCK, B. and WOLPERT, E. (1973) The influence of attention, vigilance and stimulus area on optokinetic and vestibular nystagmus and voluntary saccades. In: *The Oculomotor System and Brain Functions*, ZIKMUND, V. (Ed.). London, Bratislava, 1973.

RASHBASS, C. (1961) The relationship between saccadic and smooth tracking eye movements. *J. Physiol. (Lond.)* **159**, 326.

ROBINSON, D. A. (1972) Progress in models of eye movement control. *Int. Conf. Cybernetics and Society, Washington.*

CLINICAL ASPECTS OF OCULAR
MOTILITY

VERTIGO AND NYSTAGMUS OF INNER EAR ORIGIN: A STUDY BASED ON ELECTRON MICROSCOPIC FINDINGS†

Tetsuo Ishii and Jun-Ichi Suzuki

Nystagmus resulting from inner ear lesion may serve as a guide to more fully evaluate these pathologies. Some of these conditions have a characteristic vertigo of inner ear etiology, i.e. Ménière's disease, benign paroxysmal nystagmus and vertigo, and other vertiginous inner ear conditions.

If the frequency of the impulses in one of the lateral ampullary nerve increases, relative to the opposite labyrinth, then a deviation of the eyes to the contralateral side will appear. When the deviation lasts, a nystagmus will be resulted. The direction of this nystagmus will be toward the labyrinth with the increased output. When the whole labyrinth is involved, the induced horizontal nystagmus will have a rotating component and horizontal rotating nystagmus will be induced. This condition of the labyrinth with increased afferent impulses may be referred to as an "irritative condition" of the vestibular labyrinth and the clinically observed spontaneous nystagmus will be directed towards that side.

Conversely, the function of one of the labyrinths may be depressed, in which case the frequency of the afferent impulses decreases. This "paretic condition" of the labyrinth will generate a spontaneous nystagmus directed away from the diseased ear—towards the normal ear, namely in the exactly opposite direction to that in irritative condition.

In some pathological conditions of the inner ear, head shaking or head position change causes vertigo. This may be due to a too sensitive condition of the end-organs and it may be denominated "a hypersensitive condition" of the inner ear.

Generally, in cases of typical Ménière's disease, it is not difficult to determine the affected ear because of the concomitant unilateral cochlear symptoms. However, in cases of vertigo that are not accompanied by cochlear symptoms, such as paroxysmal positional vertigo, the affected ear is clinically difficult to determine. To ascertain the affected labyrinth of patients with no cochlear symptoms, the authors injected 4% lidocaine into the tympanic cavity of the suspected diseased ear. If the injected lidocaine temporarily abolished the patient's vertigo, then it was felt that the diseased ear had been identified.

This paper outlines the case reports of two patients who were thought to have had vertiginous inner ear lesions. These patients presented a horizontal-rotating nystagmus which changed direction during the clinical course. Ménière's disease, and other

†Partly supported by U.S.P.H.S. Research Grant No. NS 10412.

inner ear lesions as well, is thought to provoke a spontaneous nystagmus directed toward the diseased ear (irritative type) during a vertiginous attack. Between the attacks, however, nystagmus is usually directed toward the unaffected ear (paretic type). As the disease progresses with time, the presence of the irritative nystagmus declines. This phenomenon seems to have some theoretical support. Thus, in a patient with a "mature" lesion in the vestibular labyrinth, the spontaneous nystagmus is directed toward the unaffected ear (paretic type) even during a vertiginous attack and this nystagmus and the accompanying vertigo may occasionally be very active.

Case 1. A 46-year-old female. She suffered from vertiginous attacks with concomitant fullness in the left ear since 3 years ago. Hearing impairment in the left ear also appeared during vertiginous attacks. During an attack, the horizontal-rotating nystagmus towards the left was usually observed. The nystagmus between the attacks was directing to the right.

Case 2. A 36-year-old male, with an inner ear vertiginous lesion who subsequently underwent surgical treatment. A portion of the membranous labyrinth was morphologically examined by electron microscope. During vertiginous attacks, this patient presented a left-beating horizontal-rotating nystagmus. However, between attacks a right-beating nystagmus was seen. Since childhood, this patient had had a severe sensorineural hearing loss in the left ear. There were no concomitant cochlear symptoms which accompanied the attacks of vertigo. Lidocaine, injected into the left tympanic cavity, abolished the

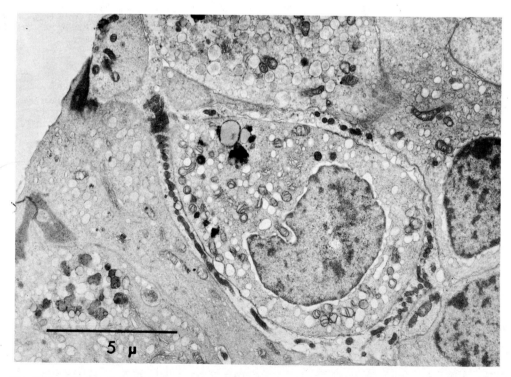

FIG. 1. Type I hair cell in the sensory epithelium of the crista ampullaris, taken from Case 2, a 36-year-old male. Sensory hairs were missing, whereas vacuolization and swollen mitochondria are observed. Contrariwise, nerve chalice (afferent nerve ending) seems normal.

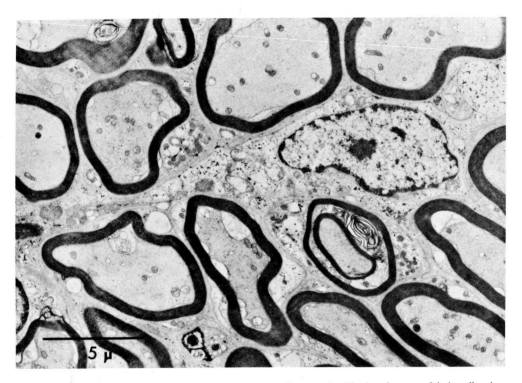

F_{IG}. 2. Nerve fibers of the crista ampullaris in Case 2. Compared with the changes of hair cells, these myelinated fibers maintained good structures. Axons and myelin sheath look normal.

vertigo for a week with a recurrence afterwards, thus indicating an inner ear lesion on this side. A left labyrinthectomy was carried out and this ultimately led to the termination of the vertiginous attacks.

The utricle and ampullae, removed from Case 2 during labyrinthectomy, were examined with an electron microscope. Ultrastructural findings indicated varying degrees of degeneration of the hair cells of the sensory epithelium, i.e. loss of the sensory hairs, vacuolization of the cytoplasm of the hair cells and swelling of the mitochondria (Fig. 1). However, the vestibular nerve fibers and nerve endings showed a less intensive degree of degeneration (Fig. 2). The axon and myelin sheath showed a nearly normal structure. These morphological findings may explain the symptom of "irritation" which existed preoperatively. Namely, the irritation, which was generated within the degenerating sensory cells, must have been conveyed up to the brainstem by the nerve which appeared relatively normal or unaffected.

DISACCOMMODATION:
HABIT REVERSAL IN ESOTROPIA

Stephen Réthy

For my topic as a clinician I have chosen the most frequent clinical cases, those with a rest angle of esotropia. After wearing the so-called full retinoscopic correction for longer periods, a convergent angle is often retained. This part of the squint is supposed to be of "non-accommodative" origin.

The theory of stabilization of the motor impulse pattern (SMIP) offers a hypothesis on the etiology and development of this esotropia with a hint to the possibility of therapy, as well. The SMIP theory claims that the esotropia in most cases is due to the fixed, automatic firing of accommodation and convergence impulses (A + C) owing to previous conditioning.

Distinct vision achieved by accommodation effort in the case of hypermetropic refraction gives a positive reinforcement, which leads, by frequent repetitions, to the automatic stabilization of this behaviour (Donders, 1866; Réthy, 1971).

Stabilization processes of accommodative esotropia can be described in terms of experimental psychology. The operant conditioning of voluntary impulses (Skinner, 1958) is, in our case, more relevant than classical conditioning (Pavlov, 1927).

In order to relax the rest angle of squint an inverse scheme of stimuli was applied for reversal of conditioning. By means of overcorrecting glasses distinct vision reinforces positively the relaxation of accommodation just opposite of the situation before, when distinct vision reinforced the effort of accommodation.

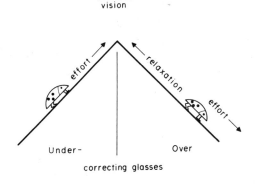

Fig. 1. The automatic robot symbolizes the conditioned use of accommodation in long-standing esotropia. The overcorrecting glasses alter the conditions completely. Now accommodation causes more blur. Distinct vision, the aim of activity, is approached by relaxation of accommodation.

MATERIAL AND METHODS

Twenty unselected children (average 5 years, range from $2\frac{1}{2}$ to $7\frac{3}{4}$ received overcorrection (average $+1.0$ dpt, range from $+0.5$ to 1.5) for a rest angle of esotropia (average $+10°$, range $+5°$ to $+25°$) during the year of 1967 in the Second Eye Clinic of the Medical University of Budapest. The spherically overcorrecting glasses allowed clear vision for the near range only, resembling the condition of low spherical myopia. The astigmatism was corrected very carefully. Atropine instillations were used regularly once a day in the fixating eye wearing the overcorrection. The deviating eye was occluded, usually in a monthly alternating manner. Alternating occlusion was maintained. An instruction sheet made the parents familiar with the purpose of the strange overcorrecting glasses.

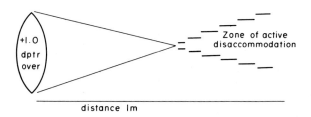

FIG. 2. Stabilized effort of accommodation for distance relaxed by overcorrecting glasses.

Exercises consisted of a series of equally sized small cards were aligned from 30 cm to a distance of 4 m, bearing simple figures. Between the single cards remained spaces of 10 cm. The child wearing the overcorrection calls the name of the nearest, first card. This requires an accommodative effort, which relaxes somewhat looking at the next distant card. The relaxation is immediately positively reinforced by distinct vision. To see the next cards more relaxation is needed, reinforced positively in the same manner. An additional encouraging word of the examiner enhances the reward of distinct vision achieved through the relaxation of the effort.

When for the time being there was no more relaxation possible, the more distant cards were not recognized, the answers were given with much hesitation. The process was repeated with first looking at the near cards. The relaxation became more complete if repeatedly tried: more distant cards in the line were recognized. The exercise is continued for several minutes until the child showed interest in the learning process. The most distant cards recognized correctly were recorded for comparison each day.

RESULTS

The range of distinct vision could be extended as "disaccommodation" was achieved gradually. The maximum relaxation achieved on a certain day was preserved and new extension added by repeated exercises the following days. The "disaccommodation" was achieved step by step. The initial overcorrection was gradually changing into full correction as hypermetropia became manifest. If esotropia was still present, a repeated overcorrection was prescribed and the exercises started again. The effect of

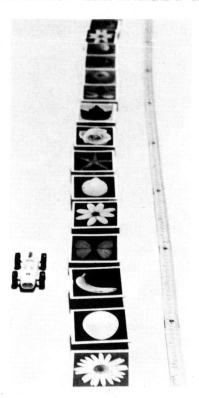

A series of equally sized cards is placed at increasing distances to test visual acuity while accommodation relaxes gradually. The child starts to call the cards one by one proceeding as far as relaxation of accommodation allows distinct vision with the overcorrecting glasses.

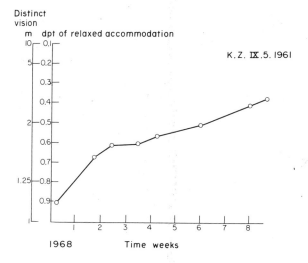

FIG. 4. Effort of accommodation relaxes during repeated exercises. The achieved "disaccommodation" is shown in diopters against the time of wearing the overcorrection. The manifest hypermetropia increases accordingly.

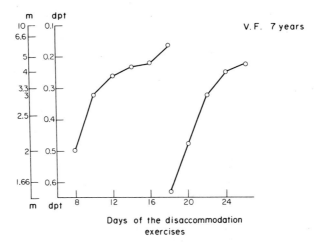

FIG. 5. The exercise can be repeated with a new overcorrection if the squint angle persists. Achievement: More distinct vision for distance by relaxation of the accommodation.

the age on the learning of "disaccommodation" was clearly shown by the sum of monthly achievements of relaxation compared in different age groups. The angle of esotropia decreased in most cases. Intermittent increases of the angle were also observed, due to the more dynamic ability of convergence. The return of intermittent character of formerly stabilized angle was observable in each case. Unfortunately, the sensorimotor treatment could not be finished in Budapest owing to unfavourable external circumstances.

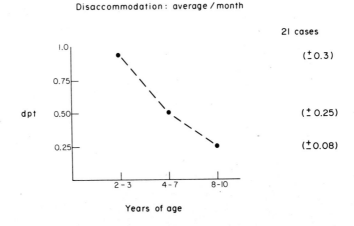

FIG. 6. Possible "disaccommodation" decreases with the increasing age of the patients from 0.9 dpt per month in the youngest age group to 0.25 dpt of relaxation in the oldest age group. The mean error of the three age groups is shown on the right side of the diagram.

DISCUSSION

It has to be stressed that exercises were started only after the "full" correction was provided once or twice and the rest angle was still present. We often see a spontaneous decrease of the angle with correcting glasses. The role of habitual accommodative effort was demonstrated by insistence of the examiner that the child read all cards correctly. Such voluntary effort caused loss of distinctness and the distances of the recognized cards decreased. The vision for distance was best if the cards were called in an effortless, playful manner. Repeated exercises helped the child to correct any of his previous mistakes. The range of distinct vision was slightly better in the morning than in the evening. Squeezing the eyelids in order to see better through a stenopeic opening had to be carefully avoided as a means to replace the relaxation. Every time it occurred, the attention was redirected to the closer region. Campbell and Westheimer (1960) have shown a constant fluctuation of the accommodation as relaxation was reinforced by more distinct vision. The region of fluctuation was moved toward the distance under the influence of the spectacle overcorrection.

The demonstration of the presence of a stabilized accommodative factor in esotropia seems to depend on the skill and determination of the ophthalmologist, who takes the trouble to detect the stabilized hypermetropia (remaining latent in spite of atropine), and to neutralize it by overcorrecting glasses. The ultimate borderlines of such skills cannot be drawn at present. The possibilities of removing the rest angle by early conservative motor therapy—as it can be safely assumed—are surprisingly high in an esotropia population.

SUMMARY

In twenty unselected esotropia patients wearing the full retinoscopic correction from atropine cycloplegia, retained an angle esotropia of $+10°$ (5 to $+25°$). Optical overcorrection from 0.5 to 1.5 diopter was worn before the fixating eye, allowing distinct vision at near only. Exercises were undertaken at home daily twice for 10 minutes teaching the children how to acquire more distinct vision by relaxation of the automatic accommodation effort.

The stabilized motor impulse pattern (SMIP) of esotropia relaxed gradually. The angle of squint was increasingly unstable, due to changes in the static motor impulse pattern. The accommodation used automatically for distant vision relaxed under the influence of the reversed conditioning by the overcorrecting glasses.

REFERENCES

CAMPBELL, F. W. and WESTHEIMER, G. (1960) Dynamics of accommodative responses of the human eye. *J. Physiol.* **151**, 285–295.
DONDERS, F. C. (1866) *Die Anomalien der Refraction und Accommodation des Auges.* Braumüller, Wien.
PAVLOV, I. P. (1927) *Conditioned Reflexes.* Oxford University Press.
RÉTHY, I. (1971) Stabilized accommodative factor in esotropia. *International Ophthal. Clinics*, vol. 11, pp. 27–38. Little Brown Co., Boston.
SKINNER, B. F. (1958) *The Behaviour of Organisms.* Appleton, New York.

OCULAR TORSION AND
THE FUNCTION OF THE VERTICAL
EXTRAOCULAR MUSCLES

Robert S. Jampel

In the physiologically integrated state the eyes in man and monkey either do not undergo conjugate counter-rolling at all or do so to a minimal degree that is wholly insufficient to compensate for head tilt or body displacement or both (Woellner and Graybiel, 1959; Miller, 1962; Davson, 1963; Levine, 1973; Petrov and Zenkin, 1973; Southhall, 1962; Levine, 1969. Even investigators who have demonstrated some slight ocular torsion have not shown that this movement represents a wheel-like rotation around the pupillary axis. This movement could take place around an axis other than the pupillary axis or be the result of translatory movement of the eye. The possibility that the movements are artifacts has not been completely eliminated (Petrov and Zenkin, 1973). With our present limited sophistication in the clinical analysis of ocular motor defects it is best to consider that no compensatory rotation or displacment of the eyes takes place.

In extensive monkey experiments, where the actions of individual and various combinations of extraocular muscles were observed, no wheel-like rotation of the eyes around the pupillary axis was ever produced (Jampel, 1966; Jampel, 1970; 1967). Stimulation of the ocular motor nuclei in the brainstem, the ampullary nerves of the labyrinths, and the frontal eye fields has never resulted in wheel-like ocular rotation (Jampel, 1966). For example, simultaneous stimulation of the SO and superior rectus muscles never produced intortion of the eyes and simultaneous stimulation of the IO and inferior rectus muscles never produced extorsion of the eyes. The mechanical and neurological mechanisms for wheel-rotation of the eyes around the pupillary axis apparently do not exist.

An oblique muscle when caused to act alone experimentally—a situation which never occurs normally—produces a rotary movement of the eye around a fixed eccentric axis which forms an angle in man of about 60 degrees with the Y-axis of Fick. This axis remains *fixed in the orbit* regardless of horizontal eye movements around the Z-axis of Fick. As a result of the location of this axis contraction of an oblique muscle produces an angular rotation of the eye that is equal to the angular displacement of the vertical corneal meridian when projected onto the frontal plane (Figs. 1 and 2). Experimentally in monkeys the oblique muscles when acting alone or in combination with the vertical rectuses never produce a wheel-rotation of the eye around the pupillary axis.

543

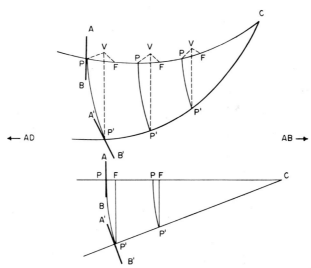

FIG. 1. Superior oblique muscle action in the monkey (*Macaca mulatta*). The anterior axis pole (C) of the rotational axis of the SO remains fixed in the orbit when the eye moves in the horizontal plane (CP) owing to the activity of the horizontal rectuses. A given contraction of the SO causes the pupillary axis (P) to transcribe larger and larger parallel arcs of latitude (P to P′) as the eye moves from a position of abduction (AB) to a position of adduction (AD). Both the outward displacement (PF) of the pupillary axis (P) and the backward displacement (PV) increase as the eye adducts. It can be seen that the angle of ocular rotation (PCP′) is equal to the angle of displacement of the vertical corneal meridian (A′P′F) in all horizontal gaze positions. The lower diagram is the eye movement projected onto a frontal plane.

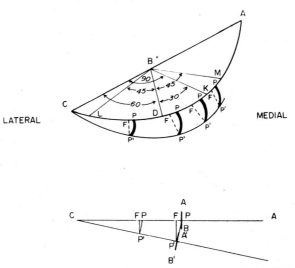

FIG. 2. Diagram of the action of the superior oblique muscle in man. Arc AMKDLC is the horizontal plane. Arc L to M is the approximate range of horizontal ocular movement in man. The rotational axis of the SO line ABC with B the center of rotation of the eye. This axis is located about 60 degrees from line BD which represents the primary position and corresponds to the Y-axis of Fick. When the SO contracts with the eye in any position in the horizontal plane the center of the pupil (P) transcribes an arc of latitude (P to P′). The arc of latitude has three components—down, lateral (PF), and back into the orbit. These components increase in magnitude until the eye rotates 90 degrees (to point K) from the rotational axis (line ABC) after which they decrease. Angle ACP′ is equal to angle A′P′F and, hence, the angle of ocular rotation is equal to the angular displacement of the corneal meridian (lines AB and A′B′ in the lower diagram).

Thus, there is no compensatory conjugate counter-rolling of the eyes to head tilt in order to maintain the retinal horizon parallel to the terrestial horizon. Also, the oblique muscles appear incapable of producing wheel-like rotation of the eyes or any significant ocular torsion, for that matter, in the normal state.

Thus, the neurological mechanisms that govern the vertical extraocular muscles and the structure of these muscles appear designed to inhibit or *prevent ocular rolling or torsion* and to maintain the eyes in a stable position relative to that of the head, i.e. to keep the vertical corneal meridian as parallel as possible to the sagittal plane of the head. Thus, when the head or body or both are inclined the vertical muscles acting together hold the eyes in a stable position. Any small residual torsional movements that may exist might be vestigial. Having maintained the eyes stable the vertical extraocular muscles, which in the normal state are neither significant tortors nor horizontal ductors, are then capable of working in concert to produce elevation or depression of the eyes with the head or body in any position or posture.

When the head or body is tilted the vertical corneal meridia are held parallel to the sagittal plane of the head. Therefore, the insertions of the extraocular muscles are displaced equal to the angle of head tilt from their original positions. The insertions of the horizontal recti, for example, are no longer parallel to the horizon and yet the eye with the head tilted as capable of a smooth pursuit or saccadic movement in the terrestial horizontal plane. Such a movement is difficult to explain employing what is already known about ocular mechanics. It is possible that there is an innervational shift or redistribution among the vertical and horizontal extraocular muscles produced by head tilt or body displacement that enables such an eye movement to take place. Also, in the head-erect position the innervations for elevation and depression of the eyes are sent to both the vertical rectuses and obliques although not necessarily equally. When the head is tilted innervation may be shifted to the vertical rectuses in the contralateral eye and to the obliques in the homolateral eye for the production of elevation and depression. This is suggested by some cases of superior oblique paralysis in man in which the oblique muscles appear to have little or no function in the homolateral eye when the head is tilted to the contralateral side (Fig. 3). The otolith organs of the vestibular apparatus may be responsible for this innervational shift.

Torsional displacement of the vertical corneal meridian takes place only in pathological conditions (not to be confused with so-called pseudotorsion seen in normal oblique gazes) such as extraocular muscle paralysis or nystagmus and in certain abnormal phorias and tropias, but this displacement has never been seen to be wheel-like, i.e. it does not take place around the pupillary axis.

Spatial orientation and the recognition of an "objective" vertical when the head tilts or when the body is displaced is maintained in spite of the fact that there are no compensatory eye movements. The mechanisms responsible for this phenomenon reside in the brain or in an interplay between the retina and the brain and not in the peripheral ocular motor apparatus. Recent experiments indicate that cyclofusion can take place without ocular movement (Kertesz, 1972). Also, wheel-like rotational eye movements (cycloduction) around the pupillary axis do not take place and torsional displacement of the vertical corneal meridian is always associated with a vertical ocular displacement. Thus visual sensory adaptations to body and head inclinations are not dependent on compensatory eye movements and certainly not on ocular torsion around the pupillary axis.

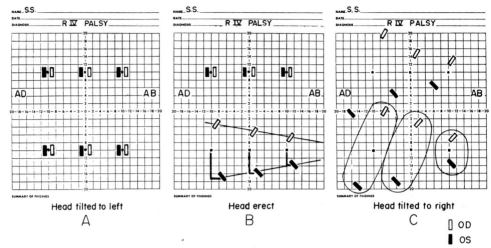

FIG. 3. The Lancaster red–green projection test in isolated superior oblique muscle paralysis (see text). (A) The projections are normal when the head is tilted to the contralateral shoulder. (B) With the head erect the projections are abnormal in horizontal gaze (not shown) and in downward gaze. In downward gaze the vertical projections undergo the greatest vertical and lateral displacement (abduction) in the position of adduction (AD). The angular displacements of the vertical projections to the horizontal plane are the same in all gaze positions. (C) The projections are abnormal in all gaze positions when the eye is tilted to the homolateral shoulder.

SUMMARY

1. The vertical corneal meridia are not kept perpendicular to the horizon in human and non-human primates when the head or body are titled, i.e. compensatory counter-rolling of the eyes does not occur. The slight torsional displacement of the vertical corneal meridia noted by many observers may be the result of rotation around an axis other than the pupillary axis or due to translation of the globe.

2. The neurological and structural systems that control the actions of the vertical muscles in human and non-human primates do not appear to provide a mechanism for wheel-rotation of the eyes around the visual line.

3. Ocular torsion is not a normal function of the vertical extraocular muscles. Their function is probably the reverse, i.e. *the inhibition or prevention of ocular torsion* and the stabilization of the eyes when the head or body inclines. Torsional displacement of a vertical corneal meridian occurs only when there is an abnormal muscle imbalance.

4. Wheel-like movements (cycloduction) around the pupillary axis or visual line do not occur. Torsional displacement of a vertical corneal meridian occurs only with a simultaneous vertical movement (8).

5. The vertical rectuses and the oblique muscles in man work together to produce vertical ocular movements regardless of head position or body posture while maintaining the vertical corneal meridia parallel to the sagittal plane of the head. It is suggested that the vestibular apparatus may be responsible for distributing innervations among these muscles enabling them to function in this manner.

REFERENCES

DAVSON, H. (1963) *The Physiology of the Eye*. London, Churchill.
JAMPEL, R. S. Unpublished observations.

JAMPEL, R. S. (1966) The action of the superior oblique muscles. *Arch. Ophthal.* **75**, 535–544.

JAMPEL, R. S. (1967) Experimental evaluation of the ocular rolling (torsion) in the Macaque. *Proceedings of the Annual Conference on Engineering in Medicine and Biology,* **9**, 76.

JAMPEL, R. S. (1970) The fundamental principle of the action of the oblique ocular muscles. *Am. J. Ophthal.* **69**, 623–638.

KERTESZ, A. E. (1972) The effect of stimulus complexity on human cyclofusional response. *Vision Res.* **12**, 699–704.

LEVINE, M. (1969) Evaluation of the Bielschowsky head-tilt test. *Arch. Ophthal.* **82**, 433–439.

LEVINE, M. (1973) Pendulum-like eye movement. *Am. J. Ophthal.* **75**, 979–987.

MILLER, E. F. (1962) Counterrolling of the human eyes produced by head tilt with respect to gravity. *Acta Oto-laryng.* **54**, 479–501.

PETROV, A. and ZENKIN, G. M. (1973) Torsional eye movements and constancy of the visual field. *Vision Res.* **13**, 2465–2477.

SOUTHALL, J. (1962) *Helmholtz's Treatise on Physiological Optics,* Vol. III, pp. 120, 139. New York, Dover Publications, Inc.

WOELLNER, R. C. and GRAYBIEL, A. (1959) Counterrolling of the eyes and its dependence on the magnitude of gravitational or inertial forces acting laterally on the body. *J. Appl. Physiol.* **14**, 632–634.

CHRONIC PROGRESSIVE EXTERNAL OPHTHALMOPLEGIA—A NEURO-MUSCULAR DISORDER?

W. Schlote and F. Körner

The question whether eye muscle paresis in chronic progressive external ophthalmoplegia (CPEO) is of neurogenic or myogenic origin is still unresolved. Clinically, progressive ophthalmoplegia may be associated with a variety of heredo-degenerative central nervous system disorders such as spinocerebellar degeneration, epilepsy, cerebral deafness, mental retardation, Refsum's syndrome and diseases of the lower motor neuron. Therefore, a nuclear atrophy was originally believed to be the cause of progressive ophthalmoplegia.

Arguments in favor of the myogenic origin coming from histologic and EMG studies were repeatedly claimed to be limited because of the special arrangement of ocular motor units (Daroff, 1969; Drachman et al., 1969).

This is to report six cases of CPEO, two of them have already been subject of a preliminary paper (Körner and Schlote, 1972). The clinical data are summarized on Table 1. The EMG was nearly uniformly myopathic with low amplitude and well-preserved interference pattern of action potentials, in contrast to the severe degree

TABLE 1

Case		1 Ja	2 Bi	3 Ni	4 Fu	5 Gr	6 Wi
Sex		M	M	F	F	M	M
Age of onset		14	14	19	12	10?	6
Heredity		−	+	−	−	−	−
Ptosis		+	+	(+)	+	+ +	+ +
External ophthalmoplegia		+ +	+ +	+ +	+ +	+ + +	+ +
Eye muscle EMG		myo	myo	myo	myo?	myo	myo
Pigmentary retinopathy		+	+ +	+	+	+ + +	−
Facial weakness		+	+	−	−	+	+
Limb muscle weakness		−	−	(+)	−	+	+
ECG abnormalities		−	−	−	(+)	+	(+)
Increase of	CPK	186	1329	271	160	20	640
muscle specific	ALD	144	224	120	55	84	113
serum enzymes	LDH	126	150	77	68	113	122
Increase of urine creatine		+	+ + +	−	+ + +	−	+ +
EEG abnormalities		−		−	−	+	+
Increase of CSF protein						−	+ +
Other neurologic disorders		−	−	−	−	−	+

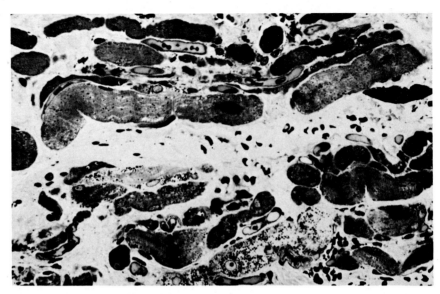

FIG. 1. Semithin section of muscle biopsy from glutaraldehyde-fixed, araldite-embedded material. CPEO, case 2. Variation of fiber diameter and of stainability of muscle fibers. Loss of cross striation over wide distances. Granular material fills some of the muscle cells. Toluidine blue staining. 320:1.

of muscular paresis. Muscle specific serum enzymes—expressed as percentage of the normal upper limit which was set at 100—were increased in all cases. In cases 5 and 6 the EEG was abnormal. In case 6 there was, in addition, a marked increase of CSF-protein, cerebellar involvement and neural hearing loss.

Histologically, all cases showed severe pathologic lesions in extraocular muscle biopsies (Fig. 1). The nerves between these degenerating muscle fibers were normal. Deltoid muscle biopsies in cases 5 and 6 with pronounced limb muscle weakness revealed an involvement of the skeletal muscle with unequivocal variability of fiber diameter and atrophic fibers with vacuolar alterations.

The electron microscope confirmed the severe alterations of extraocular muscles (Fig. 2) and showed a marked variety of type and degree of degeneration from fiber to fiber: vacuolar disintegration, focal accumulation of abnormal mitochondria with circular or linear arrangement of cristae, multinuclear muscle cells with abnormal organelles, atrophic fibers with enlarged mitochondria, lipid inclusions, dense rod-like or granular material in the sarcoplasma, disoriented and disintegrating myofilaments. The nerve fibers in these diseased extraocular muscles were nearly intact; at places, dense osmiophilic bodies were seen in the axon or inner Schwann cell cytoplasm between axon and myelin sheath.

We had the opportunity to compare these findings in cases of CPEO with those in one case of posttraumatic ocular paresis. The patient, 35 years of age, had had a traffic accident with head trauma and contusio cerebri. Immediately after the accident he suffered from a paralysis of both abducens nerves. The EMG of both lateral rectus muscles indicated a neurogenic lesion. Three months later a muscle biopsy was performed during an operative correction. Under the light microscope the fibers were small, of polygonal shape, sometimes arranged in a mosaic-like pattern, without any grouping of atrophic fibers. Electronmicroscopically, the rather uniform atrophic type

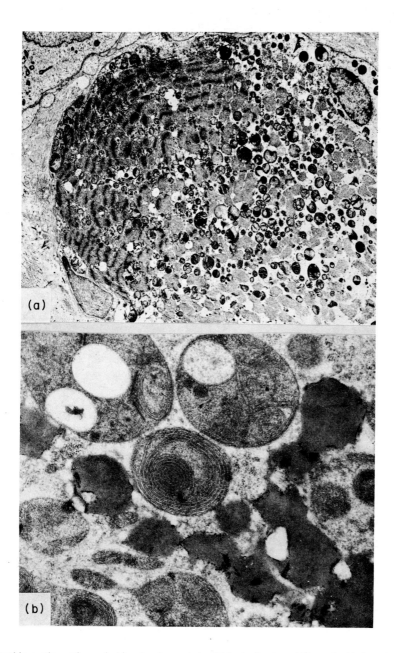

FIG. 2. Ultrathin sections of muscle biopsies from glutaraldehyde fixed, araldite embedded material. CPEO. (a) Case 2. Large muscle fiber, part of which is filled with rounded, abnormal mitochondria replacing myofibrils. 4800:1. (b) Case 1. Enlarged mitochondria with para-cristalline, circular arrangement of cristae and lipid inclusions of irregular shape in the sarcoplasm. 24,500:1.

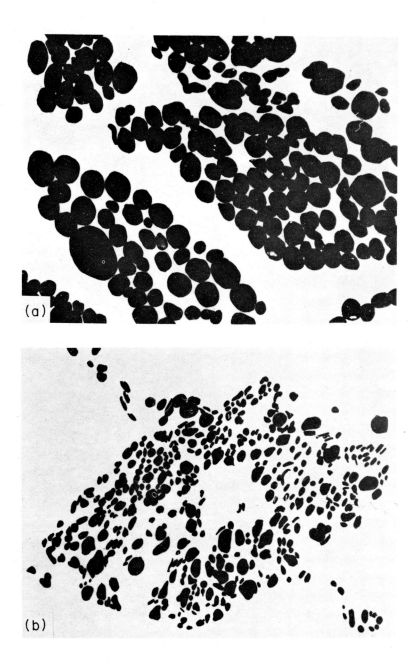

FIG. 3. Size and distribution pattern of muscle fibers in transversal sections of extraocular eye muscle biopsies. Tracings from photographed semithin sections. 380: 1. (a) Inferior oblique in CPEO, case 5. Rounded fibers of varying diameter. (b) Lateral rectus in post-traumatic paralysis with neurogenic muscle atrophy. Small fibers of polygonal shape, arranged in a mosaic-like pattern.

of the alteration was evident. The number of myofilaments was reduced without gross desorientation. Only occasionally, disintegration of myofilaments occurred. The basement membranes of the small atrophic fibers have maintained their original length, are therefore too wide and arranged in loose bands in a manner characteristic of atrophic fibers which was never seen in cases of CPEO. In the nerves, most of myelinated nerve fibers have disappeared and are replaced by connective tissue.

Tracings from transversal sections of the biopsied muscles demonstrate clearly the different size and distribution pattern of muscle fibers in one of the cases of CPEO (Fig. 3a) and in the case with the neurogenic lesion (Fig. 3b).

What do these findings mean with view of the pathogenesis of chronic progressive ophthalmoplegia? In a light microscopic study after experimental denervation of extraocular muscles in monkeys, Drachman et al. (1969) described alterations of muscle tissue which they could not distinguish from lesions in cases of CPEO. Though we have been able to show a completely different histologic pattern of neurogenic type of muscular lesion in human case, we do not believe that this finding would be crucial concerning the elucidation of pathogenesis of CPEO. If this disease is a neurogenic disorder, the muscle must not necessarily show the same type of lesion as after complete acute denervation. In slowly progressive neuro-muscular diseases, the axons do not simply disappear as in Wallerian degeneration. The axonal metabolism and transport of substances along the axon may be disturbed without axonal disintegration, the trophic influence upon the muscle may be altered and may cause structural changes of muscle tissue displaying not necessarily the picture characteristic of the pure atrophic type of lesion. Nevertheless, we feel that the severe alteration of muscle cells with abnormal organelles in the cases of CPEO, the well-preserved nerve fibers in chronic states of the disease, the involvement of the skeletal muscle in two of our cases as in many cases of the literature, are fair arguments against a neurogenic disease and in favor of a disorder of muscle cell metabolism (myopathy). In CPEO with involvement of the central nervous system (our cases 5 and 6), which are reported in increasing number (Daroff, 1969), a combined degenerative process of striated muscle and nervous system can be argued. This view is corroborated by the recent finding by Adachi et al. (1973) who found the same type of abnormal mitochondria in extraocular muscle and in the cerebellum in a case of CPEO with cerebellar ataxia. A single gene with polymorphic effects and comparable expression in muscle and brain is presumably causative in cases of this type.

REFERENCES

ADACHI, M., TORII, J., VOLK, B. W., BRIET, P., WOLINTZ, A. and SCHNECK, L. (1973) Electron microscopical and enzyme histochemical studies of cerebellum, ocular and skeletal muscles in chronic progressive ophthalmoplegia with cerebellar ataxia. Acta Neuropath. (Berlin) 23, 300–312.
DAROFF, R. B. (1969) Chronic progressive ophthalmoplegia. A critical review. Arch. Ophthal. 84, 845–850.
DRACHMAN, D. A., WETZEL, N., WASSERMANN, N. and NAITO, H. (1969) Experimental denervation of ocular muscles. A critic of the concept of "ocular myopathy". Arch. Neurol. 21, 170–183.
KÖRNER, F. and SCHLOTE, W. (1972) Chronic progressive external ophthalmoplegia. Association with retinal pigmentary changes and evidence in favor of ocular myopathy. Arch. Ophthal. 88, 155–166.

EYE POSITION CONTROL AND VISUAL ACUITY IN STRABISMUS AMBLYOPIA†

C. M. SCHOR and M. C. FLOM

INTRODUCTION

CLINICIANS and researchers frequently comment on the abnormal movements of amblyopic eyes. Two basic questions are: "What aspect of eye position control is abnormal in amblyopic eyes?" and "How do abnormal movements of amblyopic eyes relate to their reduction in visual acuity?" The two experiments that follow were conducted in an attempt to answer these two questions.

EYE POSITION DURING ATTEMPTED STEADY MONOCULAR FIXATION

Methods

In our first experiment, subjects were required to fixate for two half-minute periods a small (1.5 min arc diam.), bright (40 ft-L), stationary spot that was presented to one eye against a dim (3 ft-L) background. Infrared sensitive photodiodes (Texas Instruments LS-400) aimed at the limbus were used to signal horizontal eye movements within an accuracy of 12 min arc.

Five young-adult amblyopes and one nonamblyope were studied. Two of the amblyopes had esotropia, two had exotropia, and one had a history of strabismus and had recently lost his normal eye through injury. Acuity in the amblyopic eyes ranged from 20/40 to 20/400. Lenses which neutralized the refractive error were used during the experiment. The experimental task of monocular fixation was required of the normal and amblyopic eye of three subjects. Representative records of horizontal eye movements from one normal eye (Subject C. S.) and three amblyopic eyes (Subjects R. C., D. H. and R. M.) with acuities respectively 20/40, 20/70 and 20/400 are shown in the accompanying figure.

Results

All the normal and amblyopic eyes exhibited slow, "drifting" eye movements as well as rapid, "saccadic" eye movements. The drifts were similar (in amplitude, duration, velocity, and direction) in the normal and amblyopic eyes. Drift direction was preferentially nasalward in seven of the nine eyes tested. Nasal and temporal drifts occurred

†This research was supported by a Health Education and Welfare Postdoctoral fellowship No. 2 FO 2 EY 33987-03 sponsored by the University of California at Berkeley.

equally often for only two eyes: the normal eye of one exotrope, and the amblyopic eye of the other exotrope (Subject R. M., Fig. 1).

Saccades, on the other hand, were substantially different for the two groups of eyes, mainly in terms of amplitude. Saccades amplitudes were larger for the amblyopic eyes (medians ranging from 40 to 200 min arc) than for the normal eyes (medians ranging from 10 to 35 min arc).

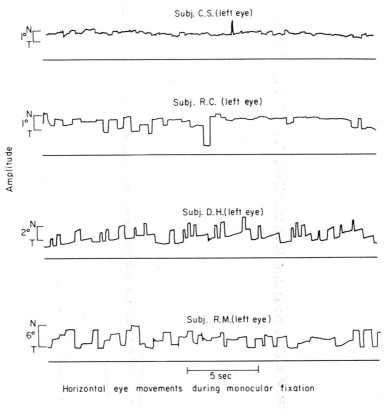

FIG. 1. Representative records of horizontal eye movements during attempted steady fixation from one normal eye (Subject C. S.) and three amblyopic eyes (Subjects R. C., D. H. and R. M.) with acuities respectively of 20/40, 20/70, and 20/400.

In analyzing the eye-movement records, movements away from the "preferred" fixation site were identified as "error producing", and movements toward this site were considered "error correcting". As already mentioned, most of the eyes tested exhibited nasalward drifts; these drift movements were typically away from the preferred fixation site and were therefore error-producing movements. Comparatively, saccades tended to be temporalward and toward the preferred fixation site, indicating that most saccades were error correcting. However, the proportion of temporal to nasal saccades was considerably less than the proportion of nasal to temporal drifts. The interpretation of this analysis is that many saccades were error producing.

Inspection of individual subject's recordings in the accompanying figure shows that although saccades most often reduced the fixation error, they frequently contributed to the fixation error. Thus, for the amblyopic eyes, fixational errors were typically produced by some combination of nasalward drifts and/or saccades; correctional eye movements consisted of one or more temporalward saccades. The error-producing and the error-correcting saccades tended to be of about the same amplitude for a given eye, this saccade amplitude being larger the worse the acuity in the amblyopic eye (Spearman rank correlation between saccade amplitude and acuity is -1.0, $p < 0.01$). Saccade amplitude is related to acuity reasonably linearly when acuity is expressed as Snell–Sterling percent efficiency. The linear regression equation from which saccade amplitude (in min arc) is predicted from the acuity (in Snell-Sterling percent) is:

$$\text{Saccade amplitude} = 167 - 1.4 \text{ (S.S.\%).}$$

Thus, for example, an amblyopic eye with acuity of 20/97 (Snellen) or 50% (Snell–Sterling) would be expected to have a median saccade amplitude of 97 min arc. Similarly, an amblyopic eye with acuity of 20/45 (Snellen) or 80% (Snell–Sterling) would be expected to have a median saccade amplitude of 54 min arc. For normal acuities of 20/20 and 20/15, the expected saccade amplitudes are, respectively, 27 and 20 min arc. From these results, it appears that one could quickly estimate the approximate median expected saccade amplitude by simply expressing the 20-foot Snellen "denominator" in minutes of arc:

$$\text{Saccade amplitude} \simeq \text{Snellen "denominator".}$$

EXPERIMENT ON VISUAL ACUITY AND RETINAL LOCUS

Methods

Single, Landolt rings (oriented in one of four positions) were presented against a bright (50 ft-L) field using the method of constant stimuli. Three retinal loci were investigated:

1. fovea of normal eye;
2. fovea of amblyopic eye;
3. usual fixing locus of amblyopic eye.

In presenting the acuity target to the fovea of the amblyopic eye, the subject viewed the entoptic image of the macula (Maxwell's spot) onto which the Landolt ring was projected through an optical system that used the subject's eye movement signals to *stabilize* the retinal image in the foveal center to within 12 min arc.

One amblyope (T.B.) was studied in the experiment. She had 10Δ of constant left esotropia with harmonious anomalous correspondence. The left amblyopic eye had acuity of 20/50 and 1 degree of unsteady, nasal eccentric fixation.

Results

Psychometric analysis of the results show the 50% threshold (corrected for guessing) acuity to be 20/10 at the normal fovea, 20/36 at the amblyopic fovea (stabilized image), and 20/65 at the usual fixing locus of the amblyopic eye. It is not surprising that the foveal acuity of the normal eye was better than the acuity obtained at the usual retinal fixing site of the amblyopic eye. Indeed, this difference in visual acuity defines the amblyopia. What is noteworthy is the acuity in the amblyopic eye being better at its fovea (20/36) than at its usual retinal fixing site (20/65).

These results raise the question of why this subject exhibits such consistent nasalward monocular fixational errors with a time-average fixational error of about 1 deg arc (60 min arc) nasal to the fovea. Surely, these eye movements on attempted steady monocular fixation cannot be occurring to enhance visual acuity—for acuity at the fovea with no target movement is 20/36, and in the eccentric nasal retina with considerable target motion across the retina acuity is 20/65.

DISCUSSION

From the results of our two experiments, we can provide at least partial answers to the two questions originally posed.

"What aspects of eye position control is abnormal in amblyopic eyes?"
Drifts during attempted steady fixation were preferentially nasalward but were normal in other respects. Saccades were larger in amblyopic than normal eyes, their amplitude being proportional to the acuity loss. Some saccades were nasalward and they caused position errors. Most saccades corrected position errors. The time average position of all amblyopic eyes tested was nasalward (eccentric fixation). The large nasalward position errors appear to result from a regional loss of position sensitivity (dead zone) which extends from the fovea onto the nasal hemiretina. Some amblyopes (Subject D. H.) compensated for their oculomotor dead zone by adopting fixation strategies of prompt firing of error producing saccades which led to detectable position errors. In this manner the eye's position was sensed and corrective movements were then able to be executed.

"How do abnormal movements of amblyopic eyes relate to their visual acuity?"
Nasalward "off foveal" position errors reduced visual acuity in the one subject tested (Subject T. B.) because the retinal image was located away from her fovea at a less sensitive eccentric retinal site. The abnormal motion itself of all amblyopic eyes tested appeared to have little affect on visual acuity. For example, saccadic motions which have high velocities (Westheimer, 1954) and are associated with visual suppression (Ditchburn, 1955; Zuber and Stark, 1966) probably did not impair visual acuity since there was adequate time for the amblyopic eye to see during the interval between the saccades (500 ms). Drifting motion of the eye during the intersaccadic interval probably did not impair resolution since drift amplitudes and velocities were identical in our normal and amblyopic eyes. Thus, the abnormal *position* of the amblyopic eye, but not its *motion* is partially responsible for reduced visual acuity.

What conditions lead to abnormal eye position control in amblyopia? Suppression of a turned eye (strabismus) during early childhood is thought to disrupt the development of normal visual acuity in amblyopia (Worth, 1921; Chavasse, 1939). The suppression associated with strabismus is regional extending from the fovea of the turned eye onto the hemiretina which normally receives the image of the fixated object (Jampolsky, 1955). Nasal hemiretinal suppression is most commonly observed in amblyopia (Irvine, 1948) since most amblyopes with strabismus (75%) have esotropia (Glover and Brewer, 1944). The oculomotor dead zone exhibited by the amblyopic eyes in our study occupied the nasal hemiretina and is presumably responsible for their abnormal eye-position control. Thus, the nasal hemiretinal suppression that occurs in esotropia constitutes a deprivation which leads to a sensory impairment in the form of reduced foveal visual acuity and reduced eye-position-error detection, the latter having an immediate consequence in the development of abnormal eye-position control.

REFERENCES

CHAVASSE, F. B. (1939) *Worth's Squint*, 7th ed. Philadelphia, Pa., Blackiston's Son and Co. Inc.

DITCHBURN, R. W. (1955) Eye movements in relation to retinal action. *Optical Acta* **1**, 171.

GLOVER, L. P. and BREWER, W. R. (1944) An ophthalmalogic review of more than twenty thousand men at the Altoona Induction Center. *Am. J. Ophthal.* **27** (4), 346.

IRVINE, S. R. (1948) Amblyopia ex anopsia: observation on retinal inhibition, scotoma, projection, light difference discrimination and visual acuity. *Trans. of Am. Ophthal. Soc.* **46**, 527.

JAMPOLSKY, A. J. (1955) Characteristics of suppression in strabismus. *A.M.A. Arch. Ophthal.* **54**, 683.

WESTHEIMER, G. (1954) Mechanism of saccadic eye movements. *Am. Arch. of Ophthal.* **52**, 710.

WORTH, C. A. (1921) Discussion on the treatment of concomitant convergent squint. *Trans. Ophthal. Soc. U.K.* **41**, 149.

ZUBER, B. L. and STARK, L. (1966) Saccadic suppression: elevation of visual threshold associated with saccadic eye movements. *Exptl Neurol.* **16**, 65.

LONG-TERM OCULOMOTOR CONSEQUENCES OF UNILATERAL COLLICULECTOMY IN MAN

S. Heywood and G. Ratcliff

P. L., a 38-year old right-handed, right-eye dominant man, had an operation for the removal of an angioma, centred on the right superior colliculus. The operation was performed by Mr. Christopher Adams at the Radcliffe Infirmary in Oxford, and we are grateful to him and to Dr. John Oxbury, into whose care P. L. came, for allowing us to see their patient. Immediately after the operation P. L. had a complete hemianopia which shrank and effectively disappeared by post-op week 7, and during the immediate post-operative period he showed loss of upward gaze, convergence, spontaneous contralateral gaze and pupillary responses to light. This was followed by the return of convergence but a persistent loss of upward gaze and a very long latency for contralateral eye movements which were sometimes led by the head. There were short-term visuo-spatial difficulties including visual neglect, and difficulties with reading, counting dot rows and closure of fragmented figures. There was also an impairment in pointing, where the difference in error between pointing to a visual target in the contralateral and ipsilateral half-field was just outside normal limits. (The visual field defect and visuo-spatial disorder are compatible with the existence of damage to the occipital lobes or LGN during the operation; some bleeding into cortex was reported.) P. L. also complained of perceptual abnormalities: objects appeared to move or displace, to stretch and to seem abnormally tall. These may have been related to his oculomotor difficulties.

We carried out, in the seventeenth post-operative week, some specific tests to see whether there were any detectable long-term oculomotor abnormalities. By this time, to ordinary inspection, there were no differences between P. L.'s horizontal eye movements and those of any normal person; his perceptual and visuo-spatial problems had cleared up and pupillary responses to light, though sluggish, were present. Unfortunately we had to use a relatively inaccurate EOG technique and to instruct P. L. to stabilize his head by holding it firmly against supporting pads at the base of the skull, since he could not remain on a bite-bar. We recorded only horizontal eye movements, with a resolution of only 2°. Three experiments were done. In the first, we looked at spontaneous saccades in the dark with no specific instructions to the subject. In the second we looked at latencies of saccades to visual targets appearing left and right of a fixation point that was extinguished at the moment of target onset. Finally we examined P. L.'s ability to use information about his own eye movements and eye position to control subsequent eye movements.

In the first experiment, we found quite abnormal distributions of saccades. In a total of 8.7 min of observation, we counted 141 saccades of which 117 were ipsilateral to the lesion. A slow drift contralateral to the lesion appeared to enable P. L. to maintain a roughly constant line of sight. None out of nine normal subjects under comparable conditions showed a similar significant asymmetry of saccades. Furthermore, P. L.'s saccade rate, for saccades greater than 2°, of 0.27/sec is about half that of normal subjects for the same size of saccades, who had a mean rate of 0.51/sec (range: 0.41–0.83/sec). There is therefore a marked reduction of frequency of spontaneous saccades contralateral to the lesion, when P. L. is sitting in the dark.

In the second experiment we examined latencies of saccades to small targets at two distances to the left and right of a central fixation point, which were presented after an auditory warning. No differences in mean latencies for saccades in either direction were found, and all latencies were within normal limits. However, two aspects of the data did distinguish between eye movements contralateral to the lesion and those ipsilateral to it. Firstly, the frequency of correction saccades was significantly higher for a target contralateral to the lesion and secondly, the proportion of trials with anticipatory eye movements (defined as saccades with a latency of less than 60 ms and which were excluded from the main analysis of latencies) rose from 10% for ipsilateral saccades to 42% for contralateral saccades.

Finally, we examined P. L.'s use of corollary discharge and/or proprioceptive information to control eye movements, by having him match saccade sizes in the dark. In this experiment, P. L. looked away to one side, paused and then looked back to where he started from. He repeated this five times in one direction, then five times in the other and so on until he completed twenty trials in each direction. We measured the error between his starting-point and the position of the eyes after the first return saccade ($Diff_1$) and after all return saccades ($Diff_2$); we also measured the numbers and sizes of saccades made. Condition OutL is the condition in which the subject looks away to the left and back to the right, and condition OutR is the opposite.

Normal right-handed, right-eye-dominant subjects show an asymmetry in the accuracy and skill with which they perform this task, being worse on condition OutL, i.e. when they are returning from the left (Heywood, 1973 a, b). P. L. and normals are compared in Table 1.

P. L. is in fact just outside normal limits for OutL on $Diff_2$. On $Diff_1$, one normal subject made massive errors by making a very small initial saccade on the return stage in condition OutL. P. L. is considerably worse on $Diff_1$ than any other normal subject.

However, there are definitely gross differences in the way P. L. performs the task. Figure 1 shows tracings of the eye movements of a representative normal subject and of P. L. in the two conditions. There is a marked difference in the number and in the sizes of P. L.'s saccades going to the left (contralateral to his lesion) compared with the normal subject. P. L. makes more saccades than any normal subject going to the left whether on the outward or return stages, significantly more than he makes going to the right (Table 2). His saccades on the outward stage going to the left are significantly smaller than those on the outward stage going to the right, unlike any normal subject. Finally, the variance of the mean total distance travelled out to the left by P. L. is significantly greater than the variance of the mean total distance to the right; again, this is not the case for any normal subject. Thus there is a disin-

TABLE 1. DIFFERENCE IN DEGREES BETWEEN MEAN ERROR FOR CONDITIONS, OutL AND OutR

Normal	Diff₁ OutL–OutR	Diff₂ OutL–OutR
N.O.	3.02	1.96
J.H.	1.74	0.18
T.T.	2.2	−1.19
G.C.	0.23	0.79
P.W.	6.25	0.95
Mean	2.69	0.54
Subject P.L.	4.26	2.09

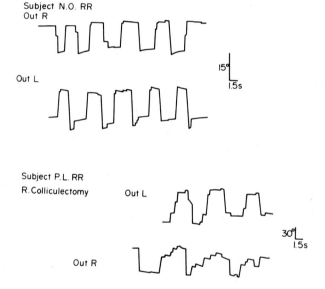

FIG. 1. Tracings of EOG recordings for a representative normal subject and for P. L., matching saccades in the dark under two conditions. Notice the fragmentation of P. L.'s leftwards saccades (contralateral to his lesion). Rightwards eye movements downwards.

TABLE 2. MEAN NUMBERS OF SACCADES PER TRIAL

		Condition OutL	OutR
Mean number of saccades on *outward* stage	Normals	1.5 (1.2–2.05)	1.63 (1.11–2.15)
	Subject P.L.	2.47	1.39
Mean number of saccades on *return* stage	Normals	1.79 (1.45–2.16)	1.48 (1.05–1.9)
	Subject P.L.	1.8	2.39

tegration of P. L.'s eye movements going contralateral to his lesion; there are more, smaller saccades and a greater variability of total distance travelled.

An alternative way of looking at the data tends to confirm that, for P. L., returning from the left is relatively less accurate than it is for normals. The mean total distance travelled out minus that travelled back per trial gives a rough measure of the extent to which over all trials the eye matches its total outward excursion with its total return distance. In condition OutL, the mean difference for normals between the distance travelled out and back is 1.2° (range: 0.87–1.66°). For P. L. it is no less than 3.18°; whereas for condition OutR there is no difference between P. L. and normals.

This major difference in condition OutL between P. L. and normals cannot be solely due to his motor problems with contralateral saccades since, of course, these are involved in both OutL and OutR conditions. It might be due, therefore, either to a specific difficulty in getting appropriate information from fragmented, multiple saccade outward stages (common in condition OutL), or to a deficit in the ability to process corollary discharge information from eye movements contralateral to the lesion. Some support for this latter hypothesis comes from the fact that the mean final position error ($Diff_2$) on trials with multiple saccade outward stages to the left (5.87°) is significantly greater than on those few with multiple saccade outward stages to the right (2.87°). However, the very small samples and the large variance must make this conclusion tentative.

In summary, after marked short-term oculomotor deficits, P. L. shows residual abnormalities of upward gaze, and of contralateral saccades in terms not only of frequency, but of size and consistency. There may also be losses in the skill with which he can use information about his eye movements and eye position contralateral to his lesion.

REFERENCES

HEYWOOD, S. P. (1973a) Asymmetries in returning the eyes to specified target positions in the dark. *Vision Res.* **13**, 81–94.

HEYWOOD, S. P. (1973b) Retinal and extra-retinal control of eye movements. Unpublished D. Phil. Thesis, Oxford University.

NON-VISUAL CONTROL OF
HUMAN SACCADIC EYE
MOVEMENTS

F. H. Körner

INTRODUCTION

The trajectory of saccadic eye movements depends on the processing of visual sensory information and on the specific activity of a pool of oculomotor units. In clinical cases, a slow-down of saccades, for instance, may indicate peripheral, nuclear, or supranuclear disorders of the oculomotor system. However, visual sensory deficits may also change certain characteristics of saccadic eye movements and this should be differentiated from impairments of primary motor centers. A comparative analysis of visually guided saccades and "non-visual saccades" that were executed in the dark, could provide new aspects for our clinical diagnosis of oculomotor disorders and also may increase information about our knowledge of the physiological control of saccadic eye movements.

In former investigations "non-visual" saccadic eye movements have already been studied (Jeannerod et al., 1965; Jeannerod, 1971; Becker and Fuchs, 1969; Dichgans et al., 1969; Becker and Klein, 1972; Ron et al., 1972). Essentially the authors agree, that saccades (including quick phases of nystagmus) are slower in the dark and even slower with the eyes closed. It has also been shown that it is impossible to accurately reproduce the amplitude of saccades under non-visual conditions.

Less attention has been paid to the relationship between amplitudes and velocity or duration of non-visual saccades, to the possible influence of non-visual sensory inputs, and to the significance of secondary or so-called corrective saccades in the dark.

CHARACTERISTICS OF
NON-VISUAL HUMAN SACCADIC
EYE MOVEMENTS

Saccades were recorded electro-oculographically from fifty subjects with normal oculomotor functions. After a training-period of ten saccades with lights on at an angular distance of 10°, 20°, or 30° the subjects tried to reproduce at least twenty same sized saccades in total darkness either with eyes open or closed.

Instead of a visual training-period alternating auditory or tactile cues were presented, in another section of the experiment, at an angular distance of 30°, and the subjects tried to saccade between these non-visual stimuli in the dark.

The results of the experiments will later be published in detail (Körner, 1975) and shall be summarized here briefly.

1. The reproduced mean amplitudes of dark-saccades exceeded the 10°, 20° and 30° visual training saccades by $+100\%$, $+58\%$, and $+38\%$ respectively with the eyes open, and by $+489\%$, $+302\%$ and $+224\%$ with the eyes closed.

2. Compared to visually controlled saccades, the relative velocity of dark saccades with the eyes open was slower. Eye closure led to a further decrease of saccade velocity. For the two non-visual conditions the maximum velocity was different but behaved according to a lawful function of amplitudes (Fig. 1). The duration of saccades was a linear function of the amplitude with slopes of approximately 2.9 for the visual condition, 3.9 for saccades with eyes open in the dark and 4.3 with eyes closed.

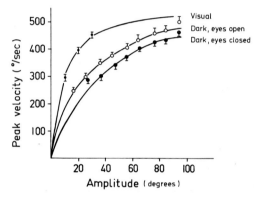

FIG. 1. Maximum velocity of human saccadic eye movements as a function of amplitudes under visual and non-visual conditions. Means and standard errors of twelve to fifty subjects. Each mean represents 50 to 1050 saccades.

3. Neither auditory nor tactile inputs could improve the accuracy or increase the reduced velocity of non-visual saccades.

4. In the dark with the eyes open positive or negative secondary or so-called corrective saccades appeared with a similar percentage as under visual conditions. These small adjustments are to be seen even after a prolonged execution of many saccades in the dark.

It is hard to interpret the results. It is possible that, in the dark, saccadic eye movements are mediated by a different corticotectal pathway than under normal viewing conditions. In that case a lower firing rate of oculomotor brainstem neurons would have to be the result. The frontal lobe has been considered for a long time as the center of voluntary saccadic eye movements. But this suggestion does not agree with Bizzi's findings (1968): frontal eye field neurons only discharge after onset of saccades, in the light as well as in the dark. Another suggestion demands attention—visual information may increase vigilance and therefore might activate brainstem neurons. An inhibition of oculomotor neurons could be the consequence of an interruption of such a reduced secondary activating pathway in darkness. In line with Harms' finding that the pupillary light reflex is inhibited after lesions of the visual cortex, a similar facilitating effect of primary visual centers on pupillomotor brainstem neurons must be discussed (Harms, 1951; Körner and Teuber, 1973).

Secondary positive or negative saccadic corrections with a latency far below the visual reaction time cannot be considered to correct primarily a remaining retinal error signal, since they also accompany non-visual saccades performed over a long period with the eyes open in the dark. They seem to be evoked by an extrastriate internal feedback-loop, which perhaps would send proprioceptive afferent information from the eye muscles to the cerebellum. Thus they might correct an inaccurately executed visual or non-visual cortical signal for voluntary saccades. As already discussed by Jeannerod (1965) eye closure leads to reduced tonic activity of oculomotor units. In case a gamma-efferent system existed for the eye muscles, its activity would also be reduced by lid closure. This would explain the totally insufficient control of saccades with eyes closed.

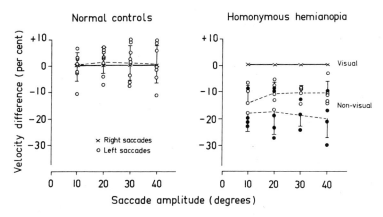

FIG. 2. *Left hand graph.* Side differences of saccade velocity in eight normal subjects. Mean velocity of left saccades is given in per cent of the velocity of right saccades. *Right hand graph.* Mean velocity of 10 to 15 saccades per subject towards the blind part of the visual field in per cent of the mean velocity of saccades towards the seeing half-field. Six patients with complete homonymous hemianopia (dots) and five patients with partial hemianopia (circles). Bars represent standard deviations.

CLINICAL IMPLICATIONS

If saccadic eye movements are slower in the dark than under normal viewing conditions, one would expect that visual field defects of patients with hemianopia have a similar effect on saccades which are directed towards the defective part of the field.

We observed eleven patients with homonymous hemianopia. Alternating right and left saccades of 10°, 20°, 30° and 40° were recorded. Six patients had a complete hemianopia. Five patients had a field defect in both eyes which did not occupy the entire half field but extended over more than one half of a quadrant.

A symmetrical distribution of right–left differences of saccade velocity was found in eight normal subjects. The range was about ±10%. All patients with hemianopia had slower saccades towards the defective half of the visual field with a range of −3 to −30% (Fig. 2). Patients with complete hemianopia tended to have slower saccades than those with partial hemianopia. This slow-down might have been caused either by a primary disturbance of oculomotor centers or by the visual deficit. The latter conclusion would imply that visual information from the hemisphere which also receives the retinal input from the peripheral visual target for a saccade, induces highest firing rates of oculomotor units for maximum saccade velocities. This would agree with the above-mentioned findings that saccades are generally slower in the dark.

This sensoric interpretation of a slow-down of saccades in hemianopic patients could be proved in patients with bitemporal hemianopia. We recorded saccadic eye movements from five such patients under three conditions: with both eyes open, with the right eye open or with the left eye open. A primary oculomotor disorder would have appeared equally under all three conditions. However, right saccades were only slower when the left eye was closed, and left saccades were slower, when the right eye was closed (Fig. 3). That means that eye movement velocity is reduced only with saccades towards the temporal blind half field of each eye. Under binocular viewing conditions, however, the two remaining nasal half-fields yielded to normal saccade velocities to the right and to the left.

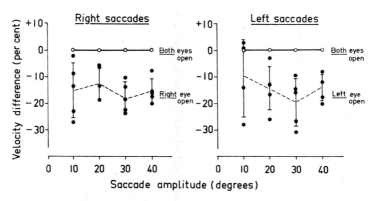

FIG. 3. Saccade velocity differences of five patients with bitemporal hemianopia. With one eye open, saccades towards the blind temporal half-field of this eye are slower than with both eyes open. Differences of means of 10 to 15 saccades in per cent (dots) and standard deviations (bars).

In the case of these patients recordings of the optokinetic nystagmus (OKN) at five different stimulus speeds proved the following. With both eyes open the OKN was symmetrical. With one eye covered OKN became asymmetric, although nystagmus frequency remained constant: with the right eye open OKN to the right showed lower amplitudes and a decrease of slow-phase velocity. With the left eye open a corresponding decrease of amplitude and slow-phase velocity was to be seen for the nystagmus to the left. In normal subjects such an asymmetry of the OKN following closure of one eye is not known. An asymmetry of the OKN was also found in our patients with complete homonymous field defects.

CONCLUSIONS

Human saccadic eye movements executed in the dark are slower than under normal viewing conditions. The maximum velocity does not only depend on a small visual target but on structured visual input to that cerebral hemisphere which also receives information from the visual goal. The reason for a directional slow-down of saccadic eye movements of hemianopic patients could be a lack of visuo-sensory facilitation of oculomotor neurons via a cortico-tectal pathway. Bitemporal hemianopia would then, under monocular viewing conditions, have the same effect as homonymous hemianopia with both eyes open. It has been proved that quick phases of nystagmus were slower in the dark just like voluntary saccades (Dichgans et al., 1969; Ron et al., 1972). Asymmetric optokinetic responses in patients with homonymous hemianopia could be explained by a slow-down of the quick phases towards the blind half-field and not by a primary disorder of the oculomotor system's components. This assumption is confirmed by the fact that in patients with bitemporal hemianopia, optokinetic asymmetries can be found only after closure of one eye.

The results shown here have to be confirmed through further investigations of a larger number of cases.

REFERENCES

BECKER, W. and KLEIN, H.-M. (1972) Accuracy of saccadic eye movements and maintenance of eccentric eye positions in the dark. *Vision Res.* **13,** 1021.

BECKER, W. and FUCHS, A. F. (1969) Further properties of the human saccadic system: Eye movements and correction saccades with and without visual fixation points. *Vision Res.* **9,** 1247.

BIZZI, E. (1968) Discharge of frontal eye field neurons during saccadic and following eye movements in unanesthetized monkeys. *Exptl Brain Res.* **6,** 69.

DICHGANS, H., NAUCK, B. and BROOKS, B. (1969) Blickbewegungen mit sichtbarem Fixationsziel, intendierte Blickbewegungen im Dunkeln und nach Lidschluß, Beziehungen zu den raschen Phasen des opto-kinetischen und vestibulären Nystagmus. *Pflügers Arch. Ges. Physiol.* **312,** R 143.

JEANNEROD, M., GERIN, P. and MOURET, J. (1965) Influence de l'obscurité et de l'occlusion des paupières sur le control des movements oculaires. *L'année Psychol.* **65,** 309.

JEANNEROD, M. (1971) Control de movements oculaires par les afférences visuelles. In: *La Function du Regard,* DUBOIS POULSEN, A., LAIRY, G. C. and REMOND, A. (Eds.). Inserm, Paris, 15.

HARMS, H. (1951) Hemianopische Pupillenstarre. *Klin. Mbl. Augenheilkunde,* **118,** 133.

JUNG, J. and KORNHUBER, H. H. (1964) Results of electronystagmography in man: the value of optokinetic, vestibular, and spontaneous nystagmus for neurologic diagnosis and research. In: *The Oculomotor System,* BENDER, M. B. (Ed.), p. 428. Harper & Row.

KÖRNER, F. (1975) Untersuchungen über die nicht-visuelle Kontrolle von Augenbewegungen. *Adv. Ophthal.* (in preparation).

KÖRNER, F. and TEUBER, H.-L. (1972) Visual field defects after missile injuries to the geniculo-striate pathway in man. *Exptl Brain Res.* **18,** 88.

RON, S., ROBINSON, D. A. and SKAVENSKI, A. A. (1972) Saccades and the quick phase of nystagmus. *Vision Res.* **12,** 2015.

SUBJECT INDEX